Mennonite Church USA

2005 Directory

J.Ron Byler, editor
James E. Horsch, publishing editor

Karen Bachman, database consultant
Merrill R. Miller, designer
Deb Ratzlaff, ministerial editor
Kathryn Rodgers, churchwide and agency editor
Doris Mendel Schmidt, congregational editor
Cindy Snider and Jo-Ann Schmidt, ad editors

Mennonite Church USA

Faith & Life Resources
A division of Mennonite Publishing Network

Scottdale, Pennsylvania
Waterloo, Ontario

MENNONITE CHURCH USA 2005 DIRECTORY
Copyright © 2004 by Faith & Life Resources, Scottdale, Pa. 15683
    Published simultaneously in Canada by Faith & Life Resources, Waterloo, Ont. N2L 6H7
International Standard Book Number: 0-8361-9294-X (Squareback)
International Standard Book Number: 0-8361-9295-8 (Spiral)
International Standard Serial Number: 1527-1722
Printed in the United States of America
Book and cover design: Merrill R. Miller

To order or request information, please call 1-800-245-7894
Website: www.mph.org

Welcome!

Mennonite Church USA is a tree with many branches. Its root system is nourished by a common Anabaptist heritage. Its trunk of missional purpose and design gives life and meaning to many branches of faithfulness and ministry.

This book is designed to get us acquainted with this organism of mission and ministry. It helps us navigate from branch to branch, and to know how, all together, the roots, trunk, and branches form the organism called Mennonite Church USA.

Church leaders, from congregational leaders to churchwide leaders, will find this book invaluable. It is meant to connect us with one another and inform us about one another so we see the tree, not just the branches.

As you use this directory, give thanks to God for the faithful leaders and important ministries it contains.

James Schrag

Jim Schrag
Executive Director
Mennonite Church USA

**Mennonite
Church
USA**

Our vision

Vision: Healing and Hope

God calls us
to be followers of Jesus Christ
and, by the power
of the Holy Spirit,
to grow as communities
of grace, joy, and peace,
so that God's healing and hope
flow through us to the world.

Joining in God's work in the world

Our priorities

As congregations, area conferences, church-wide ministries, and executive leadership of Mennonite Church USA, we are called to become a missional church by discerning God's purpose in the world and joining in that work. To help us become a missional church, we are challenged to develop leaders among us and to strengthen relationships with Mennonites around the globe and to work with other Christians to extend the reign of God on earth.

Affirmed by the Mennonite Church USA Delegate Assembly, July 2003.

Advocacy:
reinforcing the
church-school
bond

Leadership:
calling
and nurturing
education leaders

Access:
ensuring education
opportunities
for all

Networking:
enhancing
school-school
collaboration

Advancement:
developing
resources for
the future

Research:
providing
information to
shape planning

Our partners:

The area conferences/districts of Mennonite Church USA and
their congregations, and individuals passionate about education.

Associated Mennonite Biblical Seminary, Bethel College, Bluffton
University, Eastern Mennonite University, Goshen College, Hesston
College, Mennonite Elementary Education Council, Mennonite
Secondary Education Council.

Mennonite Education
Agency

Strengthening Mennonite Church USA through education

T: 574-642-3164 or toll-free 866-866-2872
E: info@MennoniteEducation.org
W: MennoniteEducation.org

MEA staff from left: Ruth Schrock, Lisa Heinz,
J. David Yoder, Cheryl Zehr Walker, Jennie Kauffman,
Carlos Romero and Diane Lockwood.

Contents

Check the online Mennonite Directory at www.MennoniteUSA.org for regularly updated congregational and ministerial information, and easily accessed websites for conferences and agencies.

Mennonite Church USA

Time after time, the Spirit in the form of a dove announces the coming of God to us. As Mennonites we recognize the centrality of Christ as proclaimed in Scripture, revealed through the Holy Spirit, and discerned in Christian community. This symbol, which has been specially designed for the Mennonite Church, reflects these basic tenents.

For information about the use and application of the logo, visit the Mennonite Church USA web site at www.MennoniteUSA.org and click on Visual Identity for Mennonite Church USA in the resources section.

One Mennonite's reflection on the meaning of our symbol:

A strength of the image for the Mennonite Church is that it "touches down" at a number of places in our salvation history.

• It brings to mind Genesis 1 and creation—the flood and the dove returning with the olive branch—the biblical themes of hope and creation.

• It brings to mind the prophets' aspiration for a kingdom of peace. I think of Isaiah and Micah's visions.

• It brings to mind Jesus's baptism, where the dove appears with a voice from God affirming, "this is my beloved Son."

• It brings to mind the experience of Pentecost, with the descent of the Holy Spirit, bringing the message of new life.

• It brings to mind the Anabaptist vision, with its theme of peace and renewal in the 16th century.

• It points us to God and the Holy Spirit, inviting us to move forward with Christ and seek the kingdom, encouraging us to aspire to a new heaven and new earth. The image suggests to me the biblical pilgrimage, enveloping us with a reference to past, present and future.

—Helmut Harder, Winnipeg, Man.*

*The logo and name "Mennonite Church" is shared with Mennonite Church Canada.

Mennonite Church USA

Many members, one body

Members
111,031 members across the United States

Congregations
943 congregations in 45 states

Area Conferences
Allegheny Mennonite Conference
Atlantic Coast Conference
Central District Conference
Central Plains Mennonite Conference
Eastern District Conference
Franconia Mennonite Conference
Franklin Mennonite Conference
Gulf States Mennonite Conference
Illinois Mennonite Conference
Indiana-Michigan Mennonite Conference
Lancaster Mennonite Conference
New York Mennonite Conference
North Central Mennonite Conference
Ohio Conference of Mennonite Church USA
Pacific Northwest Mennonite Conference
Pacific Southwest Mennonite Conference
Rocky Mountain Mennonite Conference
South Central Mennonite Conference
Southeast Mennonite Conference
Virginia Mennonite Conference
Western District Conference

Toll-free 866-866-2872

Churchwide Ministries
Executive Leadership
Mennonite Education Agency
Mennonite Mission Network
Mennonite Mutual Aid
Mennonite Publishing Network

Constituency Groups
African-American Mennonite Association
Iglesia Menonita Hispana
Native Mennonite Ministries
    Mennonite Indian Leaders Council
    United Native Ministries
Mennonite Men
Mennonite Women USA

Educational Institutions
Associated Mennonite Biblical Seminary
Bethel College
Bluffton University
Eastern Mennonite Seminary
Eastern Mennonite University
Goshen College
Hesston College
36 primary and secondary schools

Publication
The Mennonite

www.MennoniteUSA.org

Abbreviations

AAMA	African-American Mennonite Association
ACC	Atlantic Coast Conference of Mennonite Church USA
AIMM	Africa Inter-Mennonite Mission
AMBS	Associated Mennonite Biblical Seminary
ALL	Allegheny Mennonite Conference
BIC	Brethren in Christ
CAL	Center for Anabaptist Leadership (Southern California)
CDC	Central District Conference
CIM	Council of International Anabaptist Ministries
CM	Conservative Mennonite Conference
COB	Church of the Brethren
CP	Central Plains Mennonite Conference
CPT	Christian Peacemaker Teams
DC	Washington DC Area Mennonite Workers
EDC	Eastern District Conference
EMS	Eastern Mennonite Seminary
EMU	Eastern Mennonite University
FRC	Franconia Mennonite Conference
FRK	Franklin Mennonite Conference
GC	Goshen College
GS	Gulf States Mennonite Conference
HMC	Hispanic Mennonite Church
HMONG	Hmong Ministries
IMH	Iglesia Menonita Hispana
IL	Illinois Mennonite Conference
IM	Indiana-Michigan Mennonite Conference
LAN	Lancaster Mennonite Conference
LAO	Lao Mennonite Ministries
MC USA	Mennonite Church USA
MCC	Mennonite Central Committee
MDS	Mennonite Disaster Service
MEA	Mennonite Education Agency
MEDA	Mennonite Economic Development Associates
MILC	Mennonite Indian Leaders Council
MM	Mennonite Men
MMA	Mennonite Mutual Aid
MMN	Mennonite Mission Network
MPN	Mennonite Publishing Network
MUM	Mennonite Urban Ministry of Denver
MW	Mennonite Women
MWC	Mennonite World Conference
NC	North Central Mennonite Conference
NMM	Native Mennonite Ministries
NYC	New York City Council of Mennonite Churches
NY	New York Mennonite Conference
OH	Ohio Conference of the Mennonite Church
PNW	Pacific Northwest Mennonite Conference
PSW	Pacific Southwest Mennonite Conference
RM	Rocky Mountain Mennonite Conference
SC	South Central Mennonite Conference
SE	Southeast Mennonite Conference
UNM	United Native Ministries
VA	Virginia Mennonite Conference
VIET	North American Vietnamese Mennonite Fellowship
WDC	Western District Conference

OTHER ABBREVIATIONS

Ch	Church
Chr	Christian
Comm	Community
Cong	Congregation
Fell	Fellowship
Menn	Mennonite

Editor's note

I hope you'll find the new edition of the *Mennonite Directory* to be a valuable resource. In it you'll find connections to Mennonite Church USA ministers, congregations, area conferences, and churchwide ministries. You'll also find connections to other agencies, Mennonite World Conference, and sister denominations, including Mennonite Church Canada.

A new related feature is the online directory found on the home page of Mennonite Church USA (www.MennoniteUSA.org). In this online version of the *Directory*, you'll find constantly updated congregational and ministerial information, as well as easy access to the websites for conferences and agencies.

I hope you'll also regularly refer to page four, which states our churchwide vision, as well as our priority to become a missional church. As followers of Christ, we are becoming a new church, a missional church. We want to join in what God is already doing in the world. In our worship and life together, in our ministry and outreach, we want to give people a glimpse of God's intentions for the whole world. We want to welcome sinners, love our enemies, and be visibly different from the culture around us

as a sign of what God is doing in the world.

In a recent survey, more than one-quarter of us already recognize the missional vision, a broad interchurch movement more than 50 years old that has had significant input from Mennonite thinkers and leaders. In developing the survey for our church members, interviews with pastors showed strong support for becoming a missional church. Pastors want to be part of a healthy, growing church—in their own congregations and in the broader denomination.

This *Directory* includes our missional family. Please use it to pray each day for our church leaders and congregations.

The *Mennonite Church USA 2005 Directory* is the result of a lot of hard work by a lot of people. You'll find some of these persons listed on the title page. I'd also like to thank area conference staff who worked with their congregations to provide up-to-date information.

May this *Directory* help shape our life together as we seek to follow Christ's call for Mennonite Church USA and as we continue on our journey to become the missional church God wants us to become.

[signature]

J. Ron Byler, editor
Associate Executive Director
Mennonite Church USA
RonB@MennoniteUSA.org

Special days and the church year 2005

The following list includes special days that are observed by a significant number of Mennonite Church congregations. Names of these days are in italic typeface. Mennonite Church USA and Mennonite Church Canada agencies alternate annually in providing resources to support these observances. The Mennonite Church USA agency that supports the special day is indicated in parentheses after the name of the day. The seasons and some special days of the church year are also carried.

The Mennonite Church USA calendar that lists dates of area conference, churchwide agency, and other events is maintained by Mennonite Church USA Executive Leadership at www.MennoniteChurchUSA.org/calendar

JANUARY

6 Epiphany, Season of Epiphany begins. Season is January 6 – February 6.

16 *Many Peoples Sunday* (MC USA Intercultural Relations)

21 Birthday of Anabaptism, A.D. 1525

23 *Mennonite World Fellowship Sunday* (Mennonite World Conference) – 4th Sunday

FEBRUARY

6 *Church Education Sunday* (Mennonite Education Agency) – 1st Sunday

6 Transfiguration Sunday – Last Sunday of Epiphany season

9 Ash Wednesday

13 First Sunday in Season of Lent. Season is February 13 – March 24, Maundy Thursday.

13 *Congregational Life Sunday* (MC USA Congregational and Ministerial Leadership) – 2nd Sunday

March

4 World Day of Prayer – 1st Friday

20 Palm/Passion Sunday, Holy Week begins

24 Maundy Thursday

25 Good Friday

27 Easter Sunday, Season of Easter begins. Season is March 27 – May 14, Eve of Pentecost.

April

3 *Evangelism & Church Planting Sunday* (Mennonite Mission Network) – 1st Sunday after Easter

May

1 *Stewardship Sunday* (MMA) – 1st Sunday

5 Ascension Day – Thursday, 40 days after Easter Sunday

8 *Christian Family Sunday* (MC USA Congregational and Ministerial Leadership) – 2nd Sunday

15 Pentecost Sunday, 50 days after Easter Sunday

15 Season after Pentecost begins. Season is May 15 – November 20.

July

3 *Christian Citizenship Sunday* (MC USA Peace Advocate) – 1st Sunday

September

18 *Mutual Aid Sunday* (MMA) – 3rd Sunday

25 *Publishing Sunday* (Mennonite Publishing Network)
– 4th Sunday

October

2   Worldwide Communion Sunday – 1st Sunday

16 *Ministers Sunday* (MC USA Congregational and
Ministerial Leadership) – 3rd Sunday

30 *Mennonite Heritage Sunday* (MC USA Historical
Committee) – last Sunday

November

Mission Month (Mennonite Mission Network) – All
Sundays

6 *Peace Sunday* (Mennonite Mission Network
Minister of Peace and Justice) – Sunday before
November 11

20 Bible Sunday – 3rd Sunday

27 First Sunday of Advent. Season is November 27 –
December 24, Christmas eve

December

25 Christmas Day

25 Season of Christmas begins. Season is December 25
– January 6, Epiphany

Dates in the Church Year, 2005-2016

Year	Sundays after Epiphany	Ash Wed. Lent begins	Easter Sunday	Ascension Day	Pentecost Sunday	Sundays after Pentecost	Season of Advent begins
2005	5	Feb. 9	March 27	May 5	May 15	27	Nov. 27
2006	8	March 1	April 16	May 25	June 4	25	Dec. 3
2007	7	Feb. 21	April 8	May 17	May 27	26	Dec. 2
2008	4	Feb. 6	March 23	May 1	May 11	28	Nov. 30
2009	7	Feb. 25	April 12	May 21	May 31	25	Nov. 29
2010	6	Feb. 17	April 4	May 13	May 23	26	Nov. 28
2011	9	March 9	April 24	June 2	June 12	23	Nov. 27
2012	7	Feb. 22	April 8	May 17	May 27	26	Dec. 2
2013	5	Feb. 13	March 31	May 9	May 19	27	Dec. 1
2014	8	March 5	April 20	May 29	June 8	24	Nov. 30
2015	6	Feb. 18	April 5	May 14	May 24	26	Nov. 29
2016	5	Feb. 10	March 27	May 5	May 15	27	Nov. 27

Notes
The Season of Advent begins with the Sunday nearest November 30. Ash Wednesday is the Wednesday before the sixth
Sunday before Easter. Ascension Day is on the Thursday after the sixth Sunday after Easter. Pentecost Sunday is the seventh Sunday after Easter.

I have
great hope for our young church ...

Roy Williams, pastor of College Mennonite Church, Tampa, Fla., and moderator-elect of Mennonite Church USA.

Mennonite Church USA is a church of the future. As we take ever more confident steps, we are trusting in God's abiding love to help us overcome the challenges of being a faithful people in the 21st century. God has prepared a banquet for us and we are being sent out, inviting friends, neighbors and strangers to join us until we become the diverse and multi-cultural people we have dreamed of being ... the sign of God's kingdom on earth.

Mennonite Church USA

Toll-free 1-866-866-2872
www.MennoniteChurchUSA.org

Churchwide Agencies

Mennonite Church USA

All churchwide agency staff can be reached by calling the churchwide toll-free number at 1-866-866-2872.

Executive Leadership

OFFICES
info@MennoniteUSA.org,
www.MennoniteUSA.org
Toll-free 1-866-866-2872 for all staff
Great Plains office: 722 Main St, PO Box 347, Newton KS 67114-0347, 316-283-5100, fax 316-283-0454
Great Lakes office: 500 S Main St, PO Box 1245, Elkhart IN 46515-1245, 574-294-7523, fax 574-293-1892

To e-mail any staff person, use first name and first initial of last name @MennoniteUSA.org

EXECUTIVE COMMITTEE
D. Duane Oswald (doswald@avantehealth.com), moderator, 1111 E Herndon Ave, Suite 308, Fresno CA 93720-3100, 559-261-9070; Roy Williams (rrrsjw@aol.com), moderator-elect, 22642 Newfield Ct, Land O'Lakes FL 34639, 813-247-2798; Patricia Hershberger (pathershberger@msn.com), executive committee secretary, chair, board development committee, 2380 Miller Farm Rd, Woodburn OR 97071; James Harder (harderj@bluffton.edu), chair, church resources committee, 118 Sunset Dr, Bluffton OH 45817; Sharon Waltner (kswaltner@svtv.com), chair, future church committee, 28142 448th Ave, Parker SD 57053

EXECUTIVE BOARD
(in addition to Executive Committee members listed above)
B. Elaine Bryant; J. Daryl Byler; Cleon Claassen; Leslie Francisco III; Kim Vu Friesen; Kevin Goertzen; Marco Güete; Janeen Bertsche Johnson; Edith Landis; Olivette McGhee; Harold Miller; Sue E. Miller; Jane Hoober Peifer; Lois Thieszen Preheim; Edwin Rempel; Ervin Stutzman, past moderator

Executive Office
Executive@MennoniteUSA.org

STAFF
Jim Schrag, executive director (Great Plains)
J. Ron Byler, associate executive director (Great Lakes)
Phil Bergey, staff associate (771 Rte 113, Souderton PA 18964
Marty Lehman, director, financial development (Great Lakes)

Shelley Buller, executive assistant (Great Plains)
Kathryn Rodgers, executive assistant (Great
   Lakes)

INFORMATION
Executive office staff facilitate the work of the
Executive Leadership Team, Executive Board,
Constituency Leaders Council, and the delegate
body, building networks of leaders from all
parts of the church. Included in the Executive
office are the functions of Peace Advocate and
Historical Committee.

PEACE ADVOCATE
Peace@MennoniteUSA.org,
www.MennoniteUSA.org
330-683-6844, fax 330-683-6844
PO Box 173, Orrville OH 44667-0173

Staff
Susan Mark Landis, peace advocate (Orrville OH)
Lisa Amstutz, peace advocate assistant (Orrville
   OH)

Information
The peace advocate leads and organizes
prophetic witness and peace and justice advocacy on behalf of Mennonite Church USA. (See
also Peace and Justice Support Network in section 3.)

HISTORICAL COMMITTEE
Goshen Archives: 1700 S Main St, Goshen IN
   46526-4794, 574-535-7477, fax 574-535-
   7756, archives@goshen.edu/mcarchives,
   www.goshen.edu/mcarchives
North Newton Archives: 300 E 27th St, North
   Newton KS 67117-0531, 316-284-5304, fax
   316-284-5843, mla@bethelks.edu,
   www.bethelks.edu/services/mla

Staff
John Sharp, director (Goshen)
Cathy Hochstetler, assistant archivist (Goshen);
James Lynch, assistant archivist (North Newton);

Ruth Schrock, archives assistant (Goshen);
Dennis Stoesz, archivist (Goshen); John D.
Thiesen, archivist (North Newton)

Information
The Historical Committee helps the church—
individuals, congregations, conferences, and
agencies—preserve its records and discover the
significance of Mennonite history for daily life,
work, and the church's mission in the world.
(See Historical Organizations in section 3 for
individual historical groups.)

Administration
Administration@MennoniteUSA.org

STAFF
Ted Stuckey, director (Great Plains)
Karen Bachman, information technology techni-
cian (Great Plains); Larry Becker, information
technology and building manager (Great
Plains); Carol Epp, administrative assistant
(Great Lakes); Karen Kaufman, Church
Extension Services administrative assistant
(Great Plains); Marilyn Loganbill, assistant
treasurer (Great Plains); Deb Ratzlaff, recep-
tionist (Great Plains); Lela Mae Sawatzky, recep-
tionist (Great Plains); Doris Schmidt, reception-
ist (Great Plains); Robin Schrag, controller
(Great Plains); Jarrett Stucky, Church Extension
Services manager and treasurer (Great Plains)

INFORMATION
Administration staff provide for finances, asset
management, accounting, and auditing. (See
also separate listing for Church Extension
Services in section 3.)

Communications
Communications@MennoniteUSA.org

STAFF
Barth Hague, director (Great Lakes)
Ken Gingerich, art director (Great Plains); Alex
Naula, web designer (Goshen IN); Laurie

Oswald, news service director (Great Plains); Doris Schmidt, Mennonite Directory assistant (Great Plains); Jo-Ann Schmidt, administrative assistant (Great Plains); Cindy Snider, project director (Great Plains)

INFORMATION
The Communications team articulates the church's identity, communicates news and provides a public voice to others.

Congregational and Ministerial Leadership

CongregationalLife@MennoniteUSA.org or MinisterialLeadership@MennoniteUSA.org
1-866-866-2872

STAFF
Keith Harder, director (Great Plains)
Diane Zaerr Brenneman, denominational minister (1061 480th St SW, Parnell IA 52325); Evon Castro, administrative assistant (Great Lakes); Gilberto Flores, denominational minister (Great Plains); Mary Etta King and Linford King, denominational ministers (434 E Chestnut St, Lancaster PA 17602); Marlene Kropf, denominational minister (Great Lakes); Deb Ratzlaff, administrative assistant (Great Plains); Dale Stoltzfus, denominational minister (270 Ivy Terrace, Lancaster PA 17601)

INFORMATION
The Congregational and Ministerial Leadership team equips congregational leaders for ministry and supports conference ministers and pastors in their leadership roles.

Convention Planning
ConventionPlanning@MennoniteUSA.org

STAFF
Jorge Vallejos, director (Great Lakes)
Carol Epp, administrative assistant (Great Lakes); Scott Hartman, office manager (Great Lakes); Lana Miller, assistant director (Great Lakes)

INFORMATION
Convention Planning provides staff and organizational planning for the assembly of Mennonite Church USA held every two years. The assembly includes conventions for all ages—adults, young adults, youth, junior high youth, and children.
Future events: Charlotte NC, July 4-9, 2005 and San Jose CA, July 2-7, 2007.

Intercultural Relations
Intercultural@MennoniteUSA.org
2311 Tower Place, Hampton VA 23666
Toll-free 1-866-866-2872 and 757-826-0241, fax 757-825-8771

STAFF
Kenyetta Aduma Twine, director (Hampton VA)
Ammeral Johnson, administrative assistant (Hampton VA)

INFORMATION
Intercultural Relations serves the needs of racial/ethnic persons and promotes their participation in the wider church.

EXECUTIVE BOARD PUBLICATIONS
Equipping (10 issues per year) Melanie Mueller, editor; Mennonite Church USA bulletin inserts, Cindy Snider, editor; *Mennonite Church USA Directory*, Ron Byler, editor; *Mennonite Historical Bulletin* (quarterly) John E. Sharp, editor; *Mennonite Life* (online quarterly) John D. Thiesen, James C. Juhnke, and Raylene Hinz-Penner, editors; *PeaceSigns* (online monthly) Melanie Zuercher, editor

Committees/Councils

ANTI-RACISM TEAM
This team leads Mennonite Church USA to become a community of congregations, conferences, programs, and institutions that teach and preach anti-racism as a spiritual reality that is based on biblical principles related to worship, community life, and mission.

Members/Staff

Susan Mark Landis, chair
(Peace@MennoniteUSA.org), PO Box 173,
Orrville OH 44667-0173, 330-683-6844;
Kenyetta Aduma Twine, Elaine Bryant, Daryl
Byler, Ron Byler, Leslie Francisco III, Kim Vu
Friesen, Marco Güete, Jane Hoober Peifer, Jim
Schrag

CONSTITUENCY LEADERS COUNCIL (CLC)

Leaders from each area conference and recognized group meet together at least twice each
year to provide counsel and advice to the
Mennonite Church USA Executive Board and to
engage in conference-to-conference dialogue.
Representatives are listed in sections 2 and 3
with each conference and recognized group.

The representational voice and counsel of
conference and constituent group leaders is
heard through the Constituency Leaders
Council. CLC members worship and pray together, encourage faithfulness, share ideas and
resources, process concerns, and discern direction on issues of faith and life in Mennonite
Church USA. The CLC serves as a primary forum
for conference-to-conference conversation and
networking, as a place for conferences and constituency groups to talk together with churchwide agency representatives, and as a voice for
agenda from the grassroots to surface with the
Executive Board.

Each conference is invited to send up to
three representatives to the CLC, at least one of
which should be a conference minister.
Recognized constituency groups may send two
representatives to the CLC. The Mennonite
Church USA moderator-elect serves as the chair
of the group, and a vice chair is chosen by CLC
members each biennium. One role of the CLC is
to nominate half of the eight-member
Leadership Discernment Committee for election
by the Delegate Assembly.

Officers/Staff

Roy Williams, chair (rrrsjw@aol.com), 22642
Newfield Ct, Land O'Lakes FL 34639, 813-247-
2798; Susan Sommer, vice chair
(slsommer@illinois.mennonite.net), PO Box 3,
Tremont IL 61568, 309-925-2111; Bill
Zuercher, recording secretary; Jim Schrag and
Ron Byler, staff

LEADERSHIP DISCERNMENT COMMITTEE

The Leadership Discernment Committee is
charged by the Delegate Assembly to discern
persons to serve on the boards of churchwide
agencies and to bring a slate of nominees to the
Delegate Assembly for affirmation by the delegates.

Members/Staff

Ruth A. Suter, chair (rsuter@sbcglobal.net), PO
Box 88, Brisbane CA 94005; Sarah Arn; Rose
Covington; Maria Magdalena DeLeon; Ivorie G.
Lowe; Lloyd Miller; Mark Weidner; Bill
Zuercher; Ron Byler and Kathryn Rodgers, staff

INTERCHURCH RELATIONS COMMITTEE

Four groups provide leadership and give counsel to Mennonite Church USA on its relationships with Christians of other traditions. The
groups are currently: Theological Group;
Church Associations Group; Peace Group; Local
Congregations and Leaders Group.

Officers/Staff

Jim Schrag, chair (Great Plains); Albert J. Meyer
(meyer@npcc.net); 708 Emerson St, Goshen IN
46526-3904, volunteer staff

YOUTH MINISTRY COUNCIL

A group formed to promote continued youth
ministry in Mennonite Church USA. Meets annually. Next meeting, May 11-15, 2005.

Members/Staff

Shana Peachey Boshart, Kimberlee Greenawalt,
Keith Harder, Lana Miller, Merv Stoltzfus, Bob
Yoder

Mennonite Education Agency

info@MennoniteEducation.org,
www.MennoniteEducation.org
Toll-free 1-866-866-2872 and 574-642-3164,
fax 574-642-4863
63846 CR 35, Suite 1, Goshen IN 46528-9621

To e-mail any staff person, use first name and
first initial of last name
@MennoniteEducation.org.

STAFF

Carlos Romero, executive director
Lisa Heinz, associate director
Jennie Kauffman, office manager
Diane Lockwood, administrative assistant
Ruth Schrock, administrative assistant
Cheryl Zehr Walker, associate director, 219
    Brookwood Dr, Bluffton OH 45817, 419-
    230-8515
J. David Yoder, associate director, 2280 Lake
    Terrace Dr, Harrisonburg VA 22802, 540-
    421-6321

BOARD

Rosalind E. Andreas, chair
(kenda430@aol.com), 113 Ridge Top Ln, Essex
Junction VT 05452, 802-879-0012; Ed Diller,
vice chair; James L. Rosenberger, secretary;
Jesus M. Cruz, treasurer; Terri J. Plank
Brenneman; Anne Hege; Susan Schultz Huxman;
Paul Johnson; Franzie L. Loepp; John Stahl-
Wert; Connie F. Stauffer

INFORMATION

The mission of Mennonite Education Agency is
to strengthen the life, witness, and identity of
Mennonite Church USA through education. The
agency provides leadership to the educational
agenda of the church in partnership with both
church and schools of all levels.

PURPOSES

Advocate for the vision and mission of
    Mennonite-Anabaptist education in church
    and school.
Discern the educational needs of the church
    and develop schools and programs that best
    meet these needs.
Provide services to support the missions of the
    educational institutions.
Facilitate cooperation, collaboration and co-
    ordination among Mennonite Church USA
    educational institutions and between these
    institutions and other church programs.

PARTNERS

Church: Mennonite Education Agency relates to
area conferences/districts, congregations and
individuals involved in and passionate about
education.

School: Mennonite Education Agency relates to
Mennonite Elementary Education Council,
Mennonite Secondary Education Council,
Associated Mennonite Biblical Seminary, Bethel
College, Bluffton University, Eastern Mennonite
Seminary, Eastern Mennonite University, Goshen
College, and Hesston College. (See "Schools" in
section 3 for information on secondary and ele-
mentary schools, as well as the separate listing
for each college and seminary.)

Enrollment (fall 2003): MEEC and MSEC
schools (grades PreK–12): 10,758 total (4,742
Mennonite and other Anabaptist). Mennonite
Church USA colleges (BC, BU, EMU, GC, HC):
full-time undergraduate: 3,310 total (1,526
Mennonite and other Anabaptist), 3,412 full-
time equivalent (FTE), 313 degree-completion,
293 graduate studies. Mennonite Church USA
seminaries (AMBS, EMS): full-time: 139 total,
95 Mennonite Church USA/Mennonite Church
Canada, 102 other Mennonite, 175 part-time,
187 FTE.

CHURCHWIDE AGENCIES

1

FACULTY CALLING PROJECT: Helps Mennonite educational institutions locate prospective faculty members. Team: Marion Schrock, leader (mdsvs@hotmail.com), 20 Red Leaf Lane, Lancaster PA 17602, 717-394-9360; Jeremy M. Bergen, Thomas Lehman, Dale Schrag, Victor Stoltzfus. MEA staff: J. David Yoder

FUND FOR PEOPLEHOOD EDUCATION: Provides grants to support projects to strengthen church-school relationships. Reference Committee: Jesus M. Cruz, chair (jcruzconsult@aol.com), 441 Surrey Dr, Lancaster PA 17602, 717-581-7816; Tim Jost (jostt@wlu.edu), 1370 Lincolnshire Dr, Harrisonburg VA 22802, 540-564-2524. MEA staff: Cheryl Zehr Walker

INVESTMENT COMMITTEE: Manages long-term investment funds for some educational institutions of Mennonite Church USA. Members: Phillip J. Rich, chair (prich@richford.tv), 1201 Lindau St, Archbold OH 43502, 419-446-2215; Charles Bishop, Tom Bishop, Wilbur Bontrager, Robert Carlson, Jesus M. Cruz, Carl Harman, Curtis D. Hartman, Lowell Herr. Institutional Staff: Jeff Miller, Willis Sommer, Ron Piper, Jim Histand, Wendell Sauder. MEA staff: Lisa Heinz

RACIAL/ETHNIC LEADERSHIP EDUCATION (RELE) PROGRAMS: Hispanic Education in Theology and Leadership (with Iglesia Menonita Hispana and Goshen College), Lark Leadership Scholarship program (with African-American Mennonite Association and Eastern Mennonite University), Native Education and Training program (with United Native Ministries and Hesston College). Advisory Council: Rafael Barahona, Karla Francisco, Leslie Francisco III, Marco Güete, Ray Horst, Olivette McGhee, Clark Roth, Anita Stalter, Shirley Yoder, Kenyetta Aduma Twine (Executive Leadership staff). MEA staff: Carlos Romero

YOUTH CENSUS: Collects and makes available to Mennonite groups demographic and contact information about Mennonite students of all ages in the United States, to promote access to church programs and activities. MEA staff: Cheryl Zehr Walker

MENNONITE ELEMENTARY EDUCATION COUNCIL (MEEC): www.MennoniteSchools.org. Organized to interpret, coordinate, and promote the work of Mennonite elementary schools, both among the schools and their sponsoring groups and throughout Mennonite Church USA. Executive committee: Matt McMullen, chair (Lake Center Christian School), 12893 Kaufman Ave NW, Hartville OH 44632, lccsprincipal@yahoo.com, 330-877-2049; Elvin Kennel, secretary (West Fallowfield Christian School), 310-593-5011; Neal Eckert, treasurer (Lititz Area Mennonite School), 717-626-9551. Members: Ann Kanagy (Belleville Mennonite School), 717-935-2154; Joyce Taylor (Central Christian Learning Center), 330-857-2686; Ken Hawkley (Chicago Mennonite Learning Center), 773-735-9304; David L. Sauder (Ephrata Mennonite School), 717-738-4266; Melvin L. Weaver (Gehmans Mennonite School), 717-484-4222; Larry Crossgrove (Greenwood Mennonite School), 302-349-4131; Tom Burnett (Hinkletown Mennonite School), 717-354-6705; Andrew Meiser (Juniata Mennonite School), 717-463-2898; John Weber (Kraybill Mennonite School), 717-653-5236; J. Richard Thomas (Lancaster Mennonite School), 717-299-0436; Dwilyn Beiler (Linville Hill Mennonite School), 717-442-4447; Ray Kratz (Manheim Christian Day School), 717-665-4300; Carol Wenger (Mt. Pleasant Christian School), 757-482-9557; Kathy Bauman (New Covenant Christian School), 717-274-2423; Bob Rutt (Penn View Christian School), 717-723-1196; Alma J. Geosits, (Quakertown Christian School), 215-536-6970; Conrad Swartzentruber (Shalom Christian Academy), 717-375-2223;

Jean Martin (Sarasota Christian School), 941-371-6481; Gordon Zook (Warwick River Christian School), 757-877-2941.

MENNONITE SECONDARY EDUCATION COUNCIL (MSEC):

www.MennoniteSchools.org.
Consists of the chief administrator of each participating high school. Executive committee: J. Richard Thomas, chair (Lancaster Mennonite School), 2176 Lincoln Highway East, Lancaster PA 17602, thomasjr@lancastermennonite.org, 717-299-0436; Allan Dueck, secretary (Bethany Christian Schools), 574-534-2567; Wilbur Yoder, treasurer (Iowa Mennonite School), 319-656-2073. Members: Margarita Kolthoff-Benners (Academia Menonita), 787-783-1295; Ann Kanagy (Belleville Mennonite School), 717-935-2184; Frederic A. Miller (Central Christian School), 330-857-2686; Elaine A. Moyer (Christopher Dock Mennonite School), 215-362-2675; Susan Yoder (Conestoga Christian School), 610-286-0353; Paul Leaman (Eastern Mennonite High School), 540-432-4500; Marlan Kauffman (Freeman Academy), 605-925-4237; Matt McMullen (Lake Center Christian School), 330-877-2049; Kathy Bauman (New Covenant Christian School), 717-274-2423; Barbara Moses (Philadelphia Mennonite High School), 215-769-5363; Terry Schellenberg (Rockway Mennonite Collegiate), 519-743-5209; Eugene Miller (Sarasota Christian School), 941-371-6481; Conrad Swartzentruber (Shalom Christian Academy), 717-375-2223; Victor Winter (United Mennonite Educational Institute), 519-326-7448; Darrel White (Western Mennonite School), 503-363-2000

HIGHER EDUCATION INSTITUTIONS

Bethel College: E. LaVerne Epp, president, 300 E 27th St, North Newton KS 67117, www.bethelks.edu, 316-283-2500. Bluffton University: Lee Snyder, president, 1 University Dr, Bluffton OH 45817, www.bluffton.edu, 419-358-3000. Eastern Mennonite University: Loren E. Swartzendruber, president, 1200 Park Rd, Harrisonburg VA 22802, www.emu.edu, 540-432-4000. Goshen College: John D. Yordy, interim president, 1700 S Main St, Goshen IN 46526, www.goshen.edu, 574-535-7000. Hesston College: Howard Keim, president, 325 S College, Hesston KS 67062, www.hesston.edu, 620-327-4221

SEMINARIES

Associated Mennonite Biblical Seminary: Nelson Kraybill, president, 3003 Benham Ave, Elkhart IN 46517, www.ambs.edu, 574-295-3726. Eastern Mennonite Seminary: Ervin Stutzman, dean, 1200 Park Rd, Harrisonburg VA 22802, www.emu.edu, 540-432-4260

CHURCHWIDE AGENCIES

1

Mennonite Mission Network

info@MennoniteMission.net,
www.MennoniteMission.net
Toll-free 1-866-866-2872

Great Lakes office: 500 S Main St, PO Box 370, Elkhart IN 46515-0370. In the Great Lakes region, call the toll-free number or fax 574-294-8669

Great Plains office: 722 Main St, PO Box 347, Newton KS 67114-0347, 316-283-5100, fax 316-283-0454

Mennonite Media office: 1251 Virginia Ave, Harrisonburg VA 22802-2497, 540-434-6701, fax 540-434-5556, info@MennoMedia.org, www.MennoMedia.org

To e-mail any staff person, use first name and first initial of last name @MennoniteMission.net.

EXECUTIVE STAFF

Stanley W. Green, executive director/CEO

Erwin Rempel, associate executive director and senior executive for Mission Network Services

Cindy Yoder, corporate secretary

James R. Krabill, senior executive for Global Ministries

Peter Graber, senior executive for Missional Church Advancement

BOARD

Lee Schmucker, chair (LeeSchmuckerMMN@aol.com), 9404 W Wyncroft, Wichita KS 67205, 316-721-2443; N. Leroy Kauffman, vice chair; Richard W. Baum; Tesfatsion Dalellew; Roma J. Eicher; Bill Hochstetler; Loren E. Horst; Heidi Regier Kreider; Craig Maven; Chuwang Pam; Alice Ruth Ramseyer; Steve Cheramie Risingsun; Tonya Ramer Wenger

INFORMATION

Mennonite Mission Network, the mission agency of Mennonite Church USA, exists to lead, mobilize and equip the church to participate in holistic witness to Jesus Christ in a broken world. We envision every congregation and all parts of the church being fully engaged in God's mission—across the street, all through the marketplaces and around the world. The Mission Network supports ministries in more than 55 countries.

Mennonite Mission Network has three priorities: (1) engage people and cultures with the gospel of Jesus Christ, (2) start and cultivate missional congregations and (3) foster a missional identity in the church. For more information about the Mission Network, request a copy of *Mission Mosaic: The People and Ministries of Mennonite Mission Network* by telephone, e-mail, or mail.

DEPARTMENTS

Africa, Steve Wiebe-Johnson, director (Africa@MennoniteMission.net)

Church Relations and Partnership Formation, Dean Heisey, director (Partnership@MennoniteMission.net)

Communications, John D. Yoder, director (Communications@MennoniteMission.net)

Development, Jennifer Szambecki, director (Development@MennoniteMission.net)

East Asia, Sheldon Sawatzky, director (EastAsia@MennoniteMission.net)

Europe, J. Robert Charles, director (Europe@MennoniteMission.net)

Finance, David Weaver, director (Finance@MennoniteMission.net)

Human Resources, Rachel Stoltzfus, director (StaffRecruitment@MennoniteMission.net)

Information Technology, Ed Smolsky, director (IT@MennoniteMission.net)

Latin America, Linda Shelly, director (LatinAmerica@MennoniteMission.net)

Leadership Development, Gilberto Flores, director (Leadership@MennoniteMission.net)

Marketing, Tom Price, director (Marketing@MennoniteMission.net)

Mennonite Media, Burton Buller, director (info@MennoMedia.org)

Missional Church Development, John Powell, director (MissionalDevelopment@MennoniteMission.net)

Service, Learning and Discipleship, Del Hershberger, director (Service@MennoniteMission.net)

West Asia and Middle East, John F. Lapp, director (WestAsia@MennoniteMission.net).

STAFF DISPERSED FROM OUR THREE OFFICES

Contact dispersed staff by calling the churchwide toll-free telephone number: 1-866-866-2872.

Anabaptist Biblical Institute José Elizaldé, instructor, Instituto Bíblico Anabautista, 1417 Monarch Oaks St, Houston TX 77055

DEO (Discipleship, Encounter, Outreach) Dwight Regier, interim program director, Box 306, North Newton KS 67117, fax 316-283-0620, www.d-e-o.org

DOOR (Discovering Opportunities for Outreach and Reflection) Glenn Balzer, national director, 430 W Ninth Ave, Denver CO 80204, fax 303-295-8952, www.citymissions.org

East Asia director Sheldon Sawatzky, SheldonS@MennoniteMission.net, PO Box 12-89, Taoyuan City, 330-99 TAIWAN, Phone 011-886-3-217-2577

Group Venture Jenny Bishop, program director, fax 303-295-8952, www.citymissions.org

Missional Church Development John Powell, director, 184 Barton St, Buffalo NY 14213, fax 716-881-2789; Shirley Powell, assistant (Buffalo office); Karl McKinney, minister of church planting, 4206 LaSalle Ave, Baltimore MD 21206, fax 410-485-5124; Kuaying Teng, minister of Asian ministries, 71 Lakeshore Rd, St Catharines ON L2N 2T3 Canada, fax 905-646-1068

Peace & Justice Support Network C. Leo Hartshorn, minister of peace and justice, 202 S Ann St, Lancaster PA 17602, fax 717-391-6512; Valerie Weidman, administrative assistant

Prayer Network Marietta Sawatzky, prayer network facilitator, MariettaS@MennoniteMission.net, PO Box 12-89, Taoyuan City, 330-99 TAIWAN, Phone 011-886-3-217-2577

RAD (Reaching and Discipling) Mike Fox, training coordinator; Krissy Peterson, development and program assistant; Bob Sprunger, program director; Great Lakes Discipleship Center, 407 Broadway, New Haven IN 46774, www.GLDC.org

INTERNATIONAL MINISTRIES

Mennonite Mission Network places more than 170 long-term workers (those serving terms of one year or longer) in 46 countries. Many ministries and personnel placements occur in partnership with Mennonite Church Canada Witness, Eastern Mennonite Missions, Virginia Mennonite Board of Missions or Mennonite Central Committee. In six African countries—Botswana, Burkina Faso, Democratic Republic of Congo, Lesotho, Senegal and South Africa—program is administered through Africa Inter-Mennonite Mission. The Mission Network also places workers through multi-agency partnerships in Afghanistan (International Assistance Mission), China (China Educational Exchange), Lithuania (Lithuania Christian College), Mongolia (Joint Christian Services International) and Nepal (United Mission to Nepal). The Mission Network has founded six Mennonite or Anabaptist centers in London; Paris; Brussels, Belgium; Seoul, South Korea; and Tokyo.

PARTNERSHIPS

Mennonite Mission Network has 10 operating mission partnerships involving congregations, area conferences and other national and international groups organized to accomplish specific mission objectives. More than 80 Mennonite Church USA congregations join with other partners to lead and support mission partnerships, which coordinate their efforts through a facilitator and a council. In addition, there are 11 support networks involving more than 20 congregations plus individuals, and another 182 congregations support 51 workers and provide $850,000 in financial contributions through the Ministry Partners program.

Argentina—Evangelistic Missionary Vision Western Zone (VEMZO): Mennonites in participating congregations of Atlantic Coast Conference join with Argentine churches in Visión Evangelistica y Misionera de la Zona Oeste (VEMZO) to encourage and mutually support one another in mission and ministry together with Mennonite Mission Network. H. A. Penner, facilitator

Argentina—Patagonia: Mennonites in Illinois and Argentina's Patagonia region join together to mutually encourage and support church planting in Argentina and church renewal in Illinois. Mission Network partners include the Argentina Mennonite Church (IEMA), Arm in Arm (a cluster of congregations in Illinois), and Mennonite Churches in Patagonia (IMPA). Delbert and Frieda Erb, facilitators

Benin Bible Institute (Benin) brings together representatives of Benin Bible Institute and members of Waterford Mennonite Church in Goshen, Ind., to ensure adequate resource development and alleviate the ongoing financial commitment of Mennonite Mission Network.

DEO (Discipleship, Encounter, Outreach) is an initiative involving Mennonite Mission Network, Hesston (Kan.) College, Bethel (Kan.) College, Western District, and South Central Conference to equip young people to become whole-life disciples of Jesus Christ. Del Hershberger, interim board chair

Ecuador: Colombian Mennonite Church, Central Plains Mennonite Conference, and Mennonite Mission Network seek to be instruments of reconciliation in the world through supporting church development and the holistic development of indigenous people to demonstrate the love of God in Ecuadorian society. Ely Soto Albrecht, facilitator

Great Lakes Discipleship Center equips young adults to become lifelong, radical disciples of Jesus Christ. Mission Network partners include congregations from the Great Lakes region, Illinois Mennonite Conference, Indiana-Michigan Mennonite Conference, Ohio Mennonite Conference, and the Fellowship of Evangelical Churches. Earl Cecil, board president

Mongolia Mission Partnership is a coalition of Ohio congregations that support ministry through Joint Christian Services International in Mongolia. Burt Parks, facilitator

Senegal mobilizes a movement to Christ among the Wolof people of Senegal, leading to the planting of churches. Mission Network partners include Africa Inter-Mennonite Mission and Friends of the Wolof. Earl Roth, facilitator

South Africa/New Zion is a leadership and people exchange focused on church planting in South Africa and Virginia conference. Mission Network partners include New Zion Church movement based in Pietermaritzburg, South Africa, Calvary Community Church in Hampton, Va., and Virginia Mennonite Board of Missions.

Tabasaran (Russia) is a partnership with the Friends of the Tabasaran (based in west-central Ohio) to support Christian leadership among the Tabasaran people and build long-term relationships. Joe Henson, facilitator

SERVICE PROGRAMS

The Mission Network facilitates annual short-term assignments for more than 2,000 volunteers through its Service, Learning, and Discipleship programs. For more information on any programs or opportunities, visit http://service.MennoniteMission.net or e-mail service@MennoniteMission.net

DEO (Discipleship, Encounter, Outreach) challenges young adults (ages 18 to 30) to experience an intimate encounter with Jesus, radical outreach, and practical service. Dwight Regier, interim program director

DOOR (Discovering Opportunities for Outreach and Reflection) Through weeklong and weekend opportunities in major urban cities, groups immerse themselves in city life, encounter the living urban church, serve in community-based ministries, and reflect on the message of the psalmist: "God is in the midst of the city" (Psalm 46:5). Cities include Atlanta, Chicago, Denver, Miami, and San Antonio. Glenn Balzer, national program director

Group Venture, linking groups to options for service and spiritual reflection in North America. Jenny Bishop, program director

Mennonite Voluntary Service, providing one- or two-year opportunities for individuals to live out their faith through service in communities across North America. Tonia Stutzman, program co-director

RAD (Reaching and Discipling), for young adults (ages 18-30) in team-based discipleship training and outreach in Africa, Asia, Europe, Latin America, or North America. Bob Sprunger, program director

Service Adventure, promoting service, learning, and spiritual growth for post-high school students in eight U.S. communities. Susan Nisly, program director

SOOP (Service Opportunities for Older People), short-term service opportunities for adults age 50 and up—a partnership with Mennonite Association of Retired Persons and Mennonite Central Committee Canada. Arloa Bontrager, program director

Youth Venture, a one- to three-week short-term mission experience for teens (ages 14-20) in North America or internationally. Arloa Bontrager, program director

RESOURCES

Books Abroad, a grassroots ministry coordinated by the Mission Network but carried out by groups and individual volunteers in six locations. (Cindy Yoder, contact) BooksAbroad@MennoniteMission.net

City on a Hill, providing church planting and ministry grants to urban locations (Marty Bender, administrator) CityOnAHill@MennoniteMission.net

Conference Mission Leaders, an annual meeting for input, resources and networking for mission leaders from area conferences.

(Marty Bender, facilitator)
EquippingCongregations@
MennoniteMission.net

Instituto Bíblico Anabautista
(Anabaptist Biblical Institute), a leadership-training program in cooperation with more than two dozen congregations for Spanish-speaking lay people in North America. (Gilberto Flores, director)
Leadership@MennoniteMission.net

Mennonite Media acts on behalf of Mennonite Church USA to promote an Anabaptist understanding in secular media through television documentaries, public-service announcements and websites, and creates resources, such as educational videos to assist congregations in their ministry. (Burton Buller, director)
info@MennoMedia.org

Ministry Partners and **Support Networks** organize congregations and individuals into groups that provide personal, prayerful, and financial support for specific ministries and/or workers. (Marlene Kroeker, coordinator)
MinistryPartners@MennoniteMission.net

Mission Musicians Doug and Jude Krehbiel (Road Less Travelled) give musical and multimedia presentations to spread the vision of a missional church and share about ministries of the Mission Network.
Musicians@MennoniteMission.net or
http://Musicians.MennoniteMission.net

Missional Church Development consultants provide coaching and assistance to congregations and conferences in church planting, community development, evangelism, multiethnic ministries, peace, and urban ministry. (John Powell, director)
MissionalDevelopment@MennoniteMission.net

Peace & Justice Support Network sponsored by Mennonite Church USA Executive Leadership and the Mission Network to focus and promote the vision of peace in the denomination, providing resources to congregations and individuals. (Leo Hartshorn, minister of peace and justice)
Peace@MennoniteMission.net

Prayer network ministry, inviting people to commit to regular prayer for mission. (Marietta Sawatzky, facilitator)
Prayer@MennoniteMission.net

Speakers program places mission workers, volunteers, and staff in hundreds of congregations annually. (Angela Rempel, congregational relations manager)
Speakers@MennoniteMission.net

Third Way Café, an Internet ministry produced by Mennonite Media to introduce an Anabaptist understanding of what it means to follow Jesus and the way of peace. (Sheri Hartzler, team leader) www.ThirdWay.com

Urban Leaders Network, an annual gathering of pastors and lay leaders for networking, education, consultation, and mutual enrichment. (Marty Bender, facilitator)
UrbanMinistry@MennoniteMission.net

Urban Ministry Directors, a partnership between area conferences and the Mission

Network that designates leaders in more than a dozen metropolitan areas who work to develop a network of local leadership, start new churches and ministries, and create a visible Anabaptist presence. (Marty Bender, facilitator) UrbanMinistry@MennoniteMission.net

PUBLICATIONS

Another Way (weekly column on family life, values and spirituality), Melodie M. Davis, writer; *Beyond Ourselves* (quarterly), John D. Yoder, editor; *Links@Mennomedia* (contemporary media newsletter three times per year), Melodie M. Davis, editor; *Missio Dei* (booklet series inviting reflection and dialogue on mission issues), James R. Krabill, editor; Mission Network news (weekly e-mail of news releases from Mennonite Mission Network); *Mustard Seeds* (quarterly for mission partners who provide regular support for four Mission Network projects annually); *Prayer Vine* (monthly guide of daily prayer requests available in print or by e-mail), Marietta Sawatzky, editor; *Through a Missional Lens,* a series of one-page papers with practical ideas about how different congregational activities can have a missional component (periodic); *Urban Connections* (inter-Anabaptist e-mail newsletter published six times a year), Regina Shands Stoltzfus, editor; *x-Tending God's Mission* (quarterly), Stanley W. Green, editor

To subscribe to Mission Network publications, go to http://MennoniteMission.net/subscriptions/

Mennonite Mutual Aid

mma@mma-online.org, www.mma-online.org
800-348-7468 and 574-533-9511, fax 574-533-5264
1110 N Main St, PO Box 483, Goshen IN 46527

To e-mail any staff person, use first name.last name @mma-online.org

EXECUTIVE STAFF

Howard Brenneman, president and CEO
Mel Claassen, chief financial officer
Eunice Culp, vice president, human resources
Rod Diller, senior vice president, trust services and Mennonite Foundation
Ron Dueck, vice president, group business development
Steve Garboden, senior vice president, administrative services and health services
Barth Hague, vice president, marketing services
John Liechty, senior vice president, financial services
Steve Martin, senior vice president, corporate marketing
Vyron Schmidt, vice president, fraternal benefits
Barb Slagel, vice president, information technology and chief information officer
Karl Sommers, vice president, corporate planning

BOARD

Carol J. Suter, chair (csuter@kc.rr.com), 7233 N Bellefontaine, Kansas City MO 64119, 816-436-4833; LaVern Yutzy, vice chair; John L. Burkey; Carol L. Duerksen; Ken Enns; Andrew Eversole; David Faber; Natalie A. Francisco; Richard Friesen; Philip Keefer; J. David von Gunten; Arlan R. Yoder; Gene E. Yoder

INFORMATION

MMA was founded in 1945. Its mission is to lead Anabaptists toward greater practice of biblical principles of holistic stewardship.

MMA's Board of Directors is elected or appointed from Mennonite Church USA, the Missionary Church, Brethren in Christ Church, Conservative Mennonite Conference, and Mennonite Brethren Church. The organization is composed of 12 active legal entities that handle its administrative services and operate its programs.

MMA offers expertise and assistance to Mennonites and other Anabaptists in pursuing stewardship solutions through its diversified insurance and financial services, as well as charitable programs and educational resources.

Insurance includes health, life, long-term care, and disability income coverage, with plans for individuals and groups.

Financial services include mutual funds, annuities, trust services and estate consultation, Mennonite Retirement Trust, staff pension plan for congregations and church institutions, and investment management for individuals and institutions. MMA provides institutions and congregations with mortgages and other financing. All investments are guided by stewardship investing principles.

Mennonite Foundation provides planned charitable giving for individuals and planned giving services for institutions. Mennonite Foundation offers seminars and other educational events and serves members of Mennonite Church USA and other Mennonite and Anabaptist-related groups.

MMA's fraternal benefits include matching grants, educational resources, Stewardship University, and stewardship ministries. Fraternal benefits are made possible because part of MMA is a fraternal benefit association, and money that would otherwise be paid in taxes is instead channeled to members and churches. Fraternal benefits do not increase members' premiums or fees.

REGIONAL VICE PRESIDENTS—SALES

Phil Mason, Ole Town Square, 371 N Old Hwy 81,

PO Box 909, Hesston KS 67062, 620-327-4043; David Gautsche, 1110 N Main St, PO Box 483, Goshen IN 46527-0483, 574-533-9411; Leon Hoover, 201 E Oregon Rd, Suite 103, Lititz PA 17543, 717-560-6800

CHURCH RELATIONS MANAGERS

Lois Bontrager, 5358 Kidron Rd, PO Box 266, Kidron OH 44636, 800-986-9988; Barbara Borntrager, 1675-A Virginia Ave, Harrisonburg VA 22802, 800-442-7930; Steve Bustos, 1110 N Main St, PO Box 483, Goshen IN 46527-0483, 800-348-7468; Mark Fly, 569 Yoder Rd, PO Box 163, Harleysville PA 19438, 800-332-4141; Beverlee Keck, PO Box 728, Brea CA 92822, 800-276-1586; Brad Miller, 1110 N Main St, PO Box 483, Goshen IN 46527-0483, 800-348-7468; James M. Miller, 201 E Oregon Rd, Suite 103, Lititz PA 17543, 800-494-6622; Marvin J. Penner, 371 N Old Hwy 81, PO Box 909, Hesston KS 67062-0909, 877-467-7294; H. James Smith, 1110 N Main St, PO Box 483, Goshen IN 46527-0483, 800-348-7468

MENNONITE FOUNDATION REGIONAL REPRESENTATIVES

Marion Beyeler, 5358 Kidron Rd, PO Box 266, Kidron OH 44636, 800-986-9988; Stan Brown, 9111 W 21st St N, #5, Wichita KS 67205-1809, 316-841-5777; Marlin Hershey, 201 E Oregon Rd, Suite 103, Lititz PA 17543, 800-494-6622; John Hess-Yoder, J. D., West Professional Plaza, 8655 SW Citizens Dr, Suite 102, PO Box 1010, Wilsonville OR 97070, 800-888-6053; Todd Holsopple, 1110 N Main St, PO Box 483, Goshen IN 46527, 800-348-7468; Steve Hunsberger, 569 Yoder Rd, PO Box 163, Harleysville PA 19438, 800-332-4141; Joseph Lapp, 1675-A Virginia Ave, Harrisonburg VA 22802, 800-442-7930; Arlin Lapp, 569 Yoder Rd, PO Box 163, Harleysville PA 19438, 800-332-4141; Greg Miller, 1110 N Main St, PO Box 483, Goshen IN 46527, 800-348-7468; Mike Miller, Ole Town Square, 371 N Old Hwy 81, PO Box 909, Hesston KS 67062, 877-467-7294

MMA TRUST COMPANY REPRESENTATIVES

Tim Braun, 103 Johnson St, Suite A, PO Box 607, Goshen IN 46528, 574-537-8773; Rod Diller, 1110 N Main Street, PO Box 483, Goshen IN 46528, 800-348-7468; Bill Hartman, 201 E Oregon Road, Suite 103, Lititz PA 17543, 800-494-6622; John King, 1110 N Main Street, PO Box 483, Goshen IN 46528, 800-348-7468; Joseph Lapp, 1675-A Virginia Ave, Harrisonburg VA 22802, 800-442-7930; Mike Miller, Ole Town Square, 371 North Old Hwy 81, PO Box 909, Hesston KS 67062, 877-467-7294; Darin Short, 1110 N Main Street, PO Box 483, Goshen IN 46528, 800-348-7468

Mennonite Publishing Network

MPN is a joint ministry of Mennonite Church USA and Mennonite Church Canada. www.mph.org

OFFICES—USA

1. **Scottdale** (info@mph.org)
   724-887-8500, fax 724-887-3111
   616 Walnut Ave, Scottdale PA 15683-1999
2. **Newton** (flr@mph.org)
   316-283-5100, fax 316-283-0454
   718 Main St, PO Box 347, Newton KS 67114-0347

OFFICES—CANADA

1. **Waterloo** (offices of executive director and director of Faith & Life Resources)
   519-888-7512, fax 519-888-7605
   490 Dutton Dr, Suite C7, Waterloo ON N2L 6H7
2. **Waterloo** (distribution centre, hpcan@mph.org)
   519-747-5722, fax 519-747-5721
   490 Dutton Dr, Suite C8, Waterloo ON N2L 6H7

ORDER/CONTACT INFORMATION

Faith & Life Resources—church resources, flr@mph.org, 800-245-7894

Herald Press—trade books, hp@mph.org, 800-245-7894

Provident Bookstores—pbsorder@mph.org, 800-759-4447

For more detail including phone and e-mail directory of staff, see the MPN website www.mph.org.

MANAGEMENT TEAM

Ron Rempel, executive director
Chris Ronallo (controller); Cathy Depta (order fulfillment); Terry Graber (printing/production); Eleanor Snyder (director, Faith & Life Resources); Levi Miller (director, Herald Press); Ken Reinford (director, Provident Bookstores)

BOARD

Ron Sawatsky, chair (ronsawat@earthlink.net), 224 Harvard Ct, Souderton PA 18964, *Laverne Brubacher, vice chair; Phil Bontrager, treasurer; Curtis R. Berry, secretary; June Krehbiel; Sheri Hostetler; *Abe Bergen; *Carry Dueck. Five members are elected or appointed by MC USA and three (*) by MC Canada.

VISION/PURPOSE

The name Mennonite Publishing Network was adopted in 2002 after a 2001 merger of Mennonite Publishing House (founded in 1908) and Faith & Life Press (founded in 1860).

The vision and purpose of Mennonite Publishing Network is to provide materials that equip the church to experience and share the gospel from an Anabaptist perspective and to provide simple access to materials that shape Christian identity and mission in a U.S. and Canadian Mennonite context.

MPN seeks to fulfill its mission through its three divisions: Faith & Life Resources (congregational publishing), Herald Press (trade publishing) and Provident Bookstores (retail sales).

FAITH & LIFE RESOURCES

Eleanor Snyder, director; Cynthia Linscheid, marketing; Merrill Miller, design; Debbie Cameron and Lisa Burkhart, administrative assistants. Editors include: Carol Duerksen (*With*); James E. Horsch (*Purpose* and *Adult Bible Study*); Mary Meyer (*On the Line*); Byron Rempel-Burkholder (*Leader* and *Rejoice!*); Susan Swan (*Story Friends*). This division also produces curriculum and other resources for the church.

HERALD PRESS

Levi Miller, director; Sarah Kehrberg, editor; Patricia Weaver, marketing; Sandy Johnson, design; Michelle Cannillo, proofreader; Joshua Byler, administrative assistant; Kathy Shantz, Canadian distribution.

PROVIDENT BOOKSTORES

Ken Reinford, director of the bookstore chain and manager of the Lancaster PA store. Other store managers: Nate Humbert (New Holland and Ephrata, Pa.); Doug Landis (Souderton, Pa.); Mary Jo Kapper (Wooster, Ohio); Christine Litwiller (Bloomington, Ill.); Jilaine Graber (Berne, Ind.); Jeryl Weaver (Goshen, Ind.); Alma Unrau (Newton, Kan.). For further information, including store locations, see www.providentbookstores.com

Mennonite Church USA
Congregations and Members

For congregations affiliated with two area conferences, the "inclusive" columns includes all members and all congregations in both area conferences. The "exclusive" columns attribute half of the members and half of these congregations to each conference to give accurate figures for total members and congregations affiliated with Mennonite Church USA.

Area Conference	# of member congregations (inclusive)	# of member congregations (exclusive)	# of members (inclusive)	# of members (exclusive)
Allegheny	32	32.0	3,121	3,121
Atlantic Coast	30	29.5	4,070	4,046
Central District	57	44.0	7,457	6,356
Central Plains	55	54.5	7,969	7,961
Eastern District	15	14.5	2,151	2,176
Franconia	44	44.0	6,700	6,700
Franklin	14	14.0	1,186	1,186
Gulf States	14	14.0	654	654
Illinois	45	38.0	6,710	6,108
Ind.-Michigan	85	81.0	10,283	10,065
Lancaster	186	186.0	17,496	17,496
New York	17	17.0	1,304	1,304
North Central	13	12.5	504	496
Ohio	75	72.0	10,736	10,454
Pacific NW	34	34.0	2,685	2,685
Pacific SW	45	45.0	3,293	3,293
Rocky Mtn	20	18.0	1,521	1,384
South Central	46	39.5	3,974	3,620
Southeast	29	29.0	2,700	2,700
Virginia	67	67.0	8,817	8,817
Western District	66	57.5	10,900	10,409
TOTALS		**943**		**111,031**

Note: Twenty-six church plants listed in the directory are not included in these membership totals.

Conferences and congregations

2

Mennonite Church USA includes 21 area conferences with more than 900 congregations in the United States and northern Mexico. The chart on the previous page gives you an overview of the number of congregations and members in each area conference.

A comprehensive listing of abbreviations used in this section can be found on page 10.

Updated congregational information is available in the online directory at www.MennoniteUSA.org. Links to area conference websites also are included in the online directory. If your congregational information is not up-to-date, ask your church office to update the information online.

SAMPLE LISTING:

Name	(ID number)	(Affiliation/s)	Membership
Lindale Menn Ch	(18655)	(VA)	338

Mailing address
PO Box 1082, Harrisonburg VA 22803

Telephone, fax, e-mail, web
540-833-5171, fax 540-833-2212, admin@lindale.org, http://www.lindale.org

Location of meetingplace (if different from mailing address)
6255 Jesse Bennett Way in Linville

Name(s) of pastoral team member(s), title
Duane Allen Yoder, Pastor
Howard Miller, Associate Pastor

FOR EXAMPLE
Lindale Menn Ch (18655) (VA) **338**
PO Box 1082, Harrisonburg VA 22803
540-833-5171, fax 540-833-2212,
admin@lindale.org, http://www.lindale.org
6255 Jesse Bennett Way in Linville
   Duane Allen Yoder, Pastor
   Howard Miller, Associate Pastor

Allegheny Mennonite Conference

OFFICE
officeamc@cs.com
814-443-2007, fax 814-445-3418
111 E Main St, PO Box 12, Somerset PA 15501

STAFF
Kathy Holsopple, administrator assistant
(officeamc@cs.com)
Kurt Horst, conference minister
(kurtamc@cs.com)
Joy Cotchen, conference minister of children
and youth (jcotchenamc@cs.com)

GENERAL INFORMATION
Year founded: 1876
Members: 3,121
Congregations: 32
Ministers: 69
CLC reps: Kurt Horst, Carl Geissinger, and
Donna Mast
Annual Conference: August 4-7, 2005

EXECUTIVE COMMITTEE
Gloria Rosenberger, moderator, 464 E Foster
Ave, State College PA 16801, 814-234-2167
Carl Geissinger, moderator-elect; Brenda
Benner, James Brubaker, Wayne Lasure, Mary
Beth Lind, Enos Tice

PUBLICATION
Conference News (monthly) Donna Mast, editor (Kingview@westol.com), 513 Scottdale Ave,
Scottdale PA 15683, 724-887-5563

COMMISSIONS
Faith, Life, and Procedures Commission.
Enos Tice, chair (enostice@gcnet.net), 117
Mineral St, Salisbury PA 15558, 814-662-
4331. Members: Melvin Blough, Lynette
Plank, Trish Yoder
Finance and Stewardship Commission.
Brenda Benner, chair (blbenner66@
hotmail.com) 1462 Listie Rd, Friedens PA

15541, 814-443-3265. Members: Roger
Oswald, Tony Kanagy
Leadership Commission. James Brubaker,
chair (jnbru@sunlink.net), 1530 Buffalo
Rd, Lewisburg PA 17837, 570-523-3904.
Members: Daryl (Doc) Dawson, Judy Nord,
Steve Sauder
Mission and Service Commission. Wayne
Lasure, chair (WayneLSR@aol.com), 252
Keyser Rd, Boswell PA 15531, 814-629-
7216. Members: Cathy Chapman,
T. J. Tennefoss
Nurture and Education Commission. Mary
Beth Lind, chair (lmlind@meer.net), PO
Box 65, Harman WV 26270, 304-227-4427.
Members: Jeff Jones, Chester Yoder

OTHER
Mission and Service Projects
International Guest House, 1441 Kennedy St
NW, Washington DC 20011, 202-726-5808;
Annabelle Kratz, board chair
Urban Ministries, Pittsburgh PA

VS Projects:
Philippi Service Adventure Unit, 26 Beech
St, Philippi WV 26416, 304-457-4652
Johnstown Service Adventure Unit, 640
Somerset Ave, Johnstown PA 15901814-535-
8573
World's Attic Thrift and Gift Shop, 109 E
Main St, Somerset PA 814-445-4886

Congregations

Barrville Menn Ch (10140) (ALL) 81
48 Barrville Mountain Rd, Reedsville PA 17084
717-935-2583, http://www.hows.net/17084BMC
  Gerald Peachey, Pastor

Blough Menn Ch (10157) (ALL) 102
794 Woodstown Hwy, Hollsopple PA 15935
814-479-7566, bprabsimon@aol.com,
http://www.hows.net/15935BMC
  Robert Simonsick, Pastor
  David Garber, Interim Pastor

Boyer Menn Ch (10165) (ALL) 86
RR2, Box 158-C, Middleburg PA 17842
570-837-3366, johnbeachy@jdweb.com
Oak Dr, Rt 2, Middleburg
  John D. Beachy, Pastor

Canan Station Menn Ch (10173) (ALL) 50
RR 2, 455 Burns Avenue, Altoona PA 16601
814-695-0341
  Daryl Dawson, Pastor
  Jack Styer, Assistant Pastor

Carpenter Park Menn Ch (10181) (ALL) 165
2662 Carpenters Park Rd, Davidsville PA 15928
814-288-3264, fax 814-288-4624,
cpchurch@floodcity.net
  Todd Brenneman, Pastor

Cornerstone Fell of Mill Run (10330) (ALL) 62
RR 6 Box 1424, Altoona PA 16601
814-942-4003

Crossroads Community Ch (10488) (ALL) 50
1259 Scalp Ave, Johnstown PA 15904-3137
814-266-5094, russeanes@acninc.net
Just west of Rt 219 & Scalp Ave Interchange
  Russ Eanes, Pastor

First Menn Ch (10215) (ALL) 46
705 Somerset St, Johnstown PA 15901
814-535-1688

Glade Menn Ch (10231) (ALL) 114
5011 Accident Bittinger Rd, Accident MD 21520
301-245-4285, fax 301-245-4285,
gladechurch@iceweb.net,
http://www.forministry.com/21520gmc
  Christopher Z. Weaver, Pastor

Gortner Union Ch (22632) (ALL, COB) 38
PO Box 464, Oakland MD 21550
301-334-7969, ssauder@pennswoods.net
4391 Mason School Rd
  Steve Sauder, Pastor

Hyattsville Menn Ch (10223) (ALL, DC) 138
4217 East-West Hwy, Hyattsville MD 20782
301-927-7327, jroos@hyattsvillemennonite.org,
http://www.hyattsvillemennonite.org
  Cynthia Lapp, Pastor
  Joe Roos, Pastor

Kaufman Menn Ch (10256) (ALL) 132
916 Miller Picking Rd, Davidsville PA 15928-9523
814-479-7813, Kmcmenno@yahoo.com,
http://www.hows.net/15935KMC
Miller Picking Rd, 1/2 mile east of Rt 403 N
  Don Hamsher, Pastor

Living Way Fell (11434) (ALL) 0
PO Box 51, Tire Hill PA 15959
814-288-5763
Jerome, PA
  James Thomas, Pastor

Maple Grove Menn Ch (21931) (ALL) 268
PO Box 955, Belleville PA 17004
717-935-2513, fax 717-935-9900,
mgmcbe@acsworld.com
115 Maple Grove Rd
  Richard Alan Kauffman, Pastor

Martinsburg Menn Ch (10298) (ALL) 106
300 E Spring St, Martinsburg PA 16662
814-793-4211, mmc@wmsburgpa.com,
http://www.martinsburg.pa.us.mennonite.net
  Jeff Shull, Pastor

Masontown Menn Ch (10306) (ALL) 55
PO Box 683, Masontown PA 15461
724-737-6927
Smithfield-Masontown Rd

Meadow Mountain Menn Ch (10322) (ALL) 53
6302 Bittinger Rd, Swanton MD 21561
301-245-4030, revfrederick@hotmail.com
6117 Bittinger Rd
  Duane Frederick, Pastor

Morgantown Ch of the Brethren (27300)
(ALL, COB) 95
464 Virginia Ave, Morgantown WV 26505
304-292-5616, http://mcob.wv.us.mennonite.net
  Cameron Blake Kaufman-Frey, Pastor

New Life Menn Ch (10740) (ALL) 24
604 Listie Rd, PO Box 7, Listie PA 15549
814-288-5617, rls173@aol.com
  Ron Spory, Pastor

Oak Grove Menn Ch (10348) (ALL) 56
PO Box 368, Grantsville MD 21536
301-895-4054, fax 301-895-4054, tcfetterly@earthlink.net,
http://www.acountryvillage.com
188 Zehner Rd
  Tim Fetterly, Pastor

CONFERENCES AND
CONGREGATIONS

2

Otelia Menn Ch (10355) (ALL) 47
RR 2 Box 147, Mount Union PA 17066
814-543-7269, fax 814-543-7269, davidcjr@juno.com
RD 1 Rt 103

Philippi Menn Ch (26500) (ALL) 20
216 S Main St, Philippi WV 26416
304-457-2602

Pinto Menn Ch (10363) (ALL) 160
PO Box 44, Pinto MD 21556
304-726-4380, lthersh1@prodigy.net
13822 Pinto Rd SW
    Philip Dayton, Pastor
    Lester T. Hershey, Associate Pastor
    Paul T. Livengood, Associate Pastor

Pittsburgh Menn Ch (10371) (ALL) 39
4005 Murray Ave, Pittsburgh PA 15217
412-421-8007, fax 412-421-8007,
http://pittsburgh.pa.us.mennonite.net
    John Paul Bender, Pastor

Red Run Menn Ch (10397) (ALL) 31
662 Meyersdale Rd, Grantsville MD 21536
670 Meyersdale Rd (5 miles east of Grantsville)
    Carlos Reyes, Pastor

Rockville Menn Ch (10405) (ALL) 127
319 Rockville Rd, Belleville PA 17004
717-935-2796, rockmchr@juno.com
    Harold E. Sharp, Pastor

Scottdale Menn Ch (10413) (ALL) 200
801 Market St, Scottdale PA 15683
724-887-7470, fax 724-887-7470, scottmc@westol.com,
http://www.forministry.com/15323mcos
    Conrad Mast, Co-Pastor
    Donna Mast, Co-Pastor

Springs Menn Ch (10439) (ALL) 319
PO Box 127, Springs PA 15562
814-662-4201, springsmc@mapisp.com
1686 Springs Rd
    Steven Jay Heatwole, Pastor

Stahl Menn Ch (10447) (ALL) 114
1201 Soap Hollow Rd, Johnstown PA 15905
814-288-5523, tkcroyle@hotmail.com,
http://www.stahlchurch.pa.us.mennonite.net
    Tom Croyle, Pastor
    Joy Cotchen, Youth Pastor

Thomas Menn Ch (10454) (ALL) 141
112 Swank Rd, Hollsopple PA 15935
814-479-2127, waynelsr@aol.com,
http://www.pitt.edu/-kxy/Bulletin
    D. Wayne Lasure, Pastor

Tressler Menn Ch (10462) (ALL) 130
PO Box N, Greenwood DE 19950
302-349-4128, lowpegbechtel@juno.com
Owens Station, Rt 16 E
    Lowell B. Bechtel, Pastor

University Menn Ch (10470) (ALL) 72
318 S Atherton St, State College PA 16801
814-234-2039, fax 814-234-5257,
umc1963@chilitech.com,
http://www.universitymennonite.org/
    David B. Miller, Pastor

Atlantic Coast Conference

OFFICE
atlanticcoast@frontiernet.net,
www.atlanticcoastconference.org
717-355-0550 and 1-800-238-0126
115 E Main St, New Holland PA 17557

STAFF
Miriam Martin, conference minister/administrator (MiriamM@frontiernet.net)
Warren L. Tyson, conference minister (WarrenT@frontiernet.net)
Merv R. Stoltzfus, conference minister/youth ministry (woodray@aol.com)
Nelson S. Yoder, conference minister (NelsonY@frontiernet.net)

GENERAL INFORMATION
Year founded: 1978
Members: 4,070
Congregations: 30
Ministers: 57 active, 23 retired
CLC reps: Miriam Martin, Edgar Stoesz, Warren Tyson
Delegate sessions: 4th Saturday in April and 4th Saturday in October

EXECUTIVE COMMITTEE
Edgar Stoesz, moderator (edgarstoesz@juno.com), 929 Broad St, Akron PA 17501; James Wenger, moderator-elect; Nathan King, treasurer; Etta Esch, Mary Grace Shenk

PUBLICATION
ACC Currents (bimonthly), Lois E. Whisler, editor (lwhisler@supernet.com), 10 Panther Dr, Hanover PA 17331

COMMITTEES
Missions. Ruth Keidel Clemens, chair (keidel-clemens@juno.com), 5815 Stuart Ave, Baltimore MD 21215; Eileen Graybill, Nolan Good, Calvin Kurtz, Doris Martin, Wilmer Martin, Karl McKinney, Edgar Stoesz, Warren Tyson

Finance and Stewardship. Lloyd Kuhns, chair (lgkuhns@paonline.com), 1314 Main St, Akron PA 17501; Robert Bear, Ken Herr, Nathan King, Miriam Martin, Leon Miller, Ray Ranck

Ministerial Leadership. Calvin L. Yoder, chair (calyoder@yahoo.com), 100 Quarry Rd, Leola PA 17540; John Rush, Nancy Sauder, Edgar Stoesz, Warren Tyson, Lois Whisler, Nelson Yoder

Peace and Justice Task Force. co-chairs: Pat Yoder (npyoder1@juno.com), 5948 Michele Dr, Narvon PA 17555 and Julie Dunst (Julie@Lifespan.teamon.com); L. Jason Baer, Arlene Baer, Jim Dunst, Miriam Martin, Jean Senseing, Justin Shenk, Larry Shirk, J. Richard Thomas

Gifts Discernment. Anna Stoltzfus, Seth Ebersole, Julie Dunst, Warren Martin

Youth. Dwight Rohrer, chair (drohrer@neffmc.org), 2371 Lititz Pike, Lancaster PA 17601; Anne Hertzler, Michael Layton, Candace Stoltzfus, Merv R. Stoltzfus

OTHER CONFERENCE AGENCY AND REPS
Mennonite Women. Kathleen Roth, chair (dsecc@dejazzd.com), 125 Bomberger Rd, Akron PA 17501; Etta Esch, Jane Hartzler, Marilyn Langeman, Gwen Peachey, Jean Sensenig, Rosemary Shenk, Elaine Shirk, Jan Stoltzfus, Brenda Wagner

CONFERENCES AND CONGREGATIONS

2

Congregations

Akron Menn Ch (15651) (ACC) **454**
1311 Diamond St, Akron PA 17501
717-859-1488, fax 717-859-3942, amc@akronmench.org,
http://www.akronmench.org
  James S. Amstutz, Pastor
  Dawn Yoder Harms, Pastor

Ark Bible Chapel (15669) (ACC) **49**
88 Woodchoppertown Rd, Boyertown PA 19512
610-987-0429, kglick@juno.com,
http://www.forministry.com/19512abc
  Karl G. Glick, Pastor

Bethel Menn Ch (15743) (ACC) **84**
2335 Biglerville Rd, Gettysburg PA 17325
717-677-8057, fax 717-677-4847, bmurr@pa.net;
bethelchurch@pa.net,
http://www.forministry.com/17325bmc
  Robert G. Murr, Pastor

Birch Grove Menn Ch (15792) (ACC) **33**
321 Broad St, Port Allegany PA 16743
814-642-9275, bindluse@penn.com
Two-Mile Rd, RD 2
  Neil Binder, Pastor
  John H. Lapp, Minister of Visitation

Black Oak Menn Ch (15800) (ACC) **31**
2247 Stoneybreak Rd, Warfordsburg PA 17267
877-263-6105, reugenejr@msn.com
  Richard E. Rutherford Jr., Pastor

Cedar Grove Menn Ch (15834) (ACC) **235**
13343 Williamsport Pike, Greencastle PA 17225
717-597-3681, fax 717-597-1943, cedargrove@pa.net
  Stephen P. Fretz, Pastor

**Community Menn Ch of Lancaster (27441)
(ACC)** **197**
332 W Orange St, Lancaster PA 17603
717-392-7567, fax 717-392-6598, cmcl@mennonite.net,
http://cmcl.pa.us.mennonite.net
328 W Orange St
  Pamela R. Dintaman, Pastor

Conestoga Menn Ch (15875) (ACC) **289**
2779 Main Street, Morgantown PA 19543
610-286-9124, fax 610-913-0441,
conestogamc@hydrosoft.net
On Rt 23
  Alvin B. Horning, Pastor

Ephesians Menn Ch (23762) (ACC, NYC, IMH) . . .**10**
9 Kew Gardens Rd Apt 102, Queens NY 11415
718-261-4752
128 W 16th St, Manhattan
  Salomon Arias, Pastor

First Menn Ch (15958) (ACC, NYC, IMH) **18**
PO Box 278, Metro Sta, Brooklyn NY 11206
718-782-4444, fmcb1@juno.com
23 Marcus Garvey Blvd
  Moises H. Sanchez, Pastor

Forest Hills Menn Ch (16287) (ACC) **354**
100 Quarry Rd, Leola PA 17540
717-656-6227, fax 717-656-8607, fhmc@dejazzd.com,
http://www.foresthillschurch.org
  Calvin L. Yoder, Pastor
  Shawn D. Moyer, Youth and Young Adult Pastor

**Friendship Community Ch (16253) (ACC, NYC,
AAMA)** **25**
2283 Southern Blvd, Bronx NY 10460
718-933-3915, FCC2283@juno.com
  Kenneth Lee Thompson, Pastor

Hebron Menn Ch (23572) (ACC) **56**
13315 Highlane St, Hagerstown MD 21742
301-797-3697, h-mgshenk@juno.com,
http://hebron.md.us.mennonite.net
  Harold A. Shenk, Co-Pastor
  Mary Grace Shenk, Co-Pastor

Holly Grove Menn Ch (16089) (ACC) **155**
7333 Mennonite Church Rd, Westover MD 21871
410-957-3463, fax 410-957-3463, verleb@dmv.com
  Verle Alden Brubaker, Pastor
  Nathan T. Stucky, Youth Pastor

Hope Community Ch (10039) (ACC) **110**
31 Lobachsville Rd, Fleetwood PA 19522-9743
610-641-8961, pastorjim@hopecomm.org,
http://www.hopecomm.org
  James K. Beachy, Pastor

**Hope Community Fell of Phoenixville (11579)
(ACC)** **86**
224 Hall St, Phoenixville PA 19460
610-327-3109, NGlloyd@juno.com
  Gary E. Lloyd, Pastor

Hopewell Menn—Reading (25999) (ACC) **75**
45 S 6th St, Reading PA 19602
610-373-3907, fax 610-373-1604,
hopewellreadingchurch@netzero.net
6th & Cherry

**Iglesia Evangelica Menonita Eben-Ezer (28589)
(ACC, NYC, IMH)** **23**
1126 Sherman Avenue, Bronx NY 10456
718-538-9288, fax 718-538-9288
  Jorge Nin, Director of Church Council

Immanuel Community Ch (26468) (ACC, NYC) . . .**35**
15020 Barclay Ave, Flushing NY 11355
718-460-2063, fax 718-353-4266, immanuel7@juno.com,
http://www.iccnewyork.net
41-54 Murray St
  Shane Harris, Pastor
  Mark D. Perri, Pastor
  Conrad Sauers, Pastor

Manhattan Menn Fell (3602) (ACC, NYC) 35
314 E 19th St, New York NY 10003
212-673-7970, fax 212-673-7970,
mmfpastor@yahoo.com, http://www.mennohouse.org
15 Rutherford Pl

Maple Grove Menn Ch of Atglen (16188)
(ACC) 239
PO Box 480, Atglen PA 19310
610-593-6658, fax 610-593-6658, mgchurch@netzero.net
549 Swan Rd
   Nilson Assis, Interim/Transitional Pastor
   Bill D. Blank, Associate Pastor

Menn Congregation of Boston (16246)
(ACC, EDC) 49
1555 Massachusetts Ave, Cambridge MA 02138-2903
617-868-7784, biedrzycki@mindspring.com
Harvard Epworth United Methodist Church
   Gordon D. Kaufman, Pastor
   Earl Sears, Interim Pastor

Neffsville Menn Ch (16360) (ACC) 600
2371 Lititz Pike, Lancaster PA 17601-3653
717-569-0012, fax 717-569-2417, craig@neffmc.org,
http://www.stoprestpray.org
   Craig Schloneger, Pastor
   Dwight Rohrer, Youth Pastor
   Arthur P. Dyck, Minister of Music & Worship

New Life Christian Fell (29249) (ACC) 50
7401 Bernville Rd, Bernville PA 19506
610-488-1235, fax 610-488-1235,
newlifebernville@juno.com
   Marquel Ortiz, Pastor

North Baltimore Menn Ch (27920) (ACC) 52
4615 Roland Ave, Baltimore MD 21210
410-542-0988, fax 410-542-0989, Jaswenger@aol.com,
http://www.enbmc.org
   James Rodney Wenger, Pastor

Ocean City Menn Christian Fell (26476)
(ACC) 33
11811 Ocean Gtwy, Ocean City MD 21842
410-213-1211, pastorjoe@dmv.com
Joseph M. Kolb, Pastor
   P. Melville Nafziger, Interim Pastor

Oley Valley Menn Ch (16436) (ACC) 76
1571 Memorial Highway, PO Box 394, Oley PA 19547
610-987-3315
   Harvey Z. Stoltzfus, Interim Pastor

Ridgeview Menn Ch (16576) (ACC) 411
3723 Ridge Rd, Gordonville PA 17529
717-768-3143, fax 717-768-0569,
ridgeviewchurch@paonline.com
John H. Denlinger, Pastor
   Nelson S. Yoder, Associate Pastor
   Jeff Raught, Minister of Music

Sandy Hill Menn Ch (16642) (ACC) 118
420 S Sandy Hill Rd, Coatesville PA 19320
610-857-3959, fax 610-857-4364,
pastordavek@comcast.net,
http://www.sandyhill.pa.us.mennonite.net
   Dale L. Weaver, Senior Pastor
   David P. Klingensmith Jr., Associate Pastor

Zion Menn Ch--Birdsboro (16865) (ACC) 88
582 Zion Rd, Birdsboro PA 19508
610-856-7417, steve@zionmennonite.com
   Steven Alan Musselman, Pastor

CONFERENCES AND
CONGREGATIONS

2

Central District Conference

OFFICE
cdcoffice@hoosierlink.net,
www.centraldistrict.mennonite.net
574-534-1485; 1-800-662-2664,
fax 574-534-8654
1015 Division St, Goshen IN 46528

STAFF
Lloyd Miller, conference minister
(cdcllm@hoosierlink.net)
Emma Hartman, administrative assistant
(cdcoffice@hoosierlink.net)

GENERAL INFORMATION
Year founded: 1957
Members: 7,457
Congregations: 57 + 2 church plants
Ministers: 171
CLC reps: Sue Biesecker-Mast, Lloyd Miller,
Mick Sommers
Annual Conference: June 23-25, 2005 (fourth
weekend)

BOARD OF DIRECTORS
Mick Sommers, president
(mjsommers@msn.com), 23589 Allen Dr,
Elkhart IN 46516, 574-596-6913; Alice Roth,
president-elect; John Hockman, treasurer;
Roberta Lehman, secretary; Art
Neuenschwander, Gordon Oyer

PUBLICATIONS
focus (monthly) and *The Reporter* (quarterly)

COMMITTEES
Camp Friedenswald. Curt Bechler, Jim Eicher,
John Fox, Brad Gerber, Kate Gundy, Scott
Preheim, Jane Steinmetz, Steve Stenger,
Marlene Suter, Kent Yoder
Missional Church. Leonard Beechy, Hilary
Bertsche, John A. Bertsche, John Dey, Sheryl
Dyck, Steve Gusler, Gwen Gustafson-Zook,
Lois Kaufmann-Hunsberger, Pauline Kennel,
Robin LaRue, Glenn Martin, Chuck Neufeld,
Sheryl Nisly-Nagele, John Schrock, Barry
Schmell, Bernie Wiebe
Historian. Appointment in process.
Ministerial. Kathy Neufeld Dunn, Lois
Kaufmann, Phil Mininger, Phil Waite, staff
Program. Cathy Beery Berg, Gerald Biesecker-
Mast, Janeen Bertsche Johnson
Stewardship and Finance. John Hockman,
chair (hockman@kuntrynet.com), PO Box
297, Topeka IN 46571, 260-593-2389;
Emma Hartman, Jeanne Heyerly, Lawrence
Matthews, James Mohr

OTHER CONFERENCE AGENCY AND REPRESENTATIVES
Bluffton University Board of Trustees.
David Baumgartner, David Bertsche, Floyd A.
Liechty, John Liechty, Roberta Mohr, Mark
Weidner
**Chicago Mennonite Learning Center
Board.** Barbra Gant, Linda Suter, Sueann
VonGunten
MCC Great Lakes Board. Ben Hartman
Mennonite Men. Barney Habegger
Mennonite Women. Naomi Baumgartner,
Cindy Eicher, Rosalie Grove, Gladene
Hershberger, Alice Slager

Congregations

Agora Christian Fell (11103) (CDC, OH) 0
400 W Broad St, Columbus OH 43215
614-280-1212, fax 614-280-0312, questions@
agoraministries.org, http://agoraministries.org
  Rebecca J. Bartholomew, Co-Pastor
  Richard Bartholomew Jr., Co-Pastor

Ames Menn Ch (23424) (CDC) 6
PO Box 1752, Ames IA 50010-1752
515-233-6384, allan.beatty@acm.org
233 Walnut Ave Rd, Ste B

Ann Arbor Menn Ch (13508) (CDC, IM) 7
1455 Kelly Green Dr, Ann Arbor MI 48103-2614
734-996-9815
Arrowwood Community Center, 2566 Arrowwood
  Chibuzor Vincent Ozor, Pastor

**Asian Menn Community Ch (16719) (CDC,
Church Plant)** **20**
1280 West Indian Trail Rd, Apt #1, Aurora IL 60506
630-896-9217, jaiis53@hotmail.com
    Jai Prakash Masih, Pastor

Assembly Menn Ch (22582) (CDC, IM) **137**
1201 S 11th St, Goshen IN 46526
574-534-4190, assemblymenn@juno.com,
http://assembly.in.us.mennonite.net
Corner of 11th & New York
    Lois Johns Kaufmann, Co-Pastor
    Karl S. Shelly, Co-Pastor
    Mary Lehman Yoder, Co-Pastor

Atlanta Menn Fell (10291) (CDC) **16**
c/oSusan Gascho, Menn Hospitality House, 683 Grant St,
Atlanta GA 30312
404-622-2300, gascho606@aol.com,
http://www.atlanta.ga.us.mennonite.net
St Paul's U Methodist Church, 501 Grant St SE
    Susan Gascho, Pastor

Bethel Menn Ch (2125) (CDC) **34**
18443 Illinois Rt 9, Pekin IL 61554
309-346-2726

Boynton Menn Ch (2160) (CDC) **72**
PO Box 531, 326 Jefferson St, Hopedale IL 61747
309-449-5503, fax 309-449-5503,
boyntonmennonite@hotmail.com,
http://www.boyntonmennonite.org
RR 122 & Jefferson
    Kurt Litwiller, Pastor

Calvary Menn Ch (2190) (CDC) **357**
112 E Adams St, Washington IL 61571
309-444-2722, calmen@mtco.com
115 E Jefferson St
    David Dillon, Pastor for the interim
    Paul Scott, Youth Pastor

Carlock Menn Ch (2195) (CDC) **65**
217 E Washington, PO Box 189, Carlock IL 61725-0189
309-376-2781
    Ralph Wayne Foote, Pastor

**Chicago Community Menn Ch (24653)
(CDC, IL, CAM)** **58**
425 S Central Park Ave, Chicago IL 60624
773-343-4251, pewaite@mennonite.net
    Phil Waite, Pastor

**Christ Community Menn Ch (29397)
(CDC, IL, CAM)** **35**
888 S Roselle Rd, Schaumburg IL 60193-3965
847-895-3654, fax 847-895-3654, lpkennel@msn.com,
http://www.ccmc-mennonite.org
Pauline Kennel, Pastor
    Leroy Eldon Kennel, Minister of the Word
    Janice Kennel Ropp, Minister of Counseling

Cincinnati Menn Fell (23325) (CDC, OH) **66**
4229 Brownway Ave, Cincinnati OH 45209
513-871-0035, cmfoffice@juno.com
    Pauline Ann Nofziger, Pastor

Columbus Menn Ch (16378) (CDC,OH) **196**
35 Oakland Park Ave, Columbus OH 43214
614-784-9002, office@columbusmennonite.org,
http://www.columbusmennonite.org
    Steven William Goering, Co-Pastor
    Susan Ortman Goering, Co-Pastor

Comins Menn Ch (2205) (CDC) **103**
4263 N First St W, PO Box 60, Comins MI 48619-0060
989-848-2909, cominsmennonite@netpenny.net,
http://www.geocities.com/cominsmennonite

**Community Menn Ch (28332) (CDC, IL, CAM,
AAMA)** **82**
16200 Kedzie Ave, Markham IL 60426
708-333-1358, fax 708-333-1684,
chuckneufeld@mennonite.net,
http://community.mennonite.com
    Chuck T. Neufeld, Lead Pastor
    Bonnie Beth Neufeld, Co-Pastor
    Horace McMillon, Associate Pastor

Comunidad de Fe (2207) (CDC, CAM, IMH) **27**
1322 Kingston Lane, Schaumburg IL 60193
847-534-7242
4155 S Rockwell
    Gilberto Gaytan, Pastor

Dover Christian Fell (10709) (CDC, OH) **30**
206 W 3rd St, Dover OH 44622-2904
330-364-8590, fax 330-364-8590, dcf@tusco.net
    Daniel L. King, Pastor

Eighth Street Menn Ch (2270) (CDC) **248**
602 S 8th St, Goshen IN 46526-4019
574-533-6720, fax 574-533-8324, office@
8thstmennonite.org, http://www.8thStMennonite.org
    Kevin Dale Farmwald, Pastor
    Brenda Sawatzky Paetkau, Pastor

Evanston Menn Ch (11890) (CDC, IL, CAM) **30**
736 Dobson St, Evanston IL 60202
847-846-3954, fax 847-492-1458,
mcb9476@ameritech.net
    Mitchell C. Brown, Pastor
    Doug Hostetter, Peace Pastor

Faith Menn Ch (10127) (CDC, IM) **50**
1201 S 11th St, Goshen IN 46526
574-534-1173, gwengz@aol.com
    Deron Brill Bergstresser, Pastor
    Gwen Ann Gustafson-Zook, Pastor

First Menn Ch (2344) (CDC) **1112**
566 W Main St, PO Box 111, Berne IN 46711
260-589-3108, fax 260-589-2846,
craig@firstmennonite.org, http://www.firstmennonite.org
    G. Craig Maven, Pastor
    Ray Keim, Pastor of Congregational Care
    Marie Nussbaum, Minister of Visitation
    Dennis Schmidt, Pastor of Christian Education

**CONFERENCES AND
CONGREGATIONS**

2

First Menn Ch (2347) (CDC) 561
101 S Jackson St, Bluffton OH 45817-1294
419-358-5766, fax 419-358-1616, fmc@bluffton.edu
Corner of Jackson & Church
 Steven J. Yoder, Pastor
 John L. Schrock, Associate Pastor
 Louise Renee Wideman, Associate Pastor

First Menn Ch (2359) (CDC, AAMA, CAM) 35
1477 W 73rd St, Chicago IL 60636
773-783-8280
 John H. Burke, Pastor

First Menn Ch (2401) (CDC) 87
900 W Market St, Nappanee IN 46550-1800
574-773-7294, fmc99@kconline.com,
http://www.churches.kconline.com/fmc99
 Mark William Stahl, Pastor

First Menn Ch (2324) (CDC) 102
113 W Main St, PO Box 250, Sugarcreek OH 44681
330-852-2822
NW Corner of Main & Broadway
 Jayne M. Byler, Pastor

First Menn Ch (2333) (CDC) 106
405 Trease Rd, Wadsworth OH 44281
330-334-1863, fax 330-334-3283, mohr@wadsnet.com,
http://www.firstmennonite.com
 James R. Mohr, Pastor

First Menn Ch of Champaign-Urbana (11924)
(CDC, IL) 126
902 W Springfield Ave, Urbana IL 61801
217-367-5353, fax 217-367-2716, fmc@prairienet.org,
http://www.prairienet.org/mennonite
Larry J. Wilson, Pastor
 Cynthia Massanari Breeze, Associate Pastor

Florence Ch of the Brethren-Menn (11315)
(CDC, COB) 55
17975 Centreville-Constantine Rd, Constantine MI 49042
269-435-5945, fax 269-435-7288,
florencemcob@highstream.net
 Suzanne Lind, Interim Pastor

Grace Community Ch (2400) (CDC, CAM) 42
4155 S Rockwell St, Chicago IL 60632
773-247-4782, bserve@aol.com

Grace Menn Ch (2420) (CDC) 221
502 E Main St, PO Box 387, Pandora OH 45877
419-384-3038, fax 419-384-3038, gmc@bluffton.edu,
http://grace.oh.us.mennonite.net
 John Michael Dey, Pastor
 David Thomas Maurer, Minister of Youth and Christian
  Education

Hively Avenue Menn Ch (2455) (CDC) 109
800 E Hively Ave, Elkhart IN 46517-2564
574-294-3423, fax 574-294-3423,
hivelymenno@verizon.net,
http://mysite.verizon.net/hivelymenno
 Michael Kent Sommers, Pastor

Hively Jesus Village Ch (10005) (CDC,
Church Plant) 35
57679 7th St, Elkhart IN 46517
574-294-5631, abbacom 31@hotmail.com
800 E. Hively Ave
 Jung Og Lee, Pastor
 Yoon Shik Lee, Pastor

Joy Fell Menn Ch (27391) (CDC, IL, AAMA) 30
2918 W Montana St, Peoria IL 61605
309-691-8424
 Phillip Maclin, Pastor

Lafayette Menn Fell (26021) (CDC, IM) 8
PO Box 355, Lafayette IN 47902-0355
765-743-4876, hovde@dcwi.com,
http://livingfaith.in.us.mennonite.net
102 N Chauncy (First United Methodist), West Lafayette

Lima Menn Ch (16402) (CDC, OH) 62
1318 N Main St, Lima OH 45801
419-222-2120, limamc@bright.net
 David Palmer Moser, Pastor

Living Love Ministries (11096) (CDC, IL, AV) . . .70
PO Box 5473, Peoria IL 61601
309-676-2772, pastoramariah@sbcglobal.net
811 NE Perry Ave
 Maria Hatfield, Pastor
 Walter Smeltzer, Associate Pastor

Madison Menn Ch (10078) (CDC, IL) 111
PO Box 44522, Madison WI 53744-4522
608-276-7680, mmc@madison-mennonite.org,
http://www.madison-mennonite.org
1501 Gilbert Rd
 Tonya Ramer Wenger, Pastor

Maple Avenue Menn Ch (23697) (CDC, IL, CAM) . .39
346 Maple Ave, Waukesha WI 53186
262-547-6937, clariKra@aol.com
 Clarice Kratz, Co-Pastor
 Lawrence M. Kratz, Co-Pastor

Maplewood Menn Ch (2530) (CDC) 143
4129 Maplecrest Rd, Fort Wayne IN 46815-5326
260-485-8512, fax 260-486-2831,
maplemenno@juno.com,
http://www.forministry.com/46815mmc
 Barry Lee Schmell, Pastor

Meadows Menn Ch (2540) (CDC) 130
24955 Church St, Chenoa IL 61726
309-747-2744, meadowsc@gridcom.net
Meadows
 John Ernest Heyerly, Pastor

Menn Ch of Normal (11833) (CDC, IL) 291
805 S Cottage Ave, Normal IL 61761
309-452-6622, fax 309-452-0478, normal.mennonite@
verizon.net, http://www.normalmennonite.com
 Tim E. Schrag, Pastor
 Jane Thorley Roeschley, Associate Pastor
 Stephen A. Ropp, Youth Pastor

Morning Star Ch (29652) (CDC, IM) **24**
2000 S Hoyt Ave, Muncie IN 47302
765-287-0021
  Gladys Maina, Pastor
  Simon Mungai, Associate Pastor

MSU Menn Fell (12757) (CDC, IM) **40**
PO Box 6068, East Lansing MI 48826
517-482-9961, msumennofell@juno.com,
http://msu.mi.us.mennonite.net
Alumni Memorial Chapel, MSU Campus
  June Mears-Driedger, Pastor

North Danvers Menn Ch (2620) (CDC) **142**
5517 E 1950 North Rd, Danvers IL 61732-9240
309-963-4554, northdanversch@frontiernet.net,
http://www.northdanverschurch.com
  Richard Wayne Bucher, Pastor

North Suburban Menn Ch (27557)
(CDC, IL, CAM) **24**
1500 W Hawley St, Mundelein IL 60060-1508
847-566-8386, fax 847-475-1006, dckerner@trimedia.net,
http://www.northsuburban.org
  David Kerner, Pastor

Oak Grove Menn Ch (16428) (CDC, OH) **406**
7843 Smucker Rd, Smithville OH 44677
330-669-2697, fax 330-669-2617, ogsmthvll@aol.com,
http://www.oakgrovemc.org
  Norma B. Duerksen, Pastor
  Joel A. Short, Associate Pastor

Paoli Menn Fell (22624) (CDC, IM) **75**
2589 N CR 100 W, Paoli IN 47454
812-723-2414, fax 812-723-3515, mennos@iquest.net
  Mary Mininger, Co-Pastor
  Philip A. Mininger, Co-Pastor

Pleasant Oaks Menn Ch (2645) (CDC) **147**
13307 CR 16, PO Box 447, Middlebury IN 46540
574-825-2784, pomcsec@maplenet.net
  Robin La Rue, Pastor
  Michael Miller, Youth Pastor

Plow Creek Menn Ch (22335) (CDC, IL) **30**
19183 Plow Creek Unit #2, Tiskilwa IL 61368
815-646-6600, fax 815-646-6600,
richfoss@plowcreek.org, http://www.plowcreek.org
1925 E 880 N
  Richard Gordon Foss, Lay Minister
  Neil Horning, Pastoral Elder
  Louise Stahnke, Pastoral Elder

Prairieview Menn Ch (12138) (CDC, IL) **212**
13013 North 400 Rd East, PO Box 369, Flanagan IL 61740
815-796-2824, prairieview@frontiernet.net,
http://community-2.webtv.net/bbroeschley/PRAIRIEVIEW/
  Douglas D. King, Pastor

Salem Menn Ch (2680) (CDC) **194**
3363 Zuercher Rd, PO Box 7, Kidron OH 44636
330-857-4131, fax 330-857-4196, salemex@raex.com,
http://salemmennonite.oh.us.mennonite.net
  Darrell Lee Ediger, Pastor
  Kevin S. Himes, Minister of Music

Shalom Community Ch (23242) (CDC, COB) **45**
PO Box 8080, Ann Arbor MI 48107-8080
734-761-7366, shalomcommunitychurch@yahoo.com,
http://www.shalomcommunitychurch.mi.us.mennonite.net
2796 Packard Road
  Paul Versluis, Pastor

Silverwood Menn Ch (2715) (CDC) **232**
1712 W Clinton St, Goshen IN 46526
574-533-1922, fax 574-533-4069,
silverwd2@maplenet.net
  Kenneth Bontreger, Senior Pastor
  Jonathan Corbin, Associate Pastor

Southside Fell (12930) (CDC, IM) **95**
140 W Mishawaka Rd, Elkhart IN 46517
574-293-2825, ssfellow@maplenet.net
AMBS Chapel, 3003 Benham Ave
  Jonathan Neufeld, Pastor
  Rhoda M. Schrag, Pastor

St John Menn Ch (2670) (CDC) **407**
15988 Rd 4, Pandora OH 45877
419-384-3680, fax 419-384-3640,
stjohnoffice@thewavz.com
  Rennie W. Burrus, Pastor
  Duane Weaver, Director of Children and Family
    Ministries

St Louis Menn Fell (24182) (CDC, IL) **65**
1443 Ross Ave, St Louis MO 63146-4563
314-878-2832, slmennonitef@aol.com,
http://www.slmf.org
  Melissa S. Roth, Pastor

Topeka Menn Ch (2775) (CDC) **134**
206 E Lake St, PO Box 156, Topeka IN 46571
260-593-2389, cynthiashmc@networksplus.net
  John Edward Hockman, Pastor

Trenton Menn Ch (2779) (CDC) **126**
2 E Main St, PO Box 19, Trenton OH 45067
513-988-0313, rharbaum@cinci.rr.com
  Glenn H. Martin, Pastor

Central Plains Mennonite Conference

OFFICE
cpmcsd@gwtc.net
605-925-4463, fax 605-925-7293
121 E Third St, PO Box 101, Freeman SD 57029

STAFF
Ed Kauffman, conference minister
(edkauffman@gwtc.net), Freeman SD,
605-925-4463
Tim Detweiler, east regional minister
(tdetweiler@hotmail.com), Washington IA,
319-653-4109
Sharon Kennel, west regional minister
(sharondkennel@yahoo.com), Strang NE,
402-627-4375
Shana Peachey Boshart, youth minister
(shana@netins.net), Parnell IA,
319-646-2842
Ted Widmer, financial officer
(twidmer@lisco.com), Mt Pleasant IA,
319-986-5190
Monica Friesen, office manager
(cpmcsd@gwtc.net), Freeman SD,
605-925-4463

GENERAL INFORMATION
Year founded: 2000
Members: 7,969
Congregations: 55 + 2 church plants
Ministers: 98
CLC reps: Shana Peachey Boshart, Ed Kauffman,
Roy Kaufman
Annual Meeting: June 17-20, 2004
Conference historian: Barb Troyer
Conference archivist: LaNae Waltner

CONFERENCE COUNCIL
S. Roy Kaufman, moderator
(lorokauf@gwtc.net), 28103 443rd Ave,
Freeman SD 57029, 605-925-7106; Susan
Janzen, assistant moderator; Atlee Yoder, secretary; Lois Thieszen Preheim, treasurer;
David Boshart, Carol Janzen, Nyle Kauffman,
Irvin Sether, Rodney Unruh, Martha Yoder,
Marvin Yoder

PUBLICATION
Scattered Seeds (6/year), Myrna Joy Wenger,
editor (gdw@farmtel.net), 2561 320th St,
Wayland IA 52641, 319-256-7772

COMMITTEES
Congregational Ministries. Rodney Unruh,
chair (reunruh@att.net), 214 E 29th St,
Sioux Falls SD 57105, 605-338-7906;
Lynette Block, David Brunner, Peg Burkey,
Shujii Morichi, Dawn Stahl
Outreach and Service. Marvin K. Yoder, chair
(mknfyod@netins.net), PO Box 166,
Wellman IA 52356, 319-646-2451; Patricia
Barron, Noreen Gingerich, Leslie Harder,
David Janssen, Doyle Roth, Marlene
Thieszen, Norm Unternahrer
Pastoral Leadership. David Boshart, chair
(dboshart@netins.net), 3253 305th St
Parnell IA 52325, 319-646-6004, Rachel
Friesen, Arthur Kennel, Marlin Kym,
Raymond Reimer, Pamela Gerig Unruh
Discernment. Susan Janzen,
(sejanzen@msn.com), 2116 Clay St, Cedar
Falls IA 50613, 319-277-3262; Glenda
Maury, Patrick Preheim, Reed Schrag, Frank
Yoder

OTHER CONFERENCE AGENCY AND REPS
Mennonite Women. Marcene Ratzlaff, chair,
PO Box 22, Henderson NE 68371, 402-723-
4670; Esther Buller, Dee Goertzen, Irene
Gross, Mary Litwiller, Alice Wyse
Mennonite Men. Royce Roth, chair (roth-
wood@iowatelecom.net), 3154 Hwy 281,
Crawfordsville IA 52621, 319-658-3933;
Duane Franz, Michael Friesen, Wilbur
Friesen, Ernie Wiens Neufeld, Randy Roth

Congregations

Ashland Christian Fell (4025) (CP, MILC) 9
PO Box 819, Colstrip MT 59323-0819
406-784-6130
Old Mission Rd, Ashland
  Doug Bishop, Pastor

Beemer Menn Ch (13144) (CP) 138
327 Sherman St, PO Box 421, Beemer NE 68716-0421
402-528-7255, gordmar@gpcom.net
  Gordon Scoville, Interim Pastor

Bellwood Menn Ch (13151) (CP) 218
520 B St, PO Box 66, Milford NE 68405
402-761-2709, fax 402-761-3095, bell606@juno.com
  Marlin Kym, Pastor
  Betta Kym, Assistant Pastor

Bethany Menn Ch (4055) (CP) 222
509 S Juniper Street, PO Box 396, Freeman SD 57029
605-925-7402, fax 605-925-7202, bethanym@gwtc.net,
http://www.gwtc.net/~bethanym
  Randall LaMont Tschetter, Pastor

Bethel Menn Ch (4120) (CP) 439
301 N 9th St, PO Box 542, Mountain Lake MN 56159
507-427-3075, bethelchurchmtlakemn@earthlink.net
  George Christopher O'Reilly II, Pastor

Bethel Menn Ch (13177) (CP) 196
3185 Wayland Rd, PO Box 96, Wayland IA 52654
319-256-8531, fax 319-256-8531, pslabaugh@farmtel.net,
http://bethel.ia.us.mennonite.net
  Phil L. Slabaugh, Pastor

Bethel Menn Ch (4130) (CP) 59
HC 30 Box 2071, Wolf Point MT 59201
406-392-5215
18 mi north on Hwy 250
  Marvin Wesley Penner, Pastor

Beth-El Menn Ch (13169) (CP) 169
115 N F St, PO Box 96, Milford NE 68405
402-761-3278, bethelmilford@alltel.net
  Audrun Siebert, Pastor

Bethesda Menn Ch (4135) (CP) 1152
930 16th St, PO Box 130, Henderson NE 68371-0130
402-723-4562, fax 402-723-4567,
bethesda@mainstaycomm.net,
http://www.mainstaycomm.net/bethesda
  Weldon R. Martens, Pastor
  George K. Kaufman, Associate Pastor

Casa de Oracion Emanuel (11629) (CP) 0
204 W Garfield, Davenport IA 52903-1506
jito57@netexpress.net
  Fernando Ramos, Pastor

Cedar Falls Menn Ch (24935) (CP) 39
215 West 9th Street, Cedar Falls IA 50613
319-277-5611, cfmc@cedarnet.org
  Susan E. Janzen, Pastor

Christ Community Ch (11628) (CP) 0
2315 59th Street, PO Box 31009, Des Moines IA 50310
515-276-4966, christcommunity@dwx.com
  Chad Mason, Pastor
  Kent McDougal, Pastor

Daytonville Community Ch (13201) (CP) 9
PO Box C, Wellman IA 52356
319-646-2246
300 13th Street
  Ezra W. Shenk, Pastor

Des Moines Menn Ch (13219) (CP) 73
4001 56th St, Des Moines IA 50310
515-276-2379, fax 515-276-2379, dmmc@mennonite.net
Corner of 56th & Madison
  Randall J. Roth, Pastor
  Ha Baccam, Associate Pastor

East Union Menn Ch (13243) (CP) 239
PO Box 760, Kalona IA 52247
319-656-2590, eucares@kctc.net,
http://www.eastunionmennonite.org
5615 Gable Ave SW
  Walter Jay Miiller, Pastor

Eicher Emmanuel Menn Ch (2265) (CP) 60
2670 330th St, Wayland IA 52654
319-256-2035
  Melvin J. Koehn, Pastor

Emmanuel Menn Ch (4275) (CP) 122
18507 405th Ave, Doland SD 57436
605-266-2588, wiebegd@netzero.com
  Gordon Wayne Wiebe, Pastor

Emmanuel Menn Ch (11125) (CP) 63
4715 Laura Ln, Shoreview MN 55126-6032
651-766-9759, fax 651-766-9759, emmanuel@visi.com,
http://www.emc.MennoLink.org
1501 Hendon St, St Paul
  Mathew Swora, Pastor

Evangelical Menn Ch (13250) (CP) 44
1633 N 29th Street, Fort Dodge IA 50501-7937
515-576-0022, elevers@frontiernet.net,
http://evangelical.ia.us.mennonite.net
  Larry Evers, Pastor

Faith Menn Ch (23127) (CP) 109
2720 E 22nd St, Minneapolis MN 55406
612-375-9483, faithmc@juno.com,
http://www.faithmennonite.org
  Patty Jo Friesen, Pastor
  Patrick Preheim, Pastor

First Menn Ch (13268) (CP) 98
7300 Holdrege St, Lincoln NE 68505
402-467-1526

CONFERENCES AND
CONGREGATIONS

2

First Menn Ch (4397) (CP) **131**
305 N 7th St, PO Box 473, Mountain Lake MN 56159
507-427-2237, seekfrst@rconnect.com,
http://www.mennolink.org/cong/first/
　E. Elaine Kauffman, Pastor

First Menn Ch of Iowa City (13276) (CP) **289**
405 Myrtle Ave, Iowa City IA 52246
319-338-0302, fax 319-688-5091, 1stmenno@avalon.net,
http://www.firstofiowacity.ia.us.mennonite.net
　S. Ken Beidler, Pastor
　Margaret Richer Smith, Pastor
　Robert Smith, Pastor

Friedensberg Bible Ch (4350) (CP) **52**
40602 307th St, Avon SD 57315-5825
605-286-3621, fax 605-286-3892
30996 406 Ave

Good Shepherd Community Ch (4375) (CP) **60**
2100 W Ralph Rogers Rd, Sioux Falls SD 57108-2643
605-336-9189, fax 605-336-9189,
goodshepherdsf@juno.com,
http://www.goodshepherdsf.org
　Rosella E. Epp, Pastor

**Hmong Menn Ch of St Paul (10128) (CP,
Church Plant)** **0**
706 Clearbrooks Lane, Vadnais Heights MN 55127
651-429-4692
　Neng Chue Vang, Pastor

Hutterthal Menn Ch (4490) (CP) **208**
Drawer A, Freeman SD 57029
605-925-7186, irfri@gwtc.net
27473 437th Ave, Freeman
　Ivan D. Friesen, Co-Pastor
　Rachel Friesen, Co-Pastor

**Iglesia Roca de Salvacion (10126) (CP,
Church Plant)** **0**
746 S 10th Avenue, Washington IA 52353
319-653-6540
　Ramiro Hernandez, Pastor

Julesburg Menn Ch (13300) (CP) **65**
320 W 7th St, PO Box 52, Julesburg CO 80737
970-474-2580
Corner of 8th & Elm
　Arthur J. Roth, Pastor

Kalona Menn Ch (13318) (CP) **348**
902 6th St, PO Box 819, Kalona IA 52247
319-656-2736, kmcscott@kctc.net
　Mick Murray, Pastor
　Scott Swartzendruber, Pastor

Lame Deer Menn Ch (4635) (CP, MILC) **45**
PO Box 232, Lame Deer MT 59043
406-477-8388
　Joe Walks Along Sr., Pastor

Lower Deer Creek Menn Ch (13334) (CP) **239**
1408 540th St SW, Kalona IA 52247
319-656-3336, fax 319-656-2029, ldc@kctc.net,
http://lowerdeercreek.ia.us.mennonite.net
　Donald A. Patterson, Pastor

Manson Menn Ch (13342) (CP) **132**
1310 8th Street, PO Box 627, Manson IA 50563
712-469-3387, manson.menno@juno.com
　Curtis Kuhns, Pastor

Milford Menn Ch (13367) (CP) **145**
920 3rd St, PO Box EE, Milford NE 68405
402-761-2244, fax 402-761-2269, mmc761@alltel.net
　Lewis W. Miller, Pastor

Muscatine Menn Ch (13375) (CP, IMH) **0**
122 Evergreen Lane, Fruitland IA 52749
563-264-5544
　Cruz Rada, Pastor

Neu Hutterthal Menn Ch (4610) (CP) **88**
PO Box 19, Bridgewater SD 57319
605-729-2745
Rural Bridgewater
　Kenneth Loren Ontjes, Pastor

**Northside Christian Family Center (24166)
(CP, AAMA)** **12**
PO Box 19298, Omaha NE 68119-0298
402-453-7429, fax 402-451-1312
4102 Florence Blvd
　Owen Taylor, Pastor

Peace Menn Ch (28787) (CP) **17**
2700 Division St, Burlington IA 52601
319-753-1325, fax 319-753-9333, ljstauff@aol.com

Pleasant View Menn Ch (13425) (CP) **95**
1101 N Lucas St, Mount Pleasant IA 52641
319-385-8562, pvmenno1@interlinklc.net
　Marc Hershberger, Pastor

Pulaski Menn Ch (2650) (CP) **125**
202 West St, PO Box 100, Pulaski IA 52584
641-675-3845
http://www.netins.net/showcase/pulaskimenno
　Darrell E. Zook, Pastor

Rochester Menn Ch (4667) (CP) **22**
2219 15th Ave NW, Rochester MN 55901-1569
507-529-7910, brunnerd@prodigy.net,
http://www.rmcmn.org
Schaeffer Academy, 2700 Schaeffer Drive
　David D. Brunner, Pastor

Salem Menn Ch (4675) (CP) **386**
28103 443rd Ave, Freeman SD 57029-5840
605-925-4553, southchurch@gwtc.net
　S. Roy Kaufman, Pastor
　Stacey Waltner, Associate Pastor

Salem Menn Ch (13433) (CP) 191
PO Box 165, Shickley NE 68436
402-627-4155, fax 402-627-4235, wdd@inebraska.com
820 Rd V
  Wilton Detweiler, Pastor

Salem-Zion Menn Ch (4690) (CP) 362
27844 443rd Ave, PO Box 67, Freeman SD 57029
605-925-7410, fax 605-925-7410
  Robert L. Engbrecht, Pastor

Sermon on the Mount Menn Ch (24018) (CP) . .33
1512 E Mulberry St, Sioux Falls SD 57103
605-357-9125, smmc@juno.com,
http://sermononthemount-mennonite.org
  Rosella E. Epp, Pastor

St Paul Menn Fell (28555) (CP) 22
622 Bidwell St, St Paul MN 55107
651-290-9879, breckie@mtn.org
125 W Stevens St

Sugar Creek Menn Ch (13441) (CP) 325
1209 Franklin Ave, Box 146, Wayland IA 52654
319-256-8811, fax 319-256-6061,
sugarcreekmc@farmtel.net
  Nathan Luitjens, Pastor

Swiss Menn Ch (4755) (CP) 22
PO Box 135, Alsen ND 58311
701-256-5174
520 3rd Ave
  Vergil Moos, Pastor

Templo Alabanza Menonita (13284) (CP, IMH) . . .53
613 3rd St, Moline IL 61265
309-797-3808
  Felipe Cantu, Pastor

Washington Menn Ch (13458) (CP) 136
815 E Polk St, Washington IA 52353
319-653-6041, wash.mennonite@juno.com,
http://washington.ia.us.mennonite.net
  Timothy R. Detweiler, Pastor
  Grant Nebel, Associate Pastor

Wayland Menn Ch (2815) (CP) 186
104 Second St, PO Box 67, Wayland IA 52654
319-256-2743, waylandmcusa@farmtel.net
  Pamela Gerig Unruh, Co-Pastor
  Gerry Klopfenstein, Co-Pastor

Wellman Menn Ch (13466) (CP) 132
1215 8th Ave, PO Box 122, Wellman IA 52356
319-646-2532, wmchurch@netins.net
  Marvin Dean Hostetler, Pastor

West Union Menn Ch (13474) (CP) 296
3253 305th St, Parnell IA 52325
319-646-6004, fax 319-646-6046, wunion@netins.net,
http://www.westunion.ia.us.mennonite.net
  David W. Boshart, Pastor
  Helen Yoder, Staff Deacon

White Chapel Menn Ch (15594) (CP, NC) 16
106 White Chapel Rd, Glendive MT 59330
406-377-7574, nevpeter@midrivers.com
  Neville John Peterson, Pastor

**White River Cheyenne Menn Ch (4171)
(CP, MILC)** 57
PO Box 50, Busby MT 59016
406-592-3643, willisnadine@juno.com
Mennonite Church Rd
  Willis Herman Busenitz, Pastor

Wood River Menn Ch (13482) (CP) 97
14988 West Husker Hwy, Wood River NE 68883
308-382-0719
  Cloy Roth, Pastor

Zion Menn Ch (2860) (CP) 124
504 University St, Box 83, Donnellson IA 52625
319-835-9124, fax 319-836-2145,
logesbjl@interlinklc.net
720 Park St
  Richard Alvin Bentzinger, Pastor

Eastern District Conference

OFFICE
info@easterndistrict.org,
www.easterndistrict.org
215-723-5513 ext. 138, fax 215-723-1211
771 Rte 113, Souderton PA 18964

STAFF
Warren L. Tyson, conference minister
(warrent@easterndistrict.org)

GENERAL INFORMATION
Year founded: 1847
Members: 2,151
Congregations: 15 + 1 church plant
Ministers: 25
CLC reps.: James Musselman, Wayne Speigle,
Warren Tyson
Annual delegate session: November 6, 2004

OFFICERS
Wayne Speigle, moderator
(wjspeigle@aol.com), 862 Hunsicker Rd,
Telford PA 18969, 215-256-1995; James
Musselman, moderator-elect
(jbmuzz@netcarrier.com, 21 Penn Ave,
Souderton PA 18964, 215-721-9433; Lori Groff,
secretary (tandlgroff@comcast.net), 2697
Woodstream Dr, Hatfield PA 19440, 215-361-
95400; Douglas Moyer, treasurer
(dkmoyer@aol.com), 523 Gruber Rd,
Harleysville PA 19438, 215-256-4913; Ray
Hacker, member-at-large
(r.a.hacker@worldnet.att.net) 5323 Lake Dr,
East Petersburg PA 17520, 717-569-3460

PUBLICATION
The Message, Lori Groff, editor
(tandlgroff@comcast.net), 2697 Woodstream
Dr, Hatfield PA 19440, 215-361-6953

STANDING COMMITTEES
Ministerial Leadership. David W. Bartow,
chair (davewinb@aol.com), PO Box 115,
Zionsville PA 18092, 610-967-3899; Sumi
Gerhart, secretary; Rose Graber, Mary Lou
Simmons, Wayne Speigle, Charles E.
Sprunger, Warren L. Tyson
Peace and Justice. Bob Walden, chair
(rwaldenpa@entermail.net), 826 Tioga Ave,
Bethlehem PA 18016, 610-861-0653;
Carolyn Boyd (Franconia Conf. member),
Russ Darling, Becky Felton (Franconia Conf.
member), Ryan Kolb (Franconia Conf. mem-
ber), Russ Mast
Congregational Life. Sheryl Duerksen, chair
(duerksenjars@comcast.net), 14 South 9th
St, Perkasie PA 18944, 215-453-7069, Kelly
Ball, Scott Benner, Marjorie Geissinger
Gifts Discernment. Sarah K. Arn, chair
(sarahkarn1@netzero.com), 102 Highland
Ave, Lansdale PA 19446, 215-855-4584;
Philip Bergstresser, David Hersh, Beth
Rauschenberger

SUBCOMMITTEES
Finance. Doug Moyer, chair
(dkmoyer@aol.com), 523 Gruber Rd,
Harleysville PA 19438, 215-256-4913, Ray
Hacker
Communication. Lori Groff, chair
(tandlgroff@comcast.net), Meg Sabulsky

Congregations

Bethel Menn Ch of Lancaster (3100) (EDC) 89
2100 Manor Ridge Dr, Lancaster PA 17603-4216
717-392-8184, marlin.thomas@RRCINC.org
    Marlin E. Thomas, Pastor

Ch of the Good Samaritans (3200) (EDC) 27
964 Holland Rd, Holland PA 18966
215-355-1442

Cornerstone Community Ch (3543) (EDC) 68
Rt 2 Box 67, Mifflintown PA 17059
717-436-8585, fax 717-436-9346
Wagner Rd & Old Rt 22
    Albert Gray, Pastor

Deep Run West Menn Ch (3225) (EDC) 210
1008 Deep Run Rd, Perkasie PA 18944
215-766-8157, fax 215-766-8259
    Rodger K. Schmell, Pastor
    Daniel J. Graber, Interim Pastor

Emmanuel Menn Ch (3285) (EDC) 143
1200 W Swartzville Rd, PO Box 341,
Reinholds PA 17569-0341
717-336-6130, fax 717-336-3968,
davidyoung@churchrenewalservant.org
    David Young, Interim Pastor

Fairfield Menn Ch (3300) (EDC) 40
201 W Main St, PO Box 158, Fairfield PA 17320-0158
717-642-8936, fax 717-642-8936, fmc606@blazenet.net,
http://www.fairfieldmennonite.org
    Brenda Walter, Director of Ministries

First Menn Ch (3338) (EDC) 60
1213 W Chew St, Allentown PA 18102-3707
610-435-3162, FirstMennonite@hotmail.com,
http://fmc.ppjr.org
    David W. Bartow, Interim Pastor

Grace Menn Ch (3415) (EDC) 318
630 York Ave, Lansdale PA 19446-3329
215-855-7718, fax 215-855-4579,
pastor@gracemennonite.org
    Christian J. Nickels, Youth Pastor
    Samuel Claudio Sr., Pastor, Spanish Cong.
    R. Lee Delp, Lay Minister

**Iglesia Menonita Comunidad de Amor (3212)
(EDC, KB, IMH)** 70
PO Box 46332, Philadelphia PA 19160
215-368-5839, fax 215-324-6011
4617 N 5th St
    Luis E. Naranjo, Pastor

**Iglesia Menonita Ebenezer (10093)
(EDC, Church Plant)** 50
    755 Route 113, Souderton PA 18964
    215-703-0280, samclaudio@fast.net
    771 Route 113
       Samuel Claudio Sr., Pastor

**Menn Congregation of Boston (16246)
(ACC, EDC)** 49
1555 Massachusetts Avenue, Cambridge MA 02138-2903
617-868-7784, biedrzycki@mindspring.com
Harvard Epworth United Methodist Church
    Gordon D. Kaufman, Pastor
    Earl Sears, Interim Pastor

New Eden Fell (3260) (EDC) 101
609 Main St, PO Box 308, Schwenksville PA 19473-0308
610-287-7281, fax 610-287-6561, knowgod3@juno.com,
http://www.newedenfellowship.org
    Donald William Fry, Pastor

Roaring Spring Menn Ch (3665) (EDC) 20
1022 Queen Rd, Claysburg PA 16625
814-239-2566, jgnlc2@wmconnect.com
235 Main St, Roaring Spring
    Elsie M. Gonsman, Pastor

Upper Milford Menn Ch (3800) (EDC) 147
6450 King's Highway South, PO Box 36,
Zionsville PA 18092
610-965-4880, ummchurch@enter.net,
http://www.forministry.com/18092ummc
    Rose Elaine (Waltner) Graber, Pastor

West Swamp Menn Ch (3825) (EDC) 331
2501 Allentown Rd, Quakertown PA 18951
215-536-7468, fax 215-536-2783, wjspeigle@verizon.net,
http://westswamp.pa.us.mennonite.net
    Wayne Speigle, Pastor
    Kelly J. Ball, Youth Pastor

Zion Menn Ch (3880) (EDC) 527
149 Cherry Ln, PO Box 64495, Souderton PA 18964
215-723-3592, fax 215-723-0573,
melissastoner@enter.net, http://www.zionmennonite.org
    Dan Graber, Interim/Tansitional Pastor
    Scott Springer Benner, Associate Pastor-Youth

CONFERENCES AND CONGREGATIONS

2

Mennonite Church USA 2005 Directory

Franconia Mennonite Conference

OFFICE
Info@FMC-online.org, www.FMC-online.org
215-723-5513, fax 215-723-1211
771 Rte 113, Souderton PA 18964

STAFF
Philip C. Bergey, conference executive
  (philb@fmc-online.org)
James M. Lapp, conference pastor
  (jamesl@fmc-online.org)
Gay Brunt Miller, director of administration
  (gbmiller@fmc-online.org)
Conrad Martin, director of finance
  (conradm@fmc-online.org)
Richard A. Moyer, treasurer and administrative
  assistant (richm@fmc-online.org)
Walter Sawatzky, director of collaborative ministries, conference minister
  (walters@fmc-online.org)
Donella Clemens, conference minister
  (donellac@fmc-online.org)
Marlene Frankenfield, conference youth minister, (marlenef@fmc-online.org)
Noah Kolb, conference minister
  (noahk@fmc-online.org)
Noel Santiago, conference minister
  (noels@fmc-online.org)
Ertell Whigham, conference minister
  (ertellw@fmc-online.com)

GENERAL INFORMATION
Year founded: 1725
Members: 6,700
Congregations: 44
Ministers: 91
CLC reps: Phil Bergey, Marlene Frankenfield,
  Merrill Moyer
Annual Conferences: Fall conference assembly,
  November 11-12, 2005

CONFERENCE BOARD
Merrill Moyer, chair/moderator
(mernan@fast.net), 334 Fairview Ave,
Souderton PA 18964, 215-721-4517; Charles
Ness, vice chair/assistant moderator; Sharon
Fransen, Rita Hoover, Diane Kropf, John Landes,
John Nyce, Yvonne Platts, Nelson Shenk, Eileen
Viau, Roy Yoder. Staff: Philip C. Bergey, James
M. Lapp, Conrad Martin, Gay Brunt Miller,
Walter Sawatzky

PUBLICATION
Intersections (bimonthly), Craig Pelkey-Landes,
editor (CraigL@FMC-online.org)

CONFERENCE BOARD COMMITTEES
Conference Board Executive Committee: Merrill
Moyer, chair, (mernan@fast.net), 334 Fairview
Ave, Souderton PA 18964, 215-721-4517
Conference Board Finance Committee: John
Landes, chair (landesj@univest.net), 1050 Deer
Run Rd, Ottsville PA 18942, 215-721-2425
Conference Board Ministerial Committee:
Nelson Shenk, chair (bmc19512@yahoo.com),
Boyertown Mennonite Church, 275 Mill St,
Boyertown PA 19512, 610-369-1974

Congregations

Alpha Menn Ch (23051) (FRC) 27
901 East Blvd, Alpha NJ 08865-4233
908-454-8345, alphamenno@juno.com
Corner of North & East Boulevards
  Michael Alan Schaadt, Interim/Transitional Pastor

Ambler Menn Ch (11353) (FRC, AAMA) 93
90 E Mount Pleasant Ave, Ambler PA 19002
215-643-4876, pastorsharon@verizon.net,
http://www.ambler.pa.us.mennonite.net
  Sharon Wyse Miller, Pastor

Bally Menn Ch (11361) (FRC) 168
1481 Route 100, PO Box 194, Bally PA 19503
610-845-7780, fax 610-845-2716, mcbally@juno.com,
http://www.forministry.com/19503bmc
Rt 100
  James Ralph, Pastor

Bethany Menn Ch (11387) (FRC) 30
Route 100A #169, PO Box 145,
Bridgewater Corners VT 05035
802-672-3488, bethanym@sover.net
    Gwendolyn M. Groff, Pastor

Blooming Glen Menn Ch (11403) (FRC) 714
713 Blooming Glen Rd, PO Box 238,
Blooming Glen PA 18911
215-257-3431, fax 215-257-3150,
bloomingglen@comcast.net, http://www.bgmc.net
    Enid Elaine Schloneger, Lead Pastor
    Robert Schloneger, Lead Pastor
    David A. Stevens, Pastor
    Benjamin S. Stutzman, Pastor

Boyertown Menn Ch (11411) (FRC) 125
275 Mill St Rd, Boyertown PA 19512
610-369-1974, fax 610-473-2899, bmc19512@yahoo.com,
http://fm2.forministry.com/19512BMC
    Nelson J. Shenk, Pastor

Covenant Community Fell (29306) (FRC) 177
1080 Sumneytown Pike, Lansdale PA 19446
215-721-6490, fax 215-721-6429,
secretary@cc-fellowship.org, http://www.cc-fellowship.org
    Elmer S. Frederick, Pastor
    Jay Moyer, Co-Pastor
    R. Keith Nyce, Co-Pastor

Deep Run Menn Ch East (11437) (FRC) 338
350 Kellers Church Rd, Perkasie PA 18944-4242
215-766-8380, fax 215-766-2908, dre@depruneast.org,
http://deepruneast.org
Corner of Deep Run & Keller's Church in Bedminster
Township
    Emma Frederick, Interim Pastor of Pastoral Care
    J. Mark Frederick Jr., Interim Pastor
    William G. Martin, Associate Pastor

Doylestown Menn Ch (11445) (FRC) 196
590 N Broad St, Doylestown PA 18901
215-345-6377, fax 215-345-9513,
doylestownmc@juno.com
Corner of Broad St & Sandy Ridge Rd
    Randy E. Heacock, Pastor

Finland Menn Ch (11486) (FRC) 124
1685 Upper Ridge Rd, Pennsburg PA 18073
215-257-5365, finlandmennonitechurch@netcarrier.com,
http://www.finlandmennonitechurch.org
    Richard Lewman, Pastor

Franconia Menn Ch (11502) (FRC) 739
613 Harleysville Pike, Telford PA 18969-2419
215-723-3220, fax 215-723-2265,
jehst@franconiamennonite.org,
http://www.hows.net/18924FMC
    John M. Ehst, Lead Pastor
    Jeffrey B. Leaman, Youth Pastor
    Steven E. Landis, Minister of Pastoral Care
    Eric Musser, Minister of Evangelism & Young Adults

Frederick Menn Ch (11528) (FRC) 68
PO Box 309, Frederick PA 19435
610-754-7238, frederickchurch@safeplace.net
526 Colonial Rd
    R. Scott Landes, Pastor

Garden Chapel (11544) (FRC) 34
PO Box 376, Dover NJ 07802
973-361-8877
89 Washington Ave, Victory Gardens
    Jesse U. Adams, Pastor

Hersteins Menn Ch (11569) (FRC) 86
364 Neiffer Rd, Schwenksville PA 19473
610-495-2065, gotmilk45@hotmail.com
    Earl N. Anders Jr, Pastor
    Glenn W. Freed, Assistant Pastor

Lakeview Menn Ch (11577) (FRC) 64
RR 1 Box 55, Susquehanna PA 18847
570-756-2793, detwiler@epix.net
Lakeview Rd
    R. Blaine Detwiler, Pastor

Line Lexington Menn Ch (11593) (FRC) 264
80 Hilltown Pike, PO Box 217, Line Lexington PA 18932
215-822-0446, fax 215-822-8446, info@llmc.org,
http://www.llmc.org
    Lowell H. Delp, Pastor
    Dan Lorenzon, Youth Pastor

Menn Bible Fell (11619) (FRC) 26
PO Box 301, Morris PA 16938
570-353-2407, jbrod@epix.net,
http://www.forministry.com/16938mmbf
1912 Rt 287
    David M. Weaver, Interim Pastor

Methacton Menn Ch (11601) (FRC) 54
3081 Mill Rd, Norristown PA 19403
610-584-4080, wkull@comcast.net
Fairview Village
    Luke Beidler, Pastor
    Bill Kull, Pastor
    Dawn Ruth Nelson, Pastor

MillCreek Community Ch (29348) (FRC) 31
35 Millstone Court, Langhorne PA 19047-1539
215-757-3209, fax 215-757-3209,
millcreekchurch@msn.com, http://millcreek-church.org
Middletown Country Club—420 N Bellevue Ave
    Regan Savage, Pastor

**New Beginnings Community Ch (11429) (FRC,
AAMA)** 30
Lloyd St and Colonial Ave, Bristol PA 19007
215-785-2233, fax 215-785-2233,
Jonfeliciamoore@aol.com
    Jon E. Moore, Pastor

New Life Menn Ch (10013) (FRC) 26
PO Box 164, Athens PA 18810
570-888-8281
Front St, East Athens
   Philip James Maenza, Pastor

Norristown New Life Menn Ch (10125) (FRC, AAMA, IMH) 113
3 E Marshall St, Norristown PA 19401
610-279-5433, fax 610-272-7802, nnl3@juno.com,
http://www.forministry.com/19401nnlmc
Corner of Swede and Marshall streets
   Luke Beidler, Associate Pastor
   Ertell M. Whigham Jr., Associate Pastor

Perkasie Menn Ch (11627) (FRC, HMONG) 119
320 W Chestnut Street, Perkasie PA 18944
215-257-3117, fax 215-258-5950, info@perkmenno.org,
http://www.perkmenno.org
Corner of 4th & Chestnut
   Mark L. Weidner, Pastor
   Beth Ranck Yoder, Pastor

Perkiomenville Menn Ch (11635) (FRC) 121
PO Box 59, Perkiomenville PA 18074
215-234-4011, fax 215-234-9644, perkmc@juno.com,
http://www.perkmc.com
Deep Creek Rd
   Charles A. Ness, Pastor
   Dennis M. Detweiler, Associate Pastor

Plains Menn Ch (11643) (FRC) 234
50 W Orvilla Rd, Hatfield PA 19440-3643
215-362-7640, fax 215-362-4951, plainsmc@verizon.net,
http://www.plains.pa.us.mennonite.net
Welsh Rd & Orvilla Rd
   Michael L. Derstine, Pastor
   Dawn J. Ranck, Associate Pastor

Providence Menn Ch (11668) (FRC) 41
109 S Mennonite Rd, Collegeville PA 19426
215-799-0497, eanders12@juno.com
   Earl N. Anders Jr., Pastor

River of God Fell (11452) (FRC) 151
813 Reynolds St, Easton PA 18042
610-253-1853, riverofgod@verizon.net
   Justin Franklin Payne, Pastor

Rockhill Menn Ch (11692) (FRC) 148
3100 Meetinghouse Rd, Telford PA 18969
215-723-7780, rockhillmc@juno.com
   Larry G. Moyer, Pastor

Rocky Ridge Menn Ch (11684) (FRC) 160
114 Rocky Ridge Rd, Quakertown PA 18951
215-536-1269, bjcooper@epix.net,
http://www.rockyridgemennonite.org
   Robert D. Cooper, Associate Pastor

Salem Menn Ch (11700) (FRC) 85
41 E Cherry Rd, Quakertown PA 18951
215-536-1223, fax 215-536-1233, salem@netcarrier.com
   Bruce Eglinton-Woods, Pastor

Salford Menn Ch (11718) (FRC) 500
480 Groff's Mill Rd, Harleysville PA 19438
215-256-0778, fax 215-256-6562,
jim_longacre@salfordmc.org, http://www.salfordmc.org
   Miriam F. Book, Pastor
   James C. Longacre, Pastor
   Cynthia Moyer, Youth Pastor
   Anna L. Musselman, Minister of Development

Shalom Christian Fell (10018) (FRC) 17
PO Box 62, East Greenville PA 18041
215-234-8286, richfern@verizon.net
104 Main St
   Duane Hershberger, Pastor
   Richard A. Moyer, Pastor

Souderton Menn Ch (11734) (FRC) 666
105 W Chestnut St, Souderton PA 18964
215-723-3088, fax 215-723-8437,
churchoffice@soudertonmennonite.org,
http://www.soudertonmennonite.org
Corner of Chestnut St & Wile Ave
   Gary McMichael, Pastor of Youth and Young Adults
   Gerald A. Clemmer, Senior Executive Pastor
   Sandra Drescher-Lehman, Pastor of Worship and
     Congregational Care
   David Greiser, Senior Teaching Pastor
   Dan Sell, Administrative Pastor

Spring Mount Menn Ch (11742) (FRC) 54
25 Church Road, Schwenksville PA 19473-2342
610-287-5280, fax 215-721-7967, mking@netreach.net,
http://www.forministry.com/19478Smmc
   Michael A. King, Pastor

Spruce Lake Fell (26203) (FRC) 25
RR 1 Box 605, Canadensis PA 18325-9749
570-595-7505, fax 570-595-0328, mgs1050@erols.com
Spruce Lake Retreat
   Marty Sauder, Pastor

Steel City Menn Ch (11759) (FRC) 119
2137 Mixsell Ave, Bethlehem PA 18015
610-865-4899, fax 610-865-4755,
SCMCHURCH@AOL.COM,
http://www.steelcitymennonitechurch.org
   David K. Kochsmeier, Pastor

Swamp Menn Ch (11767) (FRC) 215
2125 Rosedale Rd, Quakertown PA 18951
215-536-7928, fax 215-536-7983, swamppb@fast.net,
http://swamp.pa.us.mennonite.net
   William A. Brunk, Pastor
   Eric E. Horst, Associate Pastor

Taftsville Chapel Menn Fell (11775) (FRC) 67
7505 Happy Valley Rd, PO Box 44, Taftsville VT 05073
802-457-5838, fax 802-457-5838, jrccgood@valley.net
   Randy Good, Pastor

Towamencin Menn Ch (11783) (FRC) **170**
Route 63 & Old Forty Foot Rd, PO Box 225,
Kulpsville PA 19443
215-368-2450, fax 215-368-9710,
tmencinmc@juno.com, http://towamencinmennonite.org
1980 Sumneytown Pike
   Robert L. Petersheim, Interim/Transitional Pastor
   Russell M. Detweiler, Assistant Pastor

Vietnamese Gospel Menn Ch (11128)
(FRC, VIET) **29**
811 S 6th Street, PO Box 64738, Allentown PA 18103
215-513-4117, tcpham1@netzero.com
   Thanh Cong Pham, Pastor

Vincent Menn Ch (11809) (FRC) **100**
39 Seven Stars Rd, Spring City PA 19475
610-948-6130, fax 610-948-6130 *51,
vincentmennonite@juno.com
   H. Wesley Boyer, Pastor

Wellspring Ch of Skippack (11726) (FRC) **40**
1183 Cressman Rd, PO Box 317, Skippack PA 19474
610-489-2688, fax 610-489-1535,
wellspringchurch@juno.com
   Michael A. Meneses, Pastor

West Philadelphia Menn Fell (27276)
(FRC, KB) **62**
4740 Baltimore Ave, Philadelphia PA 19143
215-729-2050, fax 215-729-2845,
JFKauffman@wpmf.com, http://www.wpmf.com
48th St & Baltimore Ave
   J. Fred Kauffman, Pastor

Whitehall Menn Ch (10114) (FRC) **50**
4138 Wilson St, Whitehall PA 18052
610-262-1270, fax 610-262-7380, wmcfun@yahoo.com,
http://wmcfun.tripod.com

CONFERENCES AND CONGREGATIONS

2

Franklin Mennonite Conference

OFFICE
frmc@earthlink.net
717-375-4544, fax 717-375-2136
4856 Molly Pitcher Hwy S, Chambersburg PA
    17201

STAFF
Darrell Baer, conference minister
Janet Martin, administrative office secretary

GENERAL INFORMATION
Members: 1,186
Congregations: 14
Ministers: 31
CLC reps: Darrell Baer, J. Allen Lehman
Annual Conference: October 3, 2004

CONFERENCE BOARD
J. Allen Lehman, moderator (jallen@pa.net),
    346 Warm Spring Rd, Chambersburg PA 17201,
    717-264-1319; Lloyd Gingrich, assistant moder-
    ator; Jerry Roth, secretary; Arnold Eby, treasur-
    er; Paul Clemmer, Larry Lehman, Joseph Martin,
    Roger Martin

PUBLICATION
The Burning Bush (monthly) Peter Zucconi,
    editor

COMMISSIONS
Leadership. Ray Geigley, chairperson
    (rdgeigley@yellowbananas.com), 3459
    Church St, Chambersburg PA 17201, 717-
    264-9490; Darrell Baer, Joanna Lehman,
    Karen Martin, Roger Martin, Ray Miller

**OTHER CONFERENCE AGENCIES AND
REPRESENTATIVES**
Franklin Mission Board. Roger Eshleman,
    president (eshleman1@earthlink.com), 506
    Clayton Ave, Waynesboro PA 17268, 717-
    762-7654; Allen Lehman, vice president;
    Richard Lehman, treasurer; Larry Lehman,

secretary; Dale Horst, fifth member
Mennonite Women. Beverly Martin, president
    1065 South Main St, Chambersburg PA
    17201; Dortha Neil, vice president; Carole
    Smith, secretary
Conference Youth Leaders. Joel and Sue
    Sollenberger (joelsollen@hotmail.com), PO
    Box 332, 188 Nelson St, Marion PA 17235,
    717-375-4225

Congregations

Bethel Community Ch (18994) (FRK) 42
PO Box 91, Warfordsburg PA 17267
301-678-6526
Bethel Church Rd
    Gary Quackenbos, Pastor
    Dale E. Lehman, Associate Pastor

Cedar Street Menn Ch (19000) (FRK) 112
430 Cedar St, Chambersburg PA 17201
717-263-9270, fax 717-263-7440,
cedarstreetmennonitechurch@juno.com
    Paul G. Conrad, Pastor
    Dale Eugene Clugston, Ordained Deacon

Chambersburg Menn Ch (19018) (FRK) 142
1800 Philadelphia Ave, Chambersburg PA 17201
717-264-5520, fax 717-264-6065, aroth@shalomca.com
    Jerry A. Roth, Pastor
    Jere A. Horst, Associate Pastor
    Preston M. Frey, Pastor Emeritus
    David Henry Martin, Ordained Deacon

Community Menn Ch (14738) (FRK) 17
5116 Main St Box 383, Marion MD 17235
717-375-2434, prclemmer@earthlink.net
21108A National Pike, Boonsboro MD
    Paul M. Clemmer, Pastor
    Lewis M. Coss, Pastor Emeritus

Faith Community Menn Ch (11309) (FRK) 0
30 W Frederick St, PO Box 143,
Walkersville MD 21793-0143
301-845-7106, fax 301-845-0800, timh98@juno.com
    Timothy S. Hampton, Pastor

Marion Menn Ch (19034) (FRK) 195
4365 Molly Pitcher Hwy, Chambersburg PA 17201
717-375-4309, fax 717-375-2950,
marionmennch@comcast.net,
http://www.marionmennonite.org
    Carl D. Kniss, Pastor
    Gerald D. Lehman, Ordained Deacon

Mercersburg Menn Ch (19109) (FRK) 132
PO Box 356, Mercersburg PA 17236
717-328-9282, mermenc@juno.com
10060 Buchanan Trail W
  Allen R. Eshleman, Pastor
  David Possinger, Associate Pastor
  Lloyd W. Gingrich, Minister of Visitation
  John A. Horst, Ordained Deacon

Mount Zion Menn Ch (14746) (FRK) 64
20544 Benevola Church Rd, Boonsboro MD 21713
717-263-7203, tallowhill@juno.com
  Larry Lehman, Pastor

North Side Menn Ch (16345) (FRK) 58
716 N Locust St, Hagerstown MD 21740
717-597-3294, zookie17225@peoplepc.com
  Gary L. Zook, Pastor

Pleasant View Menn Ch (19042) (FRK) 115
346 Warm Spring Rd, Chambersburg PA 17201
717-264-1319, jallen@pa.net
  J. Allen Lehman, Pastor
  Dean M. Lehman, Ordained Deacon

Pond Bank Menn Ch (19059) (FRK) 60
6555 Duffield Rd, Chambersburg PA 17201
717-352-2135, mdebersole@pa.net
  Marlin E. Ebersole, Pastor

Rock Hill Menn Ch (19067) (FRK) 21
1255 Candice Ln, Chambersburg PA 17201
717-264-1125, tssol@pa.net
Rock Hill Rd
  Samuel Sollenberger, Pastor

Salem Ridge Menn Ch (19075) (FRK) 128
441 Pensinger Rd, Greencastle PA 17225
717-597-8426, salemrmc@earthlink.net
  G. Joseph Martin, Pastor

Shady Pine Menn Ch (19083) (FRK) 100
14620 Shady Pine Rd, Willow Hill PA 17271
717-349-7061, mfneil@innernet.net
  Marlin A. Neil, Pastor
  Glenn D. Wise, Ordained Deacon

CONFERENCES AND CONGREGATIONS

2

Gulf States Mennonite Conference

OFFICE
secretaryGSMC@aol.com
985-758-7075
PO Box 526, Des Allemands LA 70030

STAFF
Duane Maust, moderator (duelchna@aol.com)
Patricia H. Reno, secretary
(secretaryGSMC@aol.com)

GENERAL INFORMATION
Year founded: 1979
Members: 654
Congregations: 14
Ministers: 12
CLC reps: Duane Maust, Robert Zehr
Annual delegate session: (first Saturday in
    November) November 6, 2004
Annual spring inspirational meeting: (first
    weekend in May) May 7-8, 2005
Conference historian: Robert O. Zehr

EXECUTIVE COMMITTEE
Duane Maust, moderator (duelchna@aol.com),
135 Fairchild Rd, Meridian, MS 39307, 601-
485-2248; Robert O. Zehr, moderator-elect;
Patricia H. Reno, secretary; Mark Roth, treasur-
er; David Roth, member-at-large; Shawn and
Pam Beadle, youth commission; Jeff Landis,
PLFC; Karen Yoder, Mennonite Women; Alice
Phillips, African-American rep; Carol Lee Roth,
Native American rep; Karl Barnhard, missions
commission; David Weaver Jr., leadership com-
mission

PUBLICATION
The Fellowship (quarterly) Linda Williams, edi-
tor (fellowshipgsmc@aol.com), 64320 Lake
Superior Rd, Amite LA 70422, 985-748-4481

COMMISSIONS
Finance and Stewardship. Mark Roth, chair
    (roth@netdoor.com), 11150 Rd 781,
    Philadelphia MS 39350, 601-656-9302;
    Mervin Mast, Howie Schiedel
Leadership. David Weaver Jr., chairperson
    (dweaver@starvisionsat.com), 21170
    D'Herde Rd, Gulfport MS 39503, 228-832-
    0661; Duane Maust, Glenn Myers, Harvey
    Yoder, Robert Zehr
Missions. Karl Barnhard, chairperson
    (bernhardkm@msn.com), 116 Pasadena
    Ave, Metairie LA 70001, 504-837-3599;
    Marlene Bernhard, David Roth, Connie Roth
Peace and Justice Representative. Lester
    Hackman Jr., 101 Franklin, Luling LA 70070,
    985-785-8696
Youth. Shawn and Pam Beadle, co-chairs
    (pgbeadle@msn.com), 114 Michael Dr, Des
    Allemands LA 70030, 985-758-2031; Grover
    Warren and Kiley Warren

OTHER CONFERENCE AGENCY AND REPS
Gulf States Choice Books. 7705 Smith Rd,
    Theodore AL 36582-3831, 334-653-0560;
    Dot Miller, Leo Yoder, Robert Zehr
Mennonite Women. Karen Yoder, president
    (ksywhy@pngusa.net), 311 Jensen St,
    Macon MS 39341, 662-726-2542; Carrie
    Geil, Amy Pauls, Alice Phillips, Sandy Reno,
    Connie Roth
Pine Lake Fellowship Camp. Jeff and Cheryl
    Landis, co-directors, 10371 Pine Lake Rd,
    Meridian MS 39307, 601-483-CAMP

Congregations

Choctaw Christian Ch (15891) (GS, UNMC) 3
c/o Mary Bucher, 80 Hill Rd, Macon MS 39341
662-726-5295
Louisville, MS

Cornerstone Community Ch (16212) (GS) 65
12817 Hwy 14, PO Box 728, Macon MS 39341-0728
662-726-9633 or 662-726-9633, fax 662-726-2512
Lee Hershberger, Interim Pastor

Des Allemands Menn Ch (17897) (GS) 141
PO Box 818, Des Allemands LA 70030
985-758-7550, mennoda@juno.com
17447 Old Spanish Trail
David Willis Roth, Pastor

First Menn Ch (10777) (GS, CM) 20
810 Camp St, El Dorado AR 71730
870-864-0606, fax 870-863-8661, mlmast@ipa.net
Mervin Mast, Pastor

Grace Menn Christian Fell (11144) (GS) 5
PO Box 508, Quitman MS 39355
601-776-6407

Gulfhaven Menn Ch (17947) (GS) 100
21497 Mennonite Rd, Gulfport MS 39503
228-832-6130, fax 228-832-5137,
gulfhavenchurch@wmconnect.com
Nelson M. Roth, Pastor
David W. Weaver Jr., Assistant Pastor

Iglesia Amor Viviente (28258) (GS, IMH, AV) . . .75
116 Pasedena Ave, Metairie LA 70001
504-219-0771, Amorviviente@msn.com
Carlos (Karl) Enrique Bernhard, Pastor

Jubilee Menn Ch (24547) (GS) 49
812 28th Ave, Meridian MS 39301
601-693-8073, fax 601-693-0079, duelchna@aol.com
Duane E. Maust, Co-Pastor
Elaine Maust, Co-Pastor

Lighthouse Fell Ch (25403) (GS) 12
PO Box 1392, Buras LA 70041
985-657-0929, Emmanuel_Diamond@lycos.com
37332 Hwy 11
Anthony J. Duplessis Jr., Interim Pastor

Nanih Waiya Indian Menn Ch (16352)
(GS, UNMC) 42
11150 Rd 781, Philadelphia MS 39350
601-656-9302
Preston MS
Mark Ray Roth, Senior Pastor
W. Harvey Yoder, Assistant Pastor
Ethan Joseph Good, Retiring Pastor

Native Christian Fell (11140) (GS, UNMC,
MILC) 28
6210 Jack Springs Rd, Atmore AL 36502
251-368-0280
Houma, LA
Steve W. Cheramie Risingsun, Pastor

Open Door Menn Ch (22046) (GS, AAMA) 24
403 Mt Vernon Ave, Jackson MS 39209
601-355-7523, rhodayoder@yahoo.com
555 Magnolia Road, Jackson, MS
Robert O. Zehr, Interim Pastor

Pearl River Menn Ch (21790) (GS, UNMC) 45
315 Northwood Dr, Philadelphia MS 39350
601-656-3514, gemyers@bbimail.net
State Hwy 16 W
D. Glenn Myers, Pastor

Poarch Community Ch (16535) (GS, UNMC) 45
6210 Jack Springs Rd, Atmore AL 36504-0385
251-368-0280, fax 334-368-2841
Steve W. Cheramie Risingsun, Pastor

CONFERENCES AND CONGREGATIONS

2

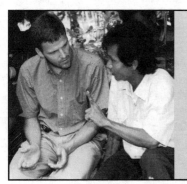

Illinois Mennonite Conference

OFFICE
info@illinois.mennonite.net,
    www.illinois.mennonite.net
309-925-2111, 309-925-2211, 309-925-5615,
    fax 309-925-5612
214 S Sampson St, PO Box 3, Tremont IL 61568

STAFF
Susan Sommer, administrator
    (slsommer@illinois.mennonite.net)
Wayne Hochstetler, conference minister
    (whochstetler@illinois.mennonite.net),
    1324 E Vernon Ave, Normal IL 61761, 309-
    862-9268; 309-925-2111
Holly Mason, secretary
    (hmason@illinois.mennonite.net)
Katrina Sommer, bookkeeper
    (ksommer@illinois.mennonite.net)

GENERAL INFORMATION
Year founded: 1872
Members: 6,710
Congregations: 45
Ministers: 81
CLC Reps: Wayne Hochstetler, Roger Kennell,
    Susan Sommer
Annual conference: Spring 2004
Conference historian: Gerlof Homan

PUBLICATION
Missionary Guide, contact Holly Mason
(hmason@illinois.mennonite.net); PO Box 3
Tremont, IL 61568, 309 925-2111

MISSIONAL LEADERSHIP TEAM
Roger Kennell, moderator; Richard Martin,
treasurer, (secretary to be named), B. Elaine
Bryant, Andres Gallardo, Gary Martin, Ray
Nachtigall, Guenetu Yigzaw

COMMISSIONS
Christian Nurture. Keith Springer, chair
    (ekeiths43@juno.com), 40364 E 600 North
    Rd, Saybrook IL 61770, 309-772-3249;
    Michael Danner, Tim Gale, Carolyn LeFevre,
    Mindy Vannaken
Committee on Faith, Life and Practice.
    Pamela Dominguez, Alice Kennell, Joel
    Nafziger, Marvin Wright
Finance and Stewardship. Richard Martin,
    chair (infcu@juno.com), 1116 Brummel St,
    Evanston IL 60202, 847-492-1467; Eldon
    Eigsti, Mark Graber, Christine Papenhause.
    Staff: Katrina Sommer
Historial. Gerlof Homan, chair,
    (homan3@juno.com), 113 Eastview Dr,
    Normal IL 61761, 309-452-5811; Elaine
    Gerber, Kenneth Ulrich, Ruth Ulrich. Staff:
    Susan Sommer
Leadership. Cindy Breeze, chair
    (cbreeze4@aol.com), 902 W Springfield
    Ave, Urbana IL 61801, 217-367-5353; Leota
    Mann, Bonnie Neufeld, Doug Roth, Elmer
    Wyse, Calvin Zehr. Staff: Wayne Hochstetler
Mission, Evangelism and Service. Rich Foss,
    chair (richfoss@plwcreek.org), 19183 Plow
    Creek #2, Tiskilwa IL 61368, 815-646-6600;
    Lori Graber, Mike Kristoff, Ken Roth, Sarah
    Sales, Duane Sears, Kay Sears, Mennonite
    Women Rep.
Nominating. Roger Kennell, chair
    (narnian@dtnspeed.net), 1220 County Rd
    1600 E, Roanoke IL 61561, 309-467-4522;
    Marilyn Eigsti, Allan Howe, Kathy Roth, Willis
    Sutter
Peace and Social Concerns. Mike Smith,
    chair (crna_mike@hotmail.com), 127 N Rt
    47, Gibson City, IL 60936, 217-784-4061;
    Ruth Anne Friesen, Cecil Graber, James
    Halteman

OTHER CONFERENCE AGENCY AND REPS

Illinois Mennonite Camp Association Inc.
David Horst, executive director
(dhorst@mennohaven.com), MennoHaven
Camp and Retreat Center, 9301 1575 East St,
Tiskilwa IL 61368-9710, 815-646-4344, fax
815-646-4301

Mennonite Women. Marian Egli, president
(egli_2@hotmail.com), 309-449-5479

CONFERENCE RELATED MINISTRIES

Chicago Mennonite Learning Center. Ken
Hawkley, principal (cmlc@juno.com), 4647
W 47th St, Chicago IL 60632, 773-735-9304,
773-735-9832

Mennonite Housing Aid. Richard Martin
(imfcu@juno.com), PO Box 6056, Evanston
IL 60204

**Chicago Opportunity for Peace in Action
(COPA).** 4647 W 47th St, Chicago IL 60632,
312-399-COPA[2672]

**Conference Advisory Board for Goshen
College.** Gene Nafziger, Rachel Zehr, CAM
appointee: David Araujo

Mennonite Financial Federal Credit Union.
(Result of a merger that included Illinois
Mennonite Federal Credit Union) Larry
Miller (larry@mennonitefinancial.com), PO
Box 10455, Lancaster PA 176052

Lombard Mennonite Peace Center.
(Admin@LMPeaceCenter.org), 1263 S
Highland Ave, Suite 1N, Lombard, IL 60148,
630-627-0507, fax 630-927-0519

MCC Great Lakes—David Ewert, IMC representative (loudarew@juno.,com) 2111 E
Luther Rd, Jansville WI 53545, 608-754-
6942. Rodolfo (Roy) Jiminez,
(rjimenez@mcc.org) Great Lakes co-ordina-
tor of Practical Ministries in Chicago and
Rigional Staff Associate for Illinois and
Wisconsin—21530 Freeport Ct, Plainfield IL
61544, 815-886-3855

Assembly Delegates: Wayne Hochstetler,
Roger Kennell, Susan Sommer, others to be
named

Congregations

Arthur Menn Ch (11817) (IL) 232
710 E Park St, Arthur IL 61911
217-543-2781, arthurmennonite@yahoo.com,
http://www.arthurmennonite.org
  Glen Rhodes, Minister of Worship & Youth
  Tony Chmiel, Minister of Community Life
  Clara King, Minister of Outreach
  Gary E. Martin, Minister of Discipling

**Berhane Wongel Ethiopian Ch (11025)
(IL, CAM)** 180
450 W Forest Ave, W Chicago IL 60185
847-869-2191, fax 630-293-7331, bwec@msn.com
1004 Greenwood and Maple St
  Guenetu Yigzaw, Pastor

**Bethel Menn Community Ch (11825) (IL, CAM,
AAMA)** 40
c/o Tony Bianchi, PO Box 5593, Chicago IL 60680-5593
312-421-3871, fax 312-421-2551, zsowell1@juno.com
1434 S Laflin
  Tony Bianchi, Pastor

Bethesda Menn Ch (17814) (IL, AAMA) 74
2823 Dayton Street, St Louis MO 63106
314-535-5336, dunigans4444@aol.com
  Jesse Dunigans, Pastor
  James Long, Pastor

Cazenovia Menn Ch (11841) (IL) 82
1634 CR 1600 E, c/o Dennis Kennell, Roanoke IL 61561
309-923-6621, kennells@mtco.com
1394 CR 1800N, Lowpoint, IL
  Dennis Kennell, Pastor

**Centro Cristiano Vida Abundante (28928)
(IL, CAM, IMH)** 1000
1321 S Austin Blvd, PO Box 50778, Cicero IL 60804
708-863-6305, fax 708-863-5954,
http://www.ccVidaabundante.com
  Andres Gallardo, Pastor
  Gamaliel Aguado, Associate Pastor
  Lilia Gallardo, Associate Pastor

**Centro Cristiano Vida Abundante Aurora
(20606) (IL)** 125
1140 Pershing Rd, Aurora IL 60506
630-844-9108, g12aurora@aol.com
  Constanzo Aguirre, Pastor

**Centro Cristiano Vida Abundante Holland
(20605) (IL)** 50
290 E 18th St, Holland MI 49424
616-399-2453, juzicarlos@aol.com,
http://www.ccvidaabundante.com

**Chicago Community Menn Ch (24653) (CDC,
IL, CAM)** 58
425 S Central Park Ave, Chicago IL 60624
773-343-4251, pewaite@mennonite.net
  Phil Waite, Pastor

**CONFERENCES AND
CONGREGATIONS**

2

Christ Community Menn Ch (29397) (CDC, IL, CAM) **35**
888 S Roselle Rd, Schaumburg IL 60193-3965
847-895-3654, fax 847-895-3654, lpkennel@msn.com, http://www.ccmc-mennonite.org
Pauline Kennel, Pastor
Leroy Eldon Kennel, Minister of the Word
Janice Kennel Ropp, Minister of Counseling

Community Menn Ch (28332) (CDC, IL, CAM, AAMA) **82**
16200 Kedzie Ave, Markham IL 60426
708-333-1358, fax 708-333-1684, chuckneufeld@mennonite.net, http://community.mennonite.com
Chuck T. Neufeld, Lead Pastor
Bonnie Beth Neufeld, Co-Pastor
Horace McMillon, Associate Pastor

East Bend Menn Ch (11874) (IL) **302**
702 CR 3300 N, PO Box 520, Fisher IL 61843
888-269-5963, fax 217-897-6386,
eastbend@earthlink.net, http://www.eastbend.org
Michael Richard Dean, Pastor
Jeffrey D. Ressler, Associate Pastor

East Peoria Menn Ch (11940) (IL) **100**
c/o Maurice Yordy, 1397 CR 700 N, Eureka IL 61530
309-699-8713, fax 309-467-6984, mpyord@mtco.com, http://www.eastpeoria.il.us.mennonite.net
125 N Norwood, E Peoria, IL
Maurice J. Yordy, Pastor

Englewood Menn Ch (11882) (IL, CAM, AAMA) **25**
PO Box 21569, Chicago IL 60621
773-483-2987, elainebryant@ameritech.net
832 W 68th St
B. Elaine Bryant, Pastor

Evanston Menn Ch (11890) (CDC, IL, CAM) **30**
736 Dobson St, Evanston IL 60202
847-846-3954, fax 847-492-1458,
mcb9476@ameritech.net
Mitchell C. Brown, Pastor
Doug Hostetter, Peace Pastor

First Menn Ch of Champaign-Urbana (11924) (CDC, IL) **126**
902 W Springfield Ave, Urbana IL 61801
217-367-5353, fax 217-367-2716, fmc@prairienet.org, http://www.prairienet.org/mennonite
Larry J. Wilson, Pastor
Cynthia Massanari Breeze, Associate Pastor

First Menn Ch of Morton (11908) (IL) **266**
250 S Baltimore Ave, Morton IL 61550
309-266-7591, fax 309-266-6344, fmmorton@mtco.com
Doane Brubaker, Pastor
Earl Smith, Youth Pastor

First Norwood Menn Ch (11916) (IL) **50**
6605 W Jones Rd, Peoria IL 61604
309-673-3026, norwoodchurch@myexcel.com
Harold J. Baer, Pastor

Freeport Menn Ch (11932) (IL) **128**
3416 E Brick School Rd, Freeport IL 61032
815-449-2498, fax 815-449-9072, fimc@aeroinc.net
Mark Vincent, Interim Pastor

Hopedale Menn Ch (11957) (IL) **308**
5192 Hopedale Rd, Hopedale IL 61747
309-449-6600, fax 309-449-5529, hmc@mtco.com
Ray Nachtigall, Lead Pastor
Kurt Walker, Associate Pastor

Iglesia Cristiana Peniel (11097) (IL) **64**
5731 S Tripp St, 1st Floor, Chicago IL 60629
773-582-6785
Juan Laureano, Pastor

Iglesia Menonita Getsemani (10638) (IL, IMH, CAM) **23**
c/o David Araujo, 506 Liberty St, East Chicago IL 46312
219-397-9936
4901 Northcotte Ave—E Chicago, IN
David Araujo, Pastor
Sonia N. Araujo, Co-Pastor

Joy Fell Menn Ch (27391) (CDC, IL, AAMA) **30**
2918 W Montana St, Peoria IL 61605
309-691-8424
Phillip Maclin, Pastor

Lawndale Menn Ch (11973) (IL, IMH, CAM) **80**
2520 S Lawndale Ave, Chicago IL 60623
773-277-6665
Angel M. Cañon, Pastor

Living Love Ministries (11096) (CDC, IL, AV) . . .**70**
PO Box 5473, Peoria IL 61601
309-676-2772, pastoramariah@sbcglobal.net
811 NE Perry Ave
Maria Hatfield, Pastor
Walter Smeltzer, Associate Pastor

Living Water Community Ch (11151) (IL, CAM, AAMA) **64**
1545 W Pratt #101, Chicago IL 60626
773-764-5872, fax 773-262-2371,
livingwatercc@juno.com,
http://livingwatercommunitychurch.org
1545 W Morse Ave, 3rd Floor (United Church of Rogers Park)
Sally Schreiner Youngquist, Senior Pastor
Joseph Maniglia, Youth Pastor

Lombard Menn Ch (11981) (IL) **163**
528 E Madison St, Lombard IL 60148
630-627-5310, fax 630-627-9893,
LombardMenno@aol.com,
http://lombard.il.us.mennonite.net
Todd K. Friesen, Lead Pastor
John M. Stoltzfus, Associate Pastor

Madison Menn Ch (10078) (CDC, IL) **111**
PO Box 44522, Madison WI 53744-4522
608-276-7680, mmc@madison-mennonite.org,
http://www.madison-mennonite.org
1501 Gilbert Rd
  Tonya Ramer Wenger, Pastor

Maple Avenue Menn Ch (23697) (CDC, IL, CAM) 39
346 Maple Ave, Waukesha WI 53186
262-547-6937, clariKra@aol.com
  Clarice Kratz, Co-Pastor
  Lawrence M. Kratz, Co-Pastor

Maple Lawn Fell (10049) (IL) **0**
700 N Main St, Eureka IL 61530
309-467-2337, fax 309-467-2594,
Doug@Maple-Lawn.com
  Richard Douglas Hicks, Pastor

Menn Ch of Dillon (11866) (IL) **55**
6349 Springfield Rd, Delavan IL 61734
309-244-7153
20549 Peach St
  Robert D. Nafziger, Pastor

Menn Ch of Normal (11833) (CDC, IL) **291**
805 S Cottage Ave, Normal IL 61761
309-452-6622, fax 309-452-0478,
normal.mennonite@verizon.net,
http://www.normalmennonite.com
  Tim E. Schrag, Pastor
  Jane Thorley Roeschley, Associate Pastor
  Stephen A. Ropp, Youth Pastor

Metamora Menn Ch (12013) (IL) **203**
1393 Mennonite Rd, Metamora IL 61548
309-367-4892, fax 309-367-4121, metmenno@mtco.com,
http://www.metmenno.org
  Michael Danner, Lead Pastor
  Melissa Danner, Associate Pastor
  Ada Nofsinger, Associate Pastor

New Life Community Ch (26732) (IL) **140**
PO Box 36, Henry IL 61537
309-364-2138, tnlf@mtco.com
  Thomas L. Schrock, Pastor

**North Suburban Menn Ch (27557) (CDC,
IL, CAM)** **24**
1500 W Hawley St, Mundelein IL 60060-1508
847-566-8386, fax 847-475-1006, dckerner@trimedia.net,
http://www.northsuburban.org
  David Kerner, Pastor

Plow Creek Menn Ch (22335) (CDC, IL) **30**
19183 Plow Creek Unit #2, Tiskilwa IL 61368
815-646-6600, fax 815-646-6600,
richfoss@plowcreek.org, http://www.plowcreek.org
1925 E 880 N
  Richard Gordon Foss, Lay Minister
  Neil Horning, Pastoral Elder
  Louise Stahnke, Pastoral Elder

Prairieview Menn Ch (12138) (CDC, IL) **212**
13013 North 400 Rd East, PO Box 369, Flanagan IL 61740
815-796-2824, prairieview@frontiernet.net,
http://community-2.webtv.net/bbroeschley/PRAIRIEVIEW/
  Douglas D. King, Pastor

Reba Place Ch (22343) (IL, CAM, AAMA) **135**
c/o Charlotte Oda, 722 Monroe St, Evanston IL 60202
847-869-0660, fax 847-328-8431, rpcoffice@juno.com,
http://www.rebaplacechurch.org
Custer and Madison
  Ric Hudgens, Pastor

Rehoboth Menn Ch (12062) (IL, CAM, AAMA) . .**25**
c/o Rose Covington, 14220 E 3000 South Rd,
St Anne IL 60964
815-944-5594, fax 815-944-5961
15729 E 3000 S Rd
  Rose Covington, Elder

Roanoke Menn Ch (12070) (IL) **400**
1195 CR 1600 E, Eureka IL 61530
309-467-3460, rmc@mtco.com, http://www.rmc4u.org
1200 N & 1600 E, corner of Woodford Co
  Rick Troyer, Pastor

Science Ridge Menn Ch (12104) (IL) **143**
1702 E 37th St, Sterling IL 61081
815-626-0538, fax 815-626-0594, sridge@cin.net
  Robert Smith, Pastor

**Sonido de Alabanza (23432) (IL, IMH,
CAM)** **800**
PO Box 50870, Cicero IL 60804-3318
815-626-0538, fax 708-780-1176,
admin@sonidodealabanza.com
5510 W Rd 25th St
  Juan Ferreras, Pastor
  Esdras Ferreras, Associate Pastor
  Maritza Ferreras, Associate Pastor
  Alejandra Mendoza, Associate Pastor

St Louis Menn Fell (24182) (CDC, IL) **65**
1443 Ross Ave, St Louis MO 63146-4563
314-878-2832, slmennonitef@aol.com,
http://www.slmf.org
  Melissa S. Roth, Pastor

Trinity Menn Ch (23549) (IL) **189**
1901 S 4th Ave, Morton IL 61550
309-263-8808, fax 309-263-0133,
trinity@trinitymennonite.org,
http://www.trinitymennonite.org
  Michael D. Hutchings, Pastor

Willow Springs Menn Ch (12146) (IL) **61**
PO Box 386, Tiskilwa IL 61368
815-646-4287, fax 815-646-4301, wsmenno@juno.com,
http://www.willowsprings.il.us.mennonite.net
16621 Kentville Rd
  Calvin Dean Zehr, Pastor
  John Gray, Associate Pastor

CONFERENCES AND CONGREGATIONS

2

Indiana-Michigan Mennonite Conference

OFFICE
imoffice@im.mennonite.net,
www.im.mennonite.net
574-534-4006; 800-288-8486,
fax 574-533-5676
212 S Main St, Goshen IN 46526

STAFF
Sherm Kauffman, executive conference minister
(sherm@im.mennonite.net)
Nancy Kauffmann, conference regional minister
(nancy@im.mennonite.net)
Tim Lichti, conference regional minister
(tim@im.mennonite.net)
Bob Yoder, conference minister of youth and
young adults (bob@im.mennonite.net)
Annette Brill Bergstresser, communication coordinator (annette@im.mennonite.net)
Diana Hershberger, secretary/receptionist
(diana@im.mennonite.net)
Heidi King, administrative coordinator
(heidi@im.mennonite.net)
Charlotte Long, bookkeeper/secretary
(charlotte@im.mennonite.net)

GENERAL INFORMATION
Year founded: 1854
Members: 10,283
Congregations: 85
Ministers: 309
CLC reps: Sherm Kauffman, Mary Ellen Meyer,
David Sutter
Annual Conference: June 16-18, 2005
Conference historian: Leonard Gross

EXECUTIVE COMMITTEE
David Sutter, moderator
(davekrmc@juno.com), 233 E Irvington, South
Bend IN 46614, 574-288-5520; Mary Swartley,
moderator-elect; Karl Cender, Terry Diener,
Brent Eash, James Gerber, Marjorie Rush
Hovde, Mary Ellen Meyer, Homer Nissley, Regina
Shands Stoltzfus, Scot Wilson

PUBLICATION
Gospel Evangel (monthly) Annette Brill
Bergstresser, editor
(annette@im.mennonite.net)

COMMISSIONS
Church Life. Ruben Chupp, chair
(rubenc@bnin.net), 1002 Beechwood Dr,
Nappanee IN 46550, 574-773-2963; Anita
Yoder Kehr, Bill Miller, Grace Whitehead
Conference Program Planning. Sandy Miller,
chair (sandy@yellowcreekmc.org), 63075
CR 17, Goshen IN 46526, 574-533-5452;
Chris Kahila, Virginia Leichty. Staff: Sherm
Kauffman
Communication Advisory. Pat McFarlane,
chair (patjm@goshen.edu), 2202
Independence Dr, Goshen IN 46526, 574-
533-7652; Bill Beck, Duane Stoltzfus. Staff:
Heidi King
Justice, Peace and Service. Rich Meyer, chair
(cptcsd@npcc.net), 13416 CR 44,
Millersburg IN 46543, 574-642-3963; Kay
Bontrager-Singer, Eldon Christophel, Bob
Whitehead, Rachel Yoder
Mission. Tim Stair, chair
(tim@collegemennonite.org), 202
Constitution Ave, Goshen IN 46526, 574-
534-4145; Michele Bollman, Robert Charles,
Eleanor Kreider, Art McPhee
Nurture. Esther Lanting, chair
(elanting@maplenet.net), 410 S Washington
St, Wakarusa IN 46573, 574-862-1910;
Randall Miller, Kathy Meyer Reimer, Ruth
Ann Wittrig, Miriam Zehr
Stewardship and Finance. Tim Burkholder,
chair (tburkholder@sharingservices.com),
508 Noelwood Dr, Goshen IN 46526, 574-
534-1593; Karl Cender, Stanley Kropf, Amy
Schrock, Doug Smoker

OTHER CONFERENCE AGENCY AND REPRESENTATIVES

Mennonite Women. Faith Slagel, president, 26408-A Banker Rd, Sturgis MI 49091, 269-651-8001; Cheryl Beachey, Eleanor Buskirk, Barb Eiler, Norma Hahn, Carolyn Lichti, Mary Sue Miller, Karen Unternahrer

Congregations

Ann Arbor Menn Ch (13508) (CDC, IM) 7
1455 Kelly Green Dr, Ann Arbor MI 48103-2614
734-996-9815
Arrowwood Community Center, 2566 Arrowwood
    Chibuzor Vincent Ozor, Pastor

Assembly Menn Ch (22582) (CDC, IM) 137
1201 S 11th St, Goshen IN 46526
574-534-4190, assemblymenn@juno.com,
http://assembly.in.us.mennonite.net
Corner of 11th & New York
    Lois Johns Kaufmann, Co-Pastor
    Karl S. Shelly, Co-Pastor
    Mary Lehman Yoder, Co-Pastor

Belmont Menn Ch (12187) (IM) 179
925 Oxford St, Elkhart IN 46516
574-293-5160, fax 574-293-2061, ninal@maplenet.net
    Duane E. Beck, Pastor
    Nina Bartelt Lanctot, Associate Pastor

Benton Menn Ch (12195) (IM) 94
15350 CR 44, Goshen IN 46528
574-642-3245, fax 574-642-0144, bmc@maplenet.net,
http://benton.in.us.mennonite.net
    Douglas D. H. Kaufman, Pastor
    Brenda Hostetler Meyer, Pastor

Berkey Avenue Menn Fell (24323) (IM) 197
2509 Berkey Ave, Goshen IN 46526
574-534-2398, fax 574-534-4748, berkeyave@juno.com,
http://berkeyavenue.in.us.mennonite.net
    Anita Yoder Kehr, Pastor
    Daniel P. Schrock, Pastor

Bethel Menn Ch (12237) (IM) 46
935 Alpine Street, Greenville MI 48838-2503
616-754-7594, joe_pendleton@hotmail.com
9785 S Bagley Rd, Ashley MI 48806
    Joe Pendleton, Pastor

Bonneyville Menn Ch (12245) (IM) 125
15273 SR 120, Bristol IN 46507
574-848-7148, fax 574-848-7148, bonvil@npcc.net
NW Corner of SR 120 & CR 131
    Eldon Stoltzfus, Interim Pastor

Burr Oak Menn Ch (12278) (IM) 64
11506 W 200 S, Rensselaer IN 47978
219-394-2339, bomc@netnitco.net
Corner of CRs 200 S & 1150 W
    Philip D. Leichty, Pastor
    James R. Armstrong, Overseer

Carroll Community Worship Center (12153) (IM) 46
4506 Carroll Rd, Fort Wayne IN 46818
260-637-2309, fax 260-637-5998, dove9@juno.com,
http://www.carrollcommunity.org
    Verlin Haarer, Pastor

Cedar Grove Menn Ch (12302) (IM) 20
5428 W River Rd, Manistique MI 49854
906-341-3435, cgmenn@up.net
1275 N Kandall Rd
    James L. Troyer, Pastor

Ch Without Walls (10244) (IM, AAMA) 80
731 Wagner Ave, Elkhart IN 46516
574-293-0776, fax 574-293-0776
    Jonathan Brown, Pastor
    Cora L. Brown, Co-Pastor
    Joe Gary, Other

Christian Fell Center (28951) (IM) 44
PO Box 416, Sturgis MI 49091
269-651-9425
    Glenn Middleton, Pastor

Clinton Brick Menn Ch (12336) (IM) 133
PO Box 713, Goshen IN 46527-0713
574-642-3805, rkennel@npcc.net
62499 SR 13
    Ronald L. Kennel, Pastor

Clinton Frame Menn Ch (12328) (IM) 608
63846 CR 35, Goshen IN 46528-9621
574-642-3165, fax 574-642-3786, cfmc@maplenet.net,
http://clintonframe.in.us.mennonite.net
    Terry L. Diener, Interim Pastor
    Marilyn Riegsecker, Minister of Christian Education
    Aldine Thomas, Minister of Visitation
    Anita Yoder, Minister of Worship and Music

Coldsprings Christian Fell (12344) (IM) 59
1381 E Phelps, Kalkaska MI 49646
231-587-0806
    Brent Bontrager, Pastor

College Menn Ch (12518) (IM) 1070
1900 S Main St, Goshen IN 46526
574-535-7262, fax 574-535-7165, cmc@
collegemennonite.org, http://www.collegemennonite.org
    Lee Dengler, Pastor
    Susan Dengler, Pastor
    Firman Gingerich, Pastor
    Wilfred Kanagy, Pastor
    Klaudia Smucker, Pastor
    Tim Stair, Pastor
    Rosemary Widmer, Pastor
    Kristen Hoober, Youth Pastor

CONFERENCES AND CONGREGATIONS

2

Community Christian Fell Ch (10243) (IM, AAMA) **250**
17330 Chandler Park Dr, Detroit MI 48224
313-882-2850, fax 313-882-4550
  Samuel A. Wilson, Pastor

East Goshen Menn Ch (12393) (IM) **219**
17861 SR 4, Goshen IN 46528
574-533-7161, fax 574-534-9974,
egmc@eastgoshenmc.org, http://eastgoshenmc.org
  Merle Hostetler, Pastor
  Steve E. Slagel, Pastor

Emma Menn Ch (12419) (IM) **275**
1900 S 600 W, Topeka IN 46571
260-593-2036, fax 260-593-2564, info@emmamc.org,
http://emmamc.org
  Gene A. Hartman, Pastor

Fairhaven Menn Ch (12435) (IM) **71**
5401 Winter St, Fort Wayne IN 46806
260-456-6997, fairhaven.mennonite@verizon.net
  Jimmie Ruffin, Pastor

Faith Menn Ch (10127) (CDC, IM) **50**
1201 S 11th St, Goshen IN 46526
574-534-1173, gwengz@aol.com
  Deron Brill Bergstresser, Pastor
  Gwen Ann Gustafson-Zook, Pastor

**Family Worship Center at the Lighthouse
(12526) (IM, OD)** **85**
306 S 27th St, Goshen IN 46528
574-831-4432, fax 574-533-6778
  Eli S. Schmucker, Pastor

Fell of Hope Menn Ch (22210) (IM) **48**
1618 S 6th St, Elkhart IN 46516
574-294-1416, fohchurch@mennonite.net,
http://ofhopechurch.in.us.mennonite.net
  Robert Weidman, Pastor
  Joshua Yoder, Pastor

First Menn Ch (12476) (IM) **73**
1213 Saint Marys Ave, Fort Wayne IN 46808
260-422-6702, mennofw@juno.com
  Kathy Colliver, Pastor

First Menn Ch (12450) (IM) **163**
4601 Knollton Rd, Indianapolis IN 46228
317-251-1980, fax 317-253-4632, fmc@indymenno.org,
http://www.indymenno.org
Corner of 46th & Knollton
  Ryan Jeffrey Ahlgrim, Pastor
  Amanda A. Yoder, Associate Pastor

First Menn Ch (12468) (IM) **369**
203 E Lawrence St, PO Box 508,
Middlebury IN 46540-0508
574-825-5135, fax 574-825-2569,
fmcoffice@firstmennonite.net,
http://www.firstmennonite.net
  Linford Martin, Pastor
  Paul D. Leichty, Associate Pastor, Music
  Pamela Yoder, Associate Pastor, Pastoral Care
  Daniel L. Yoder, Associate Pastor, Youth & Young Adults

Forks Menn Ch (12492) (IM) **151**
11435 W 025 S, Middlebury IN 46540
574-825-9333, forkspastor@bnin.net
  Mervin Miller, Intentional Interim Pastor

Germfask Menn Ch (12500) (IM) **34**
7511 County Line Rd, Germfask MI 49836
906-586-9978
  J. D. Livermore Jr., Pastor

Good News Community Chapel (12286) (IM) . . .**9**
PO Box 791, Pinckney MI 48169
734-878-3992
104 E Putnam St

Grace Chapel (12534) (IM, AAMA) **68**
2202 Janes Ave, Saginaw MI 48601
989-755-3212
  James H. Nelson, Pastor

Grand Marais Menn Ch (12542) (IM) **12**
PO Box 457, Grand Marais MI 49839
906-494-2724, smpost@jamadots.com
Randolph & Campbell
  Stephen Post, Pastor

Harlan Menn Fell (23333) (IM) **21**
PO Box 493, Ages-Brookside KY 40801
606-573-4844, erstol@kih.net
302 E Clover St, Harlan

Harmony Christian Fell (28035) (IM) **10**
c/o Judy Gingerich, 1574 Campbell Rd,
Goodletsville TN 37072
615-851-7280

Hilltop Menn Fell (12856) (IM) **14**
810 Petoskey St, Petoskey MI 49770-2935
616-347-2961, hilltopfellowship@yahoo.com

Holdeman Menn Ch (12567) (IM) **204**
65723 CR 1, Wakarusa IN 46573
574-862-4751, office@holdemanmc.org,
http://www.holdemanmc.org
  Vernard E. Guengerich, Associate Pastor

Hopewell Menn Ch (12575) (IM) **188**
PO Box 316, Kouts IN 46347
219-766-2184, hopewell@netnitco.net
805 N Main Street
  Bill Beck, Co-Pastor
  Chris Birky, Co-Pastor

House of Power (10961) (IM) 5
28103 CR 20 W, Elkhart IN 46517
574-522-7211
  Robert Crockett, Pastor
  Maria Crockett, Co-Pastor
  Shawn Lange, Minister of Outreach

Howard-Miami Menn Ch (12583) (IM) 238
3976 E 1400 S, Kokomo IN 46901
765-395-7509, fax 765-395-8192,
howardmiami@mennonite.net,
http://www.howardmiami.org
  Randy Detweiler, Pastor
  T. Lee Miller, Co-Pastor

Hudson Lake Menn Ch (12591) (IM) 40
PO Box 903, New Carlisle IN 46552
574-654-8388
7503 N Walker Rd
  Esther Lanting, Pastor

**Iglesia Menonita del Buen Pastor (12377)
(IM, IMH)** 43
523 S 6th St, Goshen IN 46526
574-537-8403
  Seferina Garcia DeLeon, Pastor
  Rolando Sosa, Pastor
  Jorge Vielman, Pastor

Kern Road Menn Ch (12617) (IM) 242
18211 Kern Rd, South Bend IN 46614
574-291-0924, fax 574-291-9437, rachelkrmc@juno.com,
http://krmc.in.us.mennonite.net
  Andre Gingerich Stoner, Pastor
  David L. Sutter, Pastor
  Janice Yordy Sutter, Pastor
  Rachel Miller Jacobs, Pastor of Faith Formation

Lafayette Menn Fell (26021) (CDC, IM) 8
PO Box 355, Lafayette IN 47902-0355
765-743-4876, hovde@dcwi.com,
http://livingfaith.in.us.mennonite.net
102 N Chauncy (First United Methodist), West Lafayette

Lake Bethel Menn Ch (12625) (IM) 12
c/o Roger Franke, 4795 S 300 E, Wolcottville IN 46795
260-351-3506, rpfranke@locl.net

Liberty Menn Ch (12641) (IM) 22
PO Box 328, Concord MI 49237
517-524-7489, fax 517-524-6696,
dtmcclin@frontiernet.net
  David McClintic, Pastor

Locust Grove Menn Ch (12666) (IM) 194
29525 Findley Rd, Burr Oak MI 49030
269-489-5041, fax 240-220-8027, office@lgrove.org,
http://www.lgrove.org
  John M. Troyer, Pastor
  James J. Carpenter, Minister of Nurture

Maple River Menn Ch (12682) (IM) 49
Attn: Pat Brubacher, 8755 Woodland Rd, Brutus MI 49716
231-529-6720, fax 231-539-8234, jskauff@freeway.net
3834 Euclid Ave

Marion Menn Ch (12708) (IM) 75
5460 N 450 W, Shipshewana IN 46565-8504
260-562-2910, marion@ligtel.com
  Daniel Z. Miller, Interim Pastor

Menn Ch of Warsaw (10007) (IM) 29
1250 Husky Trail, Warsaw IN 46582
574-269-4449
  Alan E. Leinbach, Pastor

Menn Fell of Bloomington (11426) (IM) 7
c/o Marvin Miller, 4313 N Hartstrait Rd,
Bloomington IN 47404-9682
812-876-8657, marcmill@indiana.edu
Meets in homes

Menominee River Fell (10135) (IM) 30
PO Box 542, Menominee MI 49858
715-735-0189

Michigan Avenue Menn Ch (12716) (IM) 105
PO Box 507, Pigeon MI 48755
989-453-2451, mamc@avci.net
7004 E Michigan Ave
  Scot Wilson, Pastor

Midland Menn Ch (12724) (IM) 35
2510 E Stewart Rd, Midland MI 48640
989-839-9451, fax 898-832-3303, dduford@sbcglobal.net
Corner of Stewart and Patterson
  Don Duford, Interim Pastor

Morning Star Ch (29652) (CDC, IM) 24
2000 S Hoyt Ave, Muncie IN 47302
765-287-0021
  Gladys Maina, Pastor
  Simon Mungai, Associate Pastor

MSU Menn Fell (12757) (CDC, IM) 40
PO Box 6068, East Lansing MI 48826
517-482-9961, msumennofell@juno.com,
http://msu.mi.us.mennonite.net
Alumni Memorial Chapel, MSU Campus
  June Mears-Driedger, Pastor

Naubinway Christian Fell (12807) (IM) 10
PO Box 127, Naubinway MI 49762
906-477-6553, fax 906-477-6553, tomiller@portup.com
Main St
  Timothy O. Miller, Pastor

Ninth Street Menn Ch (12815) (IM, AAMA) 40
1118 N 9th St, Saginaw MI 48601
517-752-7366, fax 517-755-4123, ninth.street@juno.com
  William L. Scott Jr., Pastor

North Goshen Menn Ch (21998) (IM) 164
PO Box 505, Goshen IN 46527-0505
574-533-4255, northgoshen@bnin.net
510 N 8th St
    Arthur E. Smoker Jr., Pastor
    Jerry Wittrig, Co-Pastor

North Leo Menn Ch (12773) (IM) 148
15419 SR 1 N, PO Box 213, Leo IN 46765
260-627-2149, fax 260-627-2370, mimsterz@aol.com,
http://www.northleomc.org
    Douglas J. Zehr, Pastor
    Miriam R. Zehr, Family Life Minister

North Main Street Menn Ch (12781) (IM) 180
504 N Main St, Nappanee IN 46550
574-773-4558, fax 574-773-5438, nmainmen@bnin.net
    Ruben Chupp, Pastor
    Derrick Devon Ramer, Youth Pastor

Olive Menn Ch (21758) (IM) 141
61081 CR 3, Elkhart IN 46517
574-293-2320, omc_office@juno.com
    Robert Martz, Pastor

Paoli Menn Fell (22624) (CDC, IM) 75
2589 N CR 100 W, Paoli IN 47454
812-723-2414, fax 812-723-3515, mennos@iquest.net
    Mary Mininger, Co-Pastor
    Philip A. Mininger, Co-Pastor

Parkview Menn Ch (12849) (IM) 68
1382 E CR 100 N, Kokomo IN 46901
765-459-5714, parkviewchurch@juno.com
    Jacob W. Elias, Co-Pastor
    Lillian Elias, Co-Pastor

Peace Community Menn Ch (12385) (IM, AAMA)61
15800 Curtis St, Detroit MI 48235
313-273-7999, fax 313-345-2285
    Evelyn E. Childs, Pastor

Pine Grove Menn Ch (12559) (IM) 45
1195 N Wattles Rd, Battle Creek MI 49014-7813
269-964-9214, fax 269-964-8718
    Thomas Schwartz, Pastor

Pleasant View Menn Ch (12872) (IM) 232
58529 CR 23, Goshen IN 46528
574-533-2872, fax 574-533-2283, pvmc@maplenet.net,
http://www.mypv.org
    Ronald Diener, Pastor
    Michael Wayne Peak, Associate Pastor
    Norman Maust, Ordained Deacon

Prairie Street Menn Ch (12880) (IM) 203
1316 Prairie St, Elkhart IN 46516-3908
574-293-0377, psmc1316@aol.com
    Andrew Kreider, Pastor

Praise Chapel Christian Fell (10079) (IM) 40
58529 CR 23, Goshen IN 46528
574-534-5568, www.praisechapel.com
Pleasant View Menn Ch
    Michael Lechlitner, Pastor

Providence Menn Ch (12898) (IM) 255
PO Box 183, Montgomery IN 47558-0183
812-486-3679, fax 812-486-3653, pmchurch@rtccom.net
    Jarvis Hochstedler, Interim Pastor

Rexton Menn Ch (12906) (IM) 44
N 7970 Church St, Naubinway MI 49762
906-595-7361, fax 906-595-7361, rexton49@hotmail.com
15 miles NE of Naubinway in Rexton
    Timothy O. Miller, Pastor

Ridgeview Menn Ch (12740) (IM) 10
1344 Lenard Oak Ch Rd, Morgantown KY 42261
270-526-3962

Shalom Menn Ch (10196) (IM) 59
6100 E 32nd St, Indianapolis IN 46226
317-549-0577, smc@iquest.net,
http://www.shalom.in.us.mennonite.net
    Dagne Assefa, Pastor

Shore Menn Ch (12963) (IM) 331
7235 W US Hwy 20, Shipshewana IN 46565
260-768-4240, fax 260-768-4255, shore@locl.net,
http://www.shore.in.us.mennonite.net
    Brent Eash, Pastor
    Carl Horner, Pastor

Soo Hill Community Ch (12971) (IM) 15
PO Box 553, Escanaba MI 49829-0553
906-786-4862

Southside Fell (12930) (CDC, IM) 95
140 W Mishawaka Rd, Elkhart IN 46517
574-293-2825, ssfellow@maplenet.net
AMBS Chapel, 3003 Benham Ave
    Jonathan Neufeld, Pastor
    Rhoda M. Schrag, Pastor

Stutsmanville Chapel (12989) (IM) 106
2988 State Rd, Harbor Springs MI 49740
231-526-2335, stuts@freeway.net
    Edward Warner, Pastor

Sunnyside Menn Ch (12997) (IM) 141
23786 Sunnyside Ave, Elkhart IN 46516
574-875-7790, fax 574-875-6336,
sunnysidemc@juno.com,
http://www.sunnysidemennonitechurch.in.us.mennonite.net
    Terry Zehr, Pastor
    Amy Kratzer, Pastor of Youth and Worship
    Dorothy Kratz, Minister of Pastoral Care and Visitation

Talcum Menn Ch (13003) (IM) 37
9365 Vest-Talcum Rd, Talcum KY 41722
606-251-3303, dabdo@hotmail.com
    Orlo J. Fisher, Pastor

True Vine Tabernacle (12914) (IM) 38
54365 Independence St, Elkhart IN 46514
574-264-0035, evoncas@juno.com
54364 Independence St
  Nancy Rodriguez-Lora, Pastor

Valparaiso Menn Ch (13037) (IM) 45
1305 Silhavy Rd, Valparaiso IN 46383
219-464-8187, fax 219-464-8187 (call first),
valpomenn@earthlink.net
  Mario Bustos, Pastor

Walnut Hill Menn Ch (13045) (IM) 112
909 N Sixth St, Goshen IN 46528
574-533-8023, S-LThomas@juno.com
  Jane Stoltzfus Buller, Pastor
  Stephen B. Thomas, Pastor

Wasepi Menn Chapel (13052) (IM) 50
PO Box 246, Centreville MI 49032
269-467-4024

Waterford Menn Ch (13060) (IM) 391
65975 SR 15, Goshen IN 46526
574-533-5642, fax 574-533-0879,
wmc@waterfordchurch.org,
http://www.waterfordchurch.org
  Kristina Marie Stoltzfus Schlabach, Pastor
  Loanne Harms, Minister to Youth
  John C. King, Minister to Older Adults
  Charlene Stoltzfus, Minister to Children

Wawasee Lakeside Chapel (13078) (IM) 192
PO Box 544, Syracuse IN 46567
574-856-2533
  Harlan Steffen, Pastor

Wildwood Menn Ch (13110) (IM) 42
W15537 Sandtown Rd, Engadine MI 49827
906-586-6421, wildwoodmc@lighthouse.net
6 miles N of Engadine on M117, 4.5 miles W on Sandtown Rd
  John L. Troyer, Pastor

Yellow Creek Menn Ch (13128) (IM) 534
64901 CR 11, Goshen IN 46526
574-862-2595, fax 574-862-2178,
info@yellowcreekmc.org, http://www.yellowcreekmc.org
NW Corner of CR 11 & CR 38
  Wes J. Bontreger, Pastor
  Harold J. Yoder, Pastor
  Ben Rheinheimer, Youth Pastor
  Sandy Miller, Minister of Worship and Music

CONFERENCES AND CONGREGATIONS

2

Lancaster Mennonite Conference

OFFICE
lmccenter@lanmenconf.org,
www.lanmenconf.org
717-293-5246 and 800-216-7249,
fax 717-431-1987
2160 Lincoln Highway East, #5, Lancaster PA
17602

STAFF
Joanne H. Dietzel, administrative coordinator
(jdietzel@lanmenconf.org)
Janet N. Gehman, interim editor, *Lancaster
Conference NEWS* (news@lanmenconf.org)
Carl A. Hess, financial administrator
(chess@lanmenconf.org)
Gloria Shenk Kniss, data manager
(gkniss@lanmenconf.org)
Karl R. Landis, director, leadership development
(klandis@lanmenconf.org)
M. Laura Livengood, administrative assistant
(llivengood@lanmenconf.org)
C. Kenneth Martin, conference treasurer
(kenc@epix.net)
James R. Martin, congregational resource staff
(jmartin@lanmenconf.org)
Lindsey A. Robinson, conference minister
(lrobinson@lanmenconf.org)
Alonna Gautsche Sprunger, congregational
resources director
(asprunger@lanmenconf.org)
Lorrie Stoltzfus, administrative assistant
(lstoltzfus@lanmenconf.org)
L. Keith Weaver, conference moderator
(kweaver@lanmenconf.org)

GENERAL INFORMATION
Year founded: 1775
Members: 17,496
Congregations: 186 + 5 church plants
Ministers (active): 385 (includes chaplains,
lead pastors, associate pastors, youth pas-
tors, those who are credentialed/no role,
and those who are active w/out charge)

Total credentialed: 703 (includes bishops, ministers, chaplains, deacons, deaconesses, mis-
sionary/church workers, staff at church
agencies, and those without an official position)
Total active credentialed: 499
CLC reps: Carl E. Horning, Samuel M. Lopez, L.
Keith Weaver

Districts. Bishops/Overseers/Supervisors:
Bishop Oversight: Nelson L. Bowman, Lloyd E.
Hoover, Freeman J. Miller; Bowmansville-
Reading: Irvin L. Martin; Conference Oversight:
Lindsey Robinson, Conference Minister;
Elizabethtown: Enos D. Martin; Ephrata: Carl E.
Horning; Groffdale: Lloyd E. Hoover;
Harrisburg: Paul W. Nisly; Juniata: Linford W.
Good; Lancaster: Linford D. King; Landisville:
Dale Stoltzfus; Lebanon: Carl E. Horning; Lititz:
Nelson W. Martin; Manheim: Donald O.
Nauman; Manor: Richard L. Buckwalter;
Martindale: Nelson L. Bowman; Mellinger: Paul
M. Zehr, Leon Oberholtzer; Millwood: Elvin J.
Ressler; New Danville: Ernest M. Hess; New
York City: Monroe J. Yoder; North Penn:
Stephen A. Haupert; Pequea Valley: Richard L.
Buckwalter; Philadelphia: Freeman J. Miller;
Spanish: Samuel M. Lopez, Jose A. Santiago,
Juan Carmona, Vincente Minino; Washington-
Baltimore: Melvin B. Delp, Lewis C. Good;
Weaverland-Northeastern PA: C. Kenneth Martin;
Williamsport-Milton area: Linford W. Good;
Willow Street-Strasburg: J. Vernon Myers; York-
Adams: Carlton D. Stambaugh

Annual conference (Celebration of Church Life):
March 18-20, 2005
Leadership assembly: March 18, 2005, and
September 17, 2005
Conference historian: Lancaster Mennonite
Historical Society

BISHOP BOARD EXECUTIVE COMMITTEE

L. Keith Weaver, moderator (kweaver@lanmenconf.org), 115 Swamp Church Rd, Reinholds PA 17569, 717-336-5253; Carl E. Horning, assistant moderator; Lloyd E. Hoover, secretary; C. Kenneth Martin, treasurer; Paul W. Nisly, member-at-large; Richard L. Buckwalter, member-at-large; Jose A. Santiago, member-at-large. Staff: Lindsey Robinson and Joanne H. Dietzel

PUBLICATIONS

Lancaster Conference *NEWS* (monthly), Janet Gehman, interim editor (news@lanmenconf.org) (same address as above)

COMMISSIONS

Finance. C. Kenneth Martin, chair (kenc@epix.net), 238 Reading Rd, East Earl PA 17519, 717-445-5736; Millard P. Garrett, vice chair; Aaron L. Groff Jr., secretary

Women in Leadership Subcommittee. Carol J. Oberholtzer, chair (doberhol@ptdprolog.net), 115 Rothsville Station Rd, Lititz PA 17543, 717-626-9361

OTHER CONFERENCE AGENCIES AND REPS

Eastern Mennonite Missions—see separate listing in section 3.

Friendship Community. George Stoltzfus, executive director (gstoltzfus@friendshipcommunity.net), 1149 E Oregon Rd, Lititz PA 17543, 717-656-2466

Lancaster Mennonite School. J. Richard Thomas, superintendent (thomasjr@lancastermennonite.org), 2176 Lincoln Hwy E, Lancaster PA 17602, 717-299-0436

Lancaster Mennonite Historical Society. Brinton L. Rutherford, director (lmhs@lmhs.org), 2215 Millstream Rd, Lancaster PA 17602, 717-393-9745

Landis Homes Retirement Community. Edward Longenecker, president (info@landishomes.org), 1001 E Oregon Rd, Lititz PA 17543, 717-569-3271

Mennonite Women. Rhoda R. Charles, president (jrcharles@bigfoot.com), 3033 Marietta Ave, Lancaster PA 17601, 717-898-7497

Sharing Programs. Carl Litwiller, president, 2160 Lincoln Highway East, PO Box 10367, Lancaster PA 17605-0367, 717-293-7100

Philhaven. LaVern Yutzy, CEO (lyutzy@philhaven.com), 283 S Butler Rd, PO Box 550, Mount Gretna PA 17064, 717-273-8871

LANCASTER AREA COUNCIL OF MENNONITE SCHOOLS (LACMS)

See separate listings for Conestoga Christian, Ephrata Mennonite, Gehmans Mennonite, Hinkletown Mennonite, Juniata Mennonite, Kraybill Mennonite, Lancaster Mennonite School, Linville Hill Mennonite, Lititz Area Mennonite, Locust Grove Mennonite, Manheim Christian Day, New Covenant Christian, New Danville Mennonite, Philadelphia Mennonite High School, West Fallowfield Christian

Congregations

Abundant Life Chinese Menn Ch (10102) (LAN, KB) 50
738 Moore St, Philadelphia PA 19148-1718
215-271-5018, fax 215-463-0909, alcmc@juno.com
1731 S Broad St
  Truong Tu, Pastor

Agape Fell (15016) (LAN) 130
485 E 3rd St, Williamsport PA 17701
570-326-5924, fax 570-326-5924, agape@chilitech.net, http://www.churchagape.com
  Michael Deal, Pastor
  James W. Mellinger, Associate Pastor

Alsace Christian Fell (13490) (LAN) 31
47 Alsace Ave, Temple PA 19560
610-775-9970, smandhm@aol.com
In village of Alsace Manor
  Sherman M. Stoltzfus, Pastor
  Daniel D. Good, Associate Pastor

Arca de Salvacion (22459) (LAN, KB, IMH) 38
2147-9 N Howard St, Philadelphia PA 19122
215-423-7642
Juan C. Carmona, Pastor

Believers Menn Garifuna Ministries (27599)
(LAN, AAMA, NYC) 24
36 Malcolm X Blvd, PO Box 210-463,
Brooklyn NY 11221-3008
718-716-6579, believersgarifuna@hotmail.com
Andrew Nunez, Pastor

Bethlehem Community Fell (29124) (LAN) 40
1417 Marvine St, Bethlehem PA 18017-6637
610-861-4409, fax 610-868-7907,
wkwendland@netcarrier.com
Wolfgang Wendland, Pastor
Richard L. Freed, Ordained Deacon

Blainsport Menn Ch (13607) (LAN) 151
7 Audubon Circle, Stevens PA 17578
717-336-8263, jnfahnestock@dejazzd.com,
http://www.forministry.com/17569bmc
85 S Blainsport Rd, Rheinholds
James R. Fahnestock, Pastor
Eric P. Marshall, Youth Pastor
Edwin Ray Martin, Ordained Deacon

Blossom Hill Menn Ch (14795) (LAN) 84
333 Delp Rd, Lancaster PA 17601
717-569-5869, jhp125@juno.com
Jane Hoober Peifer, Pastor

Bossler Menn Ch (13615) (LAN) 98
2021 Bossler Rd, Elizabethtown PA 17022-9417
717-367-5215, fgarb@juno.com
Corner of Bossler Rd & Garber Rd
Fred M. Garber, Pastor
Clair E. Good, Associate Pastor
Kenneth E. Schildt, Licensed Deacon

Boston Bethel Missionary Ch (11433) (LAN) . . .30
c/o David Cius, PO Box 255532, Dorchester MA 02125
781-396-6009
1201 Hyde Pk
David Cius, Pastor

Bowmansville Menn Ch (13623) (LAN) 278
129 Pleasant Valley Road, East Earl PA 17519
717-445-7458, krwitmer@hydrosoft.com
Kenneth R. Witmer, Co-Pastor
Chester E. Yoder, Co-Pastor
Larry H. Weber, Associate Pastor
Kenneth Duane Becker, Youth Pastor
Harold B. Eberly, Ordained Deacon

Buenas Nuevas (10732) (LAN, IMH) 29
Eduardo P Morales, 7606 Broadway Dr Apt 101, Falls
Church VA 22043-3660
703-645-8074, buenasnuevas@juno.com
Eduardo P. Morales, Pastor

Buffalo Menn Ch (13631) (LAN) 150
4445 Hoffa Mill Rd, Lewisburg PA 17837
570-523-3438, bhayes@sunlink.net
Benjamin R. Hayes, Co-Pastor
C. David Peachey, Co-Pastor
Alvin Longenecker, Ordained Deacon

Byerland Menn Ch (13656) (LAN) 104
931 Byerland Church Rd, Willow Street PA 17584
717-872-6922, fax 717-872-6922, jygarber@juno.com
SE Corner of Byerland Church Rd & Mt Hope School Rd
Joe C. Garber, Pastor

Calvary Menn Fell (14670) (LAN) 37
PO Box 25, Morris Run PA 16939-0025
570-638-2274, rkmartin@ptdprolog.net
Front St
Robert K. Martin, Pastor
Ralph N. Bender, Associate Pastor

Cambridge Menn Ch (13680) (LAN) 56
c/o Glenn Esh, 52 Evergreen St, Gordonville PA 17529
717-768-0532
Main St, Cambridge
Glenn Esh, Pastor
Edward R. Beachy, Associate Pastor
Victor R. Weaver, Associate Pastor
Isaac R. Petersheim, Ordained Deacon

Canton Menn Ch (25098) (LAN) 105
PO Box 43, Canton PA 17724
570-673-3418, dgraybil@sosbbs.com
Corner of Union & Center
Douglas C. Graybill, Pastor

Capital Christian Fell (13805) (LAN, DC) 127
8806 Eastbourne Ln, Laurel MD 20708
301-725-5692, fax 301-725-5692,
pastor@capitalchristian.org, http://www.capitalchristian.org
11301 Springfield Rd
J. David Eshleman, Pastor
Wilmer Z. Good, Associate Pastor

Carpenter Community Ch (13698) (LAN) 141
378 Glenbrook Rd, PO Box 37, Talmage PA 17580
717-656-9731, fax 717-859-4269, glennhoo@juno.com
Glenn A. Hoover, Pastor
David H. Burkholder, Evangelist
Stan Eash, Elder of Education
Daryl L. Hoover, Elder of Worship
James S. Horning, Ordained Deacon
Mel Horst, Elder of Prayer

Cedar Hill Community Ch (13706) (LAN) 35
624 Groff Ave, Elizabethtown PA 17022-2825
717-361-8990, lawtonwd@pngusa.net
5636 Bossler Rd
Wayne D. Lawton, Pastor

Cedar Lane Chapel (11580) (LAN) 4
PO Box 202, Terre Hill PA 17581
717-445-6697
208 College Ave
Marlin E. Martin, Pastor

Centro Evangelistico Cristiano (26724)
(LAN, IMH) 28
1601 W 4th St, Wilmington DE 19805
302-654-3587
Rojas Rosemberg, Pastor

Ch of the Overcomer (11590) (LAN, Church
Plant) 0
1 Princeton Av, Ridley Park PA 19078
267-784-3893, cotoministries@aol.com
First Baptist Church of Ridley Park

Chestnut Hill Menn Ch (13714) (LAN) 110
4050 Marietta Ave, Columbia PA 17512
717-684-5513, dhersh48@aol.com
Carl E. Hershey, Pastor
R. Todd Bowman, Associate Pastor
J. Donald Brubaker, Ordained Deacon
J. Leon Eshleman, Ordained Deacon

Chinese Christian Ch of Malden (10743) (LAN) . .55
50 Eastern Ave, Malden MA 02148
781-397-1092, fax 781-322-9977
Paul Cheung, Pastor

Christian Life Menn Fell (10122) (LAN, KB) 20
2045 N Carlisle St, Philadelphia PA 19121
215-765-2911
6841 Ardleigh St, Mt Airy
James Dennis, Pastor

Churchtown Menn Ch (13748) (LAN) 71
1732 Weaverland Rd, East Earl PA 17519
717-445-4107
Corner of Glick Rd & Rt 23
Clair Bennett Good, Pastor
Kenny L. Horst, Associate Pastor
Philip M. Groff, Youth Pastor
Philip R. Hollinger, Ordained Deacon

Coatesville Menn Ch (13755) (LAN) 28
625 Walnut St, Coatesville PA 19320
717-442-8394, lgroff1460@copper.net
Leonard L. Groff, Pastor
Mark C. Hickson, Pastor

Columbia Menn Ch (13771) (LAN) 38
c/o Gregory L Hershberger, 524 S 16th St,
Columbia PA 17512
717-684-5935, ghershberg@aol.com
291 S 4th St
Gregory L. Hershberger, Pastor

Community Menn Fell (13540) (LAN) 194
2985 Broadway Rd, Milton PA 17847
570-742-7315, fax 570-742-7396, office@cmfmilton.org
David Martino, Pastor
Casey Eugene Rohrer, Youth/Assistant Pastor

Cornerstone Christian Fell (27193) (LAN) 64
PO Box 126, Mountain Top PA 18707-0126
570-678-3010
Thomas H. Miller, Pastor
Michael G. Smith, Associate Pastor

Crossroads Christian Community (10631)
(LAN) 10
PO Box 424, Marlton NJ 08053
856-988-9419, atgoodnews@aol.com
9 Jefferson Ave
Andrew T Gordon, Pastor

Crossroads Community Fell (14308) (LAN) 90
1060 E Newport Rd, Lititz PA 17543
717-626-0774, erh.nh.pa@juno.com
Elvin R. Huyard, Pastor
Kyle D. Buckwalter, Associate Pastor
Donald L. Brubaker, Ordained Deacon

Crossroads Menn (15172) (LAN, AAMA) 141
420 S Christian St, Lancaster PA 17602
717-392-3713, fax 717-392-7368, scsmc2@aol.com
401 Church St
Vincent Whitman, Pastor
Alice W. Whitman, Licensed Deaconess
E. Ray Witmer, Ordained Deacon
Meredyth Ann Witmer, Licensed Deaconess

Dawsonville Menn Ch (13847) (LAN) 42
16500 Whites Ferry Rd, PO Box 487, Poolesville MD 20837
301-874-8448, pastor@dawsonvillechurch.org,
http://www.dawsonvillechurch.org
Ellis Wayne Roberson, Pastor

Delaware County Fell (11562) (LAN) 0
c/o Dave Cosden, 1552 Virginia Ave, Folcraft PA 19032
610-237-8937, teachtruth@juno.com
Woodlyn, PA
David T. Cosden, Pastor
Darlene Valerie Enns Dyck, Co-Pastor
Theodore (Ted) Russell Enns Dyck, Co-Pastor

Delaware Menn Ch (13854) (LAN) 34
RR 1 Box 32, Thompsontown PA 17094
717-463-3941, geehoss@juno.com
On Rt 333, East Salem PA
Glenn D. Hosler, Pastor

Derry Menn Ch (13862) (LAN) 55
448 S Cope Drive, Manheim PA 17545
717-665-4086, bollmbre@lycos.com
RD 8, Box 13, Danville
Mark B. Boll, Pastor
Leroy H. Erb, Associate Pastor

Diamond Street Menn Ch (13870) (LAN,
AAMA, KB) 65
1632 W Diamond St, Philadelphia PA 19121
215-769-2682, revitalization@juno.com
Otis M. Banks, Pastor

Diller Menn Ch (13888) (LAN) 49
c/o Tim Sheeler, 4275 Enola Rd, Newville PA 17241-8718
717-776-6263, fax 717-776-6263, tjsheeler@pa.net,
http://dillermennonite.org
345 Creek Rd
Dennis Lamar Witmer, Pastor
Timothy J. Sheeler, Ordained Deacon

CONFERENCES AND
CONGREGATIONS

2

Downing Hills Christian Fell (13896) (LAN) 34
107 Garris Rd, Downingtown PA 19335
610-873-1169, nate@downinghills.com
    Nathan W. Brunk, Pastor
    Brooke L. Gehman, Associate Pastor

East Chestnut Street Menn Ch (13912) (LAN) . .199
434 E Chestnut St, Lancaster PA 17602
717-392-7910, ecsmc@juno.com
    Ronald W. Adams, Pastor

East Petersburg Menn Ch (13946) (LAN) 366
6279 Main St, East Petersburg PA 17520
717-569-9931, fax 717-509-3505, epmc1@juno.com
    Karl E. Steffy, Pastor
    K. Eugene Forrey, Associate Pastor
    Derrick Garber, Youth Pastor
    Daniel W. Neff, Ordained Deacon
    Jay Todd, Ordained Deacon

El Buen Pastor (14167) (LAN, IMH) 67
645 Harrison St, Lancaster PA 17602
717-396-0346
    Juan Gonzalez, Pastor

Elizabethtown Menn Ch (13953) (LAN) 211
300 S Spruce St, PO Box 265,
Elizabethtown PA 17022-0265
717-367-7089, fax 717-367-2109,
etnmenno@earthlink.net,
http://elizabethtown.pa.us.mennonite.net
S Spruce & E Bainbridge
    Conrad L. Kanagy, Pastor
    John M. Myers, Associate Pastor
    Robert E. Fellenbaum, Ordained Deacon

Emmanuel Community Ch (24844) (LAN) 56
270 Henry St, Jersey Shore PA 17740
570-398-3455, PastorDavid@suscom.net
    David K. Kanski, Pastor

**Emmanuel Worship Center (10016) (LAN,
NYC, AAMA)** 66
c/o M Abate Woldeabe, 2407 E Tremont Ave,
Bronx NY 10461
718-822-8031, fax 718-822-2649,
ewc-ny@worldnet.att.net
    Mulugeta Abate Woldeabe, Pastor
    Mesfin Mamo, Associate Pastor

Ephrata Menn Ch (13961) (LAN) 294
510 Stevens Rd, Ephrata PA 17522
717-733-6688, fax 717-738-2769, epmech@juno.com
    Kendrick J. Scandrett, Pastor
    Jeffery L. High, Leadership Team
    L. Kenneth Hollinger, Ordained Deacon
    Clifford L. Martin, Leadership Team

Erb Menn Ch (13979) (LAN) 158
567 W Lexington Rd, Lititz PA 17543
717-665-7018, pastorwes@paonline.com
    Wesley D. Siegrist, Pastor
    Michael S. Zimmerman, Associate Pastor
    David F. High Jr., Licensed Deacon

Erisman Menn Ch (13987) (LAN) 232
8 S Erisman Rd, Manheim PA 17545
717-653-4791, fax 717-653-6270, erismanmc@juno.com
Corner of 772 (Manheim Rd) & S Erisman Rd
    John O. Yoder, Pastor
    Andrew G. Miller Jr., Associate Pastor
    Alma E. Wenger, Licensed Deaconess
    Nelson H. Wenger, Licensed Deacon
    Dale E. Witmer, Licensed Deacon
    Jeanne M. Witmer, Licensed Deaconess

**Ethiopian Evangelical Ch of Baltimore (11108)
(LAN)** 40
1005 Ingleside Ave, Baltimore MD 21228
410-663-5518, atsadik@intra.nida.nih.gov,
http://www.eecbaltimore.org
    Abraham Tsadik, Lay Leader

**Ethiopian Evangelical Ch of Philadelphia (10194)
(LAN, KB)** 30
PO Box 2078, Upper Darby PA 19082-0578
610-789-2784, merid2001@hotmail.com
69th & Chestnut St
    Endalkachew Sahle, Pastor
    Merid Seifu, Lay Leader

Evangelical Garifuna (29660) (LAN, NYC, IMH) .95
c/o Celso C Jaime, 344 Brooke Ave, Bronx NY 10462
718-792-5455, jaime4ever@aol.com
    Celso C. Jaime, Pastor

Faro Ardiente (22111) (LAN, IMH) 18
728 Wood St, Vineland NJ 08360
609-696-1399

First Deaf Menn Ch (14019) (LAN) 43
2270 Old Philadelphia Pike, Lancaster PA 17602
717-392-6752, fax 717-392-7810, fdmc340@aol.com,
http://www.hometown.aol.com/hshye/index.html
Rte 340 E

First Menn Ch of Columbia (14027) (LAN) 15
9580 Old Rt 108, Ellicott City MD 21042
410-465-1233
    J. Daniel Miller, Pastor

Fountain of Life Ch (25320) (LAN) 67
290 Newberry Rd, Middletown PA 17057
717-944-4455, fax 717-994-5952, rshonk@fol.cc,
http://www.fol.cc
    Peter L. Logan, Pastor
    Roy Lee Kenneth Shonk, Associate Pastor

Frazer Menn Ch (14050) (LAN) 125
57 Maple Linden Ln, Frazer PA 19355
610-644-3397, fax 610-644-2970,
info@frzermennonite.org, http://www.frazermennonite.org
1 mile E of Rt 30 & Rt 352; 3 miles west of Paoli
    Jason Kuniholm, Pastor
    Vernon Zehr Jr., Associate Pastor

Freedom in Christ Fell (11563) (LAN) 25
1119 Chestnut St, Lebanon PA 17042
717-270-1904, millers@paonline.com
12 N Ninth St
    Daniel G. Miller, Pastor

Friendship Menn Ch (15008) (LAN, AAMA) 35
235 N Broad St, Carney's Point NJ 08069
856-299-7900, JamesNMel@aol.com
    James L. Wenger Jr., Pastor
    Dan L. Lapp, Associate Pastor
    Paul S. Landis, Visitation Pastor

Gehman Menn Ch (14100) (LAN) 92
PO Box 842, Adamstown PA 19501
717-484-4439, fax 717-484-4473, irvinm3@juno.com
Witmer Road
    Irvin L. Martin, Pastor
    Glen D. Martin, Associate Pastor
    David W. Mohler, Ordained Deacon

Gingrichs Menn Ch (14118) (LAN) 262
100 Forney Rd, Lebanon PA 17042-9344
717-274-1521, fax 717-274-8611, jgl@mbcomp.com,
http://www.gingrichsmennonite.com
    John G. Landis, Pastor

Goods Menn Ch (14142) (LAN) 93
2563 Bainbridge Rd, Bainbridge PA 17502
717-367-1938, jnbechtold@dejazzd.com
4374 Bossler Rd
    J. Nelson Bechtold, Pastor
    Gerald E. Risser, Ordained Deacon

Goodville Menn Ch (14159) (LAN) 102
1556 Main St, PO Box 104, Goodville PA 17528-0104
717-445-6037, fax 717-445-8435
    Bruce L. Sauder, Pastor
    Nelson R. Martin, Associate Pastor
    Dale L. Buckwalter, Licensed Deacon

Grace Community Fell (14084) (LAN) 70
1483 N Colebrook Rd, Manheim PA 17545
717-664-4820, cdandrew@supernet.com
    Dennis W. Andrew, Pastor

Great Shepherd Christian Fell (13557) (LAN) . . .97
975 Benders Church Rd, Pen Argyl PA 18072
610-863-9114, fax 610-863-9114, benders@epix.net
    Jack Rice, Pastor

Green Terrace Menn Ch (14183) (LAN) 41
116 N Galen Hall Rd, Wernersville PA 19565
610-927-4668, pastorLeon@netzero.net
    Leon L. Stauffer, Pastor
    Nelson B. Zeiset, Associate Pastor
    P. Eugene Stauffer, Ordained Deacon

Groffdale Menn Ch (14191) (LAN) 244
168 N Groffdale Rd, Leola PA 17540
717-656-6388, fax 717-656-3608, jiml@groffdale.com
    James R. Leaman, Pastor
    Craig G. Sensenig, Assistant/Youth Pastor

Guilford Road Menn Ch (14209) (LAN) 32
c/o Robert C Rowe, 8614 Pine Tree Dr,
Jessup MD 20794-9530
301-725-0540, fax 410-796-5867, ssauder@ineva.com
10140 Guilford Rd
    Robert C. Rowe, Pastor
    Steven A. Sauder, Associate Pastor
    Donald M. Sauder, Ordained Deacon

Habecker Menn Ch (14217) (LAN) 106
451 Habecker Church Rd, Lancaster PA 17603
717-872-5910, giveitall@juno.com
    Randall J. Martin, Pastor
    Joshua R. VanderPlate, Youth Pastor

Halifax Community Fell (27060) (LAN) 41
852 Camp Hebron Rd, PO Box 598, Halifax PA 17032
717-896-2637, rlhm@pa.net
    Richard Huber Mininger, Pastor

Hammer Creek Menn Ch (14233) (LAN) 284
590 Hammer Creek Rd, Lititz PA 17543
717-354-4347
    Wilmer S. Musser, Pastor
    Samuel S. Burkholder, Associate Pastor
    Fred G. Heller, Associate Pastor
    Ricky L. Newswanger, Youth Pastor
    Michael D. Allgyer, Minister of Evangelism
    Mervin M. Gingrich, Ordained Deacon

Hampden Menn Ch (15354) (LAN) 44
1334 N 14th St, PO Box 14414, Reading PA 19604-1936
610-582-8915, his.servants7@juno.com
Hampden Blvd & Windsor St
    Lee Roy Ritz, Pastor
    Kenneth B. Eberly, Associate Pastor

Hernley Menn Ch (14290) (LAN) 126
746 Lebanon Rd, Manheim PA 17545
717-656-7305, fax 717-656-6481, gmchurst@yahoo.com
1 mile north of Manheim on Rt 72
    George M. Hurst, Pastor
    Jay M. Peters, Associate Pastor

Herr Street Menn Ch (14266) (LAN, AAMA) 25
c/o Harold H Lefever, 16 S Mountain Rd,
Harrisburg PA 17112
717-545-1858
1026 Herr St
    Harold H. Lefever, Pastor
    Edward L. Zook, Associate Pastor
    Louis H. Martin, Ordained Deacon

Hershey Menn Ch (14282) (LAN) 95
401 Hershey Church Rd, Kinzers PA 17535-9720
717-768-3150, toshi@hmc-kinzer.org,
http://hmc-kinzer.org
    Ramoktoshi Imchen, Pastor
    Elmer M. Martin, Ordained Deacon

CONFERENCES AND
CONGREGATIONS

2

Hinkletown Menn Ch (14316) (LAN) **400**
2031 Division Hwy, Ephrata PA 17522
717-354-5213, fax 717-354-5078, hmc2@localnet.com
Rt 322 E
  Glenn E. Sauder, Pastor
  Gerald W. Fox, Associate Pastor
  Jerold R. Martin, Associate Pastor
  Albert B. Kunkle, Ordained Deacon

**Iglesia Christiana Valle de Jesus (25338) (LAN,
NYC, IMH)** **25**
141 Manhattan Ave, Brooklyn NY 11237
718-418-7824

Iglesia el Verbo (11571) (LAN) **73**
c/o Isaias de la Cruz, PO Box 473, Robbins NC 27325
910-948-3022
  Isaias De La Cruz, Lay Leader

**Iglesia Evangelical Menonita Manantial de Vida
(29116) (LAN, IMH)** **55**
1035 N 27th St, Camden NJ 08015
856-365-9236, pastorhugo@netzero.com
  Hugo E. Garcia, Pastor
  Ivania Garcia, Pastor

Iglesia Menonita Bethel Ch (11435) (LAN) **150**
PO Box 3874, Sanford NC 27331
919-718-1776, fax 919-774-1497
622 Bragg St
  Carlos L. Villalobos Mora, Pastor
  Carlos Caleb Villalobos, Associate Pastor

**Iglesia Menonita Hispana Vida Nueva (11572)
(LAN, IMH)** **40**
c/o Vincente Minino, 10868 Oak Green Ct, Burke VA 22015
703-249-8449, fax 703-249-8449, vicarm1@juno.com
3900 King St, Alexandria
  Vincente Minino, Pastor

**Iglesia Menonita Puerta de Sion (22897)
(LAN, IMH)** **35**
c/o Nelson Colon, 328 S Broad St, Trenton NJ 08611
609-884-0445
  Nelson Colon, Lay Leader

**Iglesia Menonita Roca de Salvacion (11301)
(LAN, IMH)** **21**
637 S Prince St, Lancaster PA 17603-5615
717-299-9414
  Oscar Enrique Molina, Pastor

**Iglesia Unida de Avivamiento (22350) (LAN,
NYC, IMH)** **140**
169 Knickerbocker Ave, Brooklyn NY 11237
718-919-1588, unitedrevival@aol.com
  Nicolas Angustia, Pastor

Indiantown Menn Ch (14365) (LAN) **157**
255 Indiantown Rd, Ephrata PA 17522
717-733-3150, slm875@dejazzd.com
  Stephen L. Martin, Pastor
  Jay S. Weaver, Associate Pastor
  Paul E. Snader, Ordained Deacon

Indonesian Fell (11568) (LAN) **25**
1731 S Broad St, Philadelphia PA 19148
215-467-6001, alcmc@juno.com
  Leonard G. Burkholder, Associate Pastor
  Liem Piet In, Lay Leader

**International Christian Community Ch (11123)
(LAN, OD, NYC)** **160**
c/o Victor S Amador/ Carolina Amador, 616 Jamaica Ave,
Brooklyn NY 11208
718-235-7249, fax 718-235-2737,
victoramador2001@aol.com
  Victor S. Amador, Pastor

James Street Menn Ch (15396) (LAN) **270**
c/o Peggy Breneman, 323 W James St,
Lancaster PA 17603-2911
717-397-6707, fax 717-397-0829, info@jsmchurch.org,
http://www.jsmchurch.org
  Elizabeth G. Nissley, Associate Pastor
  L. Larry Wenger, Ordained Deacon

**Jesu Cristo Es la Respuesta (10342)
(LAN, IMH)** **44**
1116 Kittatinny St, Harrisburg PA 17104
717-233-8412
505 Hamilton St
  Emilio Montanez, Pastor

**Jesus Power and Love Ministries (10070)
(LAN, Church Plant)** **0**
715 W Birchtree Ln, Claymont DE 19703
  Reginald C. Graham, Pastor

Kapatiran Christian Ch (11102) (LAN, KB) **12**
825 Beechwood Rd, Havertown PA 19083
610-353-1002, Ling011957@yahoo.com
Corner of Beechwood & Lawndale, off Haverford Ave
  Benjamin C. Baluyot, Associate Pastor

Kauffman Menn Ch (14373) (LAN) **61**
1355 Lancaster Rd, Manheim PA 17545
717-665-3570, sfstauffer@dejazzd.com
Rt 72, 2 miles S of Manheim
  Steven B. Stauffer, Pastor
  Jay W. Nissley, Associate Pastor
  Leroy P. Beitzel, Licensed Deacon

Kennett Square Menn Ch (14381) (LAN) **34**
486 N Mill Rd, PO Box 401, Kennett Square PA 19348
610-444-0547, ejressler@kennett.net
  Harold J. Ranck, Lay Leader

**King of Glory Tabernacle (14043) (LAN,
AAMA, NYC)** **80**
c/o Michael Banks, 1114 Sherman Ave, Bronx NY 10456
718-299-1211, fax 718-583-1530, kgtbronx@localnet.com
2019 Grand Ave
  Michael E. Banks, Pastor

Kinzer Menn Ch (14399) (LAN) 53
45 N Kinzer Rd, Kinzer PA 17535
717-442-4901, paul.clark@fandm.edu
Church St & N Kinzer Rd
   Dwight L. Groff, Pastor
   Paul L. Clark, Associate Pastor
   Jeffrey G. Pauls, Associate Pastor
   Benjamin L. Clark, Ordained Deacon

Kossuth Community Chapel (25395) (LAN) 14
96 Olive St, Bolivar NY 14715-1310
585-928-2380
7150 Kossuth Rd
   John E. Boll, Pastor
   Marlin M. Miller, Associate Pastor
   John C. Hess, Ordained Deacon

Krall Menn Ch (14407) (LAN) 45
2510 S 5th Ave, Lebanon PA 17042-9701
717-535-9941, georgelois@nmax.net
2512 S 5th Ave
   George L. Zimmerman, Interim Pastor

La Luz del Mundo (10071) (LAN, Church Plant) . .0
900 12th St, Reading PA 19604

Landis Valley Menn Ch (14431) (LAN) 98
2420 Kissel Hill Rd, Lancaster PA 17601
717-560-3999, tomhorst@peoplepc.com
   Thomas A. Horst, Pastor
   Gary E. Martin, Associate Pastor

Landisville Menn Ch (14423) (LAN) 334
3320 Bowman Rd, Landisville PA 17538
717-898-0071, fax 717-898-1131,
samthomas.lmc@verizon.net,
http://landisville.pa.us.mennonite.net
   J. Samuel Thomas, Pastor
   Linda S. Helmus, Minister of Pastoral Care

Lao Menn Fell/Slate Hill (11560) (LAN) 0
1352 Slate Hill Rd, Camp Hill PA 17011
717-737-8016
Meeting at Slate Hill Mennonite Church
   Aaron S. Onelangsy, Pastor

Laurel Street Menn Ch (14449) (LAN) 67
301 Laurel St, Lancaster PA 17603-5429
717-392-7527

Lauver Menn Ch (14456) (LAN) 55
HC 63 Box 43, Richfield PA 17086
717-463-9091, fax 717-463-0064, johnwg@nmax.net
1 mi S of Evensdale on Rt 35
   John W. Gehman, Pastor
   J. Elvin Ranck, Evangelist, Orphanage Director

Lebanon Christian Fell (24562) (LAN) 30
118 N 14th St, Lebanon PA 17046-4503
717-270-9918, donymartin@juno.com
   J. Donald Martin Jr., Pastor

Lichty Menn Ch (14464) (LAN) 174
c/o Clair R. Long, 5334 Southview Dr, New Holland PA
17557-9852
717-355-2031, fax 717-354-5919
1690 Union Grove Rd, East Earl
   Clair R. Long, Pastor
   James C. Bowman, Associate Pastor
   Aaron Z. Horst, Ordained Deacon

Life Menn Fell (11294) (LAN) 62
250 Meadow Ln, Conestoga PA 17516-9750
717-871-3002, fax 717-871-0547,
mschlabach@life-ministries.com
   Mark Schlabach, Pastor
   Nevin Forry, Associate Pastor

Lititz Menn Ch (14480) (LAN) 173
165 E Front St, Lititz PA 17543-1503
717-626-8237, fax 717-626-1538, lmchurch@dejazzd.com,
http://www.forministry.com/17543lmc
NW Corner Front & Water
   Lowell Keith Gerber, Pastor
   Rodney A. Martin, Associate Pastor

Living Stones Fell (10155) (LAN) 136
2292 Robert Fulton Hwy, Peach Bottom PA 17563
717-786-3890, fax 717-786-3890, rldaed@juno.com
   Raymond L. Deiter, Pastor
   James Arnold Aukamp, Associate Pastor
   Larry E. Burkhart, Associate Pastor
   James R. Nimon, Associate Pastor
   Roger Stillman, Associate Pastor
   James Arnold Aukamp, Evangelist

Locust Lane Menn Chapel (14498) (LAN, AAMA)60
2415 Locust Ln, Harrisburg PA 17109
717-232-6252, locustlanemenn@paonline.com,
http://locustlanemennonite.org
   Lindsey A. Robinson, Pastor
   Thomas A. Neis Jr., Elder

Lost Creek Menn Ch (14506) (LAN) 127
RR 2 Box 1405, Mifflintown PA 17059
717-463-2258, kleml@verizon.net
   Kenneth Litwiller, Pastor

Love Truth Chinese Menn Ch (27995) (LAN, KB) 50
600 W Chew Ave, Philadelphia PA 19120
215-224-7622, fax 215-924-2248, lemuelso@netscape.net,
http://members.tripod.com/~ltcmc
   Lemuel So, Pastor

Luz de Salvación (26716) (LAN, IMH) 23
1401 Lehman St, Lebanon PA 17046
717-272-1231
   Luis Hernandez, Pastor

Luz Verdadera (15107) (LAN, IMH) 43
c/o Jose Gonzalez, 1003 Franklin St, Reading PA 19602
610-374-1071
   Daniel Carrion, Pastor
   Jose A. Santiago, Interim Pastor

Lyndon Menn Ch (14514) (LAN) **54**
234 Brenneman Rd, Lancaster PA 17603
717-464-4283, svanpelt1@juno.com
1930 Lyndon Ave
  Steven C. Vanpelt, Pastor
  Dwain D. Livengood, Associate Pastor
  Daniel R. Geib, Licensed Deacon

Manheim Menn Ch (14530) (LAN) **60**
5975 Reeves Rd, East Petersburg PA 17520
717-626-1566, jlstrite@yahoo.com
http://www.geocities.com/manheimmenno/index.html
201 W High St
  Kenneth A. Bucher, Pastor
  Glen M. Sell, Interim/Transitional Pastor
  D. David Martin, Associate Pastor
  James L. Strite, Ordained Deacon

**Maranatha Family Christian Fell (10119)
(LAN)** **70**
450 Jacobsburg Rd, Nazareth PA 18064
610-746-5060, fax 610-746-5060, mfcf@juno.com
  James R. Snyder, Pastor
  Leonard J. Sabatine, Ordained Deacon

Marietta Community Chapel (24224) (LAN) . . .**115**
1125 River Rd, Marietta PA 17547
717-426-4584, fax 717-426-4584,
mariettachapel@juno.com, http://www.MariettaChapel.org
  Daniel P. Althouse, Pastor

Martindale Menn Ch (14548) (LAN) **370**
958 Rettew Mill Rd, Ephrata PA 17522
717-733-0291, lweaver8@juno.com
171 Hurst Rd
  Robert L. Trupe, Pastor
  David E. Sensenig, Associate Pastor
  J. Martin Hostetter, Ordained Deacon
  Luke W. Weaver, Ordained Deacon

Masonville Menn Ch (14562) (LAN) **99**
2625 Safe Harbor Rd, Washington Boro PA 17582
717-872-4203, rakanagy@juno.com
  J. Wilmer Eby, Pastor
  Robert L. Kanagy, Pastor

Meadville Menn Ch (14571) (LAN) **47**
c/o John Meck, 109 Snake Lane, Kinzers PA 17535
717-768-8334, j6meck@dejazzd.com
5726 Meadville Rd, Gap
  John D. Meck, Pastor
  Lew K. Martin, Youth Pastor

Mechanic Grove Menn Ch (14589) (LAN) **85**
c/o Jay L Ranck, 1950 Lancaster Pk, Peach Bottom PA
17563
717-786-4730
Church Rd, Quarryville
  Jay L. Ranck, Pastor
  William E. Hershey, Associate Pastor
  Wayne E. Kreider, Associate Pastor
  Isaac E. Hostetter, Ordained Deacon

Meckville Menn Ch (14597) (LAN) **87**
Box 1020 Meckville Rd, Bethel PA 19507
717-273-8797
  J. Donald Martin Sr., Pastor
  J. Daniel Martin, Ordained Deacon

Mellinger Menn Ch (14605) (LAN) **391**
1916 Lincoln Hwy E, Lancaster PA 17602
717-397-9360, fax 717-397-9195, mmc@proclaim.net,
http://proclaim.net/~mellinger
  Leon H. Oberholtzer, Pastor
  Barry Lee Stoner, Associate Pastor
  Linford L. Good, Licensed Deacon
  Ray K. Leaman, Licensed Deacon

**Menn Evangelical Tabernacle (26849) (LAN,
NYC, IMH)** **30**
c/o Nestalis Robles De Leon, 130 3rd Ave Apt 18G,
Brooklyn NY 11207
718-522-5029
623 Wilson Ave
  Nestalis Robles De Leon, Pastor

**Meserete Wongel Ethiopian Evangelical Ch
(11565) (LAN, Church Plant)** **31**
c/o Demeke Getahun (Hempfield COB), Box MWEEC, 1186
Stevens Rd, Manheim PA 17545
717-581-9136
meets at Hempfield Church of the Brethren
  Demeke Getahun, Lay Leader

Metzler Menn Ch (14613) (LAN) **295**
120 S 10th St, Akron PA 17501
717-859-2660, richardbuch@juno.com
515 W Metzler Rd, Ephrata
  Richard E. Buch, Pastor
  Roy B. Martin, Associate Pastor
  David Eugene Zoll, Associate Pastor
  Lee Roy M. Martin, Ordained Deacon

Millersville Menn Ch (14639) (LAN) **88**
PO Box 283, Millersville PA 17551
717-872-2695, fax 717-872-2493,
millersvillemennonite@paonline.com
437 Manor Ave
  Delbert L. Kautz, Pastor
  John Henry Harnish Jr., Ordained Deacon

Millport Menn Ch (14621) (LAN) **121**
820 Log Cabin Rd, Leola PA 17540
717-627-0335, millport@dejazzd.com,
http://www.millportchurch.org
  E. Eugene Beyer, Pastor
  Clyde M. Hollinger, Associate Pastor
  Kerry D. Martin, Associate Pastor
  John A. Bender, Ordained Deacon

Millwood Menn Ch (14654) (LAN) 62
c/o Menno B Fisher Jr., 2523 Old Philadelphia Pk, Bird In
Hand PA 17505-9797
717-442-8500, fax 717-442-4247,
salliestamper@supernet.com
441 Amish Rd, Gap
   Keith L. Beiler, Associate Pastor
   Menno B. Fisher Jr., Associate Pastor
   Luke Nolt Sensenig, Associate Pastor
   M. Eugene Lapp, Licensed Deacon

Mount Joy Menn Ch (14688) (LAN) 367
10 Donegal Springs Rd, Mount Joy PA 17552-2906
717-653-5660, fax 717-653-9399, mjmenno@mjmc.org,
http://www.mjmc.org
   Joseph N. Sherer, Pastor
   Randall Shull, Associate Pastor
   Dawn R. Winey, Minister of Worship
   Richard L. Winey, Minister of Worship

Mountain View Fell (29975) (LAN) 27
1717 Pleasant Stream Rd, Trout Run PA 17771-9525
570-995-9171, erking5@juno.com
202 Old Barn Rd, Bodines
   M. Craig Zimmerman, Pastor
   J. Herbert Eby, Associate Pastor

Mountville Menn Ch (14696) (LAN) 200
205 Froelich Ave, Mountville PA 17554
717-285-3610, rayreitz@onemain.com
Corner of Fridy & Froelich
   Raymond E. Reitz, Pastor
   Philip L. Shertzer, Associate Pastor
   Jed M. Redcay, Youth Pastor

Mt Vernon Menn Ch (14720) (LAN) 207
1 Lighthouse Dr, Kirkwood PA 17536
717-529-6071, fax 717-529-6871,
mtvernonmennonite@juno.com
   Gary L. Roberts, Pastor
   Kendall Ray Keeler, Associate Pastor

Nanticoke Christian Fell (25809) (LAN) 40
112 S Prospect St, Nanticoke PA 18634
570-735-1700, davidp@epix.net,
http://www.forministry.com/18634ncf
   David A. Pegarella, Pastor

New Danville Menn Ch (14837) (LAN) 207
103 Marticville Rd, Lancaster PA 17603
717-872-8111, fax 717-872-8111, newdanville@juno.com,
http://newdanvillemc.com
1 mi S of New Danville, on Rt 324
   Curtiss Lee Kanagy, Pastor
   Shirley Kay Garber, Deaconess
   Donald W. Hess, Licensed Deacon
   Marshall Hess, Licensed Deacon

New Holland Menn Ch (14811) (LAN) 130
18 Western Ave, New Holland PA 17557
717-354-0602, fax 717-355-2787, nhmc@frontiernet.net
   Ronald E. Zook, Pastor
   Judith E. Zook, Associate Pastor

New Holland Spanish Menn (14704)
(LAN, IMH) 54
PO Box 15, New Holland PA 17557
717-354-2366, fax 717-354-9192,
marioearaya@hotmail.com
24 N Roberts Ave
   Mario E. Araya, Pastor

New Hope Community Ch (11561) (LAN) 42
333 S 13th St, Harrisburg PA 17104
717-260-0444, fax 717-232-0150,
nhccharrisburg@juno.com
The Agape Fellowship Hall—13th & Derry St
   Jason R. Rissler, Pastor

New Life Christian Fell (29157) (LAN) 48
1521-B Kam IV Road, Honolulu HI 96819
808-847-6308, fax 808-847-0808, cnlcfc@verizon.net
Community Center in urban Honolulu
   Peter K. Louis II, Pastor
   Charles W. Callahan, Associate Pastor
   Filemon B. Godoy, Associate Pastor
   Paul Tadashi Horiuchi, Associate Pastor

New Life Fell (27052) (LAN) 120
420 E Fulton St, Ephrata PA 17522
717-445-5548, nlfephrata@juno.com
   Kevin E. Horning, Pastor

New Mercies Menn Ch (10293) (LAN, KB,
AAMA) 53
PO Box 43174, Philadelphia PA 19129
215-438-0293, cmercies@aol.com
Meets at Falls Presbyterian Ch, 3462 Midvale Ave
   Charles Bulford, Pastor
   Nadine G. Smith Bulford, Associate Pastor

New Providence Menn Ch (14829) (LAN) 85
121 Main St, New Providence PA 17560
717-786-4233, bobharnish@prodigy.net
   Robert A. Harnish, Pastor
   J. Kenneth Hershey, Associate Pastor

New Revival Menn Ch (11570) (LAN) 25
1241 Church St, Reading PA 19601
610-372-1812, rafucho74@hotmail.com
Meets at Shiloh Menn, 421 Bingaman Rd
   Rafael Perez, Pastor

New Song Congregation (11581) (LAN) 40
235 N Broad St, Carney's Point NJ 08069
856-299-7900
Meets at Friendship Mennonite Chapel
   Ricky Alvira, Lay Leader

Newlinville Menn Ch (14845) (LAN) 27
145 Doe Run Rd, Coatesville PA 19320
610-593-6464
   Harold R. Engel, Pastor
   James M. Westmoreland Jr., Associate Pastor

CONFERENCES AND CONGREGATIONS

2

Norma Menn Ch (14860) (LAN) **40**
173 Almond Rd, PO Box 313, Norma NJ 08347
856-692-7441, fax 856-692-7441, nmpastor@juno.com,
http://www.forministry.com/08318nm
  Timothy E. Darling, Pastor
  Lloyd Wenger, Deacon

North Bronx Menn Ch (29561) (LAN, NYC) **22**
c/o Ruth Yoder Wenger, 3262 Rochambeau Ave,
Bronx NY 10467-3006
718-881-2824, wengermail@aol.com
302 E 206th St
  Ruth Yoder Wenger, Pastor

Nueva Vida en Cristo (11436) (LAN) **40**
762 Centre St, Trenton NJ 08611
609-396-1901
  Eugenio Matos, Pastor

Old Road Menn Ch (14928) (LAN) **141**
5795 Old Philadelphia Pike, Gap PA 17527
717-442-8630, oldroadoffice@wjtl.net
Rt 340
  Robert H. Benner, Pastor

Oxford Circle Menn Ch (14951) (LAN, KB, AAMA) **45**
PO Box 28340, Philadelphia PA 19149-0340
215-991-5805, pastorlen@verizon.net
Howell & Langdon Sts
  Leonard M. Dow, Pastor
  Lynn S. Parks, Associate Pastor

Palo Alto Menn Ch (14969) (LAN) **74**
508 E Bacon St, Pottsville PA 17901
570-622-8743, fax 570-628-3787, jerry01@dfnow.com
20 Union St & corner Cadbury St
  Ernest W. Martin, Associate Pastor
  Roy W. Musser, Ordained Deacon

Parkesburg Menn Ch (14985) (LAN) **69**
PO Box 306, Parkesburg PA 19365
610-857-1641, dlgehman@ccis.net
44 E Second Ave
  David L. Gehman, Pastor
  Kurt Eugene Hershey, Associate Pastor

Peabody Street Menn Ch (14993) (LAN, DC) . . .**24**
245 Peabody St NW, Washington DC 20011
202-829-0876, fax 202-829-0876,
112322.477@compuserve.com
Brightwood
  George R. Richards, Pastor

Peace Chapel (25353) (LAN) **8**
PO Box 1539, Harrisburg PA 17105-1539
717-393-7232
206-3rd St, New Cumberland
  Brian Eric Fountain, Pastor

Philadelphia Cambodian Menn Ch (10075) (LAN, KB) **15**
2421 S 5th St, Philadelphia PA 19148-3907
610-986-3253
  Sarin Lay, Pastor

Pilgrims Menn Ch (24513) (LAN) **55**
PO Box 217, Akron PA 17501
717-859-4596, berika@ptd.net,
http://pilgrims.pa.us.mennonite2.net
MCC Welcoming Place, 21 S 12th St
  Barry R. Kreider, Pastor

Red Run Menn Ch (15115) (LAN) **59**
J Carl Sensenig, 173 Wheatland Dr, Denver PA 17517
717-445-9641, jcsensen@yahoo.com
987 Martin Church Rd
  J. Carl Sensenig, Pastor
  Randy Fox, Ordained Deacon

Redeeming Grace Fell (24588) (LAN, NYC) **36**
539 Greeley Ave, Staten Island NY 10306-5853
718-979-5952, fax 718-351-1769, Est1man@aol.com
  Stanley Ray Sutter, Pastor

Risser Menn Ch (15123) (LAN) **77**
329 Trail Rd S, Elizabethtown PA 17022
717-367-8587, g-heistand@juno.com
2215 Elizabethtown Rd
  Gerald M. Heistand, Pastor
  Larry Eugene Ginder, Associate Pastor
  James Seibel Zimmerman, Associate Pastor

River Corner Menn Ch (15131) (LAN) **73**
PO Box 9, Conestoga PA 17516
717-872-4485, drgochnauer@paonline.com
552 River Corner Rd
  David L. Gochnauer, Pastor
  Robert A. Martin, Associate Pastor

Roedersville Menn Ch (15149) (LAN) **42**
c/o Daryl Martin, 16 Cherry St, Pine Grove PA 17963
570-345-2552, dmartin@phfa.org
Roedersville Rd, Roedersville
  Daryl G. Martin, Pastor

Rohrerstown Menn Ch (15156) (LAN) **65**
601 Rohrerstown Rd, Lancaster PA 17603
717-394-0203, davidweaver@juno.com
  David L. Weaver, Pastor
  Mauro A. Galati Jr., Pastor of Evangelism

Rossmere Menn Ch (15164) (LAN) **102**
741 Janet Ave, Lancaster PA 17601
717-397-7854, lesmarian@juno.com
  Lester K. Denlinger, Pastor
  Marilyn E. Kurtz, Associate Pastor

Salam Menn Fell (11099) (LAN, KB) **20**
8131 Washington Ln, Wyncote PA 19095
215-884-4839
  George M. Kuttab, Pastor

Schubert Menn Ch (15180) (LAN) **20**
c/o Thomas A Hess, 9310 Old 22, Bethel PA 19507-9421
717-933-8434, phess@ptd.net
Kline Rd, Schubert, PA
    Thomas A. Hess, Pastor
    John Charles Zimmerman II, Associate Pastor
    Marlin M. Zimmerman, Ordained Deacon

**Seventh Avenue Menn Ch (15198) (LAN, NYC,
AAMA)** **32**
2522 Adam Clayton Powell Jr. Blvd, New York NY 10039
212-368-1103, fax 718-653-5084,
myrybronx@earthlink.net
    Monroe J. Yoder, Pastor

Shalom Menn Ch (10076) (LAN, Church Plant) . . .**0**
PO Box 362, Milton PA 17847
    Jose A. Rosa, Pastor

Shiloh Menn Ch (10765) (LAN) **33**
1225 Fern Ave, Reading PA 19607
610-796-1528, jarhosa@juno.com
421 Bingaman St
    James Sauder, Pastor
    Merle E. Smucker, Licensed Deacon

Slate Hill Menn Ch (15206) (LAN) **200**
1352 Slate Hill Rd, Camp Hill PA 17011-8013
717-737-8150, fax 717-737-8016, slatehill@paonline.com,
http://slatehill.pa.us.mennonite.net
    W. Lynn Shertzer, Pastor
    Lena H. Brown, Associate Pastor

**South 7th Street Menn Ch (15222)
(LAN, AAMA)** **53**
415 S 7th St, Reading PA 19602
610-375-6700, smartinhoover@aol.com
    Saralee M. Hoover, Associate Pastor
    Thomas R. Hoover, Associate Pastor
    Stephen J. Good, Licensed Deacon

Stauffer Menn Ch (15230) (LAN) **32**
4295 Colebrook Rd, Hershey PA 17033
717-367-3634
    Robert J. Spayde, Pastor
    J. Frank Zeager, Associate Pastor
    Carl H. Snavely, Ordained Deacon

Steelton Menn Ch (15248) (LAN, AAMA) **40**
501 N 3rd St, Steelton PA 17113
717-787-2160
Corner of 3rd & Jefferson
    Victor H. Romain Jr., Pastor

Stony Brook Menn Ch (15255) (LAN) **110**
c/o Congregational Secretary, 15 Locust Grove Rd,
York PA 17402
717-755-8756, jcgrosh@juno.com
    Jeffrey A. Grosh, Pastor

Strasburg Menn Ch (15271) (LAN) **192**
1514 Village Rd, Strasburg PA 17579
717-687-8471, stras_men_ch@juno.com
    John Dwight Meck, Pastor
    Stephen Souder Weaver, Pastor
    John F. Mishler, Associate Pastor
    John W. Good, Ordained Deacon

Stumptown Menn Ch (15297) (LAN) **302**
2813 Stumptown Rd, Bird In Hand PA 17505
717-656-7878, donsharp@hydrosoft.net
    Donald D. Sharp, Lead Pastor
    Jansen Herr, Youth Pastor
    Andrew S. Diener Jr., Deacon
    John M. Leaman, Minister of Mission

Sunnyside Menn Ch (15305) (LAN) **116**
337 Circle Ave, PO Box 10041, Lancaster PA 17605-0041
717-293-0001, iekurtz2@juno.com
    Ira A. Kurtz, Pastor
    J. Brian Miller, Associate Pastor
    Alma M. Shultz, Licensed Deaconess

Susquehanna Menn Ch (15313) (LAN) **40**
c/o Wesley Groff, RR 1 Box 131G,
Mt Pleasant Mills PA 17853
570-539-2575
Peiffer Rd, Port Trevorton
    J. Wesley Groff, Pastor
    Albert W. Heimbach, Associate Pastor

Tinsae Kristos Evangelical Ch (11566) (LAN) . . .**20**
c/o Berhanu Kebede, 382 Dohner Dr, Lancaster PA 17602
717-898-2251, fax 717-898-8092
EMM, 53 W Brandt Blvd
    Berhanu Kebede, Pastor

University Christian Fell (10188) (LAN) **22**
Box 99 SMC, Millersville PA 17551
717-464-3361, dmetzler@marauder.millersv.edu
George St
    Duane L. Metzler, Pastor

Vietnamese Christian Fell (29215) (LAN, VIET) . . .**30**
720 N King St, Honolulu HI 96817
808-842-1089, fax 808-842-1089, pjhonuluu@juno.com
    Paul Quoccuong Luu, Pastor

Vietnamese Menn Ch (27045) (LAN, KB) **160**
6237 Woodland Ave, Philadelphia PA 19142-2005
610-352-8689, msquang@go.com
    Quang Xuan Tran, Pastor

Village Chapel Menn Ch (22491) (LAN) **73**
335 Wissler Rd, New Holland PA 17557
717-354-6075, jsjshorst@juno.com
    Jeffrey S. Horst, Pastor
    Chester L. Martin, Associate Pastor
    David L. Musselman, Associate Pastor
    Lester W. Gehman Jr., Youth Pastor

**CONFERENCES AND
CONGREGATIONS**

2

Way Thru Christ Ministry (10073) (LAN, AAMA)140
2305 Edgmont Ave, Chester PA 19013
610-872-5539
 Alvin Motley, Pastor
 Reginald C. Graham, Ordained Deacon

Weaverland Menn Ch (15420) (LAN) 589
210 Weaverland Valley Rd, PO Box 328,
East Earl PA 17519
717-445-6348, fax 717-354-9716, wmc897@juno.com
 Don R. Weaver, Pastor
 Leon R. Hurst, Associate Pastor
 Earl S. Weaver, Associate Pastor
 J. Ronald Horning, Youth Pastor
 Brian E. Martin, Ordained Deacon
 C. Kenneth Martin, Bishop
 J. Nevin Martin, Ordained Deacon

Welsh Mountain Menn Ch (22061) (LAN) 29
686 Meetinghouse Rd, New Holland PA 17557
717-354-2533, caltechdad@yahoo.com
571 Springville Rd
 J. Robert Kauffman, Pastor
 Paul M. Leaman, Ordained Deacon

West End Menn Fell (11174) (LAN) 60
20 N Charlotte St, Lancaster PA 17603
717-299-3228, berthojos@cs.com
 Josef V. Berthold, Pastor

West Franklin Menn Ch (15404) (LAN) 11
RR1 Box 248A2, Monroeton PA 18832-9622
570-364-5397
Corner Rts 414 & 514, West Franklin
 Richard B. Martin, Pastor

Wilkens Avenue Menn Ch (15081) (LAN) 60
c/o Jean Miller, 2302 Brohawn Ave, Baltimore MD 21230
410-947-7876
1616 Wilkens Ave
 Matthew Emerson Barnhart, Pastor

Willow Street Menn Ch (15461) (LAN) 278
399 E Penn Grant Rd, Willow Street PA 17584-9441
717-464-2422, fax 717-464-5332,
mcmentzer@comcast.net
Corner of Penn Grant Rd & Hans Herr Dr
 James B. Meador, Pastor
 Gerald B. Garber, Associate Pastor
 Mark W. Mentzer, Youth Pastor

Witmer Heights Menn Ch (11120) (LAN) 109
2270 Old Philadelphia Pike, Lancaster PA 17602
717-392-6698, fax 717-392-7810, whmc2270@aol.com,
http://www.witmerheights.pa.us.mennonite.net
Rt 340 East
 L. Roy Bender, Pastor

New York Mennonite Conference

OFFICE
dotconf@northnet.org, http://bfn.org/~nymennon
315-376-3734, fax 315-376-3071
PO Box 99, 5546 Alger Rd, Martinsburg NY
13404

STAFF
Milton J. Zehr, conference minister
(dotconf@northnet.org)
Dorothy L. Zehr, administrative assistant
(dotconf@northnet.org)

GENERAL INFORMATION
Year founded: 1973
Members: 1,304
Congregations: 17
Households: 673
Church Plants: 2
Active Ministers: 16
CLC reps: LeRoy Mast, Milton Zehr

DISTRICTS
Northern: Emanuel Gingerich, Overseer
(margeman@usadatanet.net), 7185 Chases
Lake Rd, Glenfield NY 13343, 315-376-7126
Southern: Don Siegrist, Overseer
(asiegrist@yahoo.com), 3465 State Route
417, Jasper NY 14855, 607-498-9330
Western: John Powell (fjpowell@aol.com)
Buffalo churches; Milton Zehr
(dotconf@northnet.org) Rochester churches

Semi-Annual Delegate Sessions
Fall meeting, Sept. 10-12, 2004 (Saturday a.m.),
CELEBRATION 2004 at Casowasco Camp,
Conference and Retreat Center, south of
Auburn, N.Y.
Spring meeting, April, 2005 (9 a.m.–3 p.m.),
Seneca Falls, N.Y.

COORDINATING COUNCIL
LeRoy Mast, moderator
(revbikeman@sg23.com), PO Box 91,
Hammondsport NY 14840, 607-569-3283; Terry
Zehr, assisting moderator; Connie Finney, secre-
tary; John Buckwalter, treasurer; E. Donald
Siegrist; Evan Zehr

PUBLICATION
Life in New York Mennonite Conference
(3 times/year) Dorothy L. Zehr, editor
(dotconf@northnet.org)

COMMISSIONS
Leadership Commission. Don Siegrist, chair
(asiegrist@yahoo.com), 3465 State Route
417, Jasper NY 14855, 607-792-3710
Finance Commission. John Buckwalter, treasurer (buckwajd@alfredstate.edu), 5744 East
Valley Rd, Alfred Station NY 14803
Congregational Resourcing Commission.
Evan Zehr, chair (eazehr@northnet.org),
5574 Highland Ave, Lowville NY 13367, 315-
376-3082
1. Peace and Justice. Sue Klassen
(SueKlassen@isp01.net), 293 Brooksboro
Dr, Webster NY 14580; 585-265-4313
2. Prayer Ministry. Ginny Gunnison
(ginjoe@infoblvd.net), 128 Hamilton Circle,
Painted Post NY 14870, 607-962-0207
3. Women's Concerns. Sherry Mast
(lsmast2@juno.com), PO Box 91,
Hammondsport NY 14840, 607-569-3283
4. Worship/Music. Marvin Zehr
(marzedos@yahoo.com), 18 N Jefferson St,
Carthage NY 13619, 315-493-4330
5. Stewardship Education. Evan Zehr
(eazehr@northnet.org), 5574 Highland Ave,
Lowville NY 13367, 315-376-3082
6. Christian Education. Edna Brugger
(ednabru@northnet.org), 8453 Number 4
Rd, Lowville NY 13367; 315-376-6249

COMMITTEES

Celebration Planning Committee. Terry Zehr, chair (tzehr1@twcny.rr.com), 7630 Park Ave, Lowville NY 13367, 315-376-5514

NYS Mennonite Medical Sharing Plan. Victor and Jewel Miller (vic-jewel@juno.com), 5210 Salt Rd, Clarence NY 14031, 716-759-6330

REPRESENTATIVES

MC USA Executive Board. Harold Miller (HNMiller@juno.com), 280 Park Ave, Corning NY 14830, 607-937-5252

MCC East Coast. Sherry Mast (lsmast2@sg23.com), PO Box 91, Hammondsport NY 14840, 607-569-3283

Eastern Mennonite Missions. Glenn Brubaker (jogle@zoominternet.net), 1580 CR 22, Whitesville NY 14897, 607-356-3379

Goshen College. Shirley Powell (sjhp@aol.com), 50 Allenhurst, Buffalo NY 14214, 716-837-1751

Eastern Mennonite University. Harold Miller (HNMiller@juno.com), 280 Park Ave, Corning NY 14830, 607-937-5252

Congregations

Alden Menn Ch (10496) (NY) 111
923 Two Rod Rd, Alden NY 14004
716-937-6977, fax 716-937-6977, AMCpastor@juno.com
Philip Martin, Pastor
Dale Meyers, Youth Pastor

Bethsaida Evangelical Ch (11118) (NY) 31
c/o Tadelech Matewos Baka, 57-C Manor Pkwy,
Rochester NY 14620
585-461-9719, tmatewos@hotmail.com
Trinity Covenant Church, 1235 S Rd Clinton

Clarence Center-Akron Menn Ch (16980) (NY) 122
11500 Clarence Center Rd, Akron NY 14001
716-542-9927, fax 716-542-1567, CCAM9927@aol.com
Keith Zehr, Pastor

Community Menn Fell of Corning (23614) (NY) 87
290 Park Ave, Corning NY 14830
607-937-5252, hnmiller@juno.com,
http://www.forministry.com/USNYMENOCCMFCM
Harold N. Miller, Pastor

Community of Faith (11479) (NY) 0
Williamson NY 14589

First Menn Ch of New Bremen (21964) (NY) . .267
PO Box 417, Lowville NY 13367
315-376-6379, fax 315-376-9385, nbmenno@northnet.org
New Bremen
Kenneth Landis, Pastor

Grace Fell (11170) (NY) .0
182 Ark Ln, Schoharie NY 12157
518-295-7891, fax 518-295-7556, wfarrell@midtel.net
William Farrell, Pastor

Harris Hill Menn Ch (10504) (NY) 25
5225 Harris Hill Rd, Williamsville NY 14221
716-688-6867, joselahai@aol.com,
http://www.forministry.com/usnymenochhmch
Elaine Haines, Co-Pastor
Joseph M. Haines, Co-Pastor

Independence Gospel Fell Menn (14357) (NY) . . .34
c/o William Dickerson, 36 Williams Ave,
Wellsville NY 14895
716-485-6923, igfchurch@hotmail.com,
http://freenet.buffalo.edu/~nymennon/independ.htm
Independence Rd in Andover
William D. Dickerson, Administrative Elder
O. Robert Mitchell, Outreach/Missions Elder
Robert Volk, Pastoral Elder

Jesus Ch (10138) (NY) 26
c/o Tim Wright Creek Hill Apts #10, 1704 Empire Blvd,
Webster NY 14580
585-670-9987, channels@frontiernet.net
Rt Rd 417
Timothy Lee Wright, Pastor

Lowville Menn Ch (10892) (NY, CM) 263
PO Box 167, Lowville NY 13367
315-376-3082, eazehr@northnet.org
7705 Ridgeroad
Evan Zehr, Pastor

Pine Grove Menn Ch (11072) (NY, CM) 53
8343 Van Amber Rd, Castorland NY 13620
315-376-2593, nrzehr@hotmail.com
Van Amber Rd, Naumburg
Nathan Zehr, Pastor

Pleasant Valley Menn Ch (15057) (NY) 41
7601 S Valley Rd, Hammondsport NY 14840
607-569-3651, revbikeman@sg23.com
LeRoy J. Mast, Pastor

Rochester Area Menn Fell (21956) (NY) 35
10 Avonmore Way, Penfield NY 14526
585-473-0220, fax 585-377-0152, RAMF@earthlink.net,
http://homepage.mac.com/RAMF
Temporary: 1650 Elmwood Ave, Rochester, NY

CONFERENCES AND CONGREGATIONS

2

Watertown Menn Ch (21980) (NY) . . . .**.65**
19089 State Rt 3, Watertown NY 13601
315-785-9861, dellreen@twcny.rr.com,
http://freenet.buffalo.edu/~nymennon/watertwn.htm
Right side of State Rt 3 south of Watertown
    Terry J. Zehr, Pastor

Westside Menn Ch (10068) (NY) **30**
c/o Shirley Powell, Elder, 184 Barton, Buffalo NY 14213
716-837-1751, fax 716-881-2789, SJHP@aol.com
    Shirley Powell, Chair, Board of Elders

Yorks Corners Menn Ch (15487) (NY) **114**
3350 CR 29, Wellsville NY 14895
585-593-3287, fax 585-593-1178, Genemile@aol.com
    Eugene N. Miller, Pastor

North Central Mennonite Conference

OFFICE
eschrock@indianheadtel.net
715-943-2317
Elwood Schrock, secretary, 166 N State Rd 40,
Exeland WI 54835-2176

GENERAL INFORMATION
Year founded: 1920
Members: 504
Congregations: 13
Ministers: 17
CLC reps.: *Galen Kauffman,
(galenkauffman@hotmail.com), PO Box
236, Surrey ND, 58785-0236, *John I.
Kauffman, (mekauffman@juno.com), 10824
W State Rd 48, Exeland WI 54835-3191
Annual Conference: June 4-6, 2004, at Lakeview
Mennonite Church, Wolford ND
Historian: Lila Kanagy,
(kanagyf@midrivers.com), 753 Road 523,
Bloomfield MT 59315, 406 583-7782

EXECUTIVE COMMITTEE
*Fred Kanagy, moderator,
(kanagyf@midrivers.com), 753 Road 523,
Bloomfield MT 59315, 406-583-7782; *Galen
Kauffman, moderator-elect; *Elwood Schrock,
secretary, *Mary Ellen Kauffman, treasurer

PUBLICATION
North Central Conference Bulletin, Elwood
and Lorene Schrock
(eschrock@indianheadtel.net), editors, 166N
State Rd 40, Exeland WI 54835

COMMISSIONS
Congregational Ministries Commission.
*David Hochstetler, chair, (davanna@
centurytel.net), W1216 County Hwy B, Stone
Lake WI 54876, 715-865-5403; Darrell
Nefzger, secretary; James Davidson
Ministerial Leadership Commission. *Ottis
Yoder, chair, 32553 County Hwy 34, Ogema

MN 56569, 218 983-3477; Alvin Stoll, secretary, David Geib
Mission and Service Commission. *Walter
Clinton, chair (clintonwjmc@aol.com),
1406 16th St South, Fargo ND 58013, 701-
298-0783; Neville Peterson, secretary; David
Book
Stewardship Commission. *Archie Stiyer,
chair, 30122 County Hwy 34, Callaway MN
56521, 218-375-3955; Arlen Gerig, secretary, Paul Kauffman

OTHER CONFERENCE AGENCY AND REPS
MCC Representative. Lorene Schrock
(eschrock@indianheadtel.net), 166N State
Rd 40, Exeland WI 54835, 715 943-2317
Mennonite Women. Dorothy Kingsley, president, 15847 25th St SE, Amenia ND 58004,
701-967-8978
Peace Representative. Ottis and Violet Yoder,
32553 County Hwy 34, Ogema MN 56569,
218-983-3477
Youth Ministers. Les and Gayle Hochstetler
(lesgayle@hotmail.com), 31837 County Hwy
34, Ogema MN 56569, 218-983-3127

* Executive Board member

Congregations

Bethlehem Menn Ch (4145) (NC) 72
183 CR 516, Bloomfield MT 59315
406-583-7583, dpnefzgr@midrivers.com
  Darrell Nefzger, Pastor

Coalridge Menn Ch (15529) (NC) 31
112 Longfellow Rd, Dagmar MT 59219
406-483-5307
108 Longfellow Rd
  David Geib, Pastor

Exeland Menn Ch (15537) (NC) 17
166 N SR 40, Exeland WI 54835-2176
715-943-2317, eschrock@indianheadtel.net
N9598 Old Murry Rd, Exeland, WI
  Elwood G. Schrock, Pastor

Lake Region Menn Ch (15578) (NC) 18
PO Box 937, Detroit Lakes MN 56502-0937
218-847-3914, mmbook@i29.net
9 miles east on State Highway 34—Detroit Lakes MN
  David Book, Pastor

Lakeview Menn Ch (15586) (NC) 47
HC 1 Box 13, Wolford ND 58385
701-583-2836
  Ron Graber, Lay Leader

Morson Community Bible Fell (15495)
(NC, UNMC) 27
RR 1, Sleeman ON P0W 1M0
807-488-5620
  Wally Detweiler, Pastor

Point O' Pines Menn Ch (15610) (NC) 12
PO Box 45, International Falls MN 56649
218-286-3316, mart-diane@juno.com
CR 93
  O. Martin Wenger, Pastor

Prairie Peace Fell (15545) (NC, COB) 82
404 1st Ave SW, PO Box 236, Surrey ND 58785-0236
701-852-4957, galenkauffman@hotmail.com,
http://www.boydenia.com/np/np
300 Pleasant Ave North
  Galen E. Kauffman, Pastor

Red Top Menn Ch (15628) (NC) 53
753 CR 523, Bloomfield MT 59315
406-583-7782, kanagyf@midrivers.com
502 CR 523
  Fred Kanagy, Pastor

Sand Lake Menn Chapel (24620) (NC) 15
W1216 County Hwy B, Stone Lake WI 54876
715-865-5403, fax 715-865-5403,
davanna@centurytel.net
6493 Old 27
  David Hochstetler, Pastor

South Lawrence Menn Ch (15636) (NC) 60
N3795 State Highway 73, Glen Flora WI 54526
715-668-5519, fax 715-668-5519, alvines@centurytel.net
N 3795 State Hwy 73, Glen Flora
  Alvin E. Stoll, Pastor

Strawberry Lake Menn Ch (15644) (NC) 54
33068 County Hwy 34, Ogema MN 56569-9557
218-983-3490
  Delmar Yoder, Pastor
  Ottis Yoder, Bishop

White Chapel Menn Ch (15594) (CP, NC) 16
106 White Chapel Rd, Glendive MT 59330
406-377-7574, nevpeter@midrivers.com
  Neville John Peterson, Pastor

CONFERENCES AND CONGREGATIONS

2

Ohio Conference of Mennonite Church USA

OFFICE

ohmc@zoominternet.net,
  www.ohio.mennonite.net
330-857-5421, fax 330-857-5485
13363 Jericho Rd, PO Box 210, Kidron OH
  44636

STAFF

Tom Kauffman, conference minister
  (tekauffman@sev.org), PO Box 140065,
  Toledo OH 43614, 419-385-6865,
  fax 419-385-6865
J. Andrew Stoner, Region I pastor
  (rpandy@juno.com), 11026 Old Oak Trail,
  Ft Wayne IN 46845, 877-321-3289 pin 7093
Mary Nitzsche and Wayne Nitzsche, Region II
  co-pastors (rpmary@juno.com;
  waynen@sssnet.com), 917 Patrick Pl,
  Wooster OH 44691, 330-264-1516,
  fax 330-264-1516
Eldon King, Region III interim pastor
  (eldor@sssnet.com), 551 Tionesta Dr,
  Dalton OH 44618, 330-828-1004
Stan Helmuth, financial coordinator
  (cboh1@zoominternet.net)
Judy King, administrative assistant
  (ohmc@zoominternet.net)
Ann Leaman, conference editor
  (ohioevan@aol.com), 5854 Sunland St NE,
  Louisville OH 44641, 330-453-3793,
  fax 330-453-3793
Jan Sohar, Choice Books director
  (soharj@oh.choicebooks.org), 330-857-
  7721. Service representatives: Daryl Arner, Jeff
  Fisher, Steve Meyer, Gordon Miller, Jim Stanco

GENERAL INFORMATION

Year founded: 1834
Members: 10,736
Congregations: 75 + 1 church plant
Ministers: 174
CLC reps: LaVonne Hartman, Tom Kauffman,
  John Rohrer

Annual Conference: March
Conference historian: Barb Crossgrove

EXECUTIVE COMMITTEE

John Rohrer, moderator
  (jrohrer@direcway.com), 11285 Converse-
  Chapel Rd, Plain City OH 43064, 614-873-8905;
  Jeff Combs, assistant moderator; LaVonne
  Hartman, secretary; Norma Duerksen, fourth
  member; fifth member-vacancy
Conference Council Members-at-Large: Jay Conn,
  Marilyn Grasse-Brubaker, Ruth Guengerich, Gerald
  Hughes, Lloyd Kauffman, Joyce Klingelsmith, Tim
  Lehman, Sid Smith, Robert Yoder

PUBLICATION

Ohio Evangel (10 times per year), Ann Leaman,
  conference editor (ohioevan@aol.com), 5854
  Sunland St NE, Louisville OH 44641, 330-453-
  3793, fax 330-453-3793

COMMISSIONS

Evangelism. Eldon King, co-chair
  (eldor@sssnet.com), 551 Tionesta Dr,
  Dalton OH 44618, 330-828-1004; Robert
  Wengerd, co-chair (bobwengerd@aol.com),
  7852 Glenwood Ave, Boardman OH 44512,
  330-758-2597; Trish André, Todd Martin,
  Mattie Marie Mast; staff: Andy Stoner
Finance. Ova Helton Jr., chair
  (ohelton@fuse.net), 8753 Daly Rd,
  Cincinnati OH 45231, 513-522-1882; Sher
  Byler, Sue Schmucker Coblentz, Art
  Neuenschwander, Gary Wyse; staff: Stan
  Helmuth and Tom Kauffman
Leadership. Mel Hathaway, chair
  (hathaway@wcoil.com), 3935 Allentown Rd,
  Elida OH 45807, 419-331-4971; Jacqui
  Rozier, Mona Sauder, Terry Shue, Alvin
  Yoder; staff: Tom Kauffman
Nurture. Jim Roynon, chair
  (njroynon@fulton-net.com), V-986 CR 20,
  Archbold OH 43502, 419-446-2967; Joyce

Combs, Eileen Lehman, Melanie Parks, Ken Miller; staff: Wayne Nitzsche

Peace-Justice-Service. Rob Burdette, chair (vorp@valkyrie.net), 17827 Carson Rd, Butler OH 44822, 740-694-1759; Lincoln Nafziger, Colin Rusel, Dana Short, Russ Smucker; staff: Mary Nitzsche

Stewardship. Jacob Nafziger, chair, 21360 B CR H, Archbold OH 43502, 419-445-2285; Benny Avena, Patrick Helmuth, Ward Mumaw, Don Taylor

OTHER CONFERENCE AGENCIES AND REPS

Choice Books Management. Paul Helmuth, chair (pjhcpapfs@aol.com), 1731 Edmar St, Louisville OH 44641, 330-875-1273; George Bixler, Jay Lehman, Marjorie King, Carol Schrock

Historical. Barb Crossgrove, chair (lockport@bright.net), 22640 CR M, West Unity OH 43570, 419-924-2068; Esther Falb, Sara Weaver

Salary and Benefits. Jeff Combs, chair (jeffcombs@mics.net), 1555 S Limestone St, Springfield OH 45505, 937-322-9130; Ova Helton Jr., Delmar Hostetler, Sid Smith, Bob Yoder

Spiritual Formation Resource. Wayne Nitzsche, chair (waynen@sssnet.com), 917 Patrick Pl, Wooster OH 44691, 330-264-1516; Beulah Steiner

Theological Resource. Ron Guengerich, chair (zionmc@bright.net), 1100 Lindau St, Archbold OH 43502, 419-446-1002; Bruce Hamsher, Andy Hook, Miriam Kratzer, Jim Mullett

Gifts Discernment. Randy Murray, chair (martinsmennonite@myfishonline.net), 2522 Tannerville Rd, Orrville OH 44667, 330-683-0158; Lois Bontrager, Bruce Glick, Wilmer Hartman, Pam Matsos, Ann Nofziger, Darrel Schweitzer, Cal Short, Melanie Sims

Central Christian School. Fred Miller, superintendent (fredmiller@centralchristian.k12.oh.us),

PO Box 9, Kidron OH 44636, 330-857-7311

Ohio Mennonite Women. Nancy Roynon, president (njroynon@fulton-net.com), V-986 CR 20, Archbold OH 43502, 419-446-2967; Jean Emery, Amy Murray, Phyllis Kornhaus, Rickie Kelley, Ida Mae Weaver, Vickie Yoder

CONFERENCE RELATED MINISTRIES

Adriel Inc., Box 188, West Liberty OH 43357, 937-465-0010

Camp Luz. Deb Horst, camp director (camp.luz@juno.com), 168 Kidron Rd, Orrville OH 44667, 330-683-1246

Choice Books of Ohio. Jan Sohar, executive director (soharj@oh.choicebooks.org), PO Box 210, Kidron OH 44636, 330-857-5471

Eastern Mennonite University Constituent Conference. Eldon King and Mary Nitzsche, OMC representatives

Goshen College Conference Advisory Board. Joann Short and Denton Yoder, OMC representatives

Great Lakes Discipleship Center. Dee Custar, OMC representative

MCC Great Lakes. René Mejía, OMC representative

Mennonite and Brethren Marriage Encounter. 5437 RD 32 S, West Liberty OH 43357, 937-465-3366, Carl Newcomer

OrrVilla Retirement Community. 425 Orrvilla Dr, Orrville OH 44667, 330-683-4455, George Bixler, executive director

Shalom Ministries. 207 Vine St, Archbold OH 43502, 419-445-1552, Lenette Moshier, director

CONFERENCE REGIONS

Region I—J. Andrew Stoner, Region I pastor
Agora, Bethel (West Liberty), Central, Cincinnati, Columbus, Cornerstone, Emmanuel, Huber, Iglesia Menonita del Buen Pastor, Inlet, Jubilee, Kalida, Lima, Lockport, North Clinton, Oak Grove (West Liberty), Pike, Pine Grove, Primera Iglesia

(Defiance), Primera Iglesia (Fremont), Salem (Elida), Salem (Michigan), Sharon, Southside, South Union, Springdale Chapel, Tedrow, Toledo, West Clinton, Zion

Region II—Wayne and Mary Nitzsche, Region II pastors

Aurora, Beaverdam, Beech, Berean, Bethel (Wadsworth), Crown Hill, Dayspring, First (Canton), Friendship, Gilead, Hartville, Lee Heights, Leetonia, Maple Grove, Martins, Midway, New Mercies, North Lima, Oak Grove (Smithville), Orrville, Peace, Pleasant View, Smithville, Stoner Heights, Summit, Sunnyside, Valley View, University Euclid

Region III—Eldon King (interim) and Wayne Nitzsche, Region III pastors

Berlin, Community Christian Fellowship, Dover, Fairpoint, Fellowship Chapel, Hillside, Kidron, Lafayette Fellowship, Longenecker, Martins Creek, Millersburg, Moorhead, Owl Creek, Salem (Wooster), Sonnenberg, St. Johns, Walnut Creek, Wayside Chapel, Wooster

Congregations

Agora Christian Fell (11103) (CDC, OH) 0
400 W Broad St, Columbus OH 43215
614-280-1212, fax 614-280-0312,
questions@agoraministries.org, http://agoraministries.org
    Rebecca J. Bartholomew, Co-Pastor
    Richard Bartholomew Jr., Co-Pastor

Aurora Menn Ch (15677) (OH) 109
59 E Mennonite Rd, Aurora OH 44202
330-562-8011, fax 330-562-3186, auroramenn@juno.com,
http://www.auroramennonite.org
    Jesse Engle, Pastor
    Naomi Engle, Associate Pastor

Beaverdam Menn Ch (22004) (OH) 130
17721 Rt 89, Corry PA 16407
814-665-5465, dcharms@earthlink.net
http://www.beaverdammennonitechurch.org
Rt 89, half-mile north of US 6

Beech Menn Ch (15701) (OH) 272
10037 Easton St, Louisville OH 44641
330-875-1133, fax 330-875-1587,
beechmennochurch@cs.com, http://members.aol.com/BrnchOut
    Ronald L. Blough, Pastor

Berean Fell Ch (15719) (OH, AAMA) 33
1321 Lansdowne Blvd, Youngstown OH 44505
330-747-0471, samrewaju@msn.com
    Sam Olarewaju, Pastor

Berlin Menn Ch (15727) (OH) 234
PO Box 217, Berlin OH 44610
330-893-2320, fax 330-893-9602, Berlinmc@juno.com
4718 US Rt 62 E
    Ernest Hershberger, Pastor
    Bruce Allen Hamsher, Associate Pastor

Bethel Menn Ch (15768) (OH) 70
2684 Seville Rd, Rittman OH 44270
330-336-4559, tim19nov@hotmail.com
    Tim A. Short, Pastor

Bethel Menn Ch (15750) (OH) 175
PO Box 549, West Liberty OH 43357-0549
937-465-4587, alvinyoder@2access.net
416 Washington St Rd
    Alvin Yoder, Pastor
    Suzanne Hostetler, Youth Pastor

Central Menn Ch (15842) (OH) 439
PO Box 191, Archbold OH 43502
419-445-3856, fax 419-445-5607,
office@centralmennonite.org
21703 SR 2
    Jeffrey Wayne Smith, Pastor
    Wanda Stopher, Associate Pastor
    Dale Wyse, Minister of Visitation

Cincinnati Menn Fell (23325) (CDC, OH) 66
4229 Brownway Ave, Cincinnati OH 45209
513-871-0035, cmfoffice@juno.com
    Pauline Ann Nofziger, Pastor

Columbus Menn Ch (16378) (CDC, OH) 196
35 Oakland Park Ave, Columbus OH 43214
614-784-9002, office@columbusmennonite.org
http://www.columbusmennonite.org
    Steven William Goering, Co-Pastor
    Susan Ortman Goering, Co-Pastor

Community Christian Fell (16485) (OH) 0
PO Box 327, Rio Grande OH 45674-0327
614-388-9041

Cornerstone Menn Fell (28225) (OH) 68
11672 Lafayette Rd, Plain City OH 43064
614-873-8903, rodrmiller@earthlink.net
    Roderick Miller, Pastor

Crown Hill Menn Ch (15883) (OH) 124
9693 Benner Rd, Rittman OH 44270
330-927-1716, fax 330-927-9514, crownhill@bright.net
Corner of Benner Rd & SR 585
    Gordon Miller, Pastor

Dayspring Christian Fell (27334) (OH) 77
733 W Maple St, North Canton OH 44720
330-499-9708, jpbart@juno.com
6592 Wales Rd, Massillon
    James E. Bartholomew, Pastor
    Kenton Tod Miller, Associate Pastor

Dover Christian Fell (10709) (CDC, OH) 30
206 W 3rd St, Dover OH 44622-2904
330-364-8590, fax 330-364-8590, dcf@tusco.net
Daniel L. King, Pastor

Emmanuel Menn Ch (10037) (OH) 12
PO Box 18, Monclova OH 43542
419-445-5094, reidshort@earthlink.net
8353 Monclova Rd
Reid Short, Pastor

Fairpoint Menn Ch (15925) (OH) 54
PO Box 47, Fairpoint OH 43927
740-695-0303
Darrel McVay, Pastor

First Menn Ch of Canton (15982) (OH) 59
1935 3rd St SE, Canton OH 44707
330-453-1044, danhooley@sbcglobal.net
Daniel Hooley, Pastor
Darin Nissley, Youth Pastor

Friendship Menn Ch (16006) (OH) 100
21881 Libby Rd, Bedford Heights OH 44146
216-662-6788, friendmc@core.com,
http://www.geocities.com/friendshipmc

Gilead Menn Ch (16014) (OH) 51
PO Box 6, 6790 CR 121, Chesterville OH 43317
419-768-3469.
Howard Horton, Pastor

Hartville Menn Ch (16048) (OH) 577
1470 Smith Kramer St NE, PO Box 727, Hartville OH 44632
330-877-2050, fax 330-877-8557,
e-mail@hartvillemennonite.org,
http://www.hartvillemennonite.org
David L. Hall, Pastor
Chadwick Miller, Associate Pastor of Student Ministries
& Worship Arts
Henry Shrock Jr., Associate Pastor

Hillside Chapel (16071) (OH) 45
c/o Doug Mullet, 4358 Donald Dr, Hilliard OH 43026
614-771-1352, mullet@wowway.com
1609 SR 788

Huber Menn Ch (16097) (OH) 88
1885 S Dayton Lakeview Rd, New Carlisle OH 45344
937-849-6720, fax 937-849-6720, fishlaj@juno.com
Oswaldo Rivera, Spanish Pastor

**Iglesia Menonita del Buen Pastor (16022) (OH,
MILC)** 75
22489 CR F, Archbold OH 43502
419-445-3100, fax 419-445-3100,
goodshepherdmc@earthlink.net
David G. Tijerina, Pastor
Ismael Huerta, Associate Pastor

Inlet Menn Ch (16105) (OH) 50
13009-16-3, Wauseon OH 43567
419-445-2612, fax 419-782-0599, yfcjones@hotmail.com
Rick Jones, Pastor

Jubilee Menn Ch (11111) (OH) 60
PO Box 428, Bellefontaine OH 43311
937-592-8101, jubilee@2access.net,
http://www.jubileemennonite.com
Friendly Senior Center
Tim Lehman, Pastor

Kalida Family Outreach Center (16311) (OH) . . .150
PO Box 236, Kalida OH 45853
419-532-2525, fax 419-532-3737, office@kfoc.org,
http://www.kfoc.org
404 W Northland Dr
James Swihart, Pastor
Kenneth Benner, Associate Pastor
Derrick Wallace, Assistant Pastor

Kidron Menn Ch (16113) (OH) 700
3987 Kidron Road, PO Box 232, Kidron OH 44636
330-857-3461, fax 330-857-0593, lois@kidronmennonite.com
Terry W. Shue, Pastor
Herman F. Myers, Associate Pastor
Jeremy Shue, Youth Pastor
Laura Shue, Youth Pastor

Lafayette Christian Fell (28191) (OH) 18
108 E Main St, West Lafayette OH 43845
740-545-5234, martin_fam@sbcglobal.net
Geneva Martin, Congregational Chair

**Lee Heights Community Ch (16139) (OH,
AAMA)** 411
4612 Lee Rd, Cleveland OH 44128
216-581-2448, fax 216-581-9283, leeheights@juno.com
Robin Dean Miller, Pastor
Richard Henderson, Associate Pastor
Vikki Pruitte-Sorrells, Associate Pastor
Jacqueline Rozier, Associate Pastor

Leetonia Menn Ch (16147) (OH) 130
764 Columbia St, PO Box 226, Leetonia OH 44431
330-427-6827, fax 330-427-2750

Lima Menn Ch (16402) (CDC, OH) 62
1318 N Main St, Lima OH 45801
419-222-2120, limamc@bright.net
David Palmer Moser, Pastor

Lockport Menn Ch (16154) (OH) 418
9269 CR 21 N, Stryker OH 43557
419-682-1831, fax 419-682-0018, lockport@bright.net,
http://www.bright.net/~lockport/index.htm
Allen G. Rutter, Pastor

Longenecker Menn Ch (16162) (OH) 190
PO Box 112, Winesburg OH 44690
330-359-5155, revc@sssnet.com,
http://www.longeneckermennonite.org
8451 Holmes CR 186
Glenn Dale Coblentz, Pastor
Dennis Hostetler, Youth Pastor

CONFERENCES AND
CONGREGATIONS

2

Maple Grove Menn Ch (16170) (OH) 33
3112 St Rt 956, New Castle PA 16105
330-549-3389, fax 724-946-2579, mgrove@infonline.net
    Maxine Bartholomew, Co-Pastor
    Richard Bartholomew, Co-Pastor

Martins Creek Menn Ch (16196) (OH) 255
6111 CR 203, Millersburg OH 44654
330-674-1242, fax 330-674-0733, carl@mcmc.org,
http://www.mcmc.org
    Carl Wiebe, Pastor
    Jay Conn, Associate Pastor
    Matt Flinner, Associate Pastor

Martins Menn Ch (16204) (OH) 182
14027 Church Rd, Orrville OH 44667
330-683-1226, fax 330-683-1226,
martinsmennonite@myfishonline.net,
http://www.martinsmennonite.com
    Randy B. Murray, Pastor
    Andrew Hook, Youth Pastor

Midway Menn Ch (16261) (OH) 185
13376 Columbiana-Canfield Rd, Columbiana OH 44408
330-482-3135, fax 330-482-9688,
midwaymenno@juno.com
    Larry D. Rohrer, Pastor

Millersburg Menn Ch (16279) (OH) 157
288 E Jackson St, PO Box 16, Millersburg OH 44654
330-674-7700, fax 330-674-7700,
mbgmennoch@juno.com
    Larry Augsburger, Interim Pastor

Moorhead Menn Ch (16295) (OH) 60
4725 Township Rd 354, Millersburg OH 44654
330-674-0963, wallykyt@yahoo.com
10415 CR 329, Shreve
    Marc Hochstetler, Pastor

New Mercies Community Ch (10899) (OH) 52
12767 Butternut Rd, Burton OH 44021
440-834-8386, fax 440-834-8386, jdsutt@ncweb.com
    James Sutton, Pastor

North Clinton Menn Ch (16329) (OH) 380
831 W Linfoot St, Wauseon OH 43567-9564
419-337-4776, fax 419-337-4779,
gary.blosser@northclinton.org,
http://www.northclinton.org
    Gary S. Blosser, Lead Pastor
    Brad Faler, Associate Pastor
    Michael R. Zehr, Associate Pastor

North Lima Menn Ch (16337) (OH) 98
90 Mennonite Dr, North Lima OH 44452
330-549-2333, fax 330-549-2333, bobwengerd@aol.com
    Robert D. Wengerd, Pastor

Oak Grove Menn Ch (16428) (CDC, OH) 406
7843 Smucker Rd, Smithville OH 44677
330-669-2697, fax 330-669-2617, ogsmthvll@aol.com,
http://www.oakgrovemc.org
    Norma B. Duerksen, Pastor
    Joel A. Short, Associate Pastor

Oak Grove Menn Ch (16410) (OH) 168
1525 Mennonite Church Rd, West Liberty OH 43357
937-465-4749, oakgrove@bright.net,
http://oakgrove.oh.us.mennonite.net
    Howard S. Schmitt, Interim Pastor
    Richard Barrett, Associate Pastor

Orrville Menn Ch (16444) (OH) 252
1305 W Market St, Orrville OH 44667
330-682-5801, fax 330-682-5841, omc@mennonite.net,
http://orrville.oh.us.mennonite.net
    Bill Seymour, Pastor

Owl Creek Menn Ch (16451) (OH) 21
13249 SR 104, Lucasville OH 45648
740-259-5712, rjbapst@zoomnet.net
1442 Germany Rd
    Rodney Bapst, Pastor

Peace Menn Ch (25825) (OH) 42
9300 W Ridge Rd, Elyria OH 44035
440-322-7344, pmcpastor@aol.com
    Allan Patterson, Pastor

Pike Menn Ch (16469) (OH) 63
3995 McBride Rd, Elida OH 45807
419-339-3961, fax 419-339-0699, pikemc@bright.net
    Orlan Koehn, Interim Pastor

Pine Grove Menn Ch (16477) (OH) 61
4524 CR 2050, Stryker OH 43557
419-682-2981, cbrubaker@frontiernet.net
    Cliff Brubaker, Interim Pastor

Pleasant View Menn Ch (16527) (OH) 99
14795 Wooster St NW, North Lawrence OH 44666
330-833-0473, johnmiller1950@sbcglobal.net,
http://www.pvmom.com
    John M. Miller, Pastor
    Rebecca Martin, Youth Pastor
    Todd Martin, Youth Pastor

Primera Iglesia Menonita (15974) (OH, IMH) . . .24
PO Box 393, Defiance OH 43512
419-782-6761, 1123 Ayersville Ave

Primera Iglesia Menonita (24695) (OH, IMH) . . .19
PO Box 178, Helena OH 43435
419-638-2048
    Tony Ortiz Jr., Lay Leader

Salem Menn Ch (16634) (OH) 95
4275 W St Rd, Elida OH 45807
419-339-1505, salemmc@bright.net
    Melvin R. Hathaway, Pastor

Salem Menn Ch (16618) (OH) 80
13751 S Tripp Rd, Waldron MI 49288
517-567-8954, salemc@frontiernet.net,
http://www.frontiernet.net/~salemc
    Deanna Custar, Preaching Minister
    Robert Stuckey, Preaching Minister
    Ned Wyse, Preaching Minister

Salem Menn Ch (16626) (OH) 43
7012 Back Orrville Rd, Wooster OH 44691
330-359-5595, bobbeem@hotmail.com
   Robert L. Miller, Pastor

Sharon Menn Ch (16659) (OH) 250
7675 Amity Pike, Plain City OH 43064
614-873-8290, fax 614-873-5925, sharonmc8@juno.com
   Robert D. Yoder, Pastor

Smithville Menn Ch (16667) (OH) 200
PO Box 455, Smithville OH 44677
330-669-3601, fax 330-669-2490,
lmsmucker@smithvillemennonite.org,
http://www.smithvillemennonite.org
6097 Akron Rd
   Burt Preston Parks, Pastor

Sonnenberg Menn Ch (18846) (OH) 273
PO Box 226, Kidron OH 44636
330-857-8222, fax 330-857-8222, sonnenbergmc@juno.com
14367 Hackett Rd
   Michael M. Mast, Pastor
   Mattie Marie Mast, Associate Pastor

South Union Menn Ch (16683) (OH) 83
56 SR 508, PO Box 579, West Liberty OH 43357
937-465-6085, fax 937-465-0271, southumc@bright.net
   Keith L. Landis, Pastor

Southside Menn Ch (24034) (OH) 27
1603 S Limestone St, Springfield OH 45505
937-323-9348, fax 937-323-8126, jeffcombs@mics.net,
http://fm2.forministry.com/church/Home.asp?SiteID=45505SCF
   Jeff Combs, Co-Pastor
   Joyce Combs, Co-Pastor

Springdale Chapel (16717) (OH) 50
3001 Springdale Rd, Cincinnati OH 45251
513-851-1822, ohelton@fuse.net
   Ova Helton Jr., Pastor

St Johns Menn Chapel (16725) (OH) 20
5756 TR 430 SW, Logan OH 43138
740-385-5385
19681 SR 664
   Linda Durst, Congregational Contact

Stoner Heights Menn Ch (16733) (OH) 41
4975 Stoner Ave Rd, Louisville OH 44641-9171
330-875-1074, wmorton@neo.rr.com
   Walter L. Morton, Pastor

Summit Menn Ch (16741) (OH) 25
939 Norton Ave, Barberton OH 44203
330-753-2019, summitmenno@juno.com

Sunnyside Menn Ch (16758) (OH) 37
12981 Foust Rd, Conneaut Lake PA 16316
814-382-6060
   Russ Richardson, Pastor

Tedrow Menn Ch (16766) (OH) 145
252 Windisch St, Wauseon OH 43567
419-445-3486, fax 419-445-3486, parson@wcnet.org,
http://www.tedrowmennonite.org
252 Windisch St in Tedrow
   Randall K. Nafziger, Pastor

Toledo Menn Ch (15685) (OH) 118
5501 Nebraska Avenue, Toledo OH 43615
419-536-1251, fax 419-536-1253,
toledomennonite@accesstoledo.com,
http://www.toledomennonite.org
   Mark Bartsch, Co-Pastor
   Stephanie Bartsch, Co-Pastor

University Euclid Christ New Testament (16774)
(OH, AAMA) 26
c/o 24580 Ridgeline Dr, Bedford Heights OH 44146-4831
440-232-2519, fax 440-439-9485
1869 E 85th or 8500 Chester Ave, Cleveland
   Warner Jackson, Pastor

Valley View Menn Ch (16782) (OH) 122
PO Box 216, Spartansburg PA 16434-0216
814-664-7892, ree0817@aol.com
24313 State Hwys 89 and 77
   Robert E. Esh, Pastor

Walnut Creek Menn Ch (16808) (OH) 469
PO Box 182, Walnut Creek OH 44687
330-852-2560, fax 330-852-4731, rossamiller@juno.com,
http://www.wcmenn.org
2619 CR 144
   Ross A. Miller, Pastor
   Beau Reagan Hummel, Assistant Pastor

Wayside Chapel (16816) (OH) 35
16975 SR 93, Pedro OH 45659
740-643-2731, shauna@bright.net
17027 SR 93
   John Kelly, Pastor

West Clinton Menn Ch (16824) (OH) 310
18029 CR C, Wauseon OH 43567
419-445-1195, fax 419-445-1196, wclinton@bright.net,
http://www.westclinton.org
   James Roynon, Pastor

Wooster Menn Ch (16840) (OH) 163
1563 Beall Ave, Wooster OH 44691
330-262-3631, fax 330-262-0422,
woostermc@sssnet.com,
http://pages.sssnet.com/woostermc/
   Ralph Reinford, Pastor
   Ryan Clements, Youth Pastor

Zion Menn Ch (16873) (OH) 490
300 Short Buehrer Rd, Archbold OH 43502
419-445-3796, fax 419-445-8214, zionmc@bright.net,
http://www.zion.oh.us.mennonite.net
   Ronald D. Guengerich, Pastor
   Anne Stuckey, Associate Pastor
   Mona Sauder, Pastor of Senior Care & Small Groups

CONFERENCES AND
CONGREGATIONS

2

Pacific Northwest Mennonite Conference

OFFICE
office@pnmc.org, www.pnmc.org
503-492-4216, fax 503-492-8965
19532 NE Glisan St, Portland OR 97230

STAFF
Duncan Smith, conference minister team leader
(dsmith@pnmc.org), 19532 NE Glisan,
Portland OR 97230, 971-570-4216
Sheldon Burkhalter, conference minister
(sburkhalter@pnmc.org), 2437 Tracy Lane,
Woodburn OR 97071, 503-951-3278
Victor Vargas, Hispanic conference minister
(vvargas@pnmc.org), PO Box 185,
Woodburn OR 97071
William Higgins, conference teacher
(peacemennonite@juno.com), 19626 NE
Glisan St, Portland OR 97013, 503-667-2762

GENERAL INFORMATION
Year founded: 1994
Members: 2,685
Congregations: 34 +5 church plants
Ministers: 60
CLC reps: Duncan Smith, Jim Wenger
Annual Conference: mid-June
Conference Historian: Ray Kauffman

EXECUTIVE COMMITTEE
John Willems, moderator
(jwillems@pacifier.com), 2796 Goldfinch Loop
SE, Albany OR 97322, 541-926-2006; Jim
Wenger, assistant moderator; Harold Nussbaum,
secretary; Don Bacher, treasurer; Janet
Buschert, Rob Hanson, Anne Hege, Pat
Hershberger, Larry Hildebrand, Jeryl Hollinger,
Sheila Kauffman, Simon Rendon

PUBLICATION
Evangel (quarterly), Carey Ann Shoufler
(carey_shoufler@yahoo.com), 2312 North 27th
St, Boise ID 83702, 208-429-0924

COMMISSIONS
Congregational Nurture. Anne Hege,
chair(hecorp@ida.net), 2830 W 2000 S,
Aberdeen ID 83210, 208-397-4398
Evangelism and Missions. Jeryl Hollinger,
chair (jhollinger@montana.com), 795
Mennonite Church Rd, Kalispell MT 59901,
406-755-8772
Pastoral Leadership. Pat Hershberger, chair
(pathershberger@msn.com), 2380 Miller
Farm Rd, Woodburn OR 97071, 503-982-
6821
Peace and Justice. Rob Hanson, chair
(robeeruu@aol.com), 316 Locust St, Boise
ID 83712, 208-383-0349

OTHER CONFERENCE AGENCIES AND REPS
Hispanic Concilio. Samuel Moran, president
(samran77@hotmail.com), PO Box 68008,
Oak Grove OR 97268, 503-657-1302
Mennonite Women. Yvonne Leppert, contact
person, 226 North St, Filer ID 83328, 208-
326-3288
Mennonite Men. John Zook, president, 246
NE 130 Pl, Portland OR 97230, 503-252-
4864

Congregations

Albany Menn Ch (17434) (PNW) **140**
3405 Kizer Ave NE, Albany OR 97322-4351
541-926-1443, fax 541-926-0522, amc@proaxis.com
Matthew Charles Friesen, Pastor

Anawim Christian Community (11602) (PNW) ...**0**
3733 N Williams, Portland OR 97227
503-888-4453, stevekimes@aol.com
Steve Kimes, Pastor

Calvary Menn Ch (5180) (PNW, IMH) **129**
6711 Lone Elder Rd, Aurora OR 97002
503-266-2202, fax 503-263-3126,
calvarymc@integrity.com
Kevin John Schumacher, Pastor

**Centro Cristiano Pentecostes de McMinnville
(11620) (PNW, Church Plant)** **0**
115 NW 9th Street, McMinnville OR 97128
503-472-6264
Simon Rendon, Pastor

**Comunidad Cristiana de Vida Nueva (11533)
(PNW)** **0**
Box 679, Woodburn OR 97071
503-982-5731
Gilberto Estrada, Pastor

Corvallis Menn Fell (10141) (PNW) **55**
101 NW 23rd St, Corvallis OR 97330
541-754-5388, fax 541-754-9106,
cmf@corvallismennonite.org, http://corvallismennonite.org

**Emmaus Christian Fell (11305) (PNW, Church
Plant)** **0**
2743 W Wave Ct, Meridian ID 83642-8515
208-288-2378, cdmort@velocitus.net
Craig Daniel Morton, Co-Pastor
Karla Morton, Co-Pastor

Eugene Menn Ch (17517) (PNW) **57**
3590 W 18th Ave, Eugene OR 97402
541-343-9548, eugmenno@efn.org
Gayle Sheller, Pastor

**Evergreen Heights Mennonite Ch (10050)
(PNW)** **0**
c/oMike Oesch, 16448 W Oak St, Caldwell ID 83607
208-455-3212, hdoesch@widaho.net
Mike Oesch, Contact Person

Evergreen Menn Ch (10145) (PNW) **26**
PO Box 100, Bellevue WA 98009-0100
425-452-8007, djrempel@aol.com,
http://evergreen.wa.us.mennonite.net
9825 NE 24th St
Jeanne Rempel, Pastor

Filer Menn Ch (17525) (PNW) **75**
109 Fifth St, PO Box 157, Filer ID 83328-0157
208-326-5150

First Menn Ch (5335) (PNW) **223**
381 Washington & 4th, PO Box 246, Aberdeen ID 83210
208-397-4239, mepluseight@juno.com
Monty Dell Ledford, Pastor

First Menn Ch (10278) (PNW) **34**
903 SW Cedarwood Ave, McMinnville OR 97128
503-472-0217
Simon Rendon, Pastor

First Menn Ch (17533) (PNW) **100**
1211 6th St N, Nampa ID 83687
208-466-9174, fax 208-463-4344, ecclespath@msn.com
George Leppert, Pastor

Hyde Park Menn Fell (23663) (PNW) **60**
1520 N 12th St, Boise ID 83702
208-336-9872, hydepark2@mindsprng.com,
http://www.netnow.micron.net/~hpmf
Linda E. Nafziger-Meiser, Pastor

**Iglesia Cristiana Roca de Salvación (17493)
(PNW, IMH, Church Plant)** **0**
c/o 6711 Lone Elder Rd, Aurora OR 97002
503-651-2576
Calvary Menn Ch

**Iglesia Menonita Pentecostes (23556)
(PNW, IMH)** **150**
PO Box 185, Woodburn OR 97071
503-390-1944, fax 503-390-0392
198 E Lincoln St
Victor M. Vargas, Pastor
Marjorie Mendez, Youth Pastor

**Iglesia Pentecostes Maranatha (17520) (PNW,
Church Plant)** **0**
PO Box 576, Moses Lake WA 98837
Roberto Labarador, Pastor

**Iglesia tu Unica Esperanza (17521) (PNW, Church
Plant)** **0**
PO Box 2296, Warden WA 98857
509-762-6853
G. Rafael Gallardo, Pastor

Jerusalem Iglesia (28315) (PNW) **0**
763 NE 18th, Salem OR 97301
503-363-8687
Jose Campoz, Pastor

Lebanon Menn Ch (17574) (PNW) **246**
2100 S 2nd Street, PO Box 575, Lebanon OR 97355
541-258-5789, fax 541-451-5958,
martintroyer@hotmail.com
J. Brent Kauffman, Pastor

Logsden Neighborhood Ch (17582) (PNW) **35**
6631 Logsden Rd, Logsden OR 97357
541-444-2820
Randy Eisele, Pastor

CONFERENCES AND
CONGREGATIONS

2

Menno Menn Ch (5550) (PNW, NYC) 147
1378 N Damon Rd, Ritzville WA 99169-8717
509-659-0926, fax 509-659-0926, menno@ritzcom.net,
http://menno.wa.us.mennonite.net
   Terry Ray Rediger, Pastor

Ministerios Restauración (11073) (PNW, IMH) . . .0
c/o Samuel Moran, 9345 SW Quinault Lane, Tualatin OR
97062-7306
503-691-9634, samran@uswest.net
   Samuel Moran, Pastor

Mountain View Menn Ch (10082) (PNW) 95
795 Mennonite Church Rd, Kalispell MT 59901
406-755-8772, jhollinger@montana.com
   Jeryl Hollinger, Pastor

Pacific Covenant Menn Ch (10142) (PNW) 40
2180 NE Territorial Rd, PO Box 609, Canby OR 97013
503-266-8646, jzyoder@web-ster.com
   Jon Yoder, Pastor

Peace Menn Ch (24380) (PNW) 24
19626 NE Glisan St, Portland OR 97230
503-667-2762, peacemennonite@juno.com
   William S. Higgins, Pastor

Plainview Menn Ch (17590) (PNW) 0
241 1st Ave W, Albany OR 97321-2223
541-926-1946, fax 541-926-1161,
pastorrob@plainview.org,
http://www.plainview.plainview.org
34414 Plainview Dr
   Rob L. Angerman, Pastor
   Scott Anthony Henderson, Youth Pastor

Portland Menn Ch (17608) (PNW) 212
1312 SE 35th Ave, Portland OR 97214
503-234-0559, fax 503-235-5548,
pmcadmin@teleport.com
   Rod Stafford, Pastor
   Charlene Schrag, Youth Pastor

Prince of Peace Community Ch (17509) (PNW) . .54
7234 NE Arnold Ave, Adair Village OR 97330
541-745-5840, princeofpeace@exchange.net
   Scott Dyer, Pastor

Prince of Peace Menn Ch (10051) (PNW) 18
PO Box 241312, Anchorage AK 99524-1312
907-346-2909, johndavidthacker@hotmail.com
10980 Hillside Dr
   John David Thacker, Pastor

River of Life Fell (10270) (PNW) 85
PO Box 873, Sweet Home OR 97386
541-367-6855, rol@centurytel.net
1658 Long St
   Gary Dean Hooley, Pastor

Salem Menn Ch (17616) (PNW) 127
1045 Candlewood Dr NE, Salem OR 97303
503-390-2715, menno@open.org,
http://www.open.org/~menno
   John Woodson Knox, Pastor

Seattle Menn Ch (28381) (PNW) 120
3120 NE 125th St, Seattle WA 98125-4515
206-361-4630, fax 206-361-6076,
smcmarsha@netsmc.net,
http://seattle.wa.us.mennonite.net
   Weldon D. Nisly, Pastor

Shalom Ch (5723) (PNW) 17
c/o Reanette Boese, PO Box 5519, Spokane WA 99205
509-747-1887, reaboese@juno.com
35 W Main St

Spring Valley Menn Ch (5730) (PNW) 69
4912 Spring Valley Rd, Newport WA 99156
509-447-3588, fax 509-447-3753, svmennonite@juno.com
   Frank Woelk, Pastor

Warden Menn Ch (5810) (PNW) 63
720 S Pine, PO Box 766, Warden WA 98857
509-349-2444, dmmorrow@mennonite.net,
http://warden.wa.us.mennonite.net
   David Marvin Morrow, Pastor

Western Menn Ch (17632) (PNW) 79
9045 Wallace Rd NW, Salem OR 97304
503-363-2595, fax 503-370-9455, MGB180@hotmail.com,
http://www.wmchurch.org
   David J. Stutzman, Pastor
   Matt Baker, Youth Pastor

Zion Menn Ch (17640) (PNW) 205
6124 S Whiskey Hill Rd, Hubbard OR 97032
503-651-2274, zionmc@canby.com
   Todd Lehman, Pastor
   Jana Gingerich, Associate/Youth Pastor

Pacific Southwest Mennonite Conference

OFFICE
admin@pacificsouthwest.org,
www.pacificsouthwest.org
626-720-8100, fax 626-720-8101
Box CAL, 1539 East Howard St, Pasadena CA
91104

STAFF
Gloria Newton, administrator
(admin@pacificsouthwest.org)
Clare Ann Ruth-Heffelbower, interim conference
minister—Northern California
(clareann@pacificsouthwest.org)
Vivian Schwartz, bookkeeper
(veschwartz@msn.com)
Al Whaley, conference minister—Arizona
(al@pacificsouthwest.org)
Jeff Wright, conference minister—Southern
California
(wrightstuff@pacificsouthwest.org)

GENERAL INFORMATION
Year founded: 1994
Delegate sessions: first weekend in Feb. and
third weekend in June
Regions: Arizona, Northern California, Southern
California
Members: 3,293
Congregations: 45
Ministers: 74
CLC Representatives: Art Montoya, Jeff Wright

PUBLICATION
Panorama: Published 3-4 times a year, available on www.pacificsouthwest.org, Doreen
Martens, editor
(panorama@pacificsouthwest.org)

EXECUTIVE COMMITTEE
Officers (executive@pacificsouthwest.org)
Ruth Suter, moderator
(moderator@pacificsouthwest.org), PO Box
88, Brisbane CA 94005, 415-468-9676; Leah

Ann Alcazar, assistant moderator; open—
secretary; Scott Engmann, treasurer
Board Members—Class of 2005: Doris Greer,
Slamet Mustangin, Karl Kauffman, Ben
Bolanos
Board Members—Class of 2006: Nehemiah
James Chigoji, Will Friesen, Chuwang Pam,
Sam Snyder

COMMISSIONS
Gift Discernment. Steve Penner, chair
(sngpenner@telis.org)
Mission Team. Jeff Wright, chair
(wrightstuff@pacificsouthwest.org)
Pastoral Leadership. Will Friesen, chair
(wfriesen@fresno.edu)

OTHER CONFERENCE AGENCIES AND REPS
Center for Anabaptist Leadership (CAL).
See separate listing in section 3.
Mennonite Men. Arlen Godshall, president
(arlengodshall@aol.com)
Mennonite Women. Nita Kimel, president
(netachiro@hotmail.com)
**Pacific Southwest Mennonite Retreat
Ministries.** George Harper, executive director (admin@campkeola.org)

Congregations

Abundant Life Miracle Christian Center (11318) (PSW, AAMA, CAL) **70**
2926 W Florence Ave, Los Angeles CA 90043
323-778-4063, clevychic@yahoo.com
Clement Nwani, Co-Pastor
Evelyn Nwani, Co-Pastor

All Souls Christian Center (11583) (PSW, CAL, AAMA) **175**
5125 S Crenshaw Blvd, Los Angeles CA 90043-1853
323-291-2235, fax 323-291-2153
Charles Opong, Pastor

Bethel Community Ch (5075) (PSW, CAL) **60**
9845 Orr & Day Rd, Santa Fe Springs CA 90670
562-860-3464
John Melendrez, Pastor

Calvary Christian Fell (18242) (PSW, CAL, AAMA) **150**
2400 W 85th St, Inglewood CA 90305-1816
323-752-8552, aisaacs837@aol.com
Alvin Isaacs, Pastor
Richard Reese, Associate Pastor

Cupertino Menn Ch (5697) (PSW) **15**
10084 Adriana Ave, Cupertino CA 95014
408-253-3638, fax 408-255-2392

Emmanuel Faith Chapel (10123) (PSW, CAL, AAMA) **25**
4232 Laurel Hill Drive, North Las Vegas NV 89032
702-638-1857, fax 702-638-1857, cjud@maxxconnect.net

Emmanuel Menn Ch (18325) (PSW) **36**
PO Box 1679, Surprise AZ 85378-1679
623-583-9902
16002 N Verde St
D. C. Seville, Pastor

Faith and Love Christian Center (11584) (PSW, AAMA, CAL) **20**
5400 S 11th Ave, Los Angeles CA 90043
323-292-8503, fax 323-294-6600, FaithnLoveCC@aol.com
Ray McCullough, Co-Pastor
Nathaniel Payton, Co-Pastor

Faith Menn Ch (18259) (PSW, CAL) **20**
11821 Old River School Rd, Downey CA 90241
fax 562-927-1219, jbixler@co.la.ca.us

Family Menn Ch (11109) (PSW, CAL, AAMA) . .**152**
PO Box 621087, Los Angeles CA 90062
323-750-1744, fax 323-750-4955, addie7662@yahoo.com
6520 S Normandie Ave
Claude Flowers, Pastor

First Menn Ch of Paso Robles (5409) (PSW) . . .**116**
2343 Park St, Paso Robles CA 93446
805-238-2445, 1stmc@iolwest.com
http://members.xoom/1stmennonite.com
J. Stanley Friesen, Ministry Team
Andy Johnson, Ministry Team

First Menn Ch of Phoenix (5312) (PSW) **45**
1612 W Northern Ave, Phoenix AZ 85021
602-944-0875, fax 602-944-1732, menn1ofphx@aol.com
Alan H. Whaley, Pastor

First Menn Ch of Reedley (5321) (PSW) **257**
1208 L St, PO Box 111, Reedley CA 93654
559-638-2917, fax 559-637-8826, sngpenner@telis.org,
http://www.firstmennonitereedley.ca.us.mennonite.net
Stephen J. Penner, Pastor
Juan V. Montes, Associate Pastor

First Menn Ch of San Francisco (23226) (PSW) . .**61**
PO Box 410656, San Francisco CA 94141
415-695-2812, FMCSF@aol.com, http://www.menno.org
601 Dolores St
Sheri Hostetler, Pastor

First Menn Ch of Upland (5330) (PSW, CAL) **61**
PO Box 338, Upland CA 91785-0338
909-982-1669, fax 909-982-1669,
kathleenkrecklow@aol.com,
http://www.forministry.com/91786fmc
379 N Campus Ave
Jeff Wright, Pastoral Team Leader
Nehemiah James Chigoji, Associate Pastor

Gereja Kristen Injili Indonesia Zion (10311) (PSW, CAL) **75**
14732 Dunnet Ave, LaMirada CA 90638
714-521-5742, fax 714-968-9432, janasria@aol.com
2000 W Valencia, Fullerton
Frederik Jan Kouttjie, Pastor

Gereja Kristus Injili (11079) PSW **40**
826 Woodward Blvd, Pasadena CA 91107
626-584-3935, mustangin@hotmail.com
1200 E Huntington Dr, Duarte
Yusak Kusuma, Pastor
Rina Kusuma, Pastor
Mathilda Koeshadi, Associate Pastor
Slamet Mustangin, Associate Pastor

Great Commission Deliverance Ch (11172) (PSW, CAL, AAMA) **40**
3939 Ursula Ave #4, Los Angeles CA 90008
323-291-8233, fax 323-291-7741, aebere@earthlink.net
166 E 45th St, San Bernardino CA
George Ahanonu, Pastor

Hmong Community Ch (10247) (PSW, HMONG) . .**46**
5015 E Olive Ave, Fresno CA 93727
559-486-0227, suemoua@wlgdirect.com
Sue Moua, Pastor

Hollywood Christian Center (11586) (PSW, CAL) . .**0**
PO Box 2542, Los Angeles CA 90028
310-674-4559

House of the Lord Fell (24885) (PSW, CAL) 50
328 S Azusa Ave, La Puente CA 91744
626-912-1983, fax 626-913-2128,
17403 E Villa Park St
 Justo Moreno, Senior Pastor
 Irene Mendoza, Associate Pastor
 Fernando Kuan, Youth Pastor

Iglesia Evangelica Bethel (25429) (PSW, CAL, IMH) 154
PO Box 1201, Sun Valley CA 91353
818-508-6467, fax 818-508-9217
6226 Colfax, North Hollywood
 Eliseo Franco, Pastor
 Daniel Gonzalez, Associate Pastor

Iglesia Monte Sinai (24232) (PSW, CAL, IMH) ..30
3119 Liberty Blvd, South Gate CA 90280
323-569-2029
2019 S Ellendale, Los Angeles
 Salvador Arana, Pastor

Indonesian Worship Ch (11078) (PSW) 70
1419 South 3rd St, Alhambra CA 91803
626-588-2102, bususy@netzero.com
www.indonesianworshipchurch.com
3000-B West Valley Blvd, Alhmbra
 Buddy Hannanto, Pastor

Jemaat Kristen Indonesia Anugrah (10289) (PSW, CAL) 100
1632 Locust St, Pasadena CA 91106
626-564-9869, fax 626-564-9869,
vhandojo@sbcglobal.net
191 W Sierra Madre Blvd
 Virgo Handoyo, Pastor
 Stephen Zacheus, Assistant/Associate Pastor

Jemaat Kristen Indonesia Hosana (10282) (PSW, CAL) 64
12027 E End Ave, Chino CA 91710
909-902-9278, fax 909-613-5803,
sutantoadi@worldnet.att.net
1120 W 13th St, Upland
 Rudy Gunawan, Associate Pastor

Jemaat Kristen Indonesia Imanuel (10309) (PSW, CAL) 60
11821 Old River School Rd, Downey CA 90241
626-333-2033, fax 562-928-8033, stevejachin@juno.com
 Stephen M. Jachin, Pastor

Jemaat Kristen Indonesia Maranatha (10259) (PSW, CAL) 80
18419 Sherman Way, Reseda CA 91335
818-757-3580, fax 818-342-6777, haryono@juno.com,
http://www.jkimaranatha.faithweb.com
 Petrus Haryono, Pastor

Koinonia Menn Ch (23044) (PSW) 84
2505 N Dobson Rd, Chandler AZ 85224
480-963-2416, azmennos@juno.com,
http://koinonia.az.us.mennonite.net
 Richard Sisco, Pastor

Labor for Christ Ministry (11269) (PSW, CAL, AAMA) 65
4915 ½ Second Ave, Los Angeles CA 90043
323-292-8139
2420 W 3rd St in Los Angeles
 Albert Asante, Pastor

Los Angeles Faith Chapel (11088) (PSW, IMH, CAL, AAMA) 155
3818 W Imperial Hwy, Inglewood CA 90303
310-677-0270, fax 310-677-3586, faithchap@aol.com
 Chuwang Rwang Pam, Pastor

Menn Community Ch (28373) (PSW) 109
5015 E Olive Ave, Fresno CA 93727
559-251-5703, fax 559-251-5778, ratzlaff@att.net,
http://www.geocities.com/mennocom
 Steve C. Ratzlaff, Pastor

Miracle of Faith Menn Ch (24612) (PSW, CAL, AAMA) 60
7860 S Western Ave, Los Angeles CA 90047
323-466-4117, fax 323-758-2844
 Egbert Pascacio, Pastor

Mountain View Menn Ch (18309) (PSW, CAL) ..49
1120 W 13th St, Upland CA 91786
909-982-6238, fax 909-982-0073, rricher@juno.com
 Roger Richer, Pastor

Pasadena Menn Ch (28142) (PSW, CAL) 80
1041 N Altadena Dr, Pasadena CA 91107
626-398-8224, fax 626-398-7626, office@pmcweb.org,
http://www.pmcweb.org
 James E. Brenneman, Pastor
 Elbert Walker Newton, Associate Pastor
 Jennifer Davis Sensenig, Associate Pastor

Peace House Fell (10027) (PSW, CAL, BIC) 30
225 W Monterrey Dr, Claremont CA 91711
909-338-8666, fax 626-815-3809, daugsburger@msn.com,
http://www.forministry.com/uscamenocpfpfp/
Members' homes

Prince of Peace Anabaptist Fell (18267) (PSW, CAL, AAMA) 10
Sharon Irvin, 1654 Hi Point St, Los Angeles CA 90035
323-939-6478, reneirv4138@yahoo.com

Riches of Christ Fell (11080) (PSW) 70
417-3 West El Segundo Blvd, Los Angeles CA 90061
310-329-7460, pastorjohn_richesofchrist@juno.com
www.richesofchrist.org
 John Egwuonwu, Pastor

Royal Dominion Family Chapel (11319) (PSW, CAL, AAMA) 50
PO Box 431434, Los Angeles CA 90043
323-759-6608, fax 323-759-6858,
royaldominion@excite.com, http://www.royaldominion.org
6505 S Normandie Ave
 Windell Moody, Pastor
 Olwfemi A. Fatunmbi, Founding Pastor
 Olatunde Olanrewaju, Evangelist

CONFERENCES AND CONGREGATIONS

2

San Diego Menn Ch (10001) (PSW, CAL) 22
4361 35th St, San Diego CA 92104
619-281-3240, ann.moyer@sharp.com
3219 Adams Ave

San Francisco Chinese Menn Ch (5692) (PSW) . .36
4021 California St, San Francisco CA 94118
415-221-7115, fax 415-221-7115

Shalom Menn Fell (22418) (PSW) 61
6044 E 30th St, Tucson AZ 85711
520-748-7082, shalommennonite@cox.net,
http://members.cox.net/shalommennonite

Sunnyslope Menn Ch (18317) (PSW) 118
9835 N 7th St, Phoenix AZ 85020
602-997-7171, fax 602-331-0652,
sunnyslopemc@juno.com,
http://www.sunnyslopemennonite.org
   Steven Joe Good, Pastor

Trinity Chinese Menn Ch (5183) (PSW, CAL) 42
60 Grant, Irvine CA 92620
949-653-2785, fax 949-653-2785, jtancpa@aol.com
7000 Beach Blvd, Buena Park
   Nelson Kuang-Daw Kao, Pastor

Trinity Menn Ch (18333) (PSW, CAL) 360
4334 W Vista Ave, Glendale AZ 85301
623-931-9241, fax 623-931-4464, trinitymc@juno.com,
http://www.trinity.az.us.mennonite.net
   Stephen Intagliata, Associate Pastor

Rocky Mountain Mennonite Conference

OFFICE
rmmc@rmmc.org, www.rmmc.org
303-347-9266, fax 303-795-0090
2391 W Caley Ave, Littleton CO 80120

STAFF
Ed and Kathrine Rempel, conference ministers
(ekrempel@msn.com)
Linda Welty, administrative assistant
(lawelty@i70west.com)

GENERAL INFORMATION
Year founded: 1962
Members: 1,521
Congregations: 20
Ministers: 36
CLC reps: Lauren Martin and Leon Stutzman
Annual Conference: April 30–May 2, 2004

EXECUTIVE COMMITTEE
Leon Stutzman, moderator
(stutzman@juno.com), 6394 W Burgundy Dr,
Littleton CO 80123, 303-797-3551; Lauren
Martin, moderator elect; Linda Welty,
administrative assistant and secretary; Jim Zook,
treasurer

PUBLICATION
Conference Connections (monthly) Linda
Welty, editor (lawelty@i70west.com), 12048
Arkansas Pl, Lakewood CO 80228

COMMISSIONS
Leadership. Merv Birky, chair
(mervbirky@bethelmennonite.org), 1219
Yuma, Colorado Springs CO 80909, 719-
636-2716
Finance. Carroll Miller, chair
(cmiller107@juno.com), 5601 18th St, #28,
Greeley CO 80634, 970-330-1119
Mission. No chair at the present time. Contact
conference office.
Youth. Ron and Char Roth, co-chairs
(rcroth@juno.com), 402 11th St, Greeley
CO 80631, 970-353-7224
Nurture Commission. No chair at the present
time. Contact conference office.
Peace and Justice Commission. Bruce
Kuhns, chair (kuhnsfam@arczip.com),
1528 Conway Dr, Colorado Springs CO
80915, 719-596-1718

OTHER CONFERENCE AGENCIES AND REPS
Mennonite Women. Kim Martin, president
(lkmsplace@juno.com), 2401 Blake Ave,
Glenwood Springs CO 81601, 970-945-8851

Congregations

Albuquerque Menn Ch (11311) (RM) 34
2210 Silver SE, Albuquerque NM 87106
505-254-1824, pastor@abqmennonite.org,
http://www.rmmc.org/amc
  Anita F. Amstutz, Pastor

Beth-El Menn Ch (20792) (RM) 182
1219 Yuma St, Colorado Springs CO 80909
719-636-2716, fax 719-636-2716,
bethel@bethelmennonite.org,
http://www.bethelmennonite.org
  Mervin R. Birky, Pastor

Carlsbad Menn Ch (20818) (RM) 58
1204 W Mckay St, Carlsbad NM 88220
505-887-5104, cmchurch@cavemen.net,
http://carlsbad.nm.us.mennonite2.net
  Joe Telgren, Pastor

East Holbrook Menn Ch (20834) (RM) 66
PO Box 68, Cheraw CO 81030
719-853-6377, fax 719-853-6291,
cholsopplefroese@hotmail.com
32723 Rd 33
  Galen Penner, Pastor

Emmanuel Menn Ch (20842) (RM) 90
502 Harriett Ave, La Junta CO 81050
719-384-9673, pastor@emclj.org, http://www.emclj.org
  Steven Gary Schmidt, Pastor

**First Menn Ch of Colorado Springs (20867)
(RM)** 47
11 N 22nd St, Colorado Springs CO 80904-3431
719-635-5593, fax 719-635-5593,
thethomassens@aol.com
  Donald L. Thomassen, Pastor

First Menn Ch of Denver (20859) (RM, CM) . . .284
430 W 9th Ave, Denver CO 80204
303-892-1038, fax 303-892-6106, fmcdenver@aol.com,
http://www.fmcdenver.org
    Vernon K. Rempel, Pastor

Fort Collins Menn Fell (24687) (RM, WDC) 42
300 E Oak St, Fort Collins CO 80524-2915
970-224-4106, revjborg@juno.com,
http://www.fortnet.org/fcmf
    Jeffrey A. Borg, Pastor

**Glennon Heights Menn Ch (20883) (RM,
MUM)** 104
11480 W Virginia Ave, Lakewood CO 80226
303-985-3606, fax 303-985-3930, ghmenno@att.net,
http://glennonheights.co.us.mennonite.net
    Dean A. Linsenmeyer, Pastor

Glenwood Menn Ch (20891) (RM) 30
2306 Blake Ave, Glenwood Springs CO 81601
970-945-5245, fax 970-945-5245,
glenwoodmenno@juno.com
    Lauren R. Martin, Pastor

Greeley Menn Ch (20917) (RM) 91
402 11th Street, Greeley CO 80631
970-353-7224, fax 970-353-7224, rcroth@juno.com
    Charlene Roth, Pastor
    Ron Roth, Pastor

**Hmong Menn Ch (11119) (RM, WDC, HMONG,
MUM)** 45
c/o Shoua Moua, 8822 W 75th Pl, Arvada CO 80005-4529
303-424-6261
    Shoua Moua, Pastor

Light of Life Menn Ch (10656) (RM, UNMC) 40
PO Box 6763, Farmington NM 87499
505-327-7056
    George Wero, Pastor

Menn Ch of La Jara (20925) (RM, OD) 7
PO Box 306, La Jara CO 81140
719-843-5118, alicep@amigo.net
5th & Walnut

**Mountain Community Menn Ch (25247) (RM,
WDC)** 97
PO Box 502, Palmer Lake CO 80133
719-481-3155, mcmc@emcmc.org,
http://www.rmmc.org/mcmc
643 Hwy 105
    Don Rheinheimer, Co-Pastor
    Jan Lynette Rheinheimer, Co-Pastor

**Peace Menn Community Ch (28605) (RM, WDC,
MUM)** 90
13601 E Alameda Ave, Aurora CO 80012
303-340-1555, fax 303-766-5008,
pmccsecretary@comcast.net
    Phil Ebersole, Pastor

Perryton Menn Ch (20958) (RM) 65
2821 S Ash St, Perryton TX 79070
806-435-3817, stdon@ptsi.net
    Don Stoll, Pastor

Pueblo Menn Ch (21774) (RM) 50
634 Goodnight Ave, Pueblo CO 81005
719-561-1669
    David Foncannon, Pastor

Rocky Ford Menn Ch (20966) (RM) 90
PO Box 66, Rocky Ford CO 81067
719-254-3283, donpen@rural-rural.com
20480 CR EE 25
    Don Penner, Pastor

Walsenburg Menn Ch (20982) (RM) 9
PO Box 88, Walsenburg CO 81089
719-738-2037
6th & Leon

South Central Mennonite Conference

OFFICE
scc@mennoscc.org
316-283-7080, fax 316-283-0620
2517 N Main, PO Box 448, North Newton KS
67117

STAFF
Robert Nolt, conference minister
(rnolt@mennoscc.org)
Doug Krehbiel, youth minister
Phyllis Regier, treasurer
(pregier@mennowdc.org)
Nancy Funk, administrative assistant
(scc@mennoscc.org)
Conrado Hinojosa, UCIM (Unidad Cristiana de
Iglesias Menonitas) conference minister
(conrado_hinojosa@hotmail.com), PO Box
2120, 2408 Fern Ave, San Juan TX 78589,
956-702-4181 (home); 956-782-8057
(church)
Marco Güete, Mid-Texas Conference Minister
(marcoguete@sbcglobal.net), 815 Parkside
Dr, Cedar Hills TX 75104; 972-293-2761
(H); 972-293-1029 (Off./fax)

GENERAL INFORMATION
Year founded: 1876
Members: 3,974
Congregations: 46 + 4 church plants
Ministers: 57
CLC reps: Esther Martinez, Robert Nolt, Margie
Wiens
Districts: Arkansas-Missouri, Kansas-Oklahoma,
Mid-Texas, South Texas (UCIM)
Annual Conference: August 2004 with Western
District Conference

EXECUTIVE COMMITTEE
Heber Ramer, moderator
(hramer@wiredks.com), 502 W 15th St,
Harper KS 67058, 620-896-2792; John C.
Murray, moderator-elect; Trish Brenneman,
Grace Brunner, Leona Diener, Gilberto Flores,
Marco Güete, Israel Hernandez, Mervin
Hershberger, Conrado Hinojosa, Spike
Hostetler, Ken King, Joanne Klassen, Esther
Martinez, Robert Nolt, Victor Vargas, Peter
Wiebe

PUBLICATION
Messenger (bimonthly), Lois Loflin, editor
(loflin@mennowdc.org), Box 448, North
Newton KS 67117

COMMISSIONS
Finance and Stewardship. Ken King, chair
(kjdking@mindspring.com), 6003 E. Eales
Rd, Hutchinson KS 67501, 620-663-1470;
Dan Miller, Dave Weaver, Leona Diener
Missions. Mervin Hershberger, Sam Nance
Peace and Service. Marion Bontrager, chair
(marionb@hesston.edu), Box 3000,
Hesston KS 67062, 620-327-8291; Richard
Davis, Leona Diener
Youth Ministry. Torrey Ball, chair
(tball@ourtown.usa), 808 S Poplar, South
Hutchinson KS 67505, 620-663-4244; Pam
Gerber, Derek Yoder
Ministerial Commission. Grace Brunner,
chair (brunner@southwind.net), 441 S
Main St, Hesston KS 67062, 620-327-2125;
Marco Güete, Conrado Hinojosa, Wally Jantz,
Howard Keim, Mim Mast, Robert Nolt, Cathy
Wagler

OTHER CONFERENCE AGENCY AND REPS
Mennonite Women. Trish Brenneman, presi-
dent (jbrenneman@cox.net), 207 Kingsway,
Hesston KS 67062, 620-327-4700; Marilyn
Hartman, Miriam Huebert Stauffer, Joan
Wohlschlegel
Mexico Conference Office. Conferencia
Cristiana de Tamaulipas, Juan Jesus Garza
Ruiz, administrator, 606 Calle 11 Entre
Rayon y Zaragoza, Zona Centro Matamoros,
Tamps MEXICO

Congregations

Argentine Menn Ch (17798) (SC) **26**
3701 Metropolitan Ave, Kansas City KS 66106-2796
913-831-3621, argentinemenn@aol.com
   Mervin Hershberger, Pastor

Austin Menn Ch (28761) (SC, WDC) **64**
5801 Westminster Dr, Austin TX 78723-2640
512-926-3121, fax 512-926-3121,
http://www.mennochurch.org
   Garland L. Robertson, Pastor

Berea Menn Community Ch (17806) (SC) **21**
RR 1 Box 30A, Birch Tree MO 65438
573-292-3553, menno_9@hotmail.com,
http://bereamenn.tripod.com/bmc
3 mi north on FF Hwy

Calico Rock Menn Fell (17855) (SC) **36**
HC 79 Box 181, Calico Rock AR 72519
870-297-8091, crmf@centurytel.net
Fellowship Rd

Calvary Menn Ch (17863) (SC, IMH) **120**
PO Box 207, Mathis TX 78368
361-547-3727
719 W San Patricio Ave
   Armando J. Calderon, Pastor

Casa de Oración (26971) (SC, IMH) **42**
PO Box 3114, Alamo TX 78516
956-787-8346
   Elizabeth Hernandez, Pastor

**Centro Cristiano Menonita Jerusalem (27601)
(SC)** **0**
Calle 13 lote 19 entre calle 15 y, Dante Delgado Col
Venustiano Carranza, Cd Boca del Rio, Veracruz
abelardold@hotmail.com
   Abelardo Diaz, Pastor

**Comunidad de Esperanza (6240) (SC, WDC,
IMH)** **35**
1721 N Garrett Ave, Dallas TX 75206
214-428-7131, fax 214-828-1292,
damain_rodriguez@msn.com
   Damian Rodriguez, Pastor

Crystal Springs Menn Ch (17889) (SC) **22**
c/o Joe Zimmerman, 424 NW 90 Rd, Harper KS 67058
620-896-2962
   Lidia Zehr, Pastor

Faith Menn Ch (24356) (SC) **50**
1403 S Main St, South Hutchinson KS 67505
620-662-2502, faithmennonite@juno.com,
http://faithmennonitechurch.ks.us.mennonite.net
   James Michael Unruh, Pastor
   James M. Unruh, Pastor

Gospel Fell Ch (27425) (SC, WDC) **32**
PO Box 403, Montezuma KS 67867
620-846-2663, erdwko@yahoo.com
   Doug Harris, Pastor

Greensburg Menn Ch (17939) (SC) **82**
310 W Pennsylvania Ave, Greensburg KS 67054
620-723-2620, gburgmc@juno.com
   Jeffrey D. Blackburn, Pastor

Hesston Menn Ch (17962) (SC) **611**
309 S Main, PO Box 3000, Hesston KS 67062
620-327-4885, fax 620-327-8300,
hesstonmc@dtnspeed.net,
http://hesston.ks.us.mennonite.net
   John C. Murray, Pastor
   Cheryl Hershberger, Associate Pastor
   Martin Bradley Troyer, Associate Pastor for Youth

Hope Fell (10012) (SC, WDC) **18**
1700 Morrow, Waco TX 76707
254-754-5942, hopefellowship@grandecom.net
   Joe Gatlin, Co-Pastor
   Nancy Gatlin, Co-Pastor
   Norma Torres, Co-Pastor

Houston Menn Ch (23184) (SC, WDC) **45**
1231 Wirt Rd, Houston TX 77055
713-464-4865, pastor@houstonmennonite.org,
http://www.houstonmennonite.org
   Jose Elizalde, Pastor

Iglesia Ebenezer (27600) (SC) **0**
Rayon Y Zaragosa, Calle Benito Quijano #500, Col Nuevo
Amanecer, Cd Reynosa, Tamaulipas
   Alfonso Martinez, Pastor

Iglesia Evangelica Galilea (27604) (SC) **0**
Calle 16 de septiembre #56, esquina Zona Centro CP
88500, Reynosa, Tamaulipas
   Julio Cesar Flores Lopez, Pastor

**Iglesia Evangelica Menonita Gethsemani
(27602) SC)** **0**
Calle Lomas de Bolado #86, Col Loma Alta, H Matamoros
Tamaulipas
011-868-835-7708
   Odilon Zaleta Sanchez, Pastor

**Iglesia Menonita Buenas Nuevas (28001)
(SC, IMH)** **32**
PO Box 2120, San Juan TX 78589
956-782-8057, fax 956-782-8057,
conrado_hinojosa@hotmail.com
Corner of Raul Longoria & El Dora
   Conrado Hinojosa, Pastor

**Iglesia Menonita Casa de Dios (15303) (SC, WDC,
Church Plant)** **0**
2514 Arcady St, Garland TX 75041
972-271-9310
   Jesus Natividad Hernandez, Church Planter

**Iglesia Menonita Casa del Alfarero (15302) (SC,
WDC, Church Plant)** **0**
1701 Burke Rd, Pasadena TX 77502
713-475-2031
   Alberto Ronald Parchmont, Church Planter
   Aurora Parchmont, Church Planter

Iglesia Menonita Comunidad de Vida (27410) (SC, WDC, Church Plant) 0
1443 S St Marys, San Antonio TX 78210
210-832-0182, blancavargas@earthlink.net
  Blanca Vargas, Pastor
  Victor Serafin Vargas, Pastor

Iglesia Menonita del Cordero (17830) (SC, IMH) . .89
1033 N Minnesota Ave, Brownsville TX 78521
956-831-4404, fax 956-831-4404, rigonegron@juno.com
  Rigoberto Negron, Pastor

Iglesia Menonita Luz del Evangelio (6512) (SC, WDC, IMH) 30
c/o Juan Limones, 2459 Telegraph, Dallas TX 75228
214-324-9409
  Juan Fernando Limones, Pastor

Iglesia Menonita Monte Horeb (11273) (SC, WDC, IMH) 12
427 N Marlborough Ave, Dallas TX 75208
214-946-2910, sacaceros@sbcglobal.net
  S Antonio Caceros, Pastor

Iglesia Menonita Rey de Gloria (27111) (SC, IMH) 40
823 N Minnesota Ave, Brownsville TX 78521
956-831-7193, fax 956-831-7193, lupeaguilar@juno.com
6711 Tallowood Cr
  Guadalupe Aguilar, Pastor

Iglesia Menonita Rios de Agua Viva (10681) (SC) 0
Calle Div del Norte #156, Col Guillermo Guajardo, H
Matamoros, Tamaulipas
011-52-88-14-07-51
  Racquel Lozano Palomino, Pastor

Iglesia Menonita Sembradores de Buenas Nuevas (15304) (SC, WDC, Church Plant) 0
208 Hurst Cr, Ferris TX 75125
972-842-5798, julioedg@aol.com
  Julio E. Dueñas, Church Planter

Manhattan Menn Ch (24174) (SC, WDC, USMBC) 76
1000 Fremont St, Manhattan KS 66502-5425
785-539-4079, menno@oz-online.net,
http://www.manhattan.ks.us.mennonite.net
  Barbara Krehbiel Gehring, Co-Pastor
  Richard L. Gehring, Co-Pastor

Menn Ch of the Servant (23317) (SC, WDC) 22
1650 Fairview Ave, Wichita KS 67203
316-267-4625, mennoservant@juno.com

Mount Pisgah Menn Ch (18002) (SC) 58
892 Hwy B, PO Box 108, Leonard MO 63451-0108
660-762-4400, mtpisgah4@juno.com
892 Hwy B, NW of Leonard

New Life Christian Center (29546) (SC, IMH) . . .86
925 Zillock Rd, San Benito TX 78586-7785
956-399-3794
  Eduardo Hinojosa, Pastor

Nueva Jerusalem (27605) (SC) 0
Calle 11 entre Rayon y Zaragoza, #606, Matamoros,
Tamaulipas CP 87300
011-868-813-9297
  Hector Salinas, Pastor

Pea Ridge Menn Ch (18044) (SC) 47
3284 CR 230, Palmyra MO 63461
573-439-5827, upontheridge@juno.com

Peace Menn Ch (17921) (SC, WDC) 82
11001 Midway Rd, PO Box 59926, Dallas TX 75229
214-902-8141, fax 214-902-8141,
Dick@PeaceMennonite.org,
http://www.PeaceMennonite.org
  Richard Douglas Davis, Pastor

Peace Menn Ch (23853) (SC, WDC) 72
1204 Oread Ave, Lawrence KS 66044
785-841-8614, peacemennonite@msn.com

Pleasant Valley Menn Ch (18051) (SC) 270
1020 E 14th St, Harper KS 67058
620-896-2004, fax 620-896-7129, pvmc@cyberlodge.com
  Royce W. Vogt, Pastor
  Bob Yates, Associate Pastor

Pleasant View Menn Ch (18069) (SC) 210
RR 1 Box 152B, Hydro OK 73048
405-663-2703, josephwood@juno.com
  Darwin Hartman, Pastor

Primera Iglesia Anabautista de Valle Hermoso (27603) (SC) 0
Calle B Juarez entre Calle 3 y 4, Col Gustavo Diaz Ordaz,
Cd Valle Hermoso, Tamaulipas
  Juan Jesus Garza, Pastor

Prince of Peace Menn Ch (18077) (SC, IMH) . . .54
1802 Horne Rd, Corpus Christi TX 78415
361-853-8554
  Felipe Almodovar, Pastor

Protection Menn Ch (18085) (SC) 122
PO Box 185, Protection KS 67127
316-622-4342
  Delbert Regier, Pastor

Rogers Menn/Ch of the Brethren (29745) (SC, COB) 21
PO Box 548, Pea Ridge AR 72751
417-341-1005, fax 417-435-2031, gengle@leru.net
1618 Hwy 12 E, Rogers
  Larry E. Graber, Minister
  George W. Engle, Elder
  Eli Miller, Elder

San Antonio Menn Ch (25239) (SC, WDC) 39
1443 S Saint Marys St, San Antonio TX 78210
210-533-0642, fax 210-341-8358,
dbeachey@earthlink.net,
http://www.sanantonio.tx.us.mennonite.net
  Duane Beachey, Pastor
  Daniel Foley, Associate Pastor

Shalom Menn Ch (10130) (SC, WDC) 180
800 E 1st St, Newton KS 67114
316-283-7395, office@shalomnewton.org,
http://www.shalomnewton.org
   Eric Massanari, Pastor

South Hutchinson Menn Ch (18101) (SC) 448
808 S Poplar St, South Hutchinson KS 67505
620-663-4244, fax 620-663-4449,
shmcoffice@shmc-online.net; shmc1@ourtownusa.net,
http://www.shmc-online.net/main.html
   Howard L. Wagler, Lead Pastor
   Dustin Busick, Youth Pastor

Spring Valley Menn Ch (18127) (SC) 32
1089 29th Ave, Canton KS 67428
620-628-4818, fax 620-628-4964, lrmartin@southwind.net
2896 Frontier Rd
   Loyal Martin, Pastor

Sycamore Grove Menn Ch (18135) (SC) 170
PO Box 320, Garden City MO 64747
816-862-6477
27221 S Sycamore Rd
   Karl Michael Bates, Co-Pastor
   Kenneth Steckly, Co-Pastor

Tabernaculo de Fe (28316) (SC, IMH) 27
PO Box 1034, Mathis TX 78368
361-547-0299

United Menn Ch (18168) (SC, USMBC) 8
PO Box 1278, Premont TX 78375
361-348-2872
SW 6th at Bernice
   Lewis E. McDorman, Pastor
   Forest Whitcher, Assistant Pastor

Whitestone Menn Ch (18184) (SC) 370
629 Crescent Dr, Hesston KS 67062
620-327-4123, fax 620-327-5127,
whitestone@wmc.kscoxmail.com,
http://whitestone.ks.us.mennonite.net
   Mark A. Miller, Pastor
   Wendy Miller, Associate Pastor
   Derek Yoder, Youth Pastor

Yoder Menn Ch (18192) (SC) 173
3605 E Longview Rd, Haven KS 67543
620-663-2657, fax 620-665-0207,
yoderchurch@ourtownusa.net
   Dennis Stutzman, Pastor
   Rory Stutzman, Youth Pastor
   Daniel Kauffman, Mentoring Pastor

Southeast Mennonite Conference

OFFICE
seconference@verizon.net
941-342-9959, fax 941-342-0318
35 S Beneva Rd, Suite A, Sarasota FL 34232-1452

STAFF
Amie Kain, administrative assistant
(seconference@verizon.net)
Ken Nauman, conference minister
(kenmirna@sunline.net)

GENERAL INFORMATION
Year founded: 1967
Members: 2,700
Congregations: 29 + 2 church plants
Ministers: 65
CLC reps: Marlin Birkey, Ken Nauman
Districts: Georgia-South Carolina, North Central
Florida, Tampa Bay, Southwest Florida,
Sarasota, South Florida
Annual conference: October 2-3, 2004

CONFERENCE COUNCIL
Dale Ivy, moderator, 13691 SW CR 275,
Blountstown FL 32424, 850-674-4516,
(tuder720@yahoo.com); Dale Beachey, treasurer
and stewardship and business secretary; Marlin
Birkey, moderator and Sarasota district minister
(seconference@verizon.net), 35 S Beneva Rd,
Suite A, Sarasota FL 34232-1452, 941-342-9959;
Ambrosio Encarnacion, Hispanic advocate; Linda
Gingerich, Mennonite Women president; Dale Ivy,
assistant moderator and North Central FL district
minister; Jonathan Larson, GA/SC district minister;
Hilaire Louis Jean, Haitian advocate; Ken Nauman,
conference minister and Southwest FL district minister; Byron Pellecer, South FL district minister;
Tom Renno, congregational outreach secretary;
and Roy Williams, Tampa Bay district minister

PUBLICATION
Ventures in Faith (quarterly), Amie Kain
(seconference@verizon.net), 35 S Beneva Rd,

Suite A, Sarasota FL 34232-1452, 941-342-9959

COMMISSIONS
Congregational Leadership. Ken Nauman,
chair (kenmirna@sunline.net), 922 W
Hickory St, Arcadia FL 34266-3361, 863-
993-9353; Marlin Birkey, Dale Ivy, Jonathan
Larson, Byron Pellecer, Roy Williams
Congregational Outreach Secretary. Tom
Renno (tjrenno@comcast.net), 2156 E
Leewynn Dr, Sarasota FL 34240-8791, 941-
379-0782
Financial Planning. Marlin Birkey, chair
(seconference@verizon.net), 35 S Beneva
Rd, Suite A, Sarasota FL 34232-1452, 941-
342-9959; Dale Beachey, Ken Nauman, staff:
Amie Kain
Nominating. Members: Ricky Brock, Lewis
Overholt, Byron Pellecer, Hazel Shirk, Sara
Alice Zimmerly
Personnel. Marlin Birkey, chair
(seconference@verizon.net), 35 S Beneva
Rd, Suite A Sarasota FL 34232-1452, 941-
342-9959; Dale Beachey, Ken Nauman
Stewardship and Business Secretary. Dale
Beachey (daleb46@comcast.net), 4929 Old
Creek Dr, Sarasota FL 34233-3942, 941-
929-1483

OTHER CONFERENCE AGENCIES AND REPS
Charis Center Board. Naomi Schlabach, chair,
5885 Ibis St, Sarasota FL 34241-9282, 941-
923-1387; Dale Beachey, Doris Diener, Janet
Hamilton, Rev. Jan Henry-Rinehart, Susi Jacocks,
Yvonne Keim, Barbara Kiracofe, Dale Stoll
Haitian Advocate. Hilaire Louis Jean
(pastorh56@aol.com), 1115 NW 126th St,
North Miami FL 33168-6441, 305-688-8245
Hispanic Advocate. Jose Hernandez, 30695
SW 162nd Ave, Homestead FL 33033-4122,
305-248-1659
MCC East Coast Board Rep. Lloyd Miller
(lp_miller-sara@juno.com), 3343

Tallywood Court, Sarasota FL 34237-3224, 941-952-5062

Mennonite Disaster Service. Merle Sommers, chair (sommersmr7@juno.com), 3904 Bellwood Dr, Sarasota FL 34232-3308, 941-341-0153; C. Nelson Hosttetter, Scott Kauffman, Darrell J. Miller, Ervin Miller, Jim Miller, Lisa Miller, Andy Nisley, Paul Yoder, Paul W. Yoder, Phillip Yoder

Mennonite Women. Linda Gingerich, president (dlgingerich@earthlink.net), 502 SE 17th Ave, Cape Coral FL 33990-1609, 239-574-8382; Jiny Brutus, Carol Clark, Sally Eisner, Colleen Fisher, Sharon Lehman, Juanita Nuñez

Sunnyside Properties Board. Allen Mast, chair (mastcpa@email.com), 1001 N Washington Blvd, Suite 107, Sarasota FL 34236, 941-953-5036; Glen Denlinger, Wade Harris, Hertha Isaac, Cheryl Kornhaus, H. Greg Lee, Danny Miller, Naomi Schlabach, Paul Yoder staff: David Ray Miller

Urban Minister for South Florida. Chuck Goertz (hmstdmenno@juno.com), 30695 SW 162nd Ave, Homestead FL 33033-4122, 305-248-1659

Youth Council. Chair position vacant, (seconference@verizon.net), 35 S Beneva Rd, Suite A, Sarasota FL 34232-1452, 941-342-9959; Paula Dominguez, Jake Goertz, Michelle Kennell, Charity Miller, Nathalie Rodriguez

Congregations

Americus Menn Fell (10067) (SE) 60
PO Box 1785, Americus GA 31709
229-924-0603, dslandis@sowega.net
409 E Hill St
  Steven Farsaci, Pastor

Ashton Menn Ch (13524) (SE) 95
2895 Ashton Rd, Sarasota FL 34231
941-924-3993, fax 941-924-3321,
ashton.church@verizon.net
  Marlin Keith Birkey, Pastor
  Dion Hunt, Minister of Youth

Assemblee de la Grace (11299) (SE) 32
PO Box 1010, Immokalee FL 33934
239-867-4403

618 9th St N, Immokalee, FL
  Laurent Louis, Pastor
  Marie Gilot, Associate Pastor

Bahia Vista Menn Ch (18903) (SE) 365
4041 Bahia Vista St, Sarasota FL 34232
941-377-4041, fax 941-378-9674,
BVMenno@comcast.net, http://www.bahiavista.org
  Glenn M. Steiner, Pastor
  Joe Bradshaw, Associate Pastor
  Larry Diener, Minister of Music and Worship
  Carolyn Stoll, Parish Nurse

Bay Shore Menn Ch (15693) (SE) 525
3809 Chapel Dr, Sarasota FL 34234
941-355-4168, fax 941-351-1969,
bay.shore7@verizon.net,
http://www.theshepherd.com/bayshore
  Rocky Miller, Interim Pastor
  David M. Barkema, Youth Pastor
  Lee E. Miller, Minister of Administration
  Hazel Shirk, Minister of Special Care

Berea Menn Ch (13565) (SE) 50
PO Box 17564, Atlanta GA 30316-0564
404-244-0289, fax 404-244-0289,
BereaMennonite@juno.com,
http://www.bereamennonitechurch.com
1088 Bouldercrest Dr SE
  Jonathan Emerson-Pierce, Pastor
  Dorothy Harding, Minister of Urban Evangelism

Cape Christian Fell (28175) (SE) 500
PO Box 150777, Cape Coral FL 33915
239-772-5683, fax 239-458-4463,
Info@capechristian.com, http://www.capechristian.com
2110 Chiquita Blvd S
  Dennis D. Gingerich, Senior Pastor
  William Brock, Associate Pastor
  Jerry Sprague, Associate Pastor
  Brett Furlong, Pastor of Youth Ministries
  Rick Brock, Pastor of Adult Ministries
  Wesley Furlong, Pastor of College & Career Ministries
  Tony Hostetler, Pastor of Visitation
  David Messenger, Worship Pastor
  Loren Zehr, Pastor of Nurture

Ch of God Prince of Peace (11169) (SE) 57
210 NE 119 St, Miami FL 33161
305-981-7600, PastorH56@aol.com
  Hilaire Louis Jean, Pastor

College Hill Menn Ch (13797) (SE, AAMA) 89
3506 Machado St, Tampa FL 33605
813-247-2798, fax 813-248-4339, rrrsjw@aol.com
  Roy W. Williams, Pastor
  Carl A. Walcott, Associate Pastor
  Irene Moore, Minister of Visitation

Covenant Menn Fell (12196) (SE) 25
3205 Southgate Cr, Sarasota FL 34239
941-366-3545, fax 941-906-8884, randy118@comcast.net,
http://home.comcast.net/~covenantmennonite/
Goshen College Building
  Randall L. Spaulding, Pastor

Ebenezer Christian Ch (25049) (SE, IMH) 75
PO Box 1954, Apopka FL 32704
407-886-0020, fax 407-886-9778, church775@aol.com
9 N Park Ave

Eglise du Nouveau Testament (28449) (SE) 20
281 NW 79th St, Miami FL 33150
305-687-3949
    Simon Daux, Pastor

Emmanuel Menn Ch (25080) (SE) 38
1320 W University Ave #A, Gainesville FL 32603
352-377-6577, gnvmenno@bellsouth.net,
http://grove.ufl.edu/~menno
    Eve B. MacMaster, Pastor

Evangelical Garifuna Ch (12051) (SE) 18
4148 NW 45 Terrace, Lauderdale Lakes FL 33319
954-739-8449
    Mario Dominguez, Pastor

Good Shepherd Evangelical (10972) (SE) 21
PO Box 381282, Miami FL 33238
305-891-1651
    Martin Menard, Pastor

Homestead Menn Ch (14332) (SE) 59
30695 SW 162nd Ave, Homestead FL 33033
305-248-1659, fax 305-247-3758,
HmstdMenno@juno.com,
http://homestead.fl.us.mennonite.net
    Charles G. Goertz, Pastor
    José R. Hernández Jr., Associate Pastor

Iglesia Evangelica Nueva Vida (11622) (SE) 0
c/o Pastor Ambrosio Encarnación, 2591 Apache St,
Sarasota FL 34231-5009
1026 41st St, Bradenton, FL
    Ambrosio Encarnación, Pastor

**Iglesia Menonita Arca de Salvación (27904)
(SE, IMH)** 100
PO Box 50058, Fort Myers FL 33994-0058
239-332-7556, fax 239-332-7556
3645 Michigan Ave
    David Maldonado, Pastor
    Madeline Maldonado, Associate Pastor

**Iglesia Menonita Encuentro de Renovación
(10284) (SE, IMH)** 70
c/o Byron R. Pellecer, 135 SW 113 CT, Miami FL 33174
305-207-5299, fax 305-207-4556, bpellece@bellsouth.net
2061 NW 27 Ave
    Byron Pellecer, Pastor

**Iglesia Seguidores de Cristo (25072)
(SE, IMH)** 45
PO Box 50292, Sarasota FL 34278
941-377-8198
1001 Ponder Ave
    Juan Jose Rivera, Pastor

Luz y Verdad (10212) (SE) 18
13411 Misti Loop, Lakeland FL 33809
863-853-3878
    Artemio De Jesus, Pastor

**New Beginning Community Ch (19531) (SE,
AAMA)** 20
2701 13th St S, St Petersburg FL 33705
727-398-4211, fax 727-823-0346
    Celestin Hill Biandudi, Pastor

**New Jerusalem Menn Ch (12501) (SE, Church
Plant)** 25
7103 Mauna Loa Blvd, Sarasota FL 34241
941-371-4669, jtannelus@comcast.net
2895 Ashton Rd, Sarasota
    Jean Tannelus, Pastor

Newtown Gospel Chapel (18762) (SE, AAMA) ..30
1815 Gillespie Ave, Sarasota FL 34234
941-951-6967
    Walter Lewis Crawford, Pastor

North Tampa Christian Fell (14886) (SE) 25
206 W 131st Ave, Tampa FL 33612-3446
813-933-1288
    Isaias Robles, Pastor

Oak Terrace Menn Ch (12823) (SE) 19
16970 NW 22nd St, Blountstown FL 32424
850-674-5731, fax 850-674-2385, twodivys@gtcom.net
    Clifford Dale Ivy, Pastor

Peace Christian Fell (10241) (SE) 108
3010 Sumter Blvd, North Port FL 34287
941-423-8746, pcfnorthprt@aol.com,
http://peacechristianfellowship.org
    Tom Renno, Interim Pastor

Pine Creek Chapel (22376) (SE) 51
1267 SW Pine Chapel Dr, Arcadia FL 34266
863-494-9166, rebodem@earthlink.net
Pine Chapel Dr & SR 72
    Bob Bodem, Pastor

**Tabernacle of Bethlehem (12502) (SE, Church
Plant)** 0
PO Box 3085, Immokalee FL 33143-3085
239-657-4065
    John Brutus, Pastor

Tabernacle of Bethlehem (10253) (SE) 110
PO Box 380386, Miami-Dade FL 33238-0386
305-769-0280, express079@aol.com
900 W Dr
    Dieudonne Brutus, Pastor

Unity Pentecostal Ch of God (11153) (SE) 45
801 NW 111th St, Miami FL 33168
305-754-2900
    Ducois Forestal, Pastor

Virginia Mennonite Conference

OFFICE
info@vmconf.org, www.vmconf.org
540-434-9727 and 800-707-5535,
   fax 540-434-7627
901 Parkwood Dr, Harrisonburg VA 22802

STAFF
Owen E. Burkholder, conference minister
   (vmcmin@vmconf.org)
Steven P. Carpenter, conference coordinator
   (steve.carpenter@vmconf.org)
Kimberlee S. Greenawalt, youth minister
   (kimberlee.greenawalt@vmconf.org)
Laura A. Moyers, secretary
   (laura.moyers@vmconf.org)
Rachel A. Swartzendruber, administrative assistant (rachel.swartzendruber@vmconf.org)
Jonathan H. Trotter, communications associate
   (jon.trotter@vmconf.org)
Evelyn W. Kratz, director of financial services
   (evelyn.kratz@vmbm.org)
Lavonne Lehman, financial services associate
   (lavonne.lehman@vmbm.org)

GENERAL INFORMATION
Year founded: 1835
Members: 8,817
Congregations: 67
Ministers: 292
CLC reps: Owen Burkholder, Beryl Jantzi
Annual conference: July 2004, Harrisonburg, Va.
Districts bishops and overseers. Central,
   Richard Bowman, Paul L. Kratz; Eastern
   Carolina, Raymond Martin; Harrisonburg,
   Truman Brunk; Norfolk, Raymond Martin;
   Northern, H. Michael Shenk, II; Samuel O.
   Weaver; Ohio, Frank Nice; Potomac, Del
   Glick; Southern, Howard Miller; Tennessee-
   Carolina-Kentucky, Edward Godshall; Calvary,
   Leslie W. Francisco III; Warwick, Raymond
   Martin

EXECUTIVE COMMITTEE
Beryl Jantzi, moderator (bjantzi@aol.com),
1552 S High St, Harrisonburg VA 22801, 540-
574-4348; Steven Brown, assistant moderator;
Malinda Stoltzfus, secretary; Ronald E. Piper,
treasurer

PUBLICATION
Connections (monthly) Gloria Lehman, editor;
Rachel Smith, assistant editor (same address as
above)

COMMISSIONS AND COMMITTEES
Consitution and Bylaws Committee.
   Gordon Zook, chair, 156 Robinhood Ln,
   Newport News VA 23602, 757-866-4247
Faith and Life Commission. Elroy J. Miller,
   chair (millere@emu.edu), 1401 College
   Ave, Harrisonburg VA 22802, 540-432-9382;
   H. Michael Shenk, II, vice chair; Paul Kratz,
   secretary
Finance Committee. Ronald E. Piper, chair
   (piperr@emu.edu), 1535 Park Rd,
   Harrisonburg VA 22802, 540-434-5057
Gift Discernment Committee. Donna Van
   Horn, chair (vanhornd@emu.edu), 3008 Mt
   Clinton Pike, Harrisonburg VA 22802, 540-
   867-5194
Health and Mutual Care Commission.
   Howard Miller, chair (howard@lindale.org),
   4368 Zion Church Rd, Broadway VA 22815,
   540-896-4014; Floyd Blosser, secretary
Historical Committee. James Rush, chair, 780
   Parkwood Dr, Harrisonburg VA 22802
Nurture Commission. Sanford Snider, chair
   (snidergs@juno.com), 7140 Turner Rd,
   Richmond VA 23231, 804-705-2646; Gloria
   Lehman, secretary
Peace Coordinators. Dave and Krista Powell,
   coordinators (ecopow@ntelos.net), 4016
   Hampton Dr, Waynesboro VA 22980, 540-
   941-3798.

Young Adult Committee. Rachel Smith, chair (rsmith2627@juno.com), 1542 N College Ave, Apt 1, Harrisonburg VA 22802, 540-442-8659

OTHER CONFERENCE AGENCIES AND REPRESENTATIVES

A World of Good Thrift Shop. Ken and Deb Layman, managers (giftandthrift@att.net), 731 Mt Clinton Pike, Harrisonburg VA 22802, 540-433-8844

Congregational Resource Center. Kathy Weaver Wenger, director (wengerkw@emu.edu), 1200 Park Rd, Harrisonburg VA 22802, 540-432-4219

Eastern Mennonite High School. Paul Leaman, principal (leamanp@emhs.net), 801 Parkwood Dr, Harrisonburg VA 22802, 540-432-4500

the exchange. Chris Scott, manager (chris@exchangecoffeehouse.com), 218 S Loudon St, Winchester VA 22601, 540-723-8777

Family Life Resource Center. Lou Emswiler, executive director (Lou@flrc.org), 273 Newman Ave, Harrisonburg VA 22802, 540-434-8450

Highland Retreat. Paul Beiler, administrator (highlandrt@juno.com), 14783 Upper Highland Dr, Bergton VA 22811-9712, 540-852-3226

Pleasant View Inc. Nancy Hopkins-Garriss, executive director (nhg_pv@intelos.net), PO Box 486, Broadway VA 22815, 540-896-8255

Shalom Foundation. Dick Benner, director, (DickB@churchoutreach.com), Media Ministries, Harrisonburg VA 22802

Virginia Mennonite Auto Aid Plan and Property Aid Plan. Brent W. Eberly, executive director (beberly@vmap.org), 901 Parkwood Dr, Harrisonburg VA 22802, 540-434-9727

Virginia Mennonite Board of Missions. See separate listing in section 3.

Virginia Mennonite Relief Sale. Marv Nisly, chair (mnisly@aol.com), 1501 Virginia Ave, Harrisonburg VA 22802, 540-564-3400

Virginia Mennonite Retirement Community. Ronald E. Yoder, executive director (roney@vmrc.org), 1501 Virginia Ave, Harrisonburg VA 22802, 540-564-3400

Warwick River Christian School. Gordon Zook, administrator (gorzook@yahoo.com), 252 Lucas Creek, Newport News VA 23602, 757-877-2941

Williamsburg Christian Retreat Center. Herb Lantz, executive director (wcrc@visi.net), 9275 Barnes Rd, Toano VA 23168, 757-566-2256

Congregations

Asheville Menn Ch (24281) (VA) 77
49 Bull Mountain Rd, Asheville NC 28805
828-298-4487, avlmenno@juno.com
  Patrick J. McFarren, Pastor

Beldor Menn Ch (18341) (VA) 29
5647 Wengers Mill Rd, Linville VA 22834
540-833-8003, jahershberger@earthlink.net
Beldor Rd, Elkton
  James L. Hershberger, Pastor

Big Spring Menn Ch (18374) (VA) 48
2545 Mims Rd, Luray VA 22835
540-743-1434, bigspringmennonite@yahoo.com,
http://www.bigspringmennonite.org
  Kevin A. Clark, Pastor
  George R. Dupuy, Associate Pastor

Calvary Community Ch (27409) (VA, AAMA) . .2235
2311 Tower Pl, Hampton VA 23666
757-825-1133, fax 757-825-0567,
pastor@calvarycommunity.org,
http://www.calvarycommunity.org
  Leslie W. Francisco III, Pastor
  Natalie A. Francisco, Associate Pastor
  Nan Williams, Associate Pastor
  Robert Williams, Associate Pastor

Calvary Community Ch Chesapeake (27411)
(VA) 0
1001 West Rd, Chesapeake VA 23323
757-558-8185
  Flinn John Ranchod, Pastor

Chapel Hill Menn Fell (11621) (VA) 0
9709 Greenfield Rd, Chapel Hill NC 27516
919-479-8414, chmf@rtpnet.org,
http://www.rtpnet.org/chmf
531 Raleigh Rd

Charlottesville Menn Ch (18408) (VA) 49
701 Monitcello Ave, Charlottesville VA 22901
434-293-8306, fax 434-293-4246,
pastorcmc@earthlink.net,
http://www.charlottesvillemennonite.org
   Maren Tyedmers Hange, Co-Pastor
   Roy Hange, Co-Pastor

Chestnut Ridge Menn Ch (18416) (VA) 114
14366 Church Rd, Orrville OH 44667
330-682-3175, chmf@rtpnet.org,
http://www.pages.sssnet.com/jjziggy/chestnut
   Marvin Zuercher, Pastor

Christian Conquest Fell (10010) (VA, DC,
AAMA) 60
1205 K Street NE, Washington DC 20002
202-397-8148, fax 202-291-1759,
powell.dottie@starpower.net,
http://www.christianconquest.org
   Paul Gaskins, Pastor
   Louis N. Jones, Associate Pastor

Christiansburg Menn Fell (25296) (VA) 47
40 Farmview Rd, Christiansburg VA 24073-1165
540-382-8787, fax 540-382-8787, glenn.horst@juno.com

Community Menn Ch (22178) (VA) 225
70 S High St, Harrisonburg VA 22801
540-433-2148, fax 540-434-4430, cmchurch@ntelos.net,
http://home.ntelos.net/~cmchurch
   Ray N. Hurst, Co-Pastor
   Margaret Wightman, Co-Pastor

Concord Menn Ch (18424) (VA) 27
2720 Tsawasi Rd, Knoxville TN 37931
865-691-5347, matteson@mfire.com
Exit 374 from I-40, Lovell Rd at Dutchtown Rd
   F. Matthew Matteson, Pastor

Crest Hill Community Ch (18432) (VA) 10
PO Box 64, Wardensville WV 26851-0064
304-874-4247, mclyndaker@citlink.net
2 mi north of Wardensville on Rt 259
   Milford E. Lyndaker, Pastor
   Carolyn Z. Lyndaker, Associate Pastor

Crossroads Menn Ch (18465) (VA) 28
PO Box 396, Broadway VA 22815
540-896-3877, crossroadschurch@rica.net
7024 Crossroads Ln, Timberville
   William F. Greene, Pastor

Durham Menn Ch (18481) (VA, AAMA) 32
603 Lynn Rd, Durham NC 27703
919-596-4702, fax 919-596-4702 (call ahead),
kk4ph@juno.com, http://DurhamMennonite.org/
   Paul Godshall, Pastor
   Kevin Nice, Youth Pastor

Family of Hope (29900) (VA) 11
1135 Hamlet Dr, Harrisonburg VA 22802
540-432-0531, fax 540-433-3805, harvyoder@aol.com
House church—no one location
   Harvey Yoder, Pastor

Fell of Christ (23473) (VA, AAMA) 116
1001 Tarboro St, Rocky Mount NC 27801
919-977-1901, focrockymt@hotmail.com
   Ronnie B. Pride, Pastor

First Menn Ch of Richmond (18523) (VA) 82
2350 Staples Mill Rd, Richmond VA 23230
804-359-1340
   Barry W. Loop, Pastor

Gospel Hill Menn Ch (18549) (VA) 93
16 Grandview Dr, Harrisonburg VA 22802-2324
540-433-8584, kgood21502@aol.com
Hopkins Gap Rd
   Roy F. Good, Interim Pastor

Grace Menn Fell (11158) (VA) 101
5379 Klines Mill Rd, Linville VA 22834
540-442-6235, gracemennonite.1@juno.com
Lacey Spring
   Richard K. Early, Pastor
   Diana Breeden, Associate Pastor
   Marlon W. Breeden, Associate Pastor
   Mark Landis, Associate Pastor
   Steve Swartzendruber, Youth Pastor

Greenmonte Menn Ch (18556) (VA) 94
1661 Cold Springs Rd, Stuarts Draft VA 24477
540-337-3599, greenmontemc@ntelos.net
   Bruce W. Hankee, Pastor

Greensboro Menn Fell (29744) (VA) 19
501 S Mendenhall St, Greensboro NC 27403
336-210-0752, rws.ays@juno.com
   Randy W. Smith, Interim Pastor

Harrisonburg Menn Ch (18564) (VA) 705
1552 S High St, Harrisonburg VA 22801
540-434-4463, fax 540-433-7389, mailhmc@aol.com,
http://members.aol.com/mailhmc/hmc.htm
   Beryl M. Jantzi, Pastor
   Kathryn J. Hochstedler, Associate Pastor
   Harry Jarrett, Associate Pastor
   Mark Haven Keller, Associate Pastor

Hebron Menn Ch (18572) (VA) 76
12467 Millertown Rd, Fulks Run VA 22830
540-896-1149
   Donald Bare, Pastor

Hickory Menn Ch (18580) (VA) 46
1405 Second St Dr SW, PO Box 3369, Hickory NC 28603
828-328-4761, kenbarbmoyer@yahoo.com
   James L. Roth, Pastor
   Chaiya Hadtasunsern, Associate Pastor

Huntington Menn Ch (18614) (VA) **134**
785 Harpersville Rd, Newport News VA 23601
757-595-6889, fax 757-595-6484, hmcnnva@juno.com,
http://www.huntingtonmennonite.org
    Anna S. Janzen, Interim Pastor
    Laban Peachey, Interim Pastor
    Glenda Mosemann, Director of Children's Ministries
    Jim Thornton, Minister of Preaching/Teaching

**Iglesia del Evangelio Completo Alpha y O
(23465) (VA, IMH)** **121**
17508 Black Rock Rd, Germantown DC 20874-2242
301-528-0622, alfacruz@msn.com
421 East-West Hwy, Hyattsville
    Justiniano Cruz, Pastor
    Jose Franscisco Borjas, Associate Pastor

Immanuel Menn Ch (10144) (VA, AAMA) **90**
446 E Rock St, Harrisonburg VA 22802
540-432-0711, basil@rica.net
400 Kelly St
    Basil Marin, Pastor

Knoxville Menn Ch (18622) (VA) **38**
4401 Sullivan Rd, Knoxville TN 37921-1343
865-588-8420, c4748F@aol.com
    Willis G. Hunsberger, Pastor
    John Forsyth, Congregational Leader

Lambert Menn Ch (18630) (VA) **26**
RR 3 Bx 70, Belington WV 26250
304-823-2178, fax 304-823-2178
Lambert Rd, Wymer
    Boyd Wyatt Jr., Pastor
    Richard White, Associate Pastor

Landstown Community Ch (24349) (VA) **85**
3220 Monet Dr, Virginia Beach VA 23456
757-468-6509, fax 757-468-6509, office@landstown.com
    Merlin L. Miller, Pastor

Lindale Menn Ch (18655) (VA) **338**
PO Box 1082, Harrisonburg VA 22803
540-833-5171, fax 540-833-2212, admin@lindale.org,
http://www.lindale.org
6255 Jesse Bennett Way in Linville
    Duane Allen Yoder, Pastor
    Howard Miller, Associate Pastor

Lynside Menn Ch (18671) (VA) **82**
PO Box 124, Lyndhurst VA 22952
540-949-7474, marchand@ntelos.net
648 Mt Rd Torrey Rd
    James C. Marchand, Pastor

Mathias Menn Ch (18689) (VA) **58**
20721 Lower Highland Dr, Bergton VA 22811
304-897-5930
Rt 259, Mathias
    Dean E. Williams, Pastor

Mount Clinton Menn Ch (18721) (VA) **126**
6954 Mt Clinton Pike, Harrisonburg VA 22802
540-867-5885, mcmchurch@juno.com,
http://mountclinton.va.us.mennonite.net
    Lee Martin, Pastor

Mount Pleasant Menn Ch (18747) (VA) **287**
2041 Mount Pleasant Rd, Chesapeake VA 23322
757-482-2215, fax 757-482-6485, mtplmen@exis.net
    J. Harold Bergey, Pastor

Mount Vernon Menn Ch (18754) (VA) **77**
13188 Port Republic Rd, Grottoes VA 24441-9342
540-249-4684, huyard@planetcomm.net
    Alvin M. Huyard, Co-Pastor
    Rose Huyard, Co-Pastor

Mountain View Menn Ch (18713) (VA) **87**
5252 W NC 10 Hwy, Hickory NC 28602
704-462-4760, bchjoyce@twave.net
    B. Charles Hostetter Jr., Pastor

Mountain View Menn Ch (18705) (VA) **146**
PO Box 208, Lyndhurst VA 22952
540-337-1062, rskiser@hotmail.com,
http://home.rica.net/earlshome
55 Love Rd
    Earl B. Monroe, Pastor

New Beginnings Ch (27517) (VA, HMONG) **78**
PO Box 126, Bridgewater VA 22812
540-828-1188, fax 540-828-7138,
ucanbeginagain@yahoo.com,
http://www.newbeginchurch.org
Turner Ashby High School
    Edwin M. Heatwole, Pastor
    Reuben W. Horst, Associate Pastor

Northern Virginia Menn Ch (23457) (VA, DC) . . .**27**
3729 Old Lee Hwy, Fairfax VA 22030
703-359-0990, fax 703-359-0990, nvmc1@juno.com,
http://www.nvmc.net
    Pearl Ann Hoover, Pastor

Park View Menn Ch (18788) (VA) **375**
1600 College Ave, Harrisonburg VA 22802
540-434-1604, fax 540-801-0023, office@pvmchurch.org,
http://www.pvmchurch.org
4 blocks north of EMU on Park Rd
    Philip L. Kniss, Pastor
    Ross Erb, Associate Pastor
    Barbara Moyer Lehman, Associate Pastor

Pleasant Grove Menn Ch (18796) (VA) **9**
HC 69 Box 228, Fort Seybert WV 26806
304-249-5224

Powhatan Menn Ch (18804) (VA) **127**
PO Box 220, Powhatan VA 23139
804-598-0240, fax 804-598-3365, timbev2@yahoo.com,
http://www.pmchurch.net
3540 Old Buckingham Rd
    Timothy D. Kennell, Pastor

Providence Menn Ch (16550) (VA) **72**
13101 Warwick Blvd, Newport News VA 23602
757-249-2702, providence@mennonite.net,
http://www.providence.va.us.mennonite.net
    Kenneth James Peterson, Pastor

Raleigh Menn Ch (28266) (VA) **50**
PO Box 25545, Raleigh NC 27611-5545
919-833-1182, http://www.raleighmennonite.org
1116 N Blount St
    Joseph E. Bontrager, Interim/Transition Pastor
    Mauricio Walter Chenlo, Peace Director/Youth Pastor
    Alan Reberg, Minister for Community Development

Rehoboth Menn Ch (11163) (VA) **15**
9235 Rockfish River Rd, Schuyler VA 22969
804-831-2383

Ridgeway Menn Ch (18812) (VA) **192**
546 E Franklin St, Harrisonburg VA 22801
540-434-3476, ridgewaymennonitechurch@yahoo.com,
http://www.geocities.com/ridgewaymennonite
    Ben Risser, Pastor

Riverside Menn Ch (18820) (VA) **28**
PO Box 176, Harman WV 26270
304-227-3647, rolowenger@juno.com
    Robert G. Wenger, Pastor

Shalom Menn Congregation (29009) (VA) **56**
EMU-Box 8, Harrisonburg VA 22802
540-432-1659, shalommc@shentel.net
Strite Auditorium, EMU
    Earl S. Zimmerman, Pastor

Springdale Menn Ch (18853) (VA) **197**
170 Hall School Rd, Waynesboro VA 22980
540-949-8945, muzet@ntelos.net,
http://www.terrispencer.com/springdale
    Kathryn W. Wenger, Co-Pastor
    Mark R. Wenger, Co-Pastor
    Muzet D. Felgar, Youth Pastor

Staunton Menn Ch (18861) (VA) **40**
2405 3rd St, Staunton VA 24401
540-886-5869, jdelp@surfbest.net,
http://wwrc.net/smc
    James S. Delp, Pastor

Stephens City Menn Ch (18879) (VA) **69**
5540 Valley Pike, Stephens City VA 22655
540-869-5037, scmc@visuallink.com,
http://client.visuallink.com/~scmc
    James W. Musser, Pastor
    Aldine Musser, Co-Pastor

Stuarts Draft Menn Ch (18887) (VA) **56**
PO Box 763, Stuarts Draft VA 24477
540-337-3792, sdmchurch@juno.com
Howardsville Turnpike (Rt Rd 610)
    Harold Robert Wenger, Pastor

Trissels Menn Ch (18895) (VA) **117**
PO Box 549, Broadway VA 22815
540-896-7289, Trisselsmc@juno.com
11246 Hisers Ln
    Philip C. Kanagy, Pastor
    Deborah Kilheffer, Youth Pastor

Valley View Menn Ch (18911) (VA) **77**
1345 Hillcrest Dr, Harrisonburg VA 22802
540-434-0578, shenkp@emu.edu
21806 Criders Rd, Criders
    H. Michael Shenk II, Pastor
    H. Michael Shenk III, Pastor

Vietnamese Christian Fell (10104) (VA, DC,
VIET) **73**
c/o Peter Simon Nguyen, 3022 Woodlawn Avenue, Falls
Church VA 22042
703-820-1057/703-824-4527,
fax 703-824-4527/703-820-1057, pnguyen@spa.com,
http://www25.brinkster.com/hted
    Peter Simon Nguyen, Pastor

Warwick River Menn Ch (18929) (VA) **188**
250 Lucas Creek Rd, Newport News VA 23602-6251
757-874-0794, fax 757-877-6510, wrmc1@juno.com,
http://warwickriver.va.us.mennonite.net
    Stephen H. Gibbs, Pastor
    Elizabeth Anne Gibbs, Assoicate Pastor of Youth and
    Worship

Washington Community Fell (24778) (VA, DC,
AAMA) **35**
907 Maryland Ave NE, Washington DC 20002
202-543-1926, fax 202-543-0287,
churchoffice@wcfchurch.org, http://www.wcfchurch.org
    Scott Garber, Senior Pastor
    Faith Evans, Associate Pastor for Youth

Waynesboro Menn Ch (24760) (VA) **140**
1801 Monroe St, Waynesboro VA 22980
540-949-0446, wmchurch@intelos.net
Hopeman Parkway at Monroe St
    Stanlee D. Kauffman, Senior Pastor
    John Joseph Arbaugh II, Minister of Missions
    Sharon Wenger, Minister of Music

Weavers Menn Ch (18937) (VA) **301**
2501 Rawley Pike, Harrisonburg VA 22801
540-434-7758, fax 540-434-5880,
weaversmc@weaversmc.org, http://www.weavers.mc.org
Hwy 33 W
    Jeffery Lane Kauffman, Pastor

West Liberty Menn Ch (18457) (VA) **18**
c/o James Fyffe, 292 Daisy Knob Rd,
West Liberty KY 41472
606-743-1567, jdfyffe@mrtc.com
52 Fyffe Ct

Williamsburg Menn Ch (23135) (VA) **75**
7800 Croaker Rd, Williamsburg VA 23188
757-566-3026, wmc@tni.net
    Randy Coblentz, Pastor

Woodland Menn Ch (18960) (VA) **28**
3408 Lindale Rd, Linville VA 22834
540-856-2432, malebron@juno.com
3715 Alum Springs Rd, Basye VA 22810
  Rodney Lebron, Pastor

Word of Life Menn Ch (18770) (VA, AAMA) **9**
6501 Pierce St, Norfolk VA 23513
757-895-8822
951 Widgeon Rd
  William Vaughn Jr., Pastor

Zion Hill Menn Ch (18986) (VA) **102**
PO Box 23, Singers Glen VA 22850
540-833-4207, lowellhaarer@juno.com
6311 Mayberry Rd
  Lowell W. Haarer, Pastor

Zion Menn Ch (18978) (VA) **244**
3260 Zion Church Rd, Broadway VA 22815
540-896-7577, fax 540-896-7577,
office@zionmennonitechurch.org,
http://www.zionmennonitechurch.org
  Clyde G. Kratz, Pastor

CONFERENCES AND
CONGREGATIONS

2

Western District Conference

OFFICE
wdc@mennowdc.org, www.mennowdc.org
316 283-6300, fax 316-283-0620
2517 Main, PO Box 306, North Newton KS
67117

STAFF
Dorothy Nickel Friesen, conference minister
(dorothynf@mennowdc.org)
Marco Güete, associate conference minister
(marcoguete@sbcglobal.net), 815 Parkside
Dr, Cedar Hills TX 75104, 972-293-1029
Merv and Jane Dick, interim associate confer-
ence ministers for Colorado
(mervdick@juno.com), 6195 Needlegrass
Green, Frederick CO 80530-7051, 303-833-
5073
Robert Nolt, associate conference minister for
Oklahoma (rnolt@mennoscc.org)
Marlene Bogard, minister of Christian nurture
(crlib@mennowdc.org) and Resource
Library Director
Pat Schmidt, Resource Library assistant
(crlib@mennowdc.org)
Phyllis Regier, treasurer
(pregier@mennowdc.org)
Nancy Funk, administrative assistant
(wdc@mennowdc.org)
Doug Krehbiel, conference youth minister (KS)
Hugo Saucedo, conference youth minister (TX)
Deron Nisly, camp director
(campmno@mennowdc.org), Camp
Mennoscah, Box 65, Murdock KS 67111,
316-297-3290
Torrey Ball, director of maintenance
(tball@ourtownusa.com), Camp
Mennoscah, Box 65, Murdock KS 67111,
316-297-3290

GENERAL INFORMATION
Year founded: 1892
Members: 10,900
Congregations: 66 + 4 church plants

Ministers: 188
CLC reps: Dorothy Nickel Friesen, Roger Neufeld
Smith, Debbie Schmidt
Next annual delegate session: August 12-14, 2005

EXECUTIVE COMMITTEE
Roger Neufeld Smith, moderator (southern-
hillsmc@networksplus.net), 1331 SW Jewell,
Topeka KS 66604, 785-266-9403; Jay Goering,
moderator-elect; Kay Schmidt, secretary; Bradley
Siebert, education; Bob Dalke, evangelism; Lee
Lever, home mission; Jim Stucky, ministerial;
Judy Johnson, peace/social concerns; Adolf
Neufeld, retreat; E. Fred Goering,
stewardship/budget; Dorothy Nickel Friesen, ex
officio; Nonvoting members: Jim Ostlund, youth;
Pauline Buller, personnel; John Wall, trustee

PUBLICATIONS
Western District News (monthly), Nancy Funk,
editor (wdc@mennowdc.org), Box 306, North
Newton KS 67117
*Western District Conference Monthly
Ministry Memo* (monthly), Nancy Funk, editor
(wdc@mennowdc.org), Box 306, North Newton
KS 67117

OTHER CONFERENCE AGENCIES AND REPS
Western District Women in Mission. Lois
Loflin, president (jimlof@southwind.net),
920 Spruce, Halstead KS 67056, 316-835-
2529
Mennonite Men of the Plains. Rodney Frey,
moderator (rodfrey@bethelks.edu), 112 W
26th, North Newton KS 67117, 316-283-
8422
Agri-urban. Terry Krehbiel, president, 23306 S
K-17 Hwy, Pretty Prairie KS 67570, 620-459-
6641
Oklahoma Convention. Arlee Johnson, president (arleejohnson@sbcglobal.net), 1313 N
College, Cordell OK 73632, 580-832-3435

Mid-Texas Convention. Esther Martinez, co-moderator (emartine@classicnet.net), 3701 Florest Lawn Rd, Balch Springs TX 75180, 972-285-1342; Blanca Vargas, co-moderator (blancavargas@earthlink.net), 1710 Lynette #606, San Antonio TX 78209, 210-533-0642

AMBS—Great Plains Extension. Lois Barrett, director (loisbarrett@mennowdc.org), 2517 Main St, PO Box 306, North Newton KS 67117, 316-263-6300

DEO (Discipleship, Encounter, Outreach). Dwight Regier, interim director (dwightr@mennowdc.org), 2517 Main St, PO Box 306, North Newton KS 67117, 316-283-6300; Kay Schroeder, associate director (deo@mennowdc.org); Immanuel Sila, recruiter/coordinator (isila@mennowdc.org)

Congregations

Alexanderwohl Menn Ch (6005) (WDC) **528**
1304 K-15 Hwy, PO Box 8, Goessel KS 67053-0008
620-367-8192, alexmenno@wwwebservice.net,
http://www.alexanderwohl.org
 Leland Suderman, Intentional Interim
 Mark Allen Wiens, Associate Pastor
 Nita Wilson, Youth Pastor

Arvada Menn Ch (6020) (WDC, MUM) **35**
5927 Miller St, Arvada CO 80004
303-424-6261, fax 303-424-0081,
arvadamenn@mennonite.net
 Phyllis Tribby, Pastor

Austin Menn Ch (28761) (SC, WDC) **64**
5801 Westminster Dr, Austin TX 78723-2640
512-926-3121, fax 512-926-3121,
http://www.mennochurch.org
 Garland L. Robertson, Pastor

Beatrice Menn Ch (6030) (WDC) **150**
1220 Summit St, Beatrice NE 68310-2432
402-228-3644, bm84101@alltel.net,
http://beatrice.ne.us.mennonite2.net
 Denton R. Jantzi, Pastor

Bergthal Menn Ch (6045) (WDC) **79**
PO Box 236, 501 Houck, Pawnee Rock KS 67567-0236
620-982-4886, ltschlosser@mpks.net
SW 30 Rd & SW 110 Ave
 Lynn Schlosser, Co-Pastor
 Todd Schlosser, Co-Pastor

Bethel College Menn Ch (6070) (WDC) **629**
2600 College Ave, PO Box 364,
North Newton KS 67117-0364
316-283-3667, fax 316-283-2079, bcmc@southwind.net,
http://bcmc.ks.us.mennonite.net
 Heidi Regier Kreider, Pastor
 Norma J. Johnson, Associate Pastor
 Roger Juhnke, Associate Pastor

Bethel Menn Ch (6085) (WDC, MILC) **25**
c/o Marcia Standingwater, HC 66, Box 100, Foss OK 73647

Bethel Menn Ch (6090) (WDC) **80**
RR 3 Box 84, Hydro OK 73048
405-663-2749
6th & Coffee
 Raymond Unruh, Pastor

Bethel Menn Ch (6095) (WDC) **391**
256 8th Ave, PO Box 306, Inman KS 67546
620-585-6964, fax 620-585-6958,
bethelch@southwind.net
 Allen Dick, Interim Pastor

Boulder Menn Ch (6153) (WDC, MUM, COB) **83**
3920 Table Mesa Dr, Boulder CO 80305
303-443-3889, fax 720-563-0109,
bouldermc@MX1.mennonite.net,
http://boulder.co.us.mennonite.net
 Jane Dick, Interim Pastor
 Mervin Dick, Interim Pastor

Buhler Menn Ch (6165) (WDC) **422**
220 W Ave B, PO Box 188, Buhler KS 67522
620-543-2733, bmcoffice@buhlerks.net
 Robert Eugene Dalke, Pastor
 Alan Stucky, Youth Pastor

Burrton Menn Ch (6170) (WDC) **83**
411 N Reno Ave, PO Box 227, Burrton KS 67020-0227
620-463-3415, mgundy1@cox.net
429 N Reno Ave
 James Ralph Gundy, Pastor

Calvary Menn Ch (6185) (WDC) **39**
831 S New York Ave, Liberal KS 67901
620-624-5530, fax 620-624-5530
 Ervey A. Unruh, Pastor
 David Quiring, Assistant Pastor

Comunidad de Esperanza (6240) (SC, WDC, IMH) **35**
1721 N Garrett Ave, Dallas TX 75206
214-428-7131, fax 214-828-1292,
damain_rodriguez@msn.com
 Damian Rodriguez, Pastor

Deer Creek Menn Ch (6230) (WDC) **69**
201 S Lee St, PO Box 66, Deer Creek OK 74636
580-267-3377, redsilo@pldi.net

Eden Menn Ch (6250) (WDC) **206**
21905 E 600 Rd, Inola OK 74036
918-543-2739, fax 918-543-3250,
edenmennonite@juno.com
    Dewayn Isaac, Pastor

Eden Menn Ch (6255) (WDC) **783**
109 E Hirschler St, PO Box 406, Moundridge KS 67107
620-345-8320, fax 620-345-8325, edenmc@mtelco.net,
http://edenmennonite.org
401 18th Ave
    Lawrence Lee Lever, Pastor
    James W. Ostlund, Associate Pastor

Faith Menn Ch (6325) (WDC) **370**
2000 N Anderson Rd, Newton KS 67114-1203
316-283-6370, faith@sbcglobal.net,
http://www.faithmenno.org
Corner of Northridge & Anderson Streets
    Gordon Louis Smith, Pastor
    Sam Schrag, Interim Youth Pastor

First Menn Ch (6341) (WDC) **251**
6714 W St Hwy 4, Beatrice NE 68310-6864
402-228-2231, firstmenno@yahoo.com,
http://firstmennonite.ne.us.mennonite.net
3 mi west on Hwy 4
    Florence Eileen Schloneger, Co-Pastor
    Weldon Ray Schloneger, Co-Pastor

First Menn Ch (6362) (WDC) **60**
700 S 19th St, Clinton OK 73601-5132
580-323-3694, mennoknights@itlnet.net
    David Gerbrandt, Pastor

First Menn Ch (6374) (WDC) **287**
427 W 4th St, Halstead KS 67056
316-835-2282, dnight78@hotmail.com
    Cleo H. Koop, Pastor

First Menn Ch (6376) (WDC) **326**
102 S Ash St, Hillsboro KS 67063
620-947-5662, fax 620-947-2774, fmc@wwwebservice.net
    Ernest Stanley Bohn, Interim Pastor
    Todd A. Lehman, Youth Pastor

First Menn Ch (6382) (WDC) **241**
52 Rambler Rd, Hutchinson KS 67502
620-662-9385, fax 620-662-9261,
hutchfmc@sbcglobal.net,
http://www.fmchutchinson.ks.us.mennonite.net
    Debra Ann Schmidt, Pastor
    Laverle Schrag, Associate Pastor

First Menn Ch (6391) (WDC) **207**
1161 E Ave A, McPherson KS 67460
620-241-4040, fax 620-241-1468, neilafmc@earthlink.net;
RHawk_33@hotmail.com
    Neil B. Amstutz, Pastor

First Menn Ch (6403) (WDC) **596**
429 E 1st, PO Box 291, Newton KS 67114
316-283-0273, fax 316-283-0277,
fstmenno@southwind.net
    Clarence E. Rempel, Pastor
    Joel R. Schroeder, Associate Pastor
    Joan Boyer, Minister of Outreach

First Menn Ch (6315) (WDC) **406**
315 S Ash, PO Box 127, Pretty Prairie KS 67570
620-459-6344, fax 620-459-6344, fmpp@earthlink.net
1718 W Pretty Prairie Rd
    Lester L. Zook, Pastor

First Menn Ch (6318) (WDC) **96**
RR 1 Box 69, Ransom KS 67572-9709
785-731-2758, buller@gbta.net
Corner of Ogden & Massachusetts
    Eric Buller, Pastor

First Menn Ch of Christian (6330) (WDC) **227**
719 S Christian, PO Box 66, Moundridge KS 67107
620-345-2546, fmcc@mtelco.net,
http://firstofchristian.ks.us.mennonite.net
    Marvin Zehr, Interim Pastor

Fort Collins Menn Fell (24687) (RM, WDC) **42**
300 E Oak St, Fort Collins CO 80524-2915
970-224-4106, revjborg@juno.com,
http://www.fortnet.org/fcmf
    Jeffrey A. Borg, Pastor

Goessel Menn Ch (6370) (WDC) **166**
109 S Church, PO Box 38, Goessel KS 67053-0038
620-367-2446, goesselchurch@juno.com
    Kevin T. Goertzen, Pastor

Gospel Fell Ch (27425) (SC, WDC) **32**
PO Box 403, Montezuma KS 67867
620-846-2663, erdwko@yahoo.com

Grace Hill Menn Ch (6390) (WDC) **218**
10218 SE 12th, Whitewater KS 67154
316-799-2238, fax 316-799-2238, jvoth@cox.net,
http://gracehill.ks.us.mennonite.net
    James Joel Voth, Pastor
    Brett Klingenberg, Youth Pastor

Grace Menn Ch (6410) (WDC) **100**
902 S Adams St, Enid OK 73701
580-234-2078, fax 580-234-2078 (call first),
treacd@integris-health.com
    Dennis Treat, Interim Pastor

Greenfield Menn Ch (6425) (WDC) **23**
c/o Alvin Unruh, 405 N 4th St, PO Box 655,
Ft Cobb OK 73038
405-643-5142, fax 405-643-5142

Hanston Menn Ch (6430) (WDC) **21**
RR 1 Box 45A, Hanston KS 67849
620-623-4986, cvincen@hr.state.ks.us
    Carl Vincent, Pastor

Herold Menn Ch (6445) (WDC) **129**
1313 N College St, Cordell OK 73632-1809
580-832-3435, arleejohnson@sbcglobal.net
RR, Bessie
   Arlee Johnson, Pastor

**Hmong Menn Ch (11119) (RM, WDC, HMONG,
MUM)** **45**
c/o Shoua Moua, 8822 W 75th Pl, Arvada CO 80005-4529
303-424-6261
   Shoua Moua, Pastor

Hoffnungsau Menn Ch (6460) (WDC) **278**
43 13th Ave, Inman KS 67546
620-585-6733, hmc@dtnspeed.net,
http://www.hoffnungsau.ks.us.mennonite.net
   Willmar Toews Harder, Pastor

Hope Fell (10012) (SC, WDC) **18**
1700 Morrow, Waco TX 76707
254-754-5942, hopefellowship@grandecom.net
   Joe Gatlin, Co-Pastor
   Nancy Gatlin, Co-Pastor
   Norma Torres, Co-Pastor

Hope Menn Ch (6468) (WDC) **201**
868 N Maize Rd, Wichita KS 67212
316-722-0903, fax 316-722-5173,
pastor@hopemennonite.com,
http://www.hopemennonite.com
   Douglas Ray Luginbill, Pastor
   Linda Ewert, Associate Pastor

Houston Menn Ch (23184) (SC, WDC) **45**
1231 Wirt Rd, Houston TX 77055
713-464-4865, pastor@houstonmennonite.org,
http://www.houstonmennonite.org
   Jose Elizalde, Pastor

**Iglesia Menonita Casa de Dios (15303) (SC, WDC,
Church Plant)** **0**
2514 Arcady St, Garland TX 75041
972-271-9310
   Jesus Natividad Hernandez, Church Planter

**Iglesia Menonita Casa del Alfarero (15302) (SC,
WDC, Church Plant)** **0**
1701 Burke Rd, Pasadena TX 77502
713-475-2031
   Alberto Ronald Parchmont, Church Planter
   Aurora Parchmont, Church Planter

**Iglesia Menonita Comunidad de Vida (27410)
(SC, WDC, Church Plant)** **0**
1443 S St Marys, San Antonio TX 78210
210-832-0182, blancavargas@earthlink.net
   Blanca Vargas, Pastor
   Victor Serafin Vargas, Pastor

**Iglesia Menonita Luz del Evangelio (6512) (SC,
WDC, IMH)** **30**
c/o Juan Limones, 2459 Telegraph, Dallas TX 75228
214-324-9409
   Juan Fernando Limones, Pastor

**Iglesia Menonita Monte Horeb (11273) (SC,
WDC, IMH)** **12**
427 N Marlborough Ave, Dallas TX 75208
214-946-2910, sacaceros@sbcglobal.net
   S. Antonio Caceros, Pastor

**Iglesia Menonita Sembradores de Buenas Nuevas
(15304) (SC, WDC, Church Plant)** **0**
208 Hurst Cr, Ferris TX 75125
972-842-5798, julioedg@aol.com
   Julio E. Duenas, Church Planter

Inman Menn Ch (6505) (WDC) **130**
PO Box 236, Inman KS 67546
620-585-6550, akaiser@southwind.net
304 S Pine
   Jerry Lee Kaiser, Pastor

Joy Menn Ch (6642) (WDC) **14**
504 NE 16th St, Oklahoma City OK 73104
405-236-4938, mosesmast@aol.com,
http://joy.ok.us.mennonite.net
   Moses Mast, Pastor

Kingman Menn Ch (6511) (WDC) **89**
PO Box 306, Kingman KS 67068
620-532-5330, darev@kans.com
1620 S Main St
   Bradley B. Penner, Pastor

Koinonia Menn Ch (6575) (WDC, MILC) **23**
c/o Lawrence Hart, 2501 E Modelle, Clinton OK 73601
580-323-5320
   Lawrence H. Hart, Pastor

Lorraine Avenue Menn Ch (6525) (WDC) **374**
655 S Lorraine St, Wichita KS 67211-3025
316-682-4555, fax 316-682-2644, l
amcsecretary@prodigy.net,
http://lorraineavenue.ks.us.mennonite.net
   Lois M. Harder, Co-Pastor
   Thomas L. Harder, Co-Pastor

**Manhattan Menn Ch (24174) (SC, WDC,
USMBC)** **76**
1000 Fremont St, Manhattan KS 66502-5425
785-539-4079, menno@oz-online.net,
http://www.manhattan.ks.us.mennonite.net
   Barbara Krehbiel Gehring, Co-Pastor
   Richard L. Gehring, Co-Pastor

Menn Ch of the Servant (23317) (SC, WDC) **22**
1650 Fairview Ave, Wichita KS 67203
316-267-4625, mennoservant@juno.com
   Jerry Truex, Pastor

Menn Indian Ch (6558) (WDC, MILC) **12**
c/o Norma Smith, PO Box 43, Seiling OK 73663
580-886-2664

Mountain Community Menn Ch (25247) (RM, WDC) 97
PO Box 502, Palmer Lake CO 80133
719-481-3155, mcmc@emcmc.org,
http://www.rmmc.org/mcmc
643 Hwy 105
   Don Rheinheimer, Co-Pastor
   Jan Lynette Rheinheimer, Co-Pastor

New Creation Fell (6596) (WDC) 50
221 Muse St, Newton KS 67114-3827
316-283-1363, ncfc@southwind.net,
http://www.southwind.net/~ncfc
   Ruth Penner, Pastor

Peace Menn Ch (17921) (SC, WDC) 82
11001 Midway Road, PO Box 59926, Dallas TX 75229
214-902-8141, fax 214-902-8141,
Dick@PeaceMennonite.org,
http://www.PeaceMennonite.org
   Richard Douglas Davis, Pastor

Peace Menn Ch (23853) (SC, WDC) 72
1204 Oread Ave, Lawrence KS 66044
785-841-8614, peacemennonite@msn.com
   Kathy Neufeld Dunn, Interim Pastor

Peace Menn Community Ch (28605) (RM, WDC, MUM) 90
13601 E Alameda Ave, Aurora CO 80012
303-340-1555, fax 303-766-5008,
pmccsecretary@comcast.net
   Phil Ebersole, Pastor

Rainbow Menn Ch (18093) (WDC) 207
1444 Southwest Blvd, Kansas City KS 66103
913-236-8820, fax 913-236-6838,
rainbowrev@mennonite.net,
http://rainbow.ks.us.mennonite.net
   Robert Kaufman, Pastor

Salina Menn Ch (6691) (WDC) 62
600 W State St, Salina KS 67401
785-825-2663, fax 785-825-2663, smckspg@ikansas.com,
http://salina.ks.us.mennonite2.net/
   Val R. Krehbiel, Pastor

San Antonio Menn Ch (25239) (SC, WDC) 39
1443 S Saint Marys St, San Antonio TX 78210
210-533-0642, fax 210-341-8358,
dbeachey@earthlink.net,
http://www.sanantonio.tx.us.mennonite.net
   Duane Beachey, Lead Pastor
   Gloria Beachey, Pastor
   Daniel Foley, Assistant Pastor

Shalom Menn Ch (10130) (SC, WDC) 180
800 E 1st St, Newton KS 67114
316-283-7395, office@shalomnewton.org,
http://www.shalomnewton.org
   Eric Massanari, Pastor

Southern Hills Menn Ch (6740) (WDC) 94
511 SE 37th St, PO Box 5067, Topeka KS 66605-0067
785-266-9403, fax 785-266-4512,
southernhillsmc@networksplus.net
   Roger Neufeld Smith, Pastor
   Cynthia Neufeld Smith, Associate Pastor

Tabor Menn Ch (6765) (WDC) 341
891 Chisholm Trail, Newton KS 67114-7503
620-367-2318, fax 620-367-2309,
tabor@tabormennonite.org
   Corey Lee Miller, Pastor
   Karen Andres, Associate Pastor
   Doug Krehbiel, Youth Pastor

Trinity Menn Ch (6780) (WDC) 253
211 S Elm St, Hillsboro KS 67063
620-947-3824, fax 620-947-3422,
tkliewer@southwind.net
   Tim Kliewer, Pastor

Turpin Menn Ch (6785) (WDC) 103
RR 2 Box 21, Turpin OK 73950
580-259-6440, jeffmote@yahoo.com
   Jeffrey Dale Wintermote, Pastor

West Zion Menn Ch (6830) (WDC) 218
101 S Washington Ave, PO Box 758,
Moundridge KS 67107-0758
620-345-8141, fax 620-345-8143, Westzionmc@netks.net
   John Lamar Yoder-Schrock, Co-Pastor
   Marcia Ann Yoder-Schrock, Co-Pastor

Zion Menn Ch (6865) (WDC) 144
525 N Main St, PO Box 68, Elbing KS 67041
316-799-2071, zion@iwichita.com,
http://www.zion-elbing.org
   Walt Friesen, Interim Pastor

Other Agencies

The Directory has separate sections for church-wide agencies (section 1), area conferences (section 2), Mennonite World Conference (section 4), and sister denominations (section 5). This section (3) of the *Directory* includes agencies and organizations who are a part of Mennonite Church USA or who relate in some way to Mennonite Church USA. Inclusion in this section does not signify official endorsement by Mennonite Church USA.

In this section, the visual image of the dove appears immediately following the name of those agencies that are formally affiliated with Mennonite Church USA.

A

Abbreviations
—see page 10

ACTV Christian Television and Media Ministries
info@actvonline.com, www.actvonline.com
610-378-1378
326 Penn Ave, West Reading PA 19611

STAFF
Jeff Stoltzfus, general manager
(jeff@actvonline.com)

Jon Carlson, production manager
(jon@actvonline.com)

INFORMATION
ACTV uses the media as a tool of evangelism, broadening the opportunity of the local church to fulfill the Great Commission, impacting lives with God's Word, and nurturing believers through innovative Christian programming.

ACTV works with a wide variety of churches and ministries. ACTV was founded by members of Zion Mennonite Church in 1973.

BOARD
John Rush, chair (rushjoes@aol.com), 326 Penn Ave, West Reading PA 19611, 610-208-0406; Mike Reinert, vice chair; Steve Van Vreede, treasurer; Santo Torcivia, secretary; Linda Evers, Esq.; Ken Herr; Jeffrey D. Miller; Bertha Collins

PUBLICATION
ACTV News (Quarterly)

ADNet (Anabaptist Disabilities Network)
adnet@adnetonline.org, www.adnetonline.org
877-214-9838 and 574-535-7053,
fax 574-535-7165
PO Box 959, Goshen IN 46527-0959

ADMINISTRATIVE TEAM

Cindy Warner Baker; Paul D. Leichty; Joyce
Pankratz; Sherry Wenger; Sheila S. Yoder
(to e-mail, use first name @adnetonline.org)

INFORMATION

ADNet is a network of families, individuals, and
friends touched by mental illnesses or other disabilities. Our mission is to support families and
equip congregations as they become inclusive
communities of faith.

This network is led by a board of directors
representing our connection to the Anabaptist
community through their membership in denominations related to Mennonite World Conference.

ADNet was formally established in 2002
when a group of parents saw the need for establishing a home for the Anabaptist churchwide
disability ministry. Our roots are in the former
Mennonite Developmental Disability Services
organized in the early 1970s and lodged with
Mennonite Central Committee.

BOARD

H. James Smith, president
(jim.smith@mma-online.org), 19204 Country
Creek Ct, Goshen IN 46528; John Heyerly, vice
president; Ruth Detweiler, secretary; Milton
Stoltzfus, treasurer; Dave Gullman, member

PUBLICATION

Dialogue (triennial) Paul D. Leichty, editor
ADNotes (bimonthly-electronic) Cindy Warner
Baker, editor

Africa Inter-Mennonite Mission (AIMM)

aimm@aimmintl.org, www.aimmintl.org
574-535-0077, fax 574-533-5275
Mailing address: PO Box 744,
    Goshen IN 46527-0744
Office location: 1013 Division St, Goshen IN
AIMM Canada: 440 Main St,
    Steinbach MB R5G 1Z5

STAFF

Dave Dyck, transition coordinator
    (dmdyck1@mts.net)
Leona Schrag, office administrator
    (leona@aimmintl.org)

INFORMATION

AIMM's focus centers on the church in Africa.
Its objective is to plant a church where none
exists, nurture the established church, and partner with the church in witness and service.

AIMM is a partnership of Anabaptist conferences, congregations, and other mission-mind-
ed groups. Partners are primarily, but not exclusively, from Africa and North America.

Organized as Congo Inland Mission in 1912,
AIMM began ministry in the Democratic
Republic of Congo and has expanded ministries
to various ethnic and language groups in
Botswana, Burkina Faso, Lesotho, Senegal, and
South Africa.

COUNCIL

Peter Rempel (prempel@mennonitechurch.ca),
chair, MC Canada Witness, 600 Shaftesbury
Blvd, Winnipeg MB R3P 0M4, 204-888-6781;
Len Barkman (EMC-Canada), vice chairperson;
Erwin Rempel (MC USA), financial consultant;
Steve Wiebe Johnson (MC USA), secretary;
Martini Janz (Women's Auxiliary); Henry
Klassen (at-large); Eric Olfert (at-large); Janet
Plenert (MC Canada Witness)

PUBLICATION

AIMM Messenger (annually) Leona Schrag, editor (same address as above); *AIMM to Inform*
(quarterly)

African-American Mennonite Association (AAMA)

aama_org@yahoo.com, www.aamaorg.org
757-262-0128, fax 757-825-8771
2311 Tower Pl, Hampton VA 23666

STAFF

Steven Brown, consultant

CLC rep, Yvonne Bailey

INFORMATION

The African-American Mennonite Association (AAMA) is a ministry of Mennonite Church USA serving as a voice of advocacy, informing, educating, and empowering African-Americans and integrated congregations within MC USA. AAMA holds an assembly every two years.

The African-American Mennonite Association was founded in 1982 and was preceded by the Minority Ministries Council and the Black Caucus, which date back to the early 1970s.

AAMA's membership consists of approximately 62 churches, which are included in section 2 in the appropriate conference listing with the AAMA code.

BOARD

Leslie W. Francisco III, president, 2311 Tower Pl, Hampton VA 23666; Alvin Isaacs; Jacqueline Rozier; Zenobia Sowell-Bianchi; Kenneth L. Thompson

PUBLICATION

AAMA/Lark Newsletter (semiannual)

AMAS

—see Association of Mutual Aid Societies

AMBS

—see Associated Mennonite Biblical Seminary

Anabaptist and Brethren Agency

—see Mutual Aid eXchange

Anabaptist Center for Healthcare Ethics (ACHE)

jkotva@ambs.edu, www.mennmed.org/ache.htm

c/o AMBS, 3003 Benham Ave, Elkhart IN 46517-1999

574-296-6235, fax 574-295-0092

STAFF

Joseph J. Kotva Jr. (jkotva@ambs.edu)

INFORMATION

The Anabaptist Center for Healthcare Ethics was created to serve the church and its members as they confront the morally complex world of modern healthcare and biotechnology. The center provides various services, including consulting, print resources, networking mechanisms, and social advocacy work.

ACHE is a working committee of the following church agencies and individuals who represent them: Mennonite Health Services Alliance, Rick Stiffney and Ada Hallman; Mennonite Mutual Aid, Karl Sommers; Mennonite Medical Association, George Brenneman and Jep Hostetler; Mennonite Nurses Association, Anne Krabill Hershberger; Mennonite Chaplains Association, Ray Geigley; Associated Mennonite Biblical Seminary, Ted Koontz; consultant, Willard Krabill

Anabaptist Deaf Ministries (ABDM)

adnet@adnetonline.org

Messages only, toll-free 877-214-9838

PO Box 959, Goshen IN 46527-0959

INFORMATION

The mission of Anabaptist Deaf Ministries is to facilitate, encourage, and support deaf people to receive the good news of Jesus Christ and actively participate and serve in an Anabaptist or other Christian church. This ministry relates closely to the Anabaptist Disabilities Network.

ABDM was formally established in 1995 to

OTHER AGENCIES

3

continue the work of Deaf Ministries, lodged with the former Mennonite Board of Missions since 1976. Currently ABDM is led by a board of directors who are connected to the Anabaptist community through their individual memberships in congregations related to Mennonite World Conference.

ADMINISTRATIVE SUPPORT PERSON

Sheila Stopher Yoder, MSW, 574-535-7053

BOARD

Ron Gerbrandt, 6863 West Dover Pl, McCordsville IN 46055 (indy@chilitech.com); Jan Hoffer, Tim Nafziger, Myron Yoder

PUBLICATION

Deaf Ministries NEWS (semiannual) Sheila Stopher Yoder, editor

Anabaptist Peace Center— Washington DC

admin@apcwdc.mennonite.net
www.apcwdc.mennonite.net
301-927-7327
4217 East-West Hwy, Hyattsville MD 20782

INFORMATION

The Anabaptist Peace Center—Washington DC seeks to engage in education, action, and ecumenical cooperation in order to encourage and assist both church and society to put into practice Jesus' call to peace and justice. We:

Encourage Mennonite and Brethren in Christ churches to strengthen and demonstrate their commitment to an Anabaptist witness of peace and justice;

Assist members, pastors, scholars, and activists of other denominations in strengthening their witness to peace and justice;

Help bring understanding, healing, and reconciliation where conflict and division exist in church and society;

Facilitate and disseminate theological reflection

on public policy issues and the role of government in contributing to a just society;

Coordinate nonviolent responses to injustice and aggression and advocate nonviolent strategies for social change;

Offer to churches and to the public resources that relate to peace and justice—speakers, audiovisuals, literature, and reference materials;

Link with institutions and efforts—both within and beyond the Anabaptist community—in common pursuit of peace and justice.

BOARD

Joe Roos (jroos@hyattsvillemennonite.org), chair, 4217 East-West Hwy, Hyattsville MD 20782, 301-927-7327; Ruth Zimmerman, vice chair; Marty Shupack, secretary/treasurer; Addie Banks; J. R. Burkholder; Sang Jin Choi; David Evans; Ed Hall; Lawrence Hart; Pearl Hoover; Susan Mark Landis; Jose Ortiz; Marcus Smucker

Associated Mennonite Biblical Seminary

rreschly@ambs.edu, www.ambs.edu
574-295-3726, fax 574-295-0092
3003 Benham Ave, Elkhart IN 46517

STAFF

J. Nelson Kraybill, president (nkraybill@ambs.edu)
Loren L. Johns, academic dean (ljohns@ambs.edu)
Ron Ringenberg, vice president for advancement and administration (rringenb@ambs.edu)
Jeffrey Miller, business administrator (jmiller@ambs.edu)
Eileen K. Saner, librarian and director of educational resources (esaner@ambs.edu)

INFORMATION

Associated Mennonite Biblical Seminary (AMBS) is dedicated to helping followers of Jesus Christ grow toward spiritual maturity,

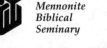

theological depth and discernment, wise pastoral practice, and personal commitment to God's reign of peace and righteousness through the enabling power of the Holy Spirit.

AMBS is a binational Mennonite educational institution committed to the Anabaptist heritage and the Christian church's global mission. AMBS is owned and supported by Mennonite Church Canada and Mennonite Church USA.

Degrees offered include master of divinity, master of arts in theological studies, master of arts in mission and evangelism, master of arts in Christian formation, master of arts in peace studies, dual-degree master of arts in peace studies and master of social work, and dual-degree master of divinity and master of social work.

Mennonite Biblical Seminary, founded in 1945, and Goshen Biblical Seminary, founded in 1946, began associating in 1958 and in 1994 incorporated as one seminary, AMBS.

AMBS is accredited by the Association of Theological Schools in the United States and Canada (ATS) and the North Central Association of College and Schools (NCA).

BOARD
David W. Boshart, chair (dboshart@netins.net), 3253 305th St, Parnell IA 42325; Jim Williams, vice chair; Teresa Moser, secretary; Robert Carlson; John A. Esau; Ray Friesen; Kathy Koop; Allon Lefever; Sherri Martin-Carman; John R. Peters; Mary Stueben; Ed Yoder

AMBS—Great Plains. AMBS—Great Plains is an extension site of AMBS, serving central Kansas with theological education programs. Lois Barrett, director, PO Box 306, 2517 Main, North Newton KS 67117, 316-283-6300 (lbarrett@ambs.edu). Board: Janette Amstutz; Susan Balzer; Palmer Becker; John A. Esau; Dorothy Nickel Friesen; Duane Friesen; Cheryl Hershberger; Heber Ramer; Deb Schmidt
Institute of Mennonite Studies—see separate listing in this section.
Pastoral Studies Distance Education. Jewel Gingerich Longenecker, director, 3003

Benham Ave, Elkhart IN 46517, 574-296-6222, fax 574-295-0092, (jglongenecker@ambs.edu); Dorothy Smucker, registrar (dsmucker@ambs.edu)

PUBLICATIONS
AMBS Window, Mary E. Klassen, editor (same address as above)
Vision: A Journal for Church and Theology, co-published by AMBS and Canadian Mennonite University, editors: Mary H. Schertz, AMBS (same address as above) and Dan Epp-Tiessen, CMU

Association of Anabaptist Risk Management (AARM)
www.aarm-web.net
717-293-7840, fax 717-293-7854
2160 Lincoln Hwy E, Suite 6, Lancaster PA 17602

STAFF
Philip B. Leaman, president/CEO (phil@aarm.net)

INFORMATION
AARM provides risk management programs and services to Anabaptist and Quaker not-for-profit institutions.

BOARD
Henry Rosenberger (HLR@rosenberger.com), chair, 818 Blooming Glen Rd, Blooming Glen PA 18911; Edgar Stoesz, secretary; Paul E. Witter, treasurer

Association of Mennonite Credit Unions
larry@mennonitefinancial.com
800-451-5719 and 717-735-8330
2160 Lincoln Hwy East, PO Box 10455, Lancaster PA 17605-0455

INFORMATION
Founded 1988. Provides a fellowship setting for those who share a common interest in

Mennonite Church based credit unions and mutual aid programs; to share experiences as formally organized financial cooperatives; to assist those communities who are interested in developing their own credit unions; and to encourage a Christian perspective in developing a credit union philosophy. For more information about Mennonite credit unions, contact one of the persons listed below.

CONTACTS

Larry Miller, Mennonite Financial Federal Credit Union (larry@mennonitefinancial.com)—see separate listing; John Beiler, Park View Federal Credit Union (jbeiler@pvfcu.org)—see separate listing; Nick Driedger, Mennonite Savings and Credit Union (ndrieger@mscu.com)

Association of Mutual Aid Societies (AMAS)

tjyousey@northnet.org
315-376-4737, fax 315-376-8433
7383M Utica Blvd, Lowville NY 13367

STAFF

Holly Yousey, conference coordinator

INFORMATION

Founded 1954. Fosters cooperation among various Anabaptist mutual aid organizations, promotes Christian mutual aid, serves as a clearinghouse for ideas and information, and fosters good management of member organizations.

Membership is open to Anabaptist mutual aid organizations and insurance companies. See separate listing under Mutual Aid and Insurance Agencies for member organizations.

BOARD

Allen Schroeder, chair; Bob Rabenstein, vice chair; Larry Litwiller, secretary; Larry Jantzi, treasurer; Ron Mathies; Holly Yousey; Joe Christophel; Nelson Scheifele; Bob Sutter

B

Bethel College

webmaster@bethelks.edu, www.bethelks.edu
316-283-2500, fax 316-284-5286
300 E 27th St, North Newton KS 67117

STAFF

E. LaVerne Epp, president (lepp@bethelks.edu)
Dale Schrag, director of church relations
(drs@bethelks.edu)

INFORMATION

A four-year, coeducational and primarily residential liberal arts college, Bethel College grants BA, BS, and BS in nursing and social work degrees. Bethel offers 28 majors, nine concentrations, and five certificate programs.

Bethel is affiliated with Mennonite Church USA, Associated Colleges of Central Kansas, Council of Christian Colleges and Universities, and Council of Independent Colleges. The oldest Mennonite College in North America, Bethel was founded in 1887 and emphasizes personal discipleship and commitment to Christian community.

Affiliated and accredited by the North Central Association of Colleges and Schools (NCA). Average enrollment is 525 students yearly.

BOARD

Dee Gaeddert, chair (dgaeddert@msn.com), 10475 Hadley Ave N, Grant MN 55110, 651-762-2837; Ray Penner, vice chair; Keith Waltner, secretary; John Penner, treasurer

PUBLICATION

Context (three times yearly)

Bluffton University

webmaster@bluffton.edu; www.bluffton.edu
800-488-3257 and 419-358-3000,
    fax 419-358-3323
1 University Dr, Bluffton OH 45817

STAFF
Lee F. Snyder, president (president@bluffton.edu)
Sally Weaver Sommer, interim dean of academic affairs (sommers@bluffton.edu)
Sue Hardwick, administrative assistant to the president (hardwicks@bluffton.edu)

INFORMATION
Bluffton University is a liberal arts school of about 1,120 students in northwest Ohio, founded by Mennonites in 1899. It offers the B.A. degree with 39 undergraduate majors, and master's degrees in education, organizational management, and business administration. Bluffton's motto from the Gospel of John, "The truth makes free," finds expression through the school's four enduring values of discovery, community, respect, and service.

Bluffton is affiliated with Mennonite Church USA and is a member of the Council for Christian Colleges and Universities. It is accredited through the North Central Association of Colleges and Schools (NCA). Program accreditations include social work, dietetics, and music.

BOARD
Morris Stutzman, chair (mstutzman@lhslaw.com), 2171-B Eagle Pass, Wooster OH 44691, 330-264-6115; Allen Yoder, vice chair; Joanne Sauder, secretary; Elaine Moyer, treasurer; Sarah Arn; James Bassett; David Baumgartner; David Bertsche; Charles Bishop; Richard Cripe; Joyce Frey; David Hersh; Edith Landis; Jerry Lewis; Floyd Liechty; John Liechty; Ronald Lora; Lawrence Milan; Roberta Mohr; Martha Augsburger Showalter; Terry Shetler; James Sommer; Mark Weidner

PUBLICATION
Bluffton magazine (quarterly), Laurie Wurth-Pressel, editor

BLUFFTON
UNIVERSITY

A community of discovery, service and respect

Preparing students for life as well as vocation and for service to God's universal kingdom.

✦ BLUFFTON
EMBRACING SPIRIT, ENGAGING MINDS

1 University Drive
Bluffton, OH 45817
1-800-488-3257
www.bluffton.edu

Books Abroad and at Home

Coordinating office
cindyy@mennonitemission.net
574-294-7523, fax 574-294-8669
Box 370, Elkhart IN 46515-0370

INFORMATION

Founded 1961. A program for sharing good used books and printed material in more than 80 countries abroad, as well as to emerging young churches in North America. Coordinated by staff at Mennonite Mission Network, and carried out by groups and individuals across the church with locally donated books and funds.

AREA OFFICES

Paxton IL: Marilyn Litwiller
(mjlitwiller@juno.com), 1415 CR 3500 N, Paxton IL 60957, 217-396-4061
Tremont IL: Julie G. Largent, 712 Prairie Ln, PO Box 1520, Tremont IL 61568-1520, 309-925-5692
Goshen/South Bend IN: Joyce Schertz
(joycems@aol.com), 705 S Ironwood Dr, South Bend IL 46615, 574-289-6864. Workroom located at The Depot, 1013 Division St, Goshen IN 46526, 574-534-4070.
Lancaster PA: Mabel Herr, 733B North Reservoir St, Lancaster PA 17602-2412, 717-299-6875. Workroom located at MCC Material Resource Center, 517 Trout Run Rd, Ephrata PA 17522
Scottdale PA: Milford and Winifred Paul, 12 Park Ave, Scottdale PA 15683, 724-887-6145. Workroom located at Mennonite Publishing Network, Scottdale PA
Harrisonburg VA: Melba Heatwole
(wilmelh@juno.com), 3351 Hill Gap Rd, Bridgewater VA 22812, 540-828-2999. Workroom located at Virginia Mennonite Conference Center, Harrisonburg.

C

CAL

—see Center for Anabaptist Leadership

Camps

—see Mennonite Camping Association

Cascadia Publishing House

(formerly Pandora Press U.S.)
mking@cascadiapublishinghouse.com,
    www.CascadiaPublishingHouse.com
215-723-9125, fax 215-721-7967
126 Klingerman Rd, Telford PA 18969

STAFF

Michael A. King, owner and publisher

INFORMATION

Founded 1997. Releases Anbaptist-related scholarly volumes; also publishes popular books under the *DreamSeeker* books imprint, and faith-related general audience articles through *DreamSeeker* magazine. Relates to Herald Press, Mennonite Church USA, Mennonite Church Canada, and Anabaptist-related colleges and seminaries, as well as other institutions.

Center for Anabaptist Leadership (CAL)

cal@uscwm.org, www.urban-anabaptist.org
626-720-8100, fax 626-720-8101
Box CAL, 1539 E Howard St, Pasadena CA 91104

STAFF

Joe Manickam, director of operations
    (roverjoe@fuller.edu)
Jeff Wright, director of strategic projects
    (wrightstuff@pacificsouthwest.org)
Gloria Newton, administrator (cal@uscwm.org)
Sara Haldeman-Scarr, staff associate, Church

Planting Systems
(shaldemanscarr@hotmail.com)
Raúl Serradell, staff associate, Urban Theological
Education (rserradell@juno.com)

INFORMATION

The Center for Anabaptist Leadership equips
church leaders through grassroots training, personal coaching, and strategic consulting, so that
congregations become vital centers of God's
mission in the city.

CAL's primary focus is serving Mennonite and
Church of the Brethren congregations and pastors
of the Pacific Southwest. However, relationships
with other Anabaptist groups both locally and
globally are actively developed and welcomed.

Founded in 1987 by Southern California pastors, the Center for Anabaptist Leadership is an
urban mission resource to congregations.

BOARD

Valentina Satvedi, chair
(vsatvedi@worldnet.att.net), 2761 W. 190th St,
Redondo Beach CA 90278, 310-371-0411; Juan
Martinez, vice chair; Joyce Welch, treasurer;
Myrna Wheeler, secretary; Jim Brenneman; Erin
Dufault-Hunter; Doris J. Greer; Tig Intagliata;
Alvin Isaacs; Steve Penner; Gilbert Romero;
Henny van der Zwaag

Center for Peace and Nonviolence

andrekrmc@juno.com
574-631-8758 or 574-291-0924
921 Eddy St., South Bend IN 46617

INFORMATION

The Center for Peace and Nonviolence is an
ecumenical group of churches in St. Joseph
County, Indiana, which "seeks to explore and
promote Jesus's nonviolent way of righting
wrong and establishing justice. We welcome
people of all faith traditions who are committed
to the values of justice and nonviolence to join

OTHER AGENCIES

3

us in action and conversation." Begun in the mid-1980s through Kern Road Mennonite Church, the Center has sponsored a variety of educational events, prayer vigils at murder sites and gun buy-backs. Presently the Center is giving primary energy to birthing a church-based community organizing project.

BOARD

Andre Gingerich Stoner, chair, (andrekrmc@juno.com), Kern Road Mennonite Church, 18211 Kern Road, South Bend IN 46614, 574-291-0924; Jay Caponigro, Pastor; Larry Fourman; Jan Jenkins; Jay Landry; Rev. Michael Patton; Rev. Gilbert Washington Sr.; Marilyn Zugish

Center on Conscience & War (NISBCO)

nisbco@nisbco.org, www.nisbco.org
800-379-2679 and 202-483-2220
1830 Connecticut Ave NW, Washington DC
    20009

STAFF

J. E. McNeil, executive director (j_e@nisbco.org)
Bill Galvin, counseling coordinator
    (bill@nisbco.org)
Theo Sitther, lobbyist, MVS
    (tsitther@nisbco.org)
Eli Bainbridge, editor, BVS
    (reporter@nisbco.org)
Michelle Williams, program assistant
    (michelle@nisbco.org)
Linda Swanson, administrator, Fund for
    Education and Training (FEAT@nisbco.org)

INFORMATION

CCW works to defend and extend the rights of conscientious objectors. CCW supports, for free, those who question participation in war: U.S. citizens, immigrants, or citizens in other countries. CCW participates in the G. I. Rights Hotline, a national referral and counseling service for military personnel. It lobbies to prevent the reinstatement of the draft. It administers a loan program for nonregistrants, called the Fund for Education and Training (FEAT).

CCW's advisory council includes Mennonite Central Committee, Church of the Brethren, and other Anabaptist traditions. CCW was formed in 1940 as the National Service Board for Religious Objectors (NSBRO) by an association of religious bodies including MCC and various Mennonite and other Anabaptist churches. From the Vietnam period until recently, CCW was known as the National Interreligious Board for Conscientious Objectors (NISBCO).

BOARD

Jonathan Ogle, chair, Philadelphia Yearly Meeting rep. (jonathanogle@westtown.edu), Westtown School, Westtown PA 19395, 610-339-1435; James Feldman, secretary; Mary Miller, Episcopal Church rep.; Ibrahim Ramey; Irving Ruderman, Jewish Peace Fellowship reps.; Phil Jones, Church of the Brethren rep.; David Miller, MCC rep.; Shannon McManimon, Pax Christie rep.

PUBLICATION

The Reporter for Conscience' Sake (quarterly)
Eli Bainbridge, editor (same address as above)

China Education Exchange

—see Council of International Anabaptist Ministries

Child Welfare Services

—see Mennonite Health Services Alliance

Choice Books

CENTRAL OFFICE

info@choicebooks.org, www.choicebooks.org
540-434-1827, fax 540-434-9894
2387 Grace Chapel Rd, Harrisonburg VA 22801

STAFF

John M. Bomberger, chief executive officer (bombergerj@choicebooks.org)

INFORMATION

Year founded: 1962

Mission statement: To share the good news of Jesus Christ in the general marketplace through inspiring and wholesome reading material. Choice Books operates through a network of nine regional distributors, working cooperatively with a central office in Harrisonburg, Va. Choice Books distributors service more than 7,500 book displays nationwide, located in a variety of retail stores (supermarkets, drugstores, mass merchandisers, travel centers, hospitals, airports, military bases, etc.). In 2003 Choice Books sold a record 4,010,325 books.

BOARD OF DIRECTORS

Norman G. Shenk (normans@emm.org), chair, 4050 Old Harrisburg Pk, Mt Joy PA 17552, 717-653-5256; Paul J. Helmuth, vice chair; Nathan Miller, secretary-treasurer; Ron L. Kennell; Harley Nisly; Duane M. Schrock; Simon N. Schrock; Ronald B. Schertz; Edgar D. Stoesz

DISTRIBUTORS

Choice Books of Great Lakes-Rosedale, 9920 Rosedale Milford Center Rd, Irwin OH 43029, Alvin Troyer, executive director, 740-857-1368, fax 520-569-8076, info@glr.choicebooks.org

Choice Books of Gulf States, 6115 Old Pascagoula Rd, Theodore AL 36582, Naaman Beiler, executive director, 251-653-0560, fax 251-653-0620, info@gs.choicebooks.org

Choice Books of Kansas, 7217 W Mills Ave, Hutchinson KS 67501, Arno Miller, executive director, 620-567-2162, fax 620-567-2419, info@ks.choicebooks.org

Choice Books of Midwest, 1705 W Mt Vernon, Metamora IL 61548, John Gerber, executive director, 309-367-2152, fax 309-367-9541, info@mw.choicebooks.org

Choice Books of Northern Virginia, PO Box 4080, Manassas VA 20108, Simon Schrock, executive director, 703-530-9993, fax 703-530-9983, info@nva.choicebooks.org

Choice Books of Ohio, Box 210, 13363 Jericho Rd, Kidron OH 44636, Jan Sohar, executive director, 330-857-5471, fax 330-857-5485, info@oh.choicebooks.org

Choice Books of Pennsylvania, 121 S Main St, Manheim PA 17545, Ray Brubaker, executive director, 717-665-3933, fax 717-665-3059, info@pa.choicebooks.org

Choice Books of Southwest, 1013 N 13th St, Phoenix AZ 85006, Vernon Hochstetler, executive director, 602-258-0977, fax 602-258-0971, info@sw.choicebooks.org

Choice Books of West Coast, 2708 Heath Rd, Bakersfield CA 93314, Ken Becker, executive director, 661-588-4487, fax 661-588-5296, info@wc.choicebooks.org

Christian Peacemaker Teams (CPT)

peacemakers@cpt.org; www.cpt.org
773-277-0253, fax 773-277-0291
PO Box 6508, Chicago IL 60680-6508

STAFF

Kryss Chupp, training coordinator (kryss@cpt.org)

Claire Evans, delegations (delegations@cpt.org)

Mark Frey, administrative coordinator (markefrey@cpt.org)

Rich Meyer, Hebron support team coordinator (richm@cpt.org)

Doug Pritchard, co-director (dougp@cpt.org)

Sara Reschly, regional groups (sarar@cpt.org)

Carol Rose, co-director for operations (carolr@cpt.org)

OTHER AGENCIES

3

INFORMATION

Founded in 1988. Sends teams of trained peace-makers into places of conflict around the world. Works through active, spiritually-centered peacemaking, including nonviolent direct action, negotiations, human rights work, and various ministries of presence. Sponsoring denominations include Mennonite Church USA, Mennonite Church Canada, Church of the Brethren, and Friends United Meeting. Congregational support and team makeup is ecumenical with 33 full-time Christian Peacemaker Corps persons and 125 reserve corps (part-time) persons.

BOARD

Lee McKenna, chair; Bob Bartel; Tony Brown; Walter Franz; David Jehnsen; Cliff Kindy; Susan Mark Landis (Mennonite Church USA appointee); Maxine Nash; Rick Polhamus; Orlando Redekopp; Jacqui Rozier; Hedy Sawasky; John Stoner; Rick Ufford Chase; Brian Young

PUBLICATION

Signs of the Times (quarterly), staff editor (same address as above)

Church Extension Services, Inc.

ces@mennoniteusa.org
316-283-5100, fax 316-283-0454
722 N Main St, PO Box 347, Newton KS 67114

STAFF

Ted W. Stuckey, president
(teds@mennoniteusa.org)
J. Jarrett Stucky, manager/treasurer
(jarretts@mennoniteusa.org)
Karen Kaufman, administrative assistant
(karenk@mennoniteusa.org)

INFORMATION

Church Extension Services is separately incor-porated and operates as an affiliate of Mennonite Church USA. Our core mission is to make loans to congregations that do not qualify for commercial loans to acquire, construct, or improve worship facilities and church-related facilities and sites. CES also makes loans to other entities and organizations that are affiliat-ed with the denomination and to denomination agencies. The mission is principally financed through investments by eligible investors of the denomination.

BOARD

Herman Bontrager, chair; N. Leroy Kauffman, secretary; Roma Eicher; Ron Geib; Jeff Wright

CIM

—see Council of International Anabaptist Ministries

Colleges

—see individual listings for Bethel, Bluffton, Eastern Mennonite, Goshen, and Hesston

Council of International Anabaptist Ministries (CIM)

204-888-6781, fax 204-831-5675
600 Shaftesbury Blvd, Winnipeg MB R3P 0M4 Canada
Peter H. Rempel, coordinator
(prempel@mennonitechurch.ca)

INFORMATION

The Council of International Anabaptist Ministries is an association of North American Mennonite and Brethren in Christ international and service agencies. The executive leadership and program administrators meet annually to exchange information, study issues, and plan joint projects.

CIM AGENCIES

Africa Inter-Mennonite Missions,
Box 744, Goshen IN 46527-0744
aimm@aimmintl.org

Brethren in Christ World Missions,
431 Grantham Rd, PO Box 390,
Grantham PA 17027-0390,
717-697-2634, fax 717-691-6053,
bicwm@messiah.edu

China Educational Exchange,
1251 Virginia Ave, Harrisonburg VA 22802-2497,
540-432-6983, fax 540-434-5556, chinaedex@aol.com

Eastern Mennonite Missions, 53 Brandt Blvd,
PO Box 458, Salunga PA 17538-0458, 717-898-2251,
fax 717-898-8092, info@emm.org

Eastern Mennonite Seminary, 1200 Park Rd,
Harrisonburg VA 22802-2462, 540-432-4466,
fax 540-432-4444, info@emu.org

**Evangelical Mennonite Conference, Board of
Missions,** 440 Main St, Steinbach MB R5G 1Z5,
204-326-6401, fax 204-326-1613, emconf@mts.net

Evangelical Mennonite Missions Conference,
PO Box 52029, Niakwa Post Office, Winnipeg MB
R2M 5P9, 204-253-7929, fax 204-256-7384,
info@emmc.ca

**Fellowship of Evangelical Churches,
International Missions,** 1420 Kerrway Ct,
Ft Wayne IN 46805-5402, 260-423-3649,
fax 260-420-1905, FECMissions@aol.com

Franconia Mennonite Conference,
771 Rte 113, Souderton PA 18964, 215-723-5513,
fax 215-723-1211, info@fmc-online.org

Global Disciples Network, 315 W James St,
Lancaster PA 17603, 717-290-7550, fax 717-290-7551,
mail@globaldisciples.org

Mennonite Brethren Biblical Seminary,
4824 E Butler Ave, Fresno CA 93727, 559-251-8628,
fax 559-251-7212, fresno@mbseminary.com

**Mennonite Brethren Missions/Services
International,** 4867 E Townsend Ave, Fresno CA
93727-5006, 559-456-4600, fax 559-251-1342,
mbmsi@mbmsinternational.org

Mennonite Central Committee,
21 S 12th St, O Box 500, Akron PA 17501-0500,
717-859-1151, fax 717-859-2171, mailbox@mcc.org

Mennonite Church Canada Witness,
600 Shaftesbury Blvd, Winnipeg MB R3P 0M4,
204-888-6751, fax 204-831-5675,
office@mennonitechurch.ca

Mennonite Economic Development Associates,
International Operations, 302-280 Smith St,
Winnipeg MB R3C 1K2, 204-956-6430,
fax 204-942-4001, meda@meda.org

Mennonite Medical Association,
193 E Frambes Ave, Columbus OH 43201,
614-299-8922, fax 614-299-8922,
mennmed@mennmed.org

Mennonite Mission Network,
Great Lakes Office: 500 S Main St, PO Box 370,
Elkhart IN 46515-0370, 574-294-7523,
fax 574-294-8869, info@mennonitemission.net
Great Plains Office: 722 Main St, PO Box 347,
Newton KS 67114-0347, 316-283-5100,
fax 316-283-0454, info@mennonitemission.net

Mission Studies Center, c/o AMBS,
3003 Benham Ave, Elkhart IN 46517-1999,
574-295-3726, fax 574-295-0092,
wsawatsky@ambs.edu

Rosedale Mennonite Missions,
9920 Rosedale Milford Center Rd,
Irwin OH 43029-9537, 740-857-1366,
fax 740-857-1605, info@rmmoffice.org

Virginia Mennonite Board of Missions,
901 Parkwood Dr, Harrisonburg VA 22801, 540-434-
9727, fax 540-434-7627, info@vmbm.org

OTHER AGENCIES

3

Council on Church and Media (CCM)

churchandmedia@mennoniteusa.org,
www.churchandmedia.org
574-523-3041, fax 574-293-1892
500 S Main St, PO Box 1245, Elkhart IN 46515-
1245

OFFICERS

Tony Krabill, chair
(tonyk@mennonitemission.net), Mennonite
Mission Network, PO Box 370, Elkhart IN
46515-0370, 574-523-3023, Rachel J. Lapp,
vice chair; Rosa Perez, treasurer; Kathryn
Rodgers, office associate

INFORMATION

A forum of Mennonite Church USA, Brethren in Christ, Church of the Brethren, and related churches founded in 1985 to foster media creativity, integrity, and quality. CCM is organized to facilitate and enhance communication, professional enrichment, fellowship, and development among its members. An annual convention is held in the spring.

PUBLICATION

Forum (three times per year) on the website

CPT

—see Christian Peacemaker Teams

Creation Care Action Network

(formerly Mennonite Environmental Task Force)
1-866-866-2872
creationcare@mennoniteusa.org,
    www.mennoniteusa.org

Creation Care Action Network, a partnership for creation care advocacy and resources, is in the process of re-forming itself within the new Mennonite Church USA and Mennonite Church Canada structures. Its leadership, membership information, and statement of purpose will be available on the Mennonite Church USA website by the fall of 2004.

D

Dallas Peace Center

admin@dallaspeacecenter.org,
www.dallaspeacecenter.org
214-823-7793, fax 214-823-8356
4301 Bryan St, Suite 202, Dallas TX 75204

STAFF

Lon Burnam, director

Valley Reed, assistant director
Phyllis Hodge, office manager
Patricia Major, communications director

INFORMATION

Founded 1981 by Peace Mennonite Church in Dallas, Texas.

BOARD

Joy Flora, president
(joy.flora@worldnet.att.net), 2034 B Greenview Ave, Carrollton TX 75010-4051, 972-492-5422; Micah Boswell; Delia Castillo; Cherry Haymes; Rev. Charles Hunter; Henry S. Irving; Hadi Jawad; Hai Thanh Ly; Iyas Maleh; Rev. Bill Matthews; Rev. Bill McElvaney; Bobbie Nehman; Armando Pacheco; Nelda Reid; Kimberly Truitt; Ron Wilhelm; Liz Wolff; Sam Nance (ex officio); Holsey Hickman (ex officio)

PUBLICATION

The Dallas Peace Times, six times a year, Patricia Major, editor

Design For Ministry

info@designforministry.com,
    www.designforministry.com
877-771-3330, fax 262-392-9002
W325S7418 Squire Ln, Mukwonago WI 53149
Souderton PA office: 771 Rte 113, Souderton PA
    18964
Pasadena CA office: Box CAL, 1539 E Howard St,
    Pasadena CA 91114

STAFF

Mark L. Vincent, lead partner
    (marklv@designforministry.com)
Philip C. Bergey, executive leadership consultant
    (philb@designforministry.com)
Mark Vincent and Lorie Vincent, joint-owners

CONSULTING NETWORK

Tana Pelkey-Landes, executive leadership consultant (tanapl@designforministry.com)

Sharon Williams, senior consultant
(sharonw@designforministry.com)
Jeff Wright, executive leadership consultant
(jeff@designforministry.com)
Consultants: Glen Goss, Sarah Halderman-
Scarr, Ken Hansen, Joe Manickam, Gina
Mujica, Isrrael Mujica, Gloria Newton, Craig
Pelkey-Landis, Meg Sabulsky, Noel Santiago,
Walter Sawatzky, Raul Serradell, Ertell
Whigam, Dwight Wyse

INFORMATION
Design For Ministry helps congregations, ministry
organizations, nonprofits and service-minded
businesses move from where they are to where
they believe they are called to go.

Services are full-orbed, including strategic
planning and follow-through, capacity-building,
capital campaigns, technology development,
funding systems, ghost writing and publication,
communications, executive search, interim
executive leadership, executive coaching, communications, group facilitation, organizational
theological formation, church planting, and
multicultural assistance. Most services are also
available in Spanish-speaking situations. Design
For Ministry is a member of the Ecumenical
Stewardship Association and the Ecumenical
Stewardship Center.

Partners include the Center for Anabaptist
Leadership, Franconia Mennonite Conference,
Mennonite Media, Cascadia Publishing House,
Christian Ministry Resources, Paraclete Video
and Ted & Lee Theaterworks.

Design For Ministry began in 2000, following the successful conclusion of The Giving
Project. In 2003 Design For Ministry purchased
the assets of Ministry Resource Network (MRN)
and absorbed the strength of its consulting network.

PUBLICATION
Depth Perception (available in English and
Spanish via e-mail and posted on the web twice
per month). Spanish edition editors: Isrrael and
Gina Mujica; English edition editor, Mark L.
Vincent. Subscriptions free for the recipient.
Reprint rights available for a fee.

Developmental Disabilities Services
—see Mennonite Health Services Alliance

OTHER AGENCIES

3

E

Eastern Mennonite Missions

info@emm.org, www.emm.org
717-898-2251, fax 717-898-8092
53 W Brandt Blvd, PO Box 458, Salunga PA
17538-0458

STAFF

Richard Showalter, president
(richards@emm.org)

INFORMATION

EMM equips, sends, and supports more than
345 workers in global witness and service in the
way of Christ. Programs include long-term and
short-term (Youth Evangelism Service, Summer
Training Action Teams).

Supported primarily by approximately 200
congregations in Lancaster Mennonite
Conference. Other churches, conferences, and
agencies in North America also participate,
including Atlantic Coast, Franklin and New York
Conferences, Global Community Network, and
Good News Fellowship.

Founded in 1894 as Home Mission
Advocates, and from 1895 to 1914 as
Mennonite Sunday School Mission. Organized
1914 and incorporated in 1916 as Eastern
Mennonite Board of Missions and Charities.

BOARD

Carlton Stambaugh, chair; RD 3 Box 425,
Hanover PA 17331, 717-632-8641; Joseph
Sherer, vice chair; Timothy E. Darling, secretary;
Terry Adams; Joe Garber; David Gingrich;
Ronald Hershey; Jay Martin; Lindsey Robinson;
Thelma Thomas; Keith Weaver

PUBLICATION

Missionary Messenger (monthly), Stephanie
Knudsen, editor (mm@emm.org)

Eastern Mennonite Seminary

info@emu.edu, www.emu.edu
540-432-4260, fax 540-432-4444
1200 Park Rd, Harrisonburg VA 22802

STAFF

Loren E. Swartzendruber, president
(lorens@emu.edu)
Ervin R. Stutzman, dean (stutzerv@emu.edu)

INFORMATION

EMS offers graduate theological education as
preparation for Christian ministries and is
accredited by the Association of Theological
Schools in the United States and Canada (ATS)
and the Southern Association of Colleges and
Schools (SACS).

Founded in 1965 as an outgrowth of Eastern
Mennonite College, EMS is under the control of
the Eastern Mennonite University Board of
Trustees and the Mennonite Education Agency.

EMS offers the master of divinity degree, the

OTHER AGENCIES

3

master of arts in Church Leadership and master of arts in Religion degrees, Clinical Pastoral Education and Certificates in Ministry and Theological Studies.

Enrollment at EMS for 2003-04 was 141 full- and part-time students.

FACULTY

George R. Brunk III; Kenton T. Derstine; James R. Engle; Brenda Martin Hurst; Wendy J. Miller; Mark T. Nation; N. Gerald Shenk; Sara Wenger Shenk; Ervin R. Stutzman; Linford L. Stutzman; Dorothy Jean Weaver; Lawrence M. Yoder; Lonnie D. Yoder; Nathan E. Yoder

Eastern Mennonite University

info@emu.edu, www.emu.edu
540-432-4000, fax 540-432-4444
1200 Park Rd, Harrisonburg VA 22802

STAFF

Loren E. Swartzendruber, president
    (lorens@emu.edu)
Beryl Brubaker, academic provost
    (brubakeb@emu.edu)
Marie Morris, undergraduate dean
    (morrisms@emu.edu)

INFORMATION

EMU is a national liberal arts school offering degrees at the undergraduate, graduate, and seminary levels. All students participate in a cross-cultural term.

EMU is affiliated with Mennonite Church USA and accredited by the Southern Association of Colleges and Schools (SACS). It is a member of the Council for Christian Colleges and Universities.

Founded in 1917 as a Bible academy, EMU has grown in size and reputation over the years, becoming a university in 1994. Total enrollment is 1,450 in undergraduate, graduate, and seminary programs.

BOARD

Susan Godshall, chair, 1891 Mt. Pleasant, Mt Joy PA 17552, 717-653-6191; Nora Hess, secretary-treasurer; Curtis D. Hartman, treasurer; J. Harold Bergey; John M. Bomberger; Andrew Dula; Shirley N. Hochstetler; Gerald R. Horst; Linford King; H. William Longacre; Herb Noll; Rosalie Rolon-Dow; Kathy Keener Shantz; J. Richard Thomas; Diane Zimmerman Umble; Paul R. Yoder Jr.

PUBLICATIONS

Crossroads (quarterly), Paul Souder, editor (same address as above); *Weather Vane* (weekly student newspaper), *Shenandoah* (annual student yearbook)

Education

—see Mennonite Education Agency in section 1, Churchwide Agencies

Environmental Task Force

—see Creation Care Action Network

Every Church A Peace Church (ECAPC)

(formerly New Call to Peacemaking)
jstoner@ecapc.org, www.ecapc.org
717-859-1958, fax 717-859-1958
PO Box 240, Akron PA 17501

STAFF

John Stoner, coordinator (jstoner@ecapc.org)

INFORMATION

ECAPC widens the peace education work of New Call to Peacemaking by inviting all denominations and Christians to embrace the nonviolent struggle at the heart of Jesus' life and teachings. The website and gatherings in conferences are the key modes of communication.

On serving the church...

"I am committed to making EMU the strongest institution it can be in service to the church and the world. Our church schools, from kindergarten through seminary and graduate programs, are critical for the future health of the church. We who are called to offer our gifts in education participate in a holy enterprise."

Loren E. Swartzendruber
EMU president

- A learning community since 1917, EMU is marked by academic excellence, professional competence and passionate Christian faith.
- Our cross-cultural programs teach students to live and serve in a global context.
- We offer 39 undergraduate majors (including communications, international business and nursing), seven pre-professional and professional programs, seminary and four master's programs (counseling, education, conflict transformation and business).
- EMU's main campus is located in the beautiful Shenandoah Valley serving more than 1200 students. Other locations are in Lancaster (Pa.) and Washington, D.C.
- EMU alumni number more than 14,000, working and serving in all 50 states and 80 countries around the world.

EASTERN
MENNONITE
UNIVERSITY
1200 Park Road
Harrisonburg, Virginia 22802

540-432-4000 • 800-368-2665 • www.emu.edu

In 2000 Every Church A Peace Church replaced the organization known as New Call to Peacemaking, which was formed in 1975 to renew the biblical teaching of peace among Friends, Mennonites, and Brethren.

The support base is individuals representing Baptist, Catholic, Lutheran, United Methodist, United Church of Christ, ecumenical fellowships, peace fellowships, and other denominations, in addition to Friends, Mennonites, and Brethren.

BOARD
Ruby Sales and John Stoner, co-chairs; Bill Price, secretary; H. A. Penner, treasurer

PUBLICATION
Online *ECAPC Newsletter* (occasional), John Stoner, editor

Executive Board
—see section 1, Churchwide Agencies

G

Global Disciples Network
mail@globaldisciples.org;
www.globaldisciples.org
717-872-7404, fax 717-872-7404
319 Manor Ave, Millersville PA 17551

STAFF
Galen Burkholder, executive director
(galen@globaldisciples.org)
Tim Pfautz, operations manager
(mail@globaldisciples.org)

INFORMATION
Global Disciples Network connects churches, businesses, and mission groups internationally to train disciples, witness to unreached peoples, mobilize and equip leaders so the world will know Jesus.

Global Disciples works in partnership with about 30 different conferences, synods, or dioceses of churches, mostly Anabaptist related groups, in Africa, Asia, Europe, Latin America, and North America. Member CIM.

Global Disciples Network was founded in 1996. The board of directors combined with the board of Mennonite Christian Leadership Foundation in 2001, and one board now governs the two organizations.

BOARD
Marlin Thomas, chair, 100 Willow Valley Lakes Dr, Willow Street PA 17584, 717-464-2741; Dale Weaver, vice chair; George Hurst, treasurer; Eugene Witmer, secretary

PUBLICATION
Connecting (bimonthly) staff editors (same address as above)

Good Books
custserve@goodbks.com, www.goodbks.com
800-762-7171 and 717-768-7171, fax 888-768-3433
PO Box 419, 3518 Old Philadelphia Pk,
Intercourse PA 17534

STAFF
Merle Good, publisher (mgood@goodbks.com)
Phyllis Pellman Good, senior book editor
(pgood@goodbks.com)

INFORMATION
Founded 1979. Good Books seeks to bring the Mennonite-related milieu to the general public. Specializes in books about parenting and family, fiction, biography, history, peace, cooking, decorative arts, children's books, and educational books about Mennonite and Amish faith and life.

OTHER AGENCIES

3

Experience the joy of the journey.

GOSHEN
COLLEGE
Admission Office
800-348-7422
admission@goshen.edu
www.goshen.edu

Goodville Mutual Casualty Company

webmaster@goodville.com, www.goodville.com
800-448-4622 and 717-354-4921,
fax 717-354-5158
625 W Main St, PO Box 489,
New Holland PA 17557-0489

STAFF

Herman D. Bontrager, president and CEO
(herman.bontrager@goodville.com)
Philip E. Nolt, vice president
(phil.nolt@goodville.com)

INFORMATION

Goodville provides auto, home, farm, business, and church insurance coverages in Delaware, Indiana, Illinois, Kansas, Maryland, Ohio, Oklahoma, Pennsylvania, and Virginia.

Founded in 1926 the company serves Mennonites, Brethren in Christ, Church of the Brethren, and others who meet company standards. Member of Association of Mutual Aid Societies (AMAS).

BOARD

Carlton L. Miller, chair; Kenneth L. Beiler, vice chair; Herman D. Bontrager, president; John L. Frankenfield, secretary; Allon H. Lefever, treasurer; Sanford L. Alderfer; John R. Buckwalter; Paul M. King; Keith W. Lehman; Donald L. Nice; Glennys H. Shouey; Mim Shirk

Goshen College

info@goshen.edu, www.goshen.edu
800-348-7422 and 574-535-7000,
fax 574-535-7660
1700 S Main St, Goshen IN 46526

STAFF

John D. Yordy, interim president
(provost@goshen.edu)
Carla F. Weldy, director of Alumni, Church and
Parent Relations (carlafw@goshen.edu)

Andrea Cook, vice president for Institutional
Advancement

INFORMATION

Goshen College is a national liberal arts college known for leadership in international education, service/learning, and peace and justice issues in the Anabaptist-Mennonite tradition. GC is recognized for its unique Study/Service Term program, and exceptional educational value.

Degrees: BA, BS, and BS in Nursing, certificate programs. Accredited by North Central Association of Colleges and Schools, National Council for Accreditation of Teacher Education, National League for Nursing, and Council on Social Work Education, Member of Council for Christian Colleges and Universities, International 50, and Council of Independent Colleges. Founded 1894. Goshen College Sarasota (FL) established in 1998.

BOARD

Virgil Miller (vmiller@saudermfg.com), chair, 22494 CR B, Archbold OH 43502, 419-445-1100; Paul Bast; Tom Bishop; Ervin Bontrager; Miriam F. Book; J. Elvin Kraybill; Ivorie Lowe; Lonnie Sears; Terry Shue; Randy Springer; Rick Stiffney; Rebecca Stoltzfus

PUBLICATION

Bulletin (quarterly alumni magazine), Rachel Lapp, editor (racheljl@goshen.edu)

H

Harmonies Workshop

office@harmonies.org, www.harmonies.org
717-656-2749, fax 717-656-8265
34 W Eby Rd, Leola PA 17540

STAFF

Glenn Lehman, executive director
Jessica Landes, events and service manager

INFORMATION
Live events and recordings, including the Table Singers, focusing on 20th-century Mennonite music, and the Foresingers, an ensemble rediscovering early Mennonite music. Educational events and materials for the promotion of church music, especially hymns. Also produces Old Order recordings. Harmonies is a fraternal organization of Lancaster Mennonite Conference, founded and incorporated in 1987.

BOARD
Steven L. Shenk, chair (stevens478@aol.com), 2268 Old Philadelphia Pk, Lancaster PA 17602, 717-295-3105; Earl Rohrer, treasurer; Stanley Godshall; Roger Ledyard; Dorcas M. Lehman; Glenn M. Lehman; Rachel Pellman; David Rempel Smucker

PUBLICATION
Notes (occasional), Jessica Landes, editor (same address as above)

Healthcare Agencies
—see Mennonite Health Services Alliance

Heritage Centers
—see Historical Centers

Hesston College
admissions@hesston.edu;
    alumni@hesston.edu, www.hesston.edu
866-437-7866, 620-327-4221, fax 620-327-8300
325 S College, PO Box 3000,
    Hesston KS 67062-2093

STAFF
Howard Keim, president
    (howardk@hesston.edu)
Marcus Yoder, executive vice president for academic affairs (marcy@hesston.edu)
Dallas Stutzman, church relations director
    (dallass@hesston.edu)

INFORMATION

Founded in 1909, Hesston is a two-year college with students from 29 states and 15 countries, including Canada. Enrollment: 394 full-time and 52 part-time.

Degrees offered: associate of arts, associate of science, and associate of applied arts and sciences with majors in Aviation, Bible, Business, Computer Information Technology, Early Childhood Education, Nursing, and Pastoral Ministries. Affiliated and accredited by the North Central Association of Colleges and Schools (NCA).

BOARD

Arlan Yoder (ayoder@southwind.net), chair, 112 Park Rd, Hesston KS 67062, 620-327-2794); Pam Boyts Gerber, vice chair; Dee Custar, secretary; Dale Beachey; Ginny Birky; Wilbur Bontrager; Jose Elizalde; Denton R. Jantzi; Harley Kooker; Phyllis Nofziger; Norm Yoder

PUBLICATION

Hesston College Today, Phil Richard, editor (philr@hesston.edu)

Hispanic Mennonite Church
—see Iglesia Hispana Menonita

Historical Committee
—see Executive Board in section 1, Churchwide Agencies

Hospitals
—see Mennonite Health Services Alliance

Historical Organizations

CHURCHWIDE

See Mennonite Church USA Archives under Executive Board in Section 1: Churchwide Agencies.

DELAWARE

Delaware Mennonite Historical Assoc.
PO Box 238, Greenwood DE 19950

ILLINOIS

Illinois Amish Interpretive Center
iaic@one-eleven.net, www.amishcenter.com
217-268-3599 or 1-888-45AMISH, fax 217-268-4810
111 S Locust St, PO Box 413, Arcola IL 61910
Stella Eads, executive director; Wilmer Otto, board chair
  Founded 1995. Interprets the Amish faith and culture through introductory video, museum, bookstore, and guided tours of the Amish community.

Illinois Mennonite Heritage Ctr
imhgs@attbi.com, www.rootsweb.com/~ilmhgs
309-392-2518, fax 309-392-2518
675 SR 116, Metamora IL 61548-7732
  Founded 1982. Mennonite museum, historical and genealogical library, farm museum, restored grandfather house and barn, amid native trees and prairie grasses.

Illinois Mennonite Historical and Genealogical Society
lmhbs@attbi.com, www.rootsweb.com/~ilmhgs
309-392-2518, fax 309-392-2518
675 SR 116, Metamora IL 61548-7732
Carolyn Nafziger, president; Gordon Oyer, museum chair; Steven R. Estes, archives chair; Ruth Ulrich, library chair
  Founded 1969. Collects, preserves, interprets, shares artifacts and information relating to faith and life of Mennonites in Illinois. Publications; operates Heritage Center.

INDIANA

Howard-Miami Counties Heritage Society, Inc.
Jjhorner@aol.com
765-628-2280
PO Box 156, Greentown IN 46936
David Rogers, president; Arlenee Rogers, treasurer
  Founded 1996. Mission is to discover and to tell the stories of the Amish, Mennonite, and other related families who settled in central Indiana in 1848ff.

Menno-Hof
mennohof@tln.net, www.mennohof.org
260-768-4117, fax 260-768-4118
510 S. Van Buren, SR 5, PO Box 701, Shipshewana IN 46565-0701
Joseph Yoder, director
  Founded 1988. An interpretive center of Mennonite and Amish history and faith. Visitors invited to consider faith and to discover others of similar faith in their home communities.

OTHER AGENCIES

3

Mennonite Historical Library (Ind.)
mhl@goshen.edu, www.goshen.edu/mhl
574-535-7418 or 574-535-7433, fax 574-535-7438
1700 S Main St, Goshen IN 46526-9989
John D. Roth, director
Founded 1906. Holdings of more than 55,000 volumes documenting Reformation and Anabaptist history and various Mennonite and related groups throughout the world. Owned by Goshen College with support from AMBS.

Mennonite Historical Society (Ind.)
bieseckermasts@bluffton.edu
574-535-7433, fax 574-535-7438
1700 Main St, Goshen IN 46526
Founded 1921. Promote Anabaptist-Mennonite studies broadly defined. Hosts local lectures, publishes *The Mennonite Quarterly Review*, Studies in Anabaptist and Mennonite History, and the C. Henry Smith Series. Also sponsors annual publication and research grants.

Michiana Anabaptist Historians
Theronfs@goshen.edu
574-533-2280
1503-1 Kentfield Way, Goshen IN 46526
Theron Schlabach, president
Founded 1992. Assists congregational and local historians and others interested in gathering and preserving Mennonite/Anabaptist-related materials. Promotes historical awareness through spring and fall meetings, tours, seminars and biannual newsletter.

IOWA

Mennonite Historical Society of Iowa and Archives
319-656-3271, 319-656-3732
PO Box 576, Kalona IA 52247-0576
Lois Swartzendruber Gugel, president
Founded 1948. Holdings include Iowa-Nebraska Conference records, local church and community historical records, genealogy and family records.

KANSAS

Kauffman Museum
kauffman@bethelks.edu, www.bethelks.edu/kauffman
316-283-1612, fax 316-283-2107
Bethel College, 27th & Main, North Newton KS 67117-0531
Rachel Pannabecker, director; Chuck Regier, curator of exhibits
Founded 1941. Interprets Mennonites in relation to the cultural and natural history of the Great Plains. Traveling exhibitions.

Mennonite Heritage Museum
mhmuseum@futureks.net,
www.skyways.lib.ks.us/museums/goessel
620-367-8200
200 N Poplar, PO Box 231, Goessel KS 67053
Kristine Schmucker, director/curator

Founded 1974. A tribute to the Alexanderwohl Mennonite Church congregation immigrants that settled in the Goessel community in 1874.

Pioneer Mennonite Adobe House Museum
316-947-3775, 316-947-3506
501 S Ash St, Hillsboro KS 67063
David F. Wiebe, director
Founded 1958. Operates a four-acre Hillsboro Heritage Park that includes Pioneer Mennonite Adobe House built in 1876 by Peter Loewen.

MARYLAND

Casselman River Area Historians
301-895-4488
PO Box 591, Grantsville MD 21536-0591
David I. Miller, chairman; Paul H.Yoder, secretary
Founded 1987. Encourages and implements the preservation of Amish/Mennonite history in the Casselman River area.

Penn Alps and Spruce Forest Artisan Village
info@pennalps.com, www.pennalps.com
301-895-5985, fax 301-895-5942
125 Casselman Rd, Grantsville MD 21536

OHIO

Amish & Mennonite Heritage Center (Ohio)
behalt@sssnet.com, www.pages.sssnet.com/behalt
330-893-3192, fax 330-893-3529
5798 CR 77, PO Box 324, Berlin OH 44610-0324
Paul J. Miller, executive director; Verna Schlabach, assistant director
Founded 1982. Presents Anabaptist history through tours of Behalt, a 265-ft. mural-in-the-round of the Mennonite, Amish, and Hutterite story, plus video, bookstore, Ten Thousand Villages crafts, art, and more.

Bluffton University Archives
weaverp@bluffton.edu, www.bluffton.edu/mlibrary
419-358-3448, fax 419-358-3384
1 University Dr, Bluffton OH 45817-1704
Paul L. Weaver, archivist
Founded 1930. Materials held pertain to Bluffton University, Central District Conference, Africa Inter-Mennonite Mission, and Mennonite Mutual Aid societies.

Kidron Community Historical Society
kidron@sssnet.com
330-857-9111
13153 Emerson Rd, PO Box 234, Kidron OH 44636-0234
Bruce Detweiler Breckbill, director
Founded 1977. Preserves the history and heritage of the Kidron-Sonnenberg community. Member of the Ohio Association of Historical Societies and Museums.

Mennonite Historical Library (Ohio)

johnsonmj@bluffton.edu, www.bluffton.edu/mlibrary
419-358-3396, fax 419-358-3384
1 University Dr, Bluffton OH 45817-1704
Mary Jean Johnson, Director of Libraries
Founded 1930. Holdings of materials dealing with Mennonites and related groups, emphasizing those of Swiss-French-South German background.

Stark County Mennonite and Amish Historical Society

330-877-9566, 1136 S Prospect Ave, Hartville OH 44632
Elmer S. Yoder, president
Founded 1979. Focuses on the history and culture of the Stark County (Ohio) Mennonite and Amish communities. Publishes *Heritage*, a quarterly paper. Administered by a five-member board of trustees.

Swiss Community Historical Society

Keith Sommer, Box 5, Bluffton OH 45817

OREGON

Oregon Mennonite Historical and Genealogical Society

Ralphshetler@juno.com, mhgsor.mennonite.net
503-363-2000, 503-873-6406
9045 Wallace Rd NW, Salem OR 97304
Willard Kennel, president; Margaret Shetler, secretary and archivist
Founded 1988. Records and preserves the history and genealogies of Mennonite and related groups in Oregon. Supervises the Oregon Mennonite Archives and Library.

Oregon Mennonite Archives and Library

503-363-2000, 503-873-6406
9045 Wallace Rd NW, Salem OR 97304
Violet Burlely, librarian; Margaret Shetler, archivist
Founded 1960. Official repository for records of the former PCC and PDC and the present Pacific Northwest Mennonite Conference. Also historical and genealogical publications.

PENNSYLVANIA

Allegheny Mennonite Conference Archives

PO Box 12, Somerset PA 15501-0012
Mark Moyer, chair, 1000 Vista Dr Apt 922, Davidsville, PA 15928, 814 288-4575
Administered by the Historical Committee of the Allegheny Conference, and preserves the records of the conference.

Eastern Mennonite Associated Libraries and Archives

ebbpinola@juno.com
717-393-9745, fax 717-530-8595
c/o Lancaster Mennonite Historical Society, 2215 Millstream Rd, Lancaster PA 17602
Edsel Burdge Jr., chair; Lloyd Zeager, secretary

Founded 1959. Consortium of Mennonite Historical Libraries/Archives in Pa., Md., and Va., including BIC Archive/Historical Society; Germantown Mennonite Historic Trust; Home Messenger Library; Juniata District Mennonite Historical Society; Lancaster Mennonite Historical Society; Menno Simons Historical Library & Archives; Mennonite Historians of Eastern Pennsylvania; Mennonite Historical Association of the Cumberland Valley; Mifflin County Mennonite Historical Society; Muddy Creek Farm Library; Pequla Bruderschaft Library; Young Center for Anabaptist and Pietist Studies.

Germantown Mennonite Historic Trust

gmht@meetinghouse.info, www.meetinghouse.info
215-843-0943, fax 215-843-6263
6133 Germantown Ave, Philadelphia PA 19144
Randall K. Nyce, executive director; James L. Derstine, chairman
Founded 1952. An inter-Mennonite historical trust that nurtures and enriches contemporary Mennonite identity through the preservation and interpretation of the historic Germantown Mennonite meetinghouse, its adjacent cemetery, grounds, and other historical materials related to North America's first Mennonite settlement.

Hans Herr House Museum

www.hansherr.org
717-464-4438
1849 Hans Herr Dr, Willow Street PA 17584
Doug Nyce, director; Julia Whitfield, educator
Founded 1974. Oldest house in Lancaster County (1719), built by Christian Herr, an early Mennonite settler. Open to the public.

Juniata Mennonite Historical Society

717-694-3543
The Historical Center, HCR 63, Richfield PA 17086
Noah L. Zimmerman, director
Founded 1977. Preserves and protects records and related materials for study and research.

Lancaster Mennonite Historical Society

lmhs@lmhs.org, www.lmhs.org
717-393-9745, fax 717-393-8751
2215 Millstream Rd, Lancaster PA 17602-1499
Brinton L. Rutherford, director; Lloyd R. Zeager, librarian
Founded 1958. Provides library, archives, research services, publications, book sales (new/used), exhibits, speakers, and educational programs (lectures, field trips, seminars, conferences). Archives for Lancaster and Atlantic Coast area conferences. Publications include *Pennsylvania Mennonite Heritage*, *Mirror*, and occasional books.

OTHER AGENCIES

3

Mennonite Heritage Center (Pa.)

info@mhep.org, www.mhep.org
215-256-3020, fax 215-256-3023
P O Box 82, 565 Yoder Rd, Harleysville PA 19438-0082
Sarah Wolfgang Heffner, director
Founded 1974. Presents the 300-year history of Mennonite life in southeastern Pennsylvania. Describes both past and present Mennonite life in eastern Pennsylvania. Operated by the Mennonite Historians of Eastern Pennsylvania. Includes gift shop, historical library, and archives.

Mennonite Historians of Eastern Pennsylvania

info@mhep.org, www.mhep.org
215-256-3020, fax 215-256-3023
565 Yoder Rd, PO Box 82, Harleysville PA 19438-0082
Sarah Wolfgang Heffner, director; Joel D. Alderfer, librarian/curator
Founded 1974. Operates the Mennonite Heritage Center, a museum, historical library and archives, and gift shop. Preserves and perpetuates the Anabaptist-Mennonite heritage of the past three centuries in eastern Pennsylvania. The historical library and archives (founded 1967) carries collections of materials on Mennonite life in Bucks, Montgomery, Lehigh, Northampton, Chester, and Philadelphia counties.

Mennonite Historical Association of the Cumberland Valley

ebbpinola@innernet.com
717-375-4544, 301-733-2184
4850 Molly Pitcher Hwy S, Chambersburg PA 17201
Roy M. Showalter, curator; Merle Cordell, chair; Edsel Burdge Jr., editor, publishes Conococheague Mennonist.
Founded 1957. Houses a historical library, archives, and small museum. The library collections focuses on Mennonite and other peace churches in Franklin County, Pa., and Washington County, Md., as well as genealogy and local history.

Mennonite Information Center (Pa.)

menninfctr@desupernet.net, mennoniteinfoctr.com
717-299-0954, fax 717-290-1585
2209 Millstream Rd, Lancaster PA 17602-1494
R. Wesley Newswanger, director
Founded 1959. Interprets the faith of Mennonites, Amish, and other Anabaptist local and worldwide groups. Offers a lecture-tour of an actual-size reproduction of the Hebrew Tabernacle.

Mifflin County Mennonite Historical Society

Zay701@acsworld.net, mifflincomhs.mennonite.net
717-935-5574
PO Box 5603, Belleville PA 17004-5603
Paul E. Bender, president, Zelda Yoder, librarian
Founded 1985. Open Wednesday and Saturday or by appointment. Call 717-935-2598.

Muddy Creek Farm Library

376 N Muddy Creek Rd, Denver PA 17517-9125
Amos B. and Nora B. Hoover

The People's Place Quilt Museum

custserv@ppquiltmuseum.com
www.ppquiltmuseum.com
800-828-8218 or 717-768-7101, fax 888-768-3433 and 717-768-3433
3513 Old Philadelphia Pk, PO Box 419, Intercourse PA 17534
Staff: Phyllis Pellman Good, curator (pgood@goodbks.com)
Founded 1988. Features a new exhibit each year of exquisite antique Amish and/or Mennonite quilts (usually pre-1940) and other decorative arts. Occasionally includes quilts from other traditions, such as African-American and antique applique quilts. Museum Shoppe adjacent.

SOUTH DAKOTA

Freeman Academy Heritage Archives

info@freemanmuseum.org, www.freemanmuseum.org
605 925-4237
748 S Main St, Freeman SD 57209
Duane Schrag and LaNae Waltner, archivists; Cleon Graber, museum curator
Founded 1955. Includes original diaries, Mennonite and local writings, genealogy books, and records of the Northern District Conference.

VIRGINIA

Menno Simons Historical Library/Archives

bowmanlb@emu.edu, www.emu.edu
540-432-4177, fax 540-432-4977
Eastern Mennonite University, 1200 Park Rd, Harrisonburg VA 22802-2462
Lois B. Bowman, librarian; Harold E. Huber, library assistant
Founded 1955. Holdings of Anabaptist, Mennonite and Amish in the Shenandoah Valley. Archives for EMU and Virginia Mennonite Conference. Member of Eastern Mennonite Associated Libraries and Archives.

Shenandoah Valley Mennonite Historians

shenkp@emu.edu
540-434-0578
H. Michael Shenk, 1345 Hillcrest Dr, Harrisonburg, VA 22802
Founded 1993. Promotes the study, preservation, and communication of the Mennonite heritage in Shenandoah Valley of Virginia. Relates to Virginia Mennonite Conference and Mennonite Church USA Historical Committee.

Valley Brethren-Mennonite Heritage Center

info@vbmhc.org, www.vbmhc.org
540-432-4255, fax 540-867-9487
711 Garbers Church Rd, PO Box 1563, Harrisonburg VA 22803
Steve Shenk, executive director; Robert Alley, board president
Founded 1999. The mission is to share and celebrate the story of Jesus Christ as it has been reflected in the lives of Mennonites and Brethren in the Shenandoah Valley. A board representing both Brethren and Mennonites directs the ministry.

I

Iglesia Menonita Hispana

jmontesimh@juno.com
559-638-7723 (iglesia), 559-637-9787 (casa),
fax 559-637-0588
1208 L St, PO Box 111, Reedley CA 93654

STAFF
Juan Montes, executive director

EXECUTIVE BOARD
Juan Montes, executive director (see staff);
Byron Pellecer, moderator
(bpellece@bellsouth.net), 135 SW 135 Ct,
Miami FL 33174, 305-207-5299; Samuel López,
secretary; Víctor Vargas, financial director

CONFERENCIA FEMENINA HISPANA MENONITA (CFHM)
Women's Committee: Seferina Garcia De León,
coordinator (seferinad@msn.com), 712 S 12th
St, Goshen IN 46526, 574-534-0362; Cecilia
Moreno, vice coordinator, 1323 Belle Valley Rd,
Lancaster PA 17603, 717- 392-6805; Sonia
Negrón, treasurer (rigonegro@juno.com),
1033 N Minnesota Ave, Brownsville TX 78521,
956-831-2338; Vilma Padilla, secretary, 710
College Ave, Goshen IN 46526, 574-534-8772;
Maria Magdalena DeLeón, representative to
Mennonite Women (Mdeleon713@aol.com),
CR 1092, Box 23207, Mathis TX 78368, 361-
547-2429

INFORMATION
Iglesia Menonita Hispana is the recognized
organization of Hispanic Mennonites. Its purpose is to strengthen the identity and unity of
Spanish congregations. IMH interprets the work
and provides opportunities for Hispanics to
relate to one another. The organization holds an
assembly every two years.

Founded in 2000 from the former Mennonite
Association of Hispanic Churches (AMIGA) and
Hispanic Mennonite Convention (HMC).
Executive Board rep: Marco Güete, until
2005; CLC reps: Juan Montes, Byron Pellecer

PUBLICATION
ENCUENTRO (bimonthly), Juan Montes, editor,
PO Box 1875, Reedley CA 93654, 559-637-
0588, (jmontesimh@juno.com)

Information Centers
—see Historical Organizations

Institute of Mennonite Studies (IMS)
ims@ambs.edu, www.ambs.edu/IMS
574-295-3726, fax 574-295-0092
c/o AMBS, 3003 Benham Ave,
Elkhart IN 46517-1999

STAFF
Mary Schertz, director (mschertz@ambs.edu);
John D. Rempel, associate director

INFORMATION
Founded in 1958, IMS is the research agency of
AMBS and sponsors consultations and publications for Anabaptist-Mennonite studies in the
areas of history, theology, ethics, mission,
church, and ministry.

EXECUTIVE COMMITTEE
Loren Johns, chair (ljohns @ambs.edu), AMBS,
3003 Benham Ave, Elkhart IN 46517-1999,
574-295-3726; Art McPhee; Walter W. Sawatsky

PUBLICATION
Vision: A Journal for Church and Theology
(with CMBC); Mary Schertz, AMBS editor
(vision@ambs.edu), www.MennoVision.org.
Vision seeks to encourage theological reflection
by church leaders on the identity, mission, and
practices of the church from an Anabaptist-
Mennonite perspective.

OTHER AGENCIES

3

Insurance
—see listing for Mutual Aid and Insurance Agencies in this section and MMA in section 1, Churchwide Agencies

Inter-Church, Inc.
MyronSA@aol.com
540-433-2151, fax 540-433-2151
1549 Hillcrest Dr, Harrisonburg VA 22802

STAFF
Myron Augsburger, president
Abram Clymer, board chair

INFORMATION
Founded 1960. Sponsors Myron and Esther Augsburger's work in evangelism, art conferences, and international seminars.

International Guest House (IGH)
igh-dc@juno.com
202-726 5808, fax 202-882 2228
1441 Kennedy St NW, Washington DC 20011

STAFF
Marvin and Vi Miller, host/hostess; Phyllis Hostetler; Raquel Colque

INFORMATION
The IGH is a nonprofit house maintained by Allegheny Conference to provide clean, inexpensive lodging for international and national visitors in a homelike atmosphere.

BOARD
Annabelle Kratz, chair, 13495 Brighton Dam Rd, Clarksville MD 21029; Gene Miller, secretary; Ilene Weinbenner, treasurer; Glen Gehman

K

Kansas Mennonite Men's Chorus
620-543-2320
102 Rainbow Ct, Buhler KS 67522
Irvin A. Pauls, historian

INFORMATION
Founded 1969. The chorus of about 375 singers presents four concerts per year.

L

Lao Mennonite Ministries
kuayingt@mennonitemission.net
905-646-3651, 905-646-3651
71 Lakeshore Rd, St Catharines ON
   L2N 2T3 Canada

STAFF
Kuaying Teng

INFORMATION
Lao Mennonite Ministries promotes fellowship and cooperation among its members for leadership development and church planting. Kuaying Teng, Minister of Asian Ministries with Mennonite Mission Network, also serves as the official liaison person between the Lao Mennonite Ministries and Mennonite agencies in the United States and Canada.

STAFF
Kuaying Teng

Lombard Mennonite Peace Center (LMPC)
admin@lmpeacecenter.org,
www.lmpeacecenter.org
630-627-0507, fax 627-0519
1263 S Highland Ave, Suite 1N, Lombard IL 60148

STAFF
Richard Blackburn, executive director
Bob Williamson, associate director
Marty Farahat, assistant director

INFORMATION
LMPC seeks to "proclaim Christ's good news, the gospel of peace and justice—and to be active in the sacred ministry of reconciliation," resourcing churches of all denominations.

Begun in 1983, LMPC has a long history of providing training in biblical foundations for peacemaking, conflict transformation, and mediation skills. LMPC works with healthy congregations and consults with conflicted churches.

BOARD
Judd Peter, chair; Anne Meyer Byler, vice chair; Elton Martin, treasurer; Kathleen Springer, secretary; Stanley Bohn; Wanda Bouwman; Laura Dube; Terry Gladstone; Steve Felt; Richard Blackburn (ex officio)

PUBLICATION
LMPC Newsletter (quarterly)

M

MAMA Project, Inc.
mamaproject@enter.net, www.mamaproject.org
215-679-4338, fax 215-679-4338
2781A Geryville Pk, Pennsburg PA 18073

STAFF
Priscilla Benner, M.D., director
Carol Linberger, administrative assistant
Rich Moyer, treasurer

INFORMATION
MAMA (Mujeres Amigas Miles Apart) coordinates health, nutrition, and education work in Honduras and Haiti. Work includes medical clinics, Vitamin A and deworming campaigns, preschools, work teams, scholarships, and rehabilitating malnourished children.

BOARD
Board members: Ruth Cole, president (rcole@mail.montcopa.org), 2276 Hieter Rd, Quakertown PA 18951, 215-538, 3245; Priscilla Benner; Marlene Frankenfield; Judy Jones; Oscar Mejia; Rich Moyer; Barbara Rice; Barbara Schieck; Tim Weaver. Board advisers: Daryl Y. Bontrager; Sarah Wolfgang Heffner; Jose Santiago; Walt Sawatzky

PUBLICATION
MAMA News (six times/year)

MAX
—see Mutual Aid eXchange

MCC
—see Mennonite Central Committee

MEDA
—see Mennonite Economic Development Associates

Menno Travel Service, Inc. d/b/a MTS TRAVEL
ephrata@mtstravel.com, www.mtstravel.com
717-733-4131 or 800-642-8315,
    fax 717-733-1909
Home office: 124 E Main St, 4th Fl,
    Ephrata PA 17522

STAFF
Kermit Yoder, president and CEO (kermity@mtstravel.com)
Jim Buddendorf, COO (jimb@mtstravel.com)
Vickie Unruh, CFO (vickieu@mtstravel.com)

OTHER AGENCIES

3

INFORMATION

The largest nationwide, full-service travel company specializing in religious, mission, and non-profit travel, MTS Travel also offers custom group tours and cruises, all types of vacations, meetings management, and corporate travel. The company was the official travel agency for Mennonite World Conference 2003 in Zimbabwe.

Branch offices: Newton, Kan. (800-835-0106); Bloomfield N.J. (800-526-6278); Claremont, Calif., (800-854-7979); Colorado Springs, Colo. (800-542-5577); Jackson, Miss. (800-647-5296); Jacksonville, Fla. (800-888-8292); Raleigh, N.C. (800-849-1759); Miami, Fla. (877-311-7331); Greenville, Miss. (800-562-6356).

Founded in 1947 as the travel department of Mennonite Central Committee. Incorporated in 1955 as a full-service travel agency.

BOARD

Daniel Hess (dhess@lmasystems.com), chair; Kermit Yoder, president; Vickie Unruh, treasurer; Jim Buddendorf, secretary; Jim Smucker, assistant chair; Linda Zuendel, assistant secretary; Byron Ediger; Richard Huneryager; Paul Kurtz; J. E. Lehman; Keith Stuckey

PUBLICATIONS

Church, Mission, Relief and Development Travel ENews (bimonthly), Todd Jarvis, editor (Ephrata, Pa. office)

Mennofolk Music Festival

wendy@mennofolk.org,
www.mennofolk.org
419-358-4326
139 N Spring St, Bluffton OH 45817

STAFF

Wendy Chappell-Dick (wendy@mennofolk.org)
Andy Chappell-Dick (andy@mennofolk.org)

INFORMATION

Mennofolk is a yearly gathering of Mennonite

folk musicians and those who love their music, serving as an outreach through music to the surrounding communities and an acknowledgment of the many fine professional and amateur musicians of various genres among us.

We are supported by the Peace, Service, and Justice Committee of the Central District Conference with the goal of becoming an independent organization.

Our website maintains a database of Mennonite folk musicians across the country, as well as giving information about location and time of the next Mennofolk festival.

BOARD

Members of the Peace, Service, and Justice Committee of Central District Conference (see section 2)

Mennonite and Brethren Marriage Encounter (M&BME)

love@marriageencounter.org,
www.marriageencounter.org
717-838-4952 or 804-795-2646
Rte 1, Box 38-F, Hershey PA 17033

STAFF

Sam Zeist and Lois Zeist, moderators
Ruth Smith, secretary

INFORMATION

Founded in 1980. M&BME fosters improved marital love between husband and wife, and with God, based upon Christian ideals of marriage. Engaged encounter is also offered. Affiliated with Brethren in Christ, Church of the Brethren, and Mennonite Church USA.

Mennonite Association of Retired Persons (MARP)

marp-soop@juno.com,
http://marp.mennonite.net
215-721-7730, fax 215-723-1590
771 Rte 113, Souderton PA 18964

STAFF

Helen L. Lapp, executive director

INFORMATION

MARP links older adults in the Anabaptist fellowship and challenges its membership to ongoing learning and service opportunities. The organization's guiding theme is "Older Adults Living with Spirit."

Founded in 1987 as an outgrowth of Inter-Mennonite Council on Aging, MARP is open to all over 50 years of age. Its vision for continuing response to Christ's call finds one expression in the cooperative short-term service project, SOOP (Service Opportunities for Older People).

BOARD

Charles B. Longenecker, chair (cbljfk@supernet.com), 730 Maple Grove Rd, New Holland PA 17557, 717-354-5271; Eleanor C. Ruth, recording secretary; Al Albrecht; Kenton K. Brubaker;

OTHER AGENCIES

3

Kay Ann Fransen; Nancy Garis; Kay Sears; Ken Schmidt; Ralph Witmer

PUBLICATION
PAGES (quarterly), Helen L. Lapp, editor

Mennonite Camping Association (MCA)
office@mennonitecamping.org;
www.mennonitecamping.org
574 523-3043, fax 574 293-1892
PO Box 1245, Elkhart IN 46515-1245

STAFF
Evon Castro, secretary
 (evonc@mennoniteusa.org)

INFORMATION
Founded 1960. Mennonite Camping Association is a binational clearinghouse for directing and promoting Christian camping in Anabaptist/ Mennonite camps and retreat centers in Canada and the United States. Vision Statement (1998): Seeking God's face in creation, receiving God's love in Christ, radiating God's Spirit in the world. Affiliated camps and retreat centers are listed below.

BOARD
Jerry Markus, president (info@driftcreek.org), PO Box 1110, Lincoln City OR 97367, 541-996-3978; Kyle Barber, president elect; Laurie Weaver, secretary/treasurer; Christine Epp, fourth member; Keith Zehr, past president; Linford King, Mennonite Church USA representative; Elsie Rempel, Mennonite Church Canada representative; Brethren in Christ and Mennonite Brethren representative positions are currently vacant.

PUBLICATION
MCA Newsletter (quarterly), Grace Nolt, editor (marketing@sprucelake.org), RR 1, Box 605, Canadensis PA 18325, 570-595-7505, fax 570-595-0328

Camps and Retreat Centers

*Member of Mennonite Camping Association

ARIZONA

Arizona Mennonite Children's Camp
632-931-9241
4334 W Vista Ave, Glendale AZ 85301
Laurie King, contact

CALIFORNIA

Camp Keola*
info@campkeola.org, www.campkeola.org
559-225-5220 or 559-893-3505 (June–Oct.),
fax 559-225-5223
PO Box 25925, Fresno CA 93729-5925
George Harper, executive director
 Founded 1964. Located in the Sierra Nevada Mountains at Huntington Lake. Offers wholesome retreat programs that draw people closer to Jesus Christ and to each other. Affiliated with Pacific Southwest Mennonite Conference.

Hartland Christian Camp
info@hartlandcamp.com, www.hartlandcamp.com
559-337-2349, fax 559-337-2251
57611 Eshom Valley Dr, Badger CA 93603
Bob Nunziazo, executive director
 Founded 1946. A Christian camp designed for evangelism, spiritual growth, fellowship, and physical refreshment.

Mile High Pines Camp
mhpcamp@aol.com, www.milehighpines.com
909-794-2824, fax 909-794-8884
42739 Hwy 38, Angelus Oaks CA 92305
Gabriel Valencia, director
 Founded 1948. A year-round camp dedicated to retreat, reflection, and renewal. Sponsored by Pacific Conference—Brethren in Christ.

COLORADO

Deer Creek Christian Camp
303-838-5647
228 S Pine Dr, Bailey CO 80421
Joe Graham, contact
 Founded 1962. Available year round for camping, family reunions, and church retreats.

Rocky Mountain Mennonite Camp*
info@rmmcamp.org, www.rmmcamp.org
719-687-9506, fax 719-687-2582
709 CR 62, Divide CO 80814
Corbin Graber, executive director
  Founded 1952. Located on the west slope of Pikes Peak and surrounded by Pike National Forest, the mission of RMMC is to provide a place of retreat encouraging the spiritual, social, physical, and intellectual Christian growth of each camper and guest. Offers year-round programs and camps for all ages with accommodations for church and family retreats. Affiliated with Rocky Mountain and South Central (Kansas) Conferences.

FLORIDA

Lakewood Retreat*
info@Lakewoodretreat.org, www.Lakewoodretreat.org
352-796-4097, fax 352-796-7577
25458 Dan Brown Hill Rd, Brooksville FL 34602
Steve Wilson, executive director
  Founded 1965. A 114-acre youth and family camp, conference, and retreat center. Offers a year-round program for congregations throughout the Southeast.

IDAHO

Palisades Mennonite Church Camp
mepluseight@juno.com
208-397-4239
PO Box 246, Aberdeen ID 83210-0246
Monty Ledford, contact
  Founded 1957. Located in the Targhee National Forest in eastern Idaho. Provides summer Bible camp and retreats for children, youth, and adults. Operated by First Mennonite Church in Aberdeen with volunteer help from other Idaho Mennonites and area churches of other denominations.

ILLINOIS

Menno Haven Camp and Retreat Center*
camp@mennohaven.com, www.mennohaven.com
815-646-4344 and 800-636-6642, fax 815-646-4301
9301 1575 East St, Tiskilwa IL 61368-9710
David Horst, executive director
  Founded 1958. Provides summer youth camps, extensive high ropes and initiatives course, as well as year-round facilities and services for family and church events.

INDIANA

Bible Memory Ministries*
biblemem@maplenet.net, www.bible-memory.org
574-533-5388, fax 574-534-6444
PO Box 823, Goshen IN 46527-0823
Lon Erb, executive director
  Founded 1953. Educates children and youth in the Word of God through Scripture memorization, correspondence lessons, summer camps, winter camps, and area youth activities. Bible Memory leases camps for our programs.

Merry Lea Environmental Learning Center*
lukeag@goshen.edu, www.goshen.edu/merrylea
260-799-5869, fax 260-799-5875
PO Box 263, Wolf Lake IN 46796-0263
Luke A. Gascho, director
  Donated to Goshen College in 1980. A 1,150-acre nature preserve of fields, forests, wetlands, bogs, lakeshores, and meadows. Managed as a nature sanctuary and serves as the "classroom" for environmental education programs for kindergartners through adults.

IOWA

Crooked Creek Christian Camp*
ccccamp@lisco.com, www.crookedcreekcamp.org
319-653-3611, fax 319-653-3611
2830 Coppock Rd, Washington IA 52353-9317
Mary Lou Farmer, administrator
  Founded 1980. Multi-purpose, year-round facility for retreats, family reunions, and children's camping programs.

KANSAS

Camp Mennoscah*
campmno@mennowdc.org, www.mennowdc.org
620-297-3290
PO Box 65, Murdock KS 67111-0065
Deron Nisly, director
  Founded 1948. Sponsors camping programs for children, senior citizens, developmentally disabled, families, and others. A year-round facility. Owned by Western District Conference.

KENTUCKY

Bethel Mennonite Camp*
grow@bethelcamp.org, www.bethelcamp.org
606-666-4911, fax 606-666-4911
2952 Bethel Church Rd, Clayhole KY 41317
Roger Voth, director
  Founded 1957. Mission is to reach kids for Christ through 8 weeks of summer camps.

MICHIGAN

Amigo Centre*
info@amigocentre.org, www.amigocentre.org
269-651-2811, fax 269-659-0084
26455 Banker Rd, Sturgis MI 49091-9355
Dana Sommers, executive director
  Founded 1957. Camp and retreat center for church and family groups. Sponsors youth, adult, and family programs. A year-round facility.

OTHER AGENCIES

3

Camp Friedenswald*
info@friedenswald.org, www.friedenswald.org
269-476-9744, fax 269-476-9745
15406 Watercress Dr, Cassopolis MI 49031-9532
Todd Kirkton, executive director; Colin and Lora Rusel,
program directors; Brad Cogdell, outdoor learning
director
    Founded 1950. A year-round facility that sponsors
various youth and family camp programs. Rents facilities to other groups.

Little Eden Camp*
LittleEden@jackpine.com
231-889-4294, fax 231-889-4294
3721 Portage Point Dr, Onekama MI 49675-9751
Wendell Beck, contact
    Founded 1944. Provides camping programs for chil-
dren, families, and seniors during the summer. Hosts
church retreats and family gatherings the rest of the year.

Miracle Camp
miraclecamp@juno.com, www.miraclecamp.com
269-624-6161, fax 269-624-1566
25281 80th Ave, Lawton MI 49065
    Established 1965 by the Evangelical Mennonite
Camping Board. Year-round camping center for groups
and families up to 320. Programs include 8 weeks of
summer camp for children and youth; four winter youth
retreats, senior adult and family camps. Available for
guest groups.

Northern Michigan Mennonite Camp
dwen@fantheflame.net, www.fantheflame.net
231-258-3402, fax 231-258-3491
6361 Myers Rd, Kalkaska MI 49646
Dwen Bontrager, contact
    Sponsors snow camps in the winter and several
retreats in the summer.

The Hermitage Community
thehermitage@juno.com
269-244-8696, fax 269-244-5856
11321 Dutch Settlement, Three Rivers MI 49093
David and Naomi Wenger, co-directors
    Founded 1985. The Hermitage mission is to provide
a place of welcoming hospitality where individuals and
small groups can explore their sense of call and deepen
their relationship with God.

MINNESOTA

Wilderness Wind Camp*
wildernesswind@juno.com
218-365-5873 or 316-283-5132 (Oct-Apr)
2945 Hwy 169, Ely MN 55731; Oct.–April: 511 W 11th
St, Newton KS 67114
Kathy Landis, director
    Founded 1986. Offers wilderness canoeing and
backpacking trips that integrate Christian spirituality,
care of the environment, cooperation, and wilderness
ethics and skills. Wilderness Wind also has lakeside
cabins available for personal and family retreats.

MISSISSIPPI

Pine Lake Fellowship Camp*
pinelakecamp@juno.com, www.pinelakecamp.com
601-483-2267
10371 Pine Lake Rd, Meridian MS 39307
Jeff and Cheryl Landis, directors
    Founded 1966. Welcomes groups or individuals to
plan their own retreat during the week or on weekends
year-round. Rustic cabins or lodge facilities available.
Owned by Gulf States Mennonite Conference.

MISSOURI

Lakeside Mennonite Camp
660-547-2512
Rt 3 Box 3065, Lincoln MO 65338
Sylvia McMillin, secretary
    One week camping program for 4th- to 8th-graders.
Sponsored by the Mennonite churches of Missouri.

NEW YORK

Beaver Camp*
info@beavercamp.org, www.beavercamp.org
315-376-2640, fax 315-376-7011
8884 Buck Point Rd, Lowville NY 13367
Marvin Zehr, executive director
    Founded 1969. Year-round children's camp and
retreat facility.

Camp Deerpark, Inc*
deerpark@warwick.net, www.campdeerpark.org
845-754-8669, fax 845-754-8217
200 Brandt Rd, PO Box 394, Westbrookville NY 12785
Ken Bontrager, administrator; Jesus Cruz, board chair
    Founded 1969. Mission is to empower youth to
serve Christ in the city. Summer children's camps. Year-
round retreat facility.

OHIO

Camp Buckeye Retreat Center*
campbuck@tusco.net, www.campbuckeye.org
330-756-2380
10055 Camp Rd NW, Beach City OH 44608
Eric Raber, administrator
    Located in wooded hills of east-central Ohio with
more than 90 acres of hiking trails. Facilities include a
lodge, cabins, and Adirondacks with accommodations
for 100 campers in summer. Program focus is for disad-
vantaged children.

Camp Luz*
camp.luz@juno.com, www.campluz.mennonite.net
330-683-1246
152 Kidron Rd, Orrville OH 44667-9699
Deb Horst, camp director
    Founded 1953. Offers summer camps for children
and youth, programmed retreats, and rental facilities
for Christian groups.

OKLAHOMA

Oklahoma Mennonite Retreat
405-663-2523
Rt 3 Box 11, Hydro OK 73048

OREGON

Drift Creek Camp*
info@driftcreek.org, www.driftcreek.org
541-996-3978, fax 541-764-5115
PO Box 1110, Lincoln City OR 97367
Jerry and Amy Markus, administrators
   Founded 1960 by Mennonite Camp Association of Oregon Inc. Provides Christian youth camp and retreat facilities in a temperate rain forest setting of the Siuslaw National Forest.

PENNSYLVANIA

Black Rock Retreat*
main@brr.org, www.brr.org
717-529-3232 and 800-858-9299, fax 717-786-6022
1345 Kirkwood Pk, Quarryville PA 17566-9539
Robert M. Bender, administrator; John E. Riddell, business manager
   Founded 1954. Dedicated to spreading the gospel of Jesus Christ and strengthening his church.

Camp Andrews*
campandrews@yahoo.com, www.campandrews.org
717-284-2624, fax 717-284-2852
1226 Silver Spring Rd, Holtwood PA 17532
Phil Herschberger, administrator
   Founded 1983. To introduce urban youth to Jesus in a rustic, affordable, natural setting.

Camp Hebron, Inc.*
hebron@camphebron.org, www.camphebron.org
717-896-3441 and 800-864-7747, fax 717-896-3391
957 Camp Hebron Rd, Halifax PA 17032-9520
Lanny Millette, executive director; Mike Ford, program director
   Founded 1957. A place where people connect with God, nature, and each other. The vision is to be a Christ-centered sanctuary where people find renewal and growth through recreation, teaching and fellowship in God's creation.

Camp Men-O-Lan*
info@menolan.org, www.menolan.org
215-679-5144, fax 215-679-0226
1415 Doerr Rd, Quakertown PA 18951-2042
Gerald C. Musselman, administrator; Robert Hartz, program director
   Founded 1941. Year-round Christian camping and retreat facilities and programs for all ages. Cottages, cabins, dormitory, RV, and tent sites. Summer overnight and day camps, trip/adventure camps. Sponsored by Eastern District.

Christian Retreat Center
crctims2@starband.net, www.crctims2.org
717-734-3627, fax 717-734-3339
RR 1 Box 13A, East Waterford PA 17021
Bud Wagner, director
   Founded 1979. A year-round camping ministry located 40 miles NW of Harrisburg, Pa. Program includes summer camps for youth, ages 8-18, as well as host of short-term missions groups. Facilities available for 130 people. Owned by Brethren in Christ.

Cove Valley Christian Youth Camp*
covevalley@pa.net
717-328-3055, fax 717-328-2350
5357 Little Cove Rd, Mercersburg PA 17236
Kent Shoffstall, director
   Founded 1967. Children's summer camps, winter retreats, adult, family, and senior retreats. Open for rental groups.

Herrbrook Farm Retreat Cottage
herrbrook@verizon.net,
www.home.supernet.com/~housers
717-872-2848
2256 New Danville Pike, Lancaster PA 17603
Mary Lou and Rod Houser, directors
   Founded 1988. A 19th-century farmstead that offers a place of aesthetic quiet surrounded by gardens, a labyrinth, and a rural landscape. Accommodates one to four persons. Spiritual direction available.

Kairos: School of Spiritual Formation
kairos@on-the-journey.org, www.on-the-journey.org
717-669-2957, fax 717-653-4976
PO Box 5022, Lancaster PA 17606-5022
Cheryl Lehman, director
   Founded 1992. Meets at a Jesuit retreat center. Explores ways people may have a more intimate relationship with God in their daily routine. Offers space and time to experience the spiritual disciplines. Training for spiritual directors is available.

Kenbrook Bible Camp
info@kenbrook.org, www.kenbrook.com
717-865-4547, fax 717-865-0995
190 Pine Meadow Road, Lebanon PA 17046
Dan Krug, director
   Founded 1949. Year-round retreat facility, 18 rooms, handicapped accessible. Summer youth camp ministry with facilities available for groups spring and fall. Emphasizes in-depth relationship with God, self, others, and the created world. Sponsored by Brethren in Christ.

Laurelville Mennonite Church Center*
info@laurelville.org, www.laurelville.org
800-839-1021 and 724-423-2056, fax 724-423-2096
RR 5 Box 145, Mt Pleasant PA 15666
Jerry Troyer, executive director; Cheryl Paulovich, program director
   Founded 1943. Year-round conference and retreat center. Owned and operated by Laurelville Mennonite Church Center Association, Gloria Horst Rosenberger, president.

OTHER AGENCIES

3

Penn Valley Christian Retreat
pvcr@juno.com
717-899-5000 and 717-899-5001, fax 717-899-7295
7980 Ferguson Valley Rd, McVeytown PA 17051
Wayne Schrock, chairman
    Founded 1986. Provides a haven for encourage-
ment, healing, and support in a structured Christian
environment.

Penn-York Camp
pennyork@penn.com, www.pennyork.com
814-848-9811, fax 814-848-7471
226 Northern Potter Rd, Ulysses PA 16948
Gene Miller, camp administrator; Brent Peters, camp
manager
    Founded 1970. Develops dedicated followers of
Jesus Christ by building spirit, mind, and body in a natural setting.

Roxbury Holiness Camp
roxburycamp@onemain.com, www.roxburycamp.com
717-532-2208, fax 717-532-9392
PO Box 28, Roxbury PA 17251
Roy Heisey, administrator
    Founded 1936. Located at the foot of the Allegheny
Mountains. Open year-round with various housing and
meeting facilities including conference center, guesthouse,
motel, dormitories, and cabins. Suitable for retreats, camping, reunions. Sponsoring organization: Brethren in Christ
Church.

Spruce Lake Retreat*
info@sprucelake.org, www.sprucelake.org
570-595-7505, 800-822-7505; fax 570-595-0328
RR 1 Box 605, Canadensis PA 18325-9749
Dan Ziegler, executive director
    Founded 1963. Christ-centered retreat center that
features outdoor school, wilderness camp and expedi-
tions, family retreat programming, and guest group
ministries. Situated on 370 acres in the Pocono
Mountains of northeastern Pennsylvania. Owned by
Franconia Mennonite Camp Association and relates to
Franconia Mennonite Conference.

Tel Hai Camp and Retreat
telhai@uscom.com, www.telhaicamp.org
610-273-3969, fax 610-273-3558
31 Lasso Dr, Honey Brook PA 19344-9261
Mike Willoughby, director
    Founded 1950. A Christian camp and retreat center
with year-round facilities for church groups.

Woodcrest Retreat*
info@woodcrestretreat.org; www.woodcrestretreat.org
717-738-2233, fax 717-738-3128
225 Woodcrest Dr, Ephrata PA 17522-9397
Cliff Martin, administrator; Phil Horning, program
director
    Founded 1959. Sharing Christ's love with children,
youth, and families in a beautiful camp setting.
Sponsored by Woodcrest Retreat Association.

SOUTH CAROLINA

Hartwell Mennonite Center
190 Stalling Ridge Rd, Pickens SC 29671

SOUTH DAKOTA

Swan Lake Christian Camp*
slcc@hcinet.net, www.myslcc.com
605-326-5690, fax 605-326-5593
45474 288th St, Viborg SD 57070
Jerry and Judi Kroeker, co-directors
    Founded 1955. A year-round facility providing youth
camping and retreat facilities. Sponsored by the Swan
Lake Christian Camp Association.

VERMONT

Bethany Birches Camp*
bbc@valley.net, www.vtchildrenscamp.com
802-672-5220
2610 Lynds Hill Rd, Plymouth VT 05056
Mike Wenger, executive director; Ann Wenger, program
director
    Founded 1965. Provides an affordable Christian
summer camp experience for children in Vermont and
surrounding states. Programming includes seven weeks
of overnight camp in the summer for boys and girls
ages 8-18, day camp, winter snow camps, and a win-
terized cabin for retreats and family gatherings.

VIRGINIA

Highland Retreat*
info@highlandretreat.org, www.highlandretreat.org
540-852-3226, fax 540-852-9272
14783 Upper Highland Dr, Bergton VA 22811-9712
Paul Beiler, administrator
    Founded 1958. Year-round camp and retreat setting
in NW Virginia. Mission is to provide an outdoor setting where people can meet Jesus Christ and explore
his creation. Includes a summer youth camping program, retreat center, youth lodge, and campground.
Relates primarily to churches of Virginia Conference.

Williamsburg Christian Retreat Center*
wcrc@wcrc.info, www.wcrc.info
757-566-2256, fax 757-566-4875
9275 Barnes Rd, Toano VA 23168
Herb Lantz, executive director
    Founded 1984. Provides Christ-centered retreat
facilities, services, and programs to encourage fellowship, growth, and renewal. Features cottages, motel
style rooms, and an RV campground. Ideal for church,
family, and personal retreats. Also has a summer camp
program for children and youth. Relates to Virginia
Mennonite Conference.

WASHINGTON

Camp Camrec*
camrec@rightathome.com,
www.camrec.mennonite.net
509-548-7245
18899 Little Chumstick Crk Rd, Leavenworth WA
98826
Roger and Carmen Reimer, managers
 Founded 1963. A Christian camping and retreat
center operated by the Mennonite churches of the
state of Washington.

WEST VIRGINIA

Harman Mt. Farm Campground*
rolowenger@juno.com
304-227-3647
HC 70 Box 67A, Harman WV 26270
Robert and Lois Wenger, campground managers
 Founded 1971. Offers camping in quiet, natural
mountain beauty with bathhouse, pavilion, and
hookups.

Mountain Retreat
lmlind@meer.net, www.mt-retreat.com
304-227-4427
PO Box 266, Harman WV 26270
Lester and Mary Beth Lind, co-directors
 Founded 1991. A retreat center offering personal
and group retreats focused on nature, prayer, and
spirituality. Facilities available for rental.

Mennonite Central Committee

mailbox@mcc.org, www.mcc.org
888-563-4676 and 717-859-1151,
fax 717-859-2171
21 S 12th St, PO Box 500, Akron PA 17501-0500

STAFF

Ronald J. R. Mathies, executive director
(rjm@mcc.org)
Bruce McCrae, director of administration and
resources (brm@mcc.org)

INFORMATION

MCC is the relief, service, and development agency of North American Mennonite and Brethren in Christ churches. Members include Beachy Amish, Brethren in Christ, Chortitzer Mennonites, Conservative Mennonite Conference, Evangelical Mennonite Church, Evangelical Mennonite Mission Church, Evangelical Mennonite Conference, Fellowship of Evangelical Churches, Lancaster Mennonite Conference, Mennonite Brethren, Mennonite Church USA, Mennonite Church Canada, Old Colony, Old Order Amish, Old Order Mennonite, Sommerfelder Mennonite. MCC was founded in 1920 in response to hunger and human need caused by war and revolution in Russia and the Ukraine.

BOARD

+*Karen Klassen Harder, chair, 118 Sunset Dr, Bluffton OH 45817, 419-358-0698; *Eric Rempel, vice chair; *Patricia Leaman, secretary; *Vidya Narimalla, treasurer; Tom Beachy; *Harriet Sider Bicksler; *Martha Burka; Harvey Chupp; +Rose Covington; Maria DeLeon; *Harold Dick; *Ron Dueck; Jacob Elias; Marty Freeburne; Louise Giesbrecht; Ann Graber Hershberger; +Stanley Green; +John Hess-Yoder; Maribel Ramirez Hinojosa; Gerald Hughes; *Vernon Jantzi; Dora Koop; Iris Kwai Hing Leung; Ronald J. R. Mathies; David Miller; Erin Morash; +Tim Penner; Carole Phillips; Dick Plett; Laura Schmidt Roberts; Don Showalter; Richard Showalter; Scott Siemens; Glenn Wiebe; *John Wiens; Greg Zimmerman
    *Executive Committee members
    +Mennonite Church USA appointees

PUBLICATIONS

A Common Place, Peace Office Newsletter, Jottings, Hello

UNITED NATIONS OFFICE

unoffice@mcc.org
212-223-4062, fax 212-750-1194
866 United Nations Plaza, Room 575, New York NY 10017

Mennonite Central Committee U.S.

mailbox@mcc.org, www.mcc.org
717-859-3889, fax 717-859-3875
21 S 12th St, PO Box 500, Akron PA 17501-0500

A window on the world
service opportunities
photo gallery
resources
news
www.mcc.org

OTHER AGENCIES

3

STAFF
Rolando Santiago, executive director
(rsantiago@mcc.org)

BOARD
*Harriet Sider Bicksler, chair, 127 Holly Dr,
Mechanicsburg PA 17055, 717-795-9151;
*Jonathan Showalter, vice chair; *Samuel
Resendez, secretary-treasurer; Dagne Assefa;
Danny Begaye; *William Braun; Harvey Chupp;
+*Rose Covington; *Maria DeLeon; Lawrence
Hart; *Ann Graber Hershberger; David Miller;
William Swartzendruber; Sharon
Swartzentruber; Greg Zimmerman (*Executive
Committee members; +Mennonite Church USA
appointees)

REGIONAL OFFICES AND MATERIAL RESOURCES CENTERS
West Coast MCC and Material Resources Center
209-638-6911, fax 209-638-6914, 1010 G St,
Reedley CA 93654
MCC Central States and Material Resources
Center
316-284-2720, fax 316-283-8727, 121 E
30th St, PO Box 235, North Newton KS 67117
MCC Great Lakes
574-534-4133, fax 574-537-9527, 1013
Division St, Goshen IN 46526,
mccgl@mcc.org
MCC East Coast
717-859-1151, fax 717-859-3875, 21 S 12th
St, PO Box 500, Akron PA 17501-0500
MCC Material Resources Center
717-733-2847, fax 717-733-7329,
517 W Trout Run Rd, Ephrata PA 17522

WASHINGTON OFFICE
202-544-6564, fax 202-544-2820
110 Maryland Ave NE #502,
Washington DC 20002
J. Daryl Byler, director (jdb@mcc.org)

PEACE AND JUSTICE MINISTRIES OFFICE
mailbox@mcc.org, www.mcc.org
717-859-1151, fax 717 859-3875
21 S 12th St, PO Box 500, Akron PA 17501-0500

Staff—Peace and Justice Ministries Office
Iris de Leon-Hartshorn, director
(idh@mcc.org)
Titus Peachey, director of Peace Education
(tmp@mcc.org)
Rebeca J. Yoder, director of Immigration
(rjy@mcc.org)
Lorraine Stutzman Amstutz, director of the
Office on Crime and Justice (lsa@mcc.org)
Linda Gehman Peachey, director of Women's
Concerns (lgp@mcc.org)
Marcia Stoesz, co-director of Anti-Racism pro-
gram (ms@mcc.org)
The Peace and Justice Ministries Office grew out
of the MCC Peace Section. Departments include
the Anti-Racism Program (including Damascus
Road), the Immigration desk, Mennonite
Conciliation Services, the Office on Crime and
Justice (including Victim Offender
Reconciliation Program—VORP), the Peace
Education Office and the Women's Concerns
desk.

Anti-racism table serves as an advisory
group to give direction and counsel. Members:
Phil Bergey; Ron Byler; Maria DeLeon; Prem
Dick; Gilberto Flores; Lynford Hershey; Zulma
Prieto; Tammerie Spires; David Whettstone

Damascus Road was founded in 1995 by
MCC as an anti-racism training program to effect
change in Anabaptist institutions. Damascus
Road provides analysis and organizing training
several times each year. Core trainers: Dionicio
Acosta, Michelle Armster, Phil Brubaker, Rick
Derksen, Calenthia Dowdy, Harley Eagle, Felipe
Hinojosa, Erica Littlewolf, Conrad Moore,
Yvonne Plats, Tobin Miller-Shearer, Regina
Shands Stoltzfus, Sharon Williams, Brenda Zook
Friesen. Core organizers: Jeff Gingerich, Ellie
Huebner. Core Chaplains: Hosley Hickman, Fred
Kauffman, Marty Shupack

OTHER AGENCIES

3

THRIFT SHOPS

bkschrag@mcc.org, www.mcc.org
717-859-1151, fax 717-859-2171
21 S 12th St, PO Box 500, Akron PA 17501-0500
For a listing of over 100 shops, go to
www.mcc.org and click on *get involved*.

Barb Schrag, U.S. coordinator
(bkschrag@mcc.org), PO Box 416,
Freeman SD 67029

The Mennonite Central Committee Thrift
Shop Network is the result of constituent concern for human need both locally and globally.
Thrift Shop volunteers commit themselves to
Christian faith in action by volunteering their
time and talent for receiving and reselling
donated items and sending shop proceeds to
benefit the work of MCC. Shops offer a friendly,
caring presence in the community and inform
the churches and community of the Mennonite
Central Committee mission.

TEN THOUSAND VILLAGES

inquiry.us@tenthousandvillages.com,
www.tenthousandvillages.org
717-859-8100, fax 717-859-2622
704 Main St, PO Box 500,
Akron PA 17501-0500
For a complete store listing, visit
www.tenthousandvillages.org.
Paul E. Myers, chief executive officer

Ten Thousand Villages provides vital, fair income
to artisans around the world by marketing their
handicrafts and telling their stories in North
America. Ten Thousand Villages, a nonprofit
program of the Mennonite Central Committee,
has been trading fairly with artisans since 1946.

PUBLICATIONS

Washington Memo, Women's Concerns Report
and *Conciliation Quarterly* (same address as
above)

Mennonite Chaplains Association

loubeellen@enter.net
610-782-0523, fax 610-395-6126
517 N Lafayette St, Allentown PA 18104

STAFF

Byron Gingrich, president
Robert Keener, president elect
Myra Raab, past president

INFORMATION

Founded 1962. Organized to provide support,
collaboration, resources, collegiality, and continuing education for chaplains affiliated with
Mennonite/Anabaptist-related congregations or
organizations and to stimulate professional
growth.

PUBLICATION

The president has an article printed quarterly in
the *Mennonite Health Journal.*

Mennonite Christian Leadership Foundation (MCLF)

mail@globaldisciples.org,
www.globaldisciples.org
315 W James St, Suite 202, Lancaster PA 17603
717-290-7550, fax 717-290-7551

STAFF

Galen Burkholder, executive director
(galen@globaldisciples.org)
Tim Pfautz, operations manager
(mail@globaldisciples.org)

INFORMATION

Mennonite Christian Leadership Foundation
helps provide teachers for local leadership
training of church groups around the world.
MCLF is a part of the leadership training
alliance facilitated by Global Disciples Network.

MCLF, with Global Disciples Network, is focused on developing an alliance of locally operated leadership training programs among 60 conferences of churches related to Mennonite World Conference.

MCLF was founded in 1969 and for 30 years provided in-service training for church leaders globally. Their board joined with Global Disciples board in 2001. One board now governs both organizations.

Mennonite Church USA Executive Board
—see section 1, Churchwide Agencies

Mennonite Disaster Service (MDS)

binational@mds.mennonite.net, www.mds.mennonite.net
717-859-2210, fax 717-859-4910
1018 Main St, Akron PA 17501

STAFF
Kevin King, executive coordinator (kking@mds.mennonite.net)
Carla Hunt, assistant coordinator (chunt@mds.mennonite.net)
John Walker, communication coordinator (jwalker@mds.mennonite.net)

INFORMATION
Mennonite Disaster Service (MDS) answers calls for disaster help in all emergencies, such as floods, tornadoes, hurricanes, earthquakes, and fires. MDS coordinates volunteers from Anabaptist constituent churches for disaster response.

BOARD
Rocky Miller, chair, 941-371-4162; Vernon Miller, vice chair; Jane Kuepfer, secretary; Millard Garrett, treasurer; Abe Ens; Gordon Friesen; Willis Hochstetler; David Hoover; Betty Kasdorf; Fred Kathler; Wilmer Leichty; Bernard Martin; Ottis Mast; William McCoy; Dan Miller; +Ross Miller; Carlos Santiago; Vernon Schmucker; Albert Schrock; Amos Schwartz; Sanford Swartzendruber; Marvin Toews; Stella Toews; Willis Troyer; Paul Unruh; Anne Wiens; Alfred Yoder (+Mennonite Church USA appointee)

PUBLICATION
Behind the Hammer (quarterly), John Walker, editor (same address as above)

Mennonite Economic Development Associates (MEDA)

www.meda.org, www.businessasacalling.org, www.saronafund.com
Use 800-665-7026 or
meda@meda.org to contact all offices
(Corporate and International Operations in Waterloo ON; Marketing and Fundraising Group in Winnipeg MB; or North American Operations in Lancaster PA)

STAFF
Allan Sauder, president
Ed Epp, vice president, resource development
Howard Good, vice president, North American operations
Kim Pityn, vice president, international operations

INFORMATION
Founded 1953. Mennonite Economic Development Associates is an organization for Christians who seek to connect their faith and daily work in a needy world. Together we help support MEDA's business-oriented development product lines in the developing world, as well as providing assistance to low-income entrepreneurs in North America.

OTHER AGENCIES

3

BOARD
John E. Yoder, president, 505 Belmont Avenue, Bryan OH 43506
Executive Committee Members: Verda Beachy; Gloria E. Eby; Ron Haarer; Ken Hochstetler

PUBLICATION
The Marketplace, six times a year, Wally Kroeker, editor

Mennonite Education Agency
—see section 1, Churchwide Agencies

Mennonite Elementary Education Council (MEEC)
—see schools in this section and Mennonite Education Agency in section 1, Churchwide Agencies

Mennonite Financial Federal Credit Union
info@mennonitefinancial.com,
www.mennonitefinancial.com
717-735-8330, 800-451-5719, fax 717-735-8331
PO Box 10455, Lancaster PA 17605

MANAGEMENT TEAM
Larry D. Miller, president/CEO
    (larry@mennonitefinancial.com)
W. Kent Hartzler, vice president of lending and business development
    (kent@mennonitefinancial.com)
Sandy Hershey, vice president of operations
    (sandy@mennonitefinancial.com)

INFORMATION
A cooperative that provides full financial services for Mennonites, Amish, Brethren in Christ, and related Anabaptist groups in the United States. Employees and family members of Mennonite organizations also are eligible for membership.

Services include loans, credit cards, savings, checking, IRAs, certificates, and other related financial products. Office locations: Lancaster, Pa., headquarters, 800-451-5719; Lancaster, Pa., Lititz Pike branch, 717-291-1364; Scottdale, Pa., branch, 800-322-0440; Belleville, Pa., branch, 717-935-0025; Ephrata, Pa., branch, 717-721-6180; Kidron, Ohio, branch, 800-315-4306

Founded in 2000 from a merger of Pennsylvania Mennonite FCU (1955), Ohio Mennonite FCU (1985), and Illinois Mennonite FCU (1988).

BOARD
Aaron Martin Jr., chair
(vze29kk9@verizon.net); Marialy Justiniano; Art Neuenschwander; Richard Reimer; Jack Scott; Dena Stauffer; Michael Zehr

Mennonite Health Assembly
info@mhsonline.org, www.mhsonline.org
800-611-4007 and 574-534-9689,
    fax 574-534-3254
234 S Main St, Suite 1, Goshen IN 46526

STAFF
Mim Shirk, director (mim@mhsonline.org)
Wendy Rohn, registrar (wendy@mhsonline.org)

INFORMATION
The annual Mennonite Health Assembly draws practitioners and leaders of Anabaptist health and human services to explore innovative ways to carry out ministry in the context of our faith. Attendees include administrators, board members, chaplains, church leaders, congregational health promoters, counselors, executives, nurses, pastors, physicians, psychologists, social workers, and students. The Assembly is cosponsored by MHS Alliance and MMA.

OTHER AGENCIES

3

A community of health and human service ministries committed to God's work of healing and hope in Christ Jesus

Mennonite Health Services Alliance is the national membership association for Anabaptist-related health and human service providers.

A **Covenant of Relationship** between MHS Alliance and Mennonite Church USA provides accountability and affirms the place of health and human service agencies in the church's mission.

MHS Alliance provides important **services and support** to link members with their founding denominations and enable them to better serve their communities.

MHS Alliance: 72 members — 15,000 employees
Serving 75,000 senior, youth, children, and adults each year

To learn more about the
quality programs and services
of MHS Alliance members or
to find out about employment
or volunteer opportunities,
visit www.mhsonline.org
or call 574-534-9689.

Mennonite Health Services Alliance ⟩ *

info@mhsonline.org, www.mhsonline.org
800-611-4007 and 574-534-9689,
   fax 574-534-3254
234 S Main St, Suite 1, Goshen IN 46526
*covenant relationship with Mennonite Church
   USA

STAFF
Rick Stiffney, president (rick@mhsonline.org)
Mim Shirk, vice president
   (mim@mhsonline.org)
Keith Stuckey, vice president
   (keith@mhsonline.org)

INFORMATION
MHS Alliance sponsors 18 organizations and
promotes networking among 70 member ministries, strengthening board and executive leadership, enhancing relationships with churches
and co-sponsoring the annual Mennonite Health
Assembly (see separate listing).
   Members include Mennonite Church USA,
Mennonite Brethren U.S., and Brethren in Christ
health and human service ministries (see separate healthcare listings below for child welfare
services, developmental disability services, hospitals, mental health agencies and retirement
centers). MHS Alliance is accountable to its
relating denominations through covenants of
mutual accountability.
   MHS Alliance was founded by MCC in 1947
as Mennonite Mental Health Services. It broad-
ened its scope in 1989 to include other
Anabaptist health and human service ministries.

BOARD
LaVern Yutzy, chair, Philhaven, PO Box 550, Mt
Gretna PA 17064; Kenneth Brubaker; +Daniel
Grimes; Nancy Hopkins-Garriss; John Martin;
+Ron Price; Valerie Rempel; Lenora Stern; Jay
Shetler; Wendell Rempel; +Bonnie Weaver;
Margaret Zook (+Mennonite Church USA
appointees)

PUBLICATION
Connections (bimonthly), Mim Shirk, editor
(same address as above)

Health Care Agencies

*Denotes members of Mennonite Health
   Services Alliance.
+Denotes organizations sponsored by MHS
   Alliance.

CHILD WELFARE SERVICES

Adriel Inc.+
www.adriel.org
937-465-0010 and 800-262-0065, fax 937-465-8690
PO Box 188, 414 N Detroit St, West Liberty OH 43357
Dave Link, board chair
   A multiservice center for children and their families
with specialized programs including residential treat-
ment, treatment foster care, and adoptions services.
Co-sponsors Shalom Ministries (see separate entries
below). Board appointed by MHS Alliance, Ohio
Conference, Central District Conference, and four local
Mennonite churches.

Associated Youth Services
dvanderpool@aysusa.org
913-831-2820, fax 913-831-0262
1620 S 37th, PO Box 6145, Kansas City KS 66106-6145
Dennis Vanderpool, CEO (dvanderpool@ayusa.org);
Alan Stevens, board chair
   Founded 1972. Serving over 1,000 youth and families
annually. AYS exists to advance the social, educational,
and emotional health and success of youth and families.

DEVELOPMENTAL DISABILITIES SERVICES

**Central California Mennonite Residential
Services Inc.***
559-227-2940, fax 559-222-1180
PO Box 5298, Fresno CA 93755
Amanda Guajardo, executive director

**Christian Residential Opportunities and
Social Services Inc.**
grace@innernet.net
717-530-1788, fax 717-530-1788
712 Pinola Rd, Shippensburg PA 17257
Jim Roberts, director
   Founded 1985. Two residential homes for MR
adults. Social services include respite care, camps for
individuals with disabilities, and coffee houses for
those with special needs.

Faith Mission Home Inc.
434-985-2294, fax 434-985-7633
3540 Mission Home Ln, Free Union VA 22940-0114
Dennis Eash, administrator
   Christian residential care and vocational training for 60 mentally handicapped children and young adults in a beautiful rural environment.

Friendship Community*
www.friendshipcommunity.org
717-656-2466 and 717-299-1795, fax 717-656-0459
1149 E Oregon Rd, Lititz PA 17543-9208
George Stoltzfus, executive director
   A Christian ministry providing residential and social services for people with developmental disabilities and their families in Lancaster County and surrounding counties.

Indian Creek Foundation Inc.*
sbechtel@indiancreekfoundation.org;
www.indiancreekfoundation.org
215-256-5900, fax 215-256-8400
573 Yoder Rd, PO Box 225, Harleysville PA 19438-0225
David H. Crosson, executive director
   Founded 1975. Provides care for the developmentally disabled including individuals with mental retardation and autism spectrum disorders through group homes, community living programs, vocational training with work activities center, job placement, and family services for all ages.

Jubilee Association of Maryland Inc.*
twiens@jubileemd.org; www.jubileemd.org
301-949-8628 and 301-949-8626, fax 301-949-4628
10408 Montgomery Ave, Kensington MD 20895
Tim Wiens, executive director
   Founded 1978. Provides group home and supported living services to adults in Montgomery County, Md.

MDC Goldenrod*
info@goldenrodonline.org; www.goldenrodonline.org
574-533-9720 and 574-534-0452, fax 574-534-9817
1518 College Ave, Goshen IN 46526
David Heusinkveld, administrator

Founded 1977. Provides respite care and long-term residential services for individuals with developmental disabilities.

Oregon Mennonite Residential Services Inc.+
omrs@mennonitevillage.org
503-474-1213, fax 503-474-1145
325 SW Elmwood Ave, McMinnville OR 97128
Karen Litwiller, executive director (omrs@mennonite-home.com); Dave Miller, board chair
   Founded 1986. Operates and maintains group homes for adults with developmental disabilities in the Willamette Valley.

Peaceful Living+
jlandis@peacefulliving.org; www.peacefulliving.org
610-287-1200, fax 610-287-7121
PO Box 154, Lederach PA 19450
Joe Landis, executive director

Pleasant View Inc.*
nhg_pv@ntelos.net; www.pleasantview-inc.com
540-896-8255, fax 540-896-8454
PO Box 426, Broadway VA 22815-0426
   Founded 1971. Serves adults with developmental disabilities. Provides group homes, apartment living, in-home services, intermediate care, specialized home services, day support, and supported employment. A mission of Virginia Mennonite Conference.

Sunshine Inc. of Northwest Ohio+
info@sunshineincnwo.org; www.sunshineincnwo.org
419-865-0251, fax 419-865-9715
7223 Maumee Western Rd, Maumee OH 43537-9656
John L. Martin, executive director
   Founded 1949. Mission is to enhance the lives of people with developmental disabilities and their families. Provide supportive, loving communities through residential and related services. Board consists of local community leaders.

HOSPITALS

BroMenn Healthcare
www.bromenn.org
309-454-1400
PO Box 2850, Bloomington IL 61702-2850
Roger Hunt, president/CEO (rhunt@bromenn.org)
Acute care hospital, primary care and pediatric physician practices, home health, hospice, rehabilitation, and behavioral health services.

Mid-Valley Healthcare*
www.samhealth.org
541-768-5009, fax 541-768-5002
525 N Santiam Hwy, PO Box 739, Lebanon OR 97355
Steve Jasperson, executive vice president of hospital operations (stevej@samhealth.org)
Founded 1952. Provides integrated health and hospital services primarily for the people of Linn County, Ore.

Samaritan Health Services Inc.*
stevej@goodsam.com; www.samhealth.org
541-757-5002 and 541-757-5009, fax 541-757-5100
PO Box 1068, Corvallis OR 97339
Larry Mullins, president/CEO

MENTAL HEALTH AGENCIES

Brook Lane Health Services+
curtm@brooklane.org; www.brooklane.org
301-733-0330 and 800-342-2992, fax 301-733-4038
13218 Brook Ln Dr, PO Box 1945, Hagerstown MD 21742
R. Lynn Rushing, CEO; Ray Geigley, board chair
Founded 1946. Provides mental health services for children, adolescents, adults, and older adults in an atmosphere reflecting God's love for each person. Governed by local church and community board.

Crown Centre for Counseling
330-927-2020, fax 330-927-2020
9693 Benner Rd, Rittman OH 44270
Dave Stauffer and Twila Zimmerly, co-directors
Founded 1984 as an independent entity. Reorganized in 2002 as an outreach of the church.

Family Life Resource Center
services@flrc.org; www.flrc.org
540-434-8450 and 800-655-2055, fax 540-433-3805
273 Newman Ave, Harrisonburg VA 22801
Lu Emswiler, executive director

Kings View Corporation+
fduerksen@kingsview.org; www.kingsview.org
559-256-0100 ext. 3006, fax 559-256-0115
575 E Locust Ave, Suite 311, Fresno CA 93720
Frank Duerksen, CEO
Founded 1951. Kings View provides community behavioral health for the people of Central and Northern California, including mental health, chemical dependency, and services for developmentally challenged individuals.

No Longer Alone Ministries*
Nlam2@earthlink.net; www.nlam.org
717-656-7358, fax 717-656-6457
1155-B E Oregon Rd, Lititz PA 17543
Founded in 1991. No Longer Alone Ministries provides supportive services to individuals experiencing long-term mental illness and their families in Lancaster County, Pa., as an expression of Christ's love.

Oaklawn+
info@oaklawn.org; www.oaklawn.org
574-533-1234 and 800-282-0809, fax 574-537-2673
330 Lakeview Dr, PO Box 809, Goshen IN 46527-0809
Harold C. Loewen, president/CEO; Daniel Kinsey, M.D., medical director
Founded 1962. Oaklawn offers a comprehensive range of mental health and addictions services for children, adolescents, adults, and older adults.

Penn Foundation Inc.+
jgoshow@pennfoundation.org;
www.pennfoundation.org
215-257-6551 and 800-245-7366, fax 215-257-9347
807 Lawn Ave, PO Box 32, Sellersville PA 18960-0032
John Goshow, president/CEO; Jay Showalter, medical director
Founded 1955. Mission is to provide comprehensive behavioral health care to persons in need of hope, healing, and compassion.

Philhaven+
dale@philhaven.com; www.philhaven.com
717-273-8871 and 717-270-2443, fax 717-270-2456
PO Box 550, 283 S Butler Rd, Mt Gretna PA 17064-0550
Founded 1952. Provides broad range of behavioral health services for persons of all ages in south central Pennsylvania. Services include inpatient, residential, day hospital, outpatient, and numerous community based services. Additional programs include Recovery of Hope, Employee Assistance Programs, and Adventure Challenge Experience.

Prairie View Inc.+
info@pvi.org; www.pvi.org
316-284-6400 and 800-362-0180, fax 316-284-6491
PO Box 467, 1901 E First St, Newton KS 67114-0467
Founded 1954. Behavioral and mental health organization providing services for persons with disorders. A not-for-profit, outcomes-based, regional behavioral and mental health system, providing inpatient, outpatient, residential, school, and consultation services in South Central Kansas.

OTHER AGENCIES

3

Shalom Ministries
lmoshier@adriel2.org
419-445-1552, fax 419-445-1401
207 Vine Street, Archbold OH 43502
Lenette Moshier, director
Founded 1998. Co-sponsored by Adriel School and Northwest Ohio Mennonite Ministers Fellowship. Serving Ohio (primarily Northwest Ohio) and Southern Michigan. Mission: to provide consultation, counseling, reconciliation, education, guidance, and other services to individuals, churches, and other groups.

Shalom Wellness Center (a program of Shalom Ministries)
Darlene Rohrer-Meck, director, LISW,
drmeck@adriel2.org
Individual, couple, children, and family therapy. Pastoral consultations, support groups, wellness education, and spiritual direction. Other services offered through Shalom Ministries: VORP (Victim Offender Reconciliation Program) and mediation services.

Upward Call*
717-355-2117, fax 717-355-2879
150 E Franklin St, New Holland PA 17557
Upward Call provides professional Christian counseling with a special emphasis on reaching the Old Order Amish and Mennonite community.

OTHER HEALTH AND HUMAN SERVICES AGENCIES

Bridge of Hope
info@bridgeofhope.org; www.bridgeofhope.org
866-670-HOPE
National Office: 311 National Rd, Exton PA 19341
Edith Yoder, executive director
Bridge of Hope ends and prevents homelessness for single mothers with the help of trained mentoring groups within Christian congregations. Will help start Bridge of Hope in other geographical areas.

RETIREMENT CENTERS

Bethesda Home*
www.bethesdahome.org
620-367-2291, fax 620-367-2294
408 E Main St, Box 37, Goessel KS 67053-0037
Linda Peters, CEO
Founded 1899. Organized to care for frail elderly and disabled. Offers assisted living, independent living, skilled nursing care, adult daycare, and Alzheimer's special care unit.

Beth-Haven Nursing Home and Residential Care*
www.bethhaven.org
573-221-6000 and 573-221-3815, fax 573-248-1523
2500 Pleasant St, Hannibal MO 63401-2699
Paul Ewert, administrator

Brementowne Manor Apartments*
Brementowne1982@covad.net
708-429-4088, fax 708-532-1397
16130 Oak Park Ave, Tinley Park IL 60477
James R. Durnbaugh, site manager
Housing for senior citizens and disabled persons.

Casa del Sol Retirement Community*
info@casadelsollj.org; www.casadelsollj.org
719-384-0342, fax 719-384-0342
1002 Casa del Sol Dr, La Junta CO 81050
Lynette Horner, manager; Howard E Stutzman, M.D., board chair
Founded in 1992. Fifty-two apartments, 6 eight-plexes and two duplexes. Community for independent living for adults over 55 years old.

Community Caring, Inc
comments@comcaring.org; www.comcaring.org
989-848-2843, fax 989-848-7590
PO Box 9, Fairview MI 48621
Chris Mulrooney, M.P.S., Ph.D., president/CEO; Ronald W. Messner, board chair
Founded 1948. A Christian service organization sponsoring health and human service ministries. Flagship ministry is AuSable Valley Community, a 170-resident community in Fairview.

Community Home Services*
dtihansky@communityhomeservices.org
715-723-1906, 888-723-3570, fax 715-723-1590
PO Box 158, Franconia PA 18924
Diane Tihansky, administrator
Founded in 1995. Provides support and services to enable persons to remain at home throughout the aging, illness, disability and hospice process. Sponsors: Dock Woods Community, Frederick Mennonite Community, Peter Becker Community, Rockhill Mennonite Community, Souderton Mennonite Homes. Related conferences: FCMC and EDC Mennonite Conferences, Atlantic Northeast COB Conference.

Dock Woods Community Inc.*
moreinfo@dockwoods.com; www.dockwoods.com
215-368-4438, fax 215-362-2682
275 Dock Dr, Lansdale PA 19446
Edward D. Brubaker, president
Founded 1942. Offers a wide range of housing for seniors and families, along with support services and ongoing activities for all residents.

Fairlawn Haven
fairlawn01@adelphia.net
419-445-3075, fax 419-446-2699
407 E Lutz Rd, Archbold OH 43502
Steven A. Ringenberg, executive director; David Lersch, board chair
Founded 1961. Provides a variety of housing facilities for the elderly; includes a 90-bed Medicare/Medicaid and 10-bed Alzheimer's unit, 25 assisted living, 49 low-income housing, 59 duplexes, 30 apartments, wood shop and wellness center.

OTHER AGENCIES

3

Frederick Mennonite Community*
khummel@frederick-mennonite.org; www.frederick-mennonite.org
610-754-7878, fax 610-754-6475
2849 Big Rd, PO Box 498, Frederick PA 19435-0498
Eighty-acre campus, 100 independent living, 106 person assisted living, 24 person Alzheimer's facility, and 62 nursing beds.

Friendship Haven*
mofelkey@transedge.com
765-459-9343, fax 765-459-9343
2600 W Jefferson, Kokomo IN 46901
Maureen Felkey, administrator

Friendship Retirement Corporation, d/b/a Glencroft+
www.glencroft.com
623-939-9475 and 623-847-3001, fax 623-842-9588
8611 N 67th Ave, Glendale AZ 85302
F. Jay Shetler, president/ceo; Ron Swartz, board chair
Founded 1970. A retirement community of 900 residents in all levels of care. Sponsored by MHS Alliance with the involvement of local Mennonite Church USA, Church of the Brethren, Apostolic Christian, and Friends congregations.

Garden Spot Village*
bgerig@gardenspotvillage.org;
www.gardenspotvillage.org
717-355-6000, fax 717-355-6006
433 S Kinzer Ave, New Holland PA 17557
Stephen Lindsey, CEO
(slindsey@gardenspotvillage.org); Philip Burkholder, CFO; Bonnie Gerig, director of marketing
Approximately 600 residents. Services include cottage and apartment living, assisted living, memory support unit, skilled nursing center. Amenities include pool and fitness area, bank, computer lab, etc.

Glencroft—see Friendship Retirement Corp.

Greencroft Retirement Communities Inc.+
info@greencroft.org; www.greencroft.org
574-537-4000, fax 574-533-8063
1721 Greencroft Blvd, PO Box 819, Goshen IN 46527-0819
Mark King, president/CEO
Founded 1962. Continuing Care Retirement Community with 1,200 residents and several levels of care. Administers Evergreen Place (assisted living), Manor II, Manor III, Manor IV, Juniper Place Court Apartments, Greencroft Health Care, a senior center, and Thelma A. Schrock Homestead adult day services.

Harmony Village Inc.*
hvillage@sky-access.com
330-482-3430, fax 330-482-0359
901 S Main St, Columbiana OH 44408
Cheryl Luli, project administrator
　　Founded 1983. A government-subsidized apartment complex for the very low-income elderly and the physically handicapped who require an especially adapted apartment.

Hickory Homes—see Schowalter Villa

Hope Village*
jwbarkman@hopevillage.org
503-266-9810, fax 503-263-7854
1535 S Ivy, Canby OR 97013
Jerry Barkman, executive director

Kidron Bethel Village
rheim@kidronbethel.org; www.kidronbethel.org
316-284-2900, fax 316-284-0173
3001 Ivy Dr, North Newton KS 67117
Richard I. Heim, president
　　Founded 1926. A continuing care retirement community with independent living residences, HUD apartments, and skilled nursing beds. Serving 285 seniors in 161 retirement townhomes and apartments, 60 skilled nursing beds, and 25 assisted living units. Includes wellness center, adult daycare, transportation, buffet dining, in-home services, recreational activities, walking trails, chaplaincy/chapel, maintenance services.

Landis Homes+
info@landishomes.org; www.landishomes.org
717-569-3271 and 717-581-3935, fax 717-569-5203
1001 E Oregon Rd, Lititz PA 17543-9206
Edward M. Longenecker, president; Virginia Musser, director of admissions
　　Founded 1964. Provides quality programs for senior adults in an environment of Christian love. An agency of the Lancaster Mennonite Conference.

Maple Lawn Homes+
rob@maple-lawn.com; www.maple-lawn.com
309-467-2337 and 309-467-9041, fax 309-467-9097
700 N Main St, Eureka IL 61530
　　Founded 1922. Organized to provide long-term care, retirement housing, and support services to the elderly of central Illinois.

Maple Lawn Manor Inc.
mlmanor@hintonet.net
405-663-2455 and 888-663-2114, fax 405-663-2443
PO Box 66, 800 Arapaho, Hydro OK 73048
Betty Palesano, administrator
(bpalesano@hotmail.com); Dale Beerwinkle, board chair
　　Founded 1968. Long-term care facility with 22 beds, locked Alzheimer's unit. Serving elderly and handicapped residents of all ages.

Meadows Mennonite Retirement Community*
rob@maple-lawn.com
309-747-2702 and 309-747-3658, fax 309-747-2944
24588 Church St, Chenoa IL 61726
　　Founded 1923. Organized to serve the long-term care need and retirement housing for the elderly of McLean and Livingston counties, Ill. Sponsored by MMRC Association of Churches. Participating denominations: MC USA and EMC.

Menno Haven Inc.*
www.mennohaven.org
717-262-1000, fax 717-261-0860
1427 Philadelphia Ave, Chambersburg PA 17201
Ray L. Miller, president/CEO
　　Founded 1964. Accredited CCRC providing care for 1,000 seniors on 3 campuses; 412 independent and 268 residential/assisted living apts, 233 skilled nursing beds, and adult day care services.

Mennonite Home Communities*
info@mennonitehome.org; www.mennonitehome.org
717-393-1301 and 717-390-4100, fax 717-393-1389
1520 Harrisburg Pk, Lancaster PA 17601
J. Nelson Kling, president/CEO; John Sauder, vice president health services
　　Founded 1903. A Continuing Care Retirement Community (CCRC) providing services to seniors in a Christian environment.

Mennonite Housing Aid Inc.
martin101@attbi.com
847-492-1458, fax 847-492-1458
PO Box 6056, Evanston IL 60204-6056
Richard E. Martin, administrator
　　Founded 1976. Promotes retirement housing, community, and service in the Chicago metropolitan area.

Mennonite Manor*
klassens@mennonitemanor.org;
www.mennonitemanor.org
620-663-7175, fax 620-663-4221
600 W Blanchard, South Hutchinson KS 67505-1599
Sheldon Klassen, CEO
　　Founded 1973. Provides healthcare services in a continuing care retirement community.

Mennonite Memorial Home/Maple Crest Senior Living Village*
mmh@wcoil.com
419-358-1015, fax 419-358-1919
410 W Elm St, Bluffton OH 45817
Lynn Thompson, administrator
　　Offers the full continuum of care within the community, with duplexes, independent apartments, assisted living and nursing. Also offers home health, mobile meals and transportation services.

OTHER AGENCIES

3

Mennonite Village+
info@mennonitevillage.org; www.mennonitevillage.org
541-928-7232, fax 541-917-1399
5353 Columbus St SE, Albany OR 97322
Ron Litwiller, executive director; Chet Patterson, chief financial officer
Founded 1947. Continuing care retirement community whose covenant is to be a Christ-centered community providing life-enriching services.

Mennowood Retirement Community
www.mennowood.com
757-249-0355, fax 757-249-7621
13030 Warwick Blvd, Newport News VA 23602
Robby Ackerman, executive director (robby@mennowood.com).
Includes 24 independent living apartments and 71 assisted living apartments on Sluice Mill Pond.

Mountain View Nursing Home
540-948-6831, fax 540-948-5402
HC 5 Box 186, Aroda VA 22709
Eldon Hochstetler, administrator
Founded 1962. Forty nursing care beds; began as a community service ministry staffed by a Voluntary Service Unit.

OrrVilla Retirement Community Inc.*
orrvilla@raex.com
330-683-4455, fax 330-683-7575
333 E Sassafras St, Orrville OH 44667
George Bixler, executive director; Morris Stutzman, board president

Pioneer Lodge*
kpcorner@midway.net
620-582-2123 and 620-823-3136, fax 620-582-2461
300 W 3rd St, PO Box 487, Coldwater KS 67029
Founded 1964. Nursing care and residential care levels.

Pleasantview Home*
sandyg@pvhome.org
319-656-2421, fax 319-656-2439
811 Third St, PO Box 309, Kalona IA 52247-0309
Sandy Gingerich, administrator; Gerald Yoder, board president
Founded 1958. A continuing care retirement community serving the elderly of Kalona and the surrounding communities.

Rock of Ages Mennonite Home/Valley View Retirement Village
delvinz@onlinemac.com
503-472-6212, fax 503-472-4797
15600 SW Rock of Ages Rd, Mc Minnville OR 97128
Delvin Zook, administrator
Founded 1949. Care center for the elderly; retirement homes; community service providing care to seniors in-home.

Rockhill Mennonite Community*
info@rockhillmennonite.org;
www.rockhillmennonite.org
215-257-2751, fax 215-257-7390
3250 State Rd, Sellersville PA 18960
Ron Sawatsky, CEO
Founded 1935. A continuing care retirement community that provides a wide range of services in an atmosphere of Christian love.

Salem Mennonite Home
smhoffice@gwtc.net
605-925-4994, fax 605-925-4764
106 W 7th St, Freeman SD 57029
Stewart Hofer, administrator
An assisted living center caring for elderly residents in the Freeman, S.D., community for over 50 years.

Schowalter Villa and Hickory Homes+
swvilla@schowalter-villa.org; www.schowalter-villa.org
620-327-4261, fax 620-327-4262
200 W Cedar, Hesston KS 67062
James M. Krehbiel, president; Lillian Claassen, vice president of health services
Founded 1961. Mission statement: Schowalter Villa provides optimal quality of life and quality of care to enrich those we serve in a Christian not-for-profit retirement community.

Sierra View Homes Inc.*
admin@sierraview.org; www.sierraview.org
559-638-9226 and 559-638-9227, fax 559-638-6857
1155 E Springfield Ave, Reedley CA 93654
Founded 1960. A retirement community offering a continuum of housing and healthcare services on a monthly rental basis.

Souderton Mennonite Homes*
margaret@soudertonhomes.org
215-723-9881, fax 215-723-9876
207 W Summit St, Souderton PA 18964
Margaret Zook, executive director; Willis A. Miller, board chair
Founded 1917. Private, not-for-profit continuing care retirement community providing a continuum of housing and services for older adults.

Southfield Village
sfinfo@southfieldvillage.org; www.southfieldvillage.org
574-231-1000, fax 574-231-5566
6450 Miami Cir, South Bend IN 46614
Sandra Yoder, executive director; J. Larry Neff, board chair
Founded 1997. Southfield Village has 60 healthcare beds and 58 assisted living apartments.

OTHER AGENCIES

3

Sunnyside Village/Health Center*
davidray08@aol.com; www.sunnysidevillage.org
941-371-2750 and 941-371-2729, fax 941-377-2571
5201 Bahia Vista St, Sarasota FL 34232
David Ray Miller, executive director
   Founded 1968. Retirement community, assisted living facility and skilled nursing facility. Sponsored by area Mennonite churches.

Swiss Village Retirement Community*
inquiries@swissvillage.org; www.swissvillage.org
260-589-3173, fax 260-589-8369
1350 W Main St, Berne IN 46711
Daryl L. Martin, executive director
   Founded 1968. Provides health care and retirement living facilities and services that enhance life with dignity, meaning, and appropriate care within a Christian environment. Sponsored by First Mennonite Church, Berne.

Tel Hai Services Inc.*
www.telhai.org
610-273-9333, fax 610-273-4141
1200 Tel Hai Cir, PO Box 190,
Honey Brook PA 19344-0190
Joseph J. Swartz, president/CEO (jswartz@telhai.org);
Paul J. King, board chair
   Founded 1950. Offers a continuum of high quality care and services for aging individuals as a demonstration of God's love to over 500 residents.

Thurston Woods Village+
theoomo@thurstonwoods.org; www.thurstonwoods.org
616-651-7841, fax 616-651-2050
307 N Franks Ave, Sturgis MI 49091
Theo Omo, CEO
   Founded 1968. Provides responsible housing, health care, and services, valuing every individual in the spirit of Christian love.

Valley View Retirement Community*
valleyview@acsworld.net; www.valleyviewretirement-community.org
717-935-2105, fax 717-935-5109
4702 E Main St, Belleville PA 17004
Randy Sheaffer, administrator
(rsheaffer@acsworld.net).
   Founded in 1963. One hundred twenty-two skilled nursing beds, 79 assisted living apartments, 118 independent living cottages. Providing a continuum of quality residential and long-term care services in a manner demonstrating Christian love and compassion.

Valley View Retirement Village
—see Rock of Ages

Virginia Mennonite Retirement Community*
roney@vmrc.org; www.vmrc.org
540-564-3400 and 888-564-VMRC, fax 540-564-3700
1501 Virginia Ave, Harrisonburg VA 22802-2452
Ronald E. Yoder, president/CEO
   Founded 1954. Offers comprehensive, high-quality service and care to the aging with Christian love and compassion in assisted living, nursing, independent housing, and wellness facilities.

Wayland Mennonite Home Association
parkview@farmtel.net
319-256-3525 and 319-256-2775, fax 319-256-4022
Parkview Home, 102 N Jackson St, Wayland IA 52654
Bill Grimm, administrator
   Founded 1961. Retirement community serving a broad spectrum of needs. Administers Parkview Home, Parkview Apartments, and Parkview Village.

Welsh Mountain Home*
wmhome@dejazzd.com
717-355-9522, fax 717-354-7103
567 Springville Rd, New Holland PA 17557
Harold E. Yoder, administrator; Paul Smoker, board chair
   Founded 1924. Provides facilities, services, and programs for older adults and dependent persons.

Mennonite Indian Leaders Council
—see Native Mennonite Ministries

Mennonite Media
info@mennomedia.org, www.mennomedia.org
800-999-3534 and 540-434-6701,
   fax 540-434-5556
1251 Virginia Ave, Harrisonburg VA 22802

STAFF
Burton Buller, director
   (burton@mennomedia.org)
Lowell Hertzler, business manager
   (lowell@mennomedia.org)

INFORMATION
Mennonite Media, a department of Mennonite Mission Network, communicates the good news through contemporary media, including national television, public service radio, Third Way Café at www.thirdway.com, educational videos, music CDs/cassettes, and print.

Mennonite Media represents Mennonite Church USA through membership in Faith & Values Media and the electronic programming division of the National Council of Churches. It also participates in the Council on Church and Media and partners with various agencies.

Mennonite Media was founded in 1951 by Eastern Mennonite College students who began a radio outreach, which was later named the *Mennonite Hour*. It became the official media agency of the Mennonite Church in 1956.

PUBLICATION

Links @ Mennomedia (three times a year), Melodie Davis, editor (melodie@mennomedia.org); *What's New* at Third Way Café, sporadically, http://www.thirdway.com/subscriptions/

Mennonite Medical Association (MMA)

mennmed@mennmed.org, www.mennmed.org
183 Grandview Dr, Harrisonburg VA 22802

STAFF

Sam Showalter, M.D., executive secretary
Jan Showalter, administrative assistant

INFORMATION

Mennonite Medical Association (MMA) is a fellowship of physicians, dentists, and medical/dental students who are members of congregations of the Mennonite Central Committee church constituency.

MMA supports the Anabaptist Center for Healthcare Ethics (www.mennmed.org/ache.htm), convenes an annual convention with Mennonite Nurses Association, connects members to short-term mission projects, and provides funding for Student Elective Term abroad. MMA was founded in 1944 by returning missionary physicians and other concerned Mennonite physicians.

BOARD

Changes biannually. Donald R. Martin, M.D., president, Baltimore MD; Daniel Nafziger, M.D., president elect, Goshen IN; Jeffrey Roth Martin, M.D., Lancaster PA, secretary-treasurer

PUBLICATION

MMA sponsors *Mennonite Health Journal* (quarterly) along with Mennonite Nurses Association, Melanie Zuercher, editor, 320 S Weaver, Hesston KS 67062, 620-327-2808, mzeeyore@southwind.net

Mennonite Men

jimg@mennoniteusa.org,
www.mennonitemen.org
316-283-5100, fax 316-283-0454
PO Box 347, 722 Main St, Newton KS 67114-0347

STAFF

Jim Gingerich, coordinator
(jimg@mennoniteusa.org)

INFORMATION

Mennonite Men aims to provide an Anabaptist perspective on manhood that speaks to current issues. It provides resources for men's groups in local congregations and develops material on specific men's issues.

Mennonite Men is a jointly owned partnership of Mennonite Church Canada and Mennonite Church USA. Mennonite Men began in the General Conference Mennonite Church in 1950. The JoinHands Mennonite Church Building program (formerly Tenth Man), which began in 1983, provides grants to young congregations acquiring their first church building.

BOARD

Don Schmidt, president (dmschmidt@wwweb-service.net), 715 Country Club Dr, Newton KS 67114, 316-283-2031; Warren (Barney) Habegger, vice president; Lowell Detweiler, secretary; Laurence Bartel, treasurer; Marvin

OTHER AGENCIES

3

Baergen, executive committee; David Bergen; Rodney Frey; Arlen Goshall; Mark A. Kniss; David L. Lehman; Royce B. Roth; John Zook; CLC reps: Jim Gingerich, Don Schmidt

Mennonite Mission Network
—see section 1, Churchwide Agencies

Mennonite Mutual Aid
—see section 1, Churchwide Agencies

Mennonite Nurses Association (MNA)
www.mna.mennonite.net
937-465-3362
183 Grandview Dr, Harrisonburg VA 22802

INFORMATION
Mennonite Nurses Association (MNA) is an organization dedicated to the promotion of nursing and the provision of support for Christian nurses within the Anabaptist tradition.

MNA supports the Anabaptist Center for Healthcare Ethics, convenes an annual convention with Mennonite Medical Association, supports scholarships for nursing students, nursing education in foreign countries, projects of missionary nurses, and other health enhancing projects. Projects are selected from Mennonite mission agencies and other health related agencies.

BOARD
Changes biannually. President: 2002-04, Barbara Landes (jblandes@logan.net), RN, BSN, CDE, West Liberty OH

PUBLICATION
MNA produces a semiannual newsletter for its members. MNA also sponsors *Mennonite Health Journal* (quarterly), along with Mennonite Medical Association, Melanie Zuercher, editor, 320 S Weaver, Hesston KS 67062, 620-327-2808, mzeeyore@southwind.net

Mennonite Press, Inc.
www.mennonitepress.com
800-536-4686 and 316-283-4680,
    fax 316-283-2068
532 N Oliver Rd, Newton KS 67114

STAFF
Steven Rudiger, managing director
    (stevenr@mennonitepress.com)

INFORMATION
Mennonite Press, Inc. is a for-profit commercial printing company founded in 1902. Mennonite Church USA is the majority stockholder. Approximately 6 percent of sales are to Mennonite Publishing Network with the balance coming from other commercial sources. Other sales concentrations include self-publishers, educational institutions, advertising agencies, and other religious organizations.

BOARD
Roger Williams (clbacctg@juno.com), chair, 2000 Evangel Way, Nappanee IN 46550, 574-773-3164; Ted Stuckey (teds@mennoniteusa.org); Steven Rudiger (stevenr@mennonitepress.com); David Weaver; Lisa Heinz

Mennonite Publishing Network
—see section 1, Churchwide Agencies

Mennonite Quarterly Review
mqr@goshen.edu, www.goshen.edu/mqr
574-535-7433, 574-535-7418, fax 574-535-7438
1700 S Main St, Goshen College,
    Goshen IN 46526

INFORMATION
An interdisciplinary journal devoted to Anabaptist-Mennonite history, thought, life, and affairs. Published jointly by Mennonite Historical Society, Goshen College and Associated Mennonite Biblical Seminary. Edited by John D. Roth. Founded 1927.

Mennonite Secondary Education Council (MSEC)
—see schools in this section and Mennonite Education Agency in section 1

Mennonite Urban Corps Pittsburgh
412-362-2268
5615 Stanton Ave, Pittsburgh PA 15206
Steve Kriss and Heather Kropf, directors

Mennonite Urban Ministries of Denver
303-892-6416, fax 303-892-6106
430 W 9th Ave, Denver CO 80204

STAFF
Gail Valetta, director

INFORMATION
Founded 1960, 1997. Mennonite Urban Ministries is a coordinating and support resource for the Denver/Boulder area Mennonite Churches. The agency helps local congregations develop, enhance and strengthen their outreach and service in their own community.

OTHER AGENCIES

3

Putting the Mennonite world together. Every week for 82 years.

MENNONITE WEEKLY REVIEW provides global coverage of Mennonite news for subscribers across the United States. ■ From an inter-Mennonite perspective, MWR gives readers the most extensive reporting of church events, missions, higher education, congregations and Mennonite Central Committee. ■ As the only weekly Mennonite periodical in America, MWR is the most frequently updated chronicle of the Mennonite world.

See news highlights on the MWR Web site:

www.mennoweekly.org

Call 1-800-424-0178 to:

■ Order a new subscription (U.S.) at half price
■ Request a free sample copy
■ Get advertising rates and data

Mennonite Weekly Review

An Inter-Mennonite Newspaper

BOARD

Eldon Mast, chair, 1528 Elmhurst Dr, Longmont CO 80513, 303-684-6733; Mike Barber; David Claasen-Wilson; Steve Friesen; Paul Johnson; Eldon Mast; Robin Ottoson; Don Sager; Ken Tribby; Sam Thornham; Rose Weaver; Dana Williams

Mennonite Weekly Review

editor@mennoweekly.org,
   www.mennoweekly.org
800-424-0178 and 316-283-3670,
   fax 316-283-6502
129 W Sixth St, PO Box 568, Newton KS 67114

STAFF

Paul Schrag, editor (editor@mennoweekly.org)
Robert Rhodes, assistant editor
   (rrhodes@mennoweekly.org)
Robert M. Schrag, publisher
   (rschrag@mennoweekly.org)
Dana Neff, editorial assistant
   (dneff@mennoweekly.org)

INFORMATION

Mennonite Weekly Review, Inc., a church-related nonprofit corporation, owns and publishes *Mennonite Weekly Review*, an inter-Mennonite newspaper providing global coverage of Mennonite news for subscribers across the U.S. Member: Associated Church Press, Meetinghouse Association and Council on Church and Media. Participating bodies: Mennonite Church USA, Mennonite Brethren U.S. Conference, and others.

   MWR, Inc. was founded as Herald Publishing Co. in 1920 by Henry P. Krehbiel and other Mennonite church leaders and laypeople.

BOARD

Patricia Swartzendruber, president (pat@advanassociates.com) 1919 Park Rd, Harrisonburg VA 22802 (540-434-5329); Raylene Hinz-Penner, vice president; James Harder, treasurer; Don Ratzlaff, secretary; Susan Biesecker-Mast; James C. Juhnke; Clarence Rempel; Steve Shenk; Paul Toews

PUBLICATION

Mennonite Weekly Review (weekly since 1923), Paul Schrag, editor (same address as above)

Mennonite Women USA

OFFICE

office@mennonitewomenusa.org
316-283-5100, fax 316-283-0454
722 Main St, PO Box 347, Newton KS 67114-0347

STAFF

Rhoda Keener, executive director
   (rhodak@mennonitewomenusa.org), 5207
   Heisey Rd, Shippensburg PA 17257,
   phone/fax 717-532-9723
Cathleen Hockman-Wert, editor
   (timbrel@mennonitewomenusa.org), 420
   SE Richland Ave, Corvallis OR 97333
   541-752-0444
Berni Kaufman, administrative assistant
   (bernik@mennonitewomenusa.org), Newton
   office
Lois Loflin, project/volunteer coordinator
   (loisl@mennonitewomenusa.org), Newton
   office

INFORMATION

Mennonite Women USA's mission is to minister to the women of Mennonite Church USA by resourcing women's groups and individual women as we nurture our life in Christ, study the Bible, utilize our gifts, hear each other, and engage in mission and service.

   Mennonite Women USA administers an International Women's Fund, connects women locally and globally through our Sister-Link program, and relates to women's groups and individual women throughout Mennonite Church USA. Year founded: 2003.

BOARD

Elaine W. Good, president (rolee-leonelaine@desupernet.net), 304 Buch Mill Rd, Lititz PA 17543, 717-626-9287; Paula Brunk Kuhns, vice president; Gail Shetler, secretary; Sue Schmucker Coblentz, treasurer; Rebecca Sommers, president elect; Yvonne Bailey; Maria Magdalena DeLeon; Anne Hege; Juel Yoder Russell; Rickey Schrag; Barbara R. Voth; Ruth Yoder Wenger; CLC reps: Elaine Good and Rhoda Keener

PUBLICATION

Timbrel (six issues/year), Cathleen Hockman-Wert, editor (address above). Mennonite Women USA also produces an annual Bible study guide. Publications are shared with Canadian Women in Mission.

Mennonite Your Way Hospitality Travel Directory

myw@mywdirectory.com
847-949-6179, fax 847-949-6179
80 West Sylvan Dr, Mundelein IL 60060-3315

STAFF

Jay and Glola Basler, editors and administrators

INFORMATION

The *Mennonite Your Way* program seeks to help fellowship happen among members of the inter-Mennonite family and across international and denominational boundaries. The *Mennonite Your Way Hospitality Travel Directory* lists more than 1,500 private homes where people across the United States and Canada and from numerous countries around the world are willing to host/assist overnight guests who travel through their area.

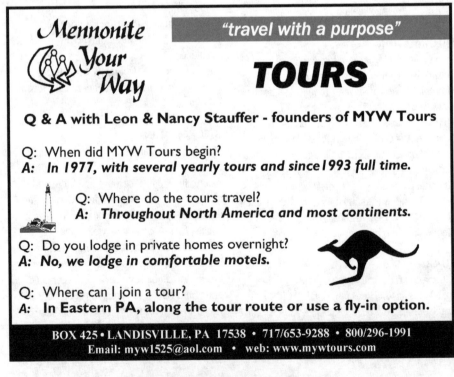

BOARD

Jay Basler and Glola Basler, editors and administrators, 80 W Sylvan Dr, Mundelein IL 60060
Leon Stauffer and Nancy Stauffer, founders and consultants, 647 N Strickler Rd, Manheim PA 17545

PUBLICATION

Mennonite Your Way Hospitality Travel Directory (published every 2-3 years)

Mennonite Your Way Tours

myw1525@aol.com, www.mywtours.com
717-653-9288 or 800-296-1991,
fax 717-653-0990
PO Box 425, Landisville PA 17538-0425

STAFF

Leon and Nancy Stauffer, founders and co-partners
Geneva Rufenacht, secretary and tour planner
Marian Brubaker, secretary and tour planner

INFORMATION

The *Mennonite Your Way* tour program seeks to help fellowship happen among members of the inter-Mennonite family and across cultural and denominational boundaries. The Tours program offers escorted tours throughout North America and numerous international locations. Begun in 1977, these "tours with a purpose" give special attention to the faith, culture, and history of local Christian groups as we visit their communities. All lodging is arranged in moderately priced motels. Efforts are made to build relationships among the tour members as we travel and fellowship together.

BOARD

Leon Stauffer and Nancy Stauffer, co-partners, 647 N Strickler Rd, Manheim PA 17545

PUBLICATION

Annual Tour Brochure
MYW Tour Notes (3 times/year), Leon Stauffer, editor

Mennonite.net

info@mennonite.net
888-868-7099, 574-535-7730, fax 574-535-7017
1700 S Main St, Goshen IN 46526

STAFF

Michael Sherer, executive director
  (msherer@goshen.edu)
Paul D. Leichty, director of user services
  (pdleichty@mennonite.net)
Peter J. Hartman, developer
  (peterjh@mennonot.net)
David Glick, developer
  (david@nonsensesoftware.com)

INFORMATION

Mennonite.net was founded in 1998 to provide low-cost technology services to the Mennonite church. Services include web hosting, a searchable online directory, and a growing suite of services for Mennonite churches, conferences, and organizations. Mennonite.net also provides web and database-oriented consulting and development services as well as database-generated, customizable websites using the Caravel content management system.

Mental Health Agencies
—see Mennonite Health Services Alliance

MHS
—see Mennonite Health Services Alliance

MILC
—see Native Mennonite Ministries

Millersville International House (MIH)

mih.usa@juno.com, www.mihusa.org
717-872-7085, fax 717-872-7085
321 Manor Ave, Millersville PA 17551

OTHER AGENCIES

3

STAFF

Raymond M. Huber, director
Sheri Brooks, director of English Language
   Programs
Daniel L. Gehman, director of Resident Services

INFORMATION

MIH was founded in 1986 as a multicultural
"home away from home" where international
students can thrive in personal relationships,
professional development, and spiritual formation. Our mission is to provide a loving, safe
community where students will not only have
positive cross-cultural experiences but also discover the abundant life that God offers through
Jesus Christ.

MIH is a student housing facility with the
capacity for 25 students located near the
Millersville University campus. It provides an
environment that engenders sensitivity to various cultural and ideological differences and
encourages students to investigate the Christian
faith. Services include English tutoring, counseling, Bible studies, and consultation with families
who host international students.

BOARD

Administered by Eastern Mennonite Missions

Mission Studies Center

formerly Mission Training Center
waltersawatsky@cs.com
574-295-3726, fax 574-295-0092
c/o AMBS, 3003 Benham Ave,
   Elkhart IN 46517-1999

STAFF

Walter Sawatsky, director

INFORMATION

The Mission Studies Center is a cooperative venture among Associated Mennonite Biblical
Seminary, Mennonite Mission Network (MC
USA), Christian Witness Council (MC Canada)
and Mennonite Central Committee. Its director
is a member of the AMBS faculty and liaison to
the mission/service agencies, consulting with
colleagues to identify and prepare workers and
consult on missiological issues.

A Coordinating Committee annually reviews
program and budget. Chaired by AMBS Dean
Loren Johns, its members are Stanley Green and
James Krabill (Mission Network), Jack
Suderman and Janet Plenert (Witness Council),
Ron Mathies and Ron Flaming (MCC), with Art
McPhee and Walter Sawatzky (ex officio).

PUBLICATION

Mission Focus: Annual Review, Walter
Sawatsky, editor (same address as above); Titus
Guenther (tguenther@cmu.ca), book review
editor

MMA

—see Mennonite Mutual Aid in section 1,
Churchwide Agencies

MRN Ministry Resouces

—see Design for Ministry

MutualAid eXchange

MAX INSURANCE AGENCY, INC.
MAX CANADA INSURANCE COMPANY
MUTUAL AID INSURANCE BROKERS
   COMPANY
(see also Association of Mutual Aid Societies—
   AMAS)
mutualaid@mutualaidexchange.com,
   www.mutualaidexchange.com
877-971-6300 and 913-338-1100,
   toll free fax 877-785-0085
8717 W. 110th St, Suite 350,
   Overland Park KS 66210

STAFF

David Wine, president/CEO
Bentley Peters, senior vice president

OTHER AGENCIES

3

Bill Williams, chief financial officer
Jim Miller, chief operations officer
Glen Welborn, director of church relations
(USA)

INFORMATION

MutualAid eXchange (MAX) is a reciprocal insurance company exclusively for Anabaptists throughout the United States and Canada. MAX provides high quality home, farm, church and business coverage. MAX Insurance Agency, Inc. is able to offer some coverages where MAX is not licensed.

MAX was founded in 2000 and MAX Canada Insurance Company was established in 2002.

BOARD

James Gascho, chair
(jgascho@sharingservices.com), 1013 Division St, PO Box 773, Goshen IN 46527-0773; David Wine, president/CEO; Phil Marner, secretary; Brent Eberly; Jay Goering; Cheryl Leis; Larry Litwiller; Jose Ortiz; Arlan Ortman; Robert Rabenstein; Nelson Scheifele; Allen Schroeder; Tim Wagler; Holly Yousey

Mutual Aid and Insurance Agencies

Mutual aid and insurance agencies that are members of Associated Mutual Aid Societies (AMAS) and/or MutualAid eXchange (MAX) are listed below. See also Association of Mutual Aid Societies and MutualAid eXchange.

OTHER AGENCIES

3

MUTUAL AID AND INSURANCE AGENCIES

Mutual aid and insurance agencies that are members of Associated Mutual Aid Societies (AMAS) and/or MutualAid eXchange (MAX) are listed below. Also see entries for Association of Mutual Aid Societies and MutualAid eXchange.
*AMAS member   +MAX member company

CALIFORNIA

Mennonite Aid Plan of the Pacific Coast*
mennonite@mennoniteinsurance.com;
www.mennoniteinsurance.com
800-447-4493 and 559-638-2327, fax 559-638-3336
1110 J St, PO Box 878, Fresno CA 93654
Ron Licata, general manager
Coverage offered: home and farm. Serves Ariz., Calif., Ore., and Wash.

INDIANA

CAM Mutual Aid Association*
cammutualaid@maplenet.net
800-363-5644 and 574-825-5644, fax 574-825-2123
13841 US 20, Middlebury IN 46540
Wayne Chupp, president
Coverage offered: home, farm, fire, and extended coverages. Serves Conservative and Amish Mennonite in 28 states. Call for more information.

Mennonite Aid Association of Indiana and Michigan*+
Sharing Services Agency, Inc.
sharing@sharingservices.com;
www.sharingservices.com
800-832-4689 and 574-533-5396, fax 574-533-5275
1013 Division St (The Depot), PO Box 733,
Goshen IN 46527
Jim Gascho, president/CEO
(jgascho@sharingservices.com)
Coverage offered: home, farm, fire, and extended coverages. Serves Anabaptists in Ind., Mich., and Ky.

Mennonite Mutual Aid Association*
memberinfo@mma-online.org; www.mma-online.org
800-348-7468 and 574-533-9511, fax 574-533-5264
1110 N Main St, PO Box 483, Goshen IN 46527
Coverage offered: health, life, mutual funds, annuities, financial services, charitable gift plans, and personal trusts. Serves U.S.

IOWA

Iowa Mennonite Mutual Aid Association*+
immaa@kctc.net
800-622-5883 and 319-656-2211, fax 319-656-2215
425 B Ave, PO Box 428, Kalona IA 52247
Phil Marner, secretary/treasurer
Coverage offered: home, farm, fire, and extended coverage. Serves Iowa.

KANSAS

The Mutual Aid Association of the Church of the Brethren*
maa@maabrethren.com; www.maabrethren.com
800-255-1243 and 785-598-2212, fax 800-238-7535
3094 Jeep Ro, Abilene KS 67410-6064
Jean Hendricks, president and general manager
(jean@maabrethren.com)
Coverage offered: home, farm, fire, and extended coverage. Serves Church of the Brethren members in the U.S.

MutualAid eXchange (MAX)*—see separate listing
MAX North America includes:
MutualAid eXchange—Overland Park Kan.
MutualAid eXchange—Hesston Kan.
MutualAid eXchange—Moundridge Kan.
MAX Insurance Agency Inc. (MAXIA)—Overland Park Kan.
MAX Canada Insurance Co.—Baden Ont.
Mutual Aid Insurance Brokers Company—Baden Ont.
MII Management Group Inc.—Overland Park Kan.

MutualAid eXchange (Hesston Branch)*
llitwiller@maxkc.com
800-585-3846 and 620-327-2761, fax 620-327-2108
371 N Old Hwy 81, PO Box 989, Hesston KS 67062
Larry Litwiller

MutualAid eXchange (Moundridge Branch)*
jgoering@maxkc.com
101 N Christian Ave, PO Box 639,
Moundridge KS 67107
Jay Goering

MINNESOTA

Mennonite Mutual Insurance Association*+
mmiaajs@rconnect.com
800-210-6168 and 507-427-2343, fax 507-427-2585
206 N 10th St, PO Box 309, Mountain Lake MN 56159
Allen Schroeder, general manager
Coverage offered: home, farm, fire and extended coverage, auto physical damage. Serves Minn. and Mont.

NEW YORK

New York Mennonite Mutual Aid Plan*+
New York Mennonite Agency, Inc
hyousey@nymai.com
315-376-4737, fax 315-376-8433
7383M Utica Blvd, Lowville NY 13367
Holly Yousey, general manager
Coverage offered: home, farm, fire, and extended coverage. Serves N.Y.

OHIO

Mutual Aid Group Insurance Agency*+
rnrmap@bright.net
937-465-5808, fax 937-465-5808 (Fax on request)
1582 SR 245 W, West Liberty OH 43357-9747
Robert Rabenstein, secretary
Coverage offered: home, farm, fire, and extended coverage. Serves Ohio.

Mennonite Mutual Aid Society*
419-358-9840, fax 419-358-9840 (fax on request)
331 N Main St, Bluffton OH 45817
Lois King, secretary
Coverage offered: home, farm, fire, and extended coverage. Serves Ohio.

PENNSYLVANIA

Goodville Mutual Casualty Company*
—see separate listing

SOUTH DAKOTA

Mennonite Aid Society*+
rarafarm@gwtc.net
605-648-3734
44760 283rd St, Hurley SD 57036
Ray Neufeld, secretary
Coverage offered: home, farm, fire, and extended coverages. Serves S.D.

VIRGINIA

Virginia Mennonite Aid Plans*+
Virginia Mennonite Aid, Inc.
info@vmap.org
800-830-0311 and 540-434-9727, fax 540-434-7627
901 Parkwood Dr, Harrisonburg VA 22802
Brent Eberly, executive director (beberly@vmap.org)
Coverage offered: home, farm, fire, and extended coverage; commercial fire; auto physical damage. Serves Fla., Ga., Ky., Md., N.C., Ohio, S.C., Tenn., Va., and W.Va.

OTHER AGENCIES

3

N

National Campaign for a Peace Tax Fund

info@peacetaxfund.org, www.peacetaxfund.org
202-483-3751 and 888-PEACETAX (732-2382),
fax 202-986-0667
2121 Decatur Place NW, Washington DC 20008

STAFF
Marian Franz, executive director

INFORMATION
Founded 1972. The National Campaign for a Peace Tax Fund advocates for legislation enabling conscientious objectors to war to pay their full federal taxes into a fund which could not be used for the military. A lobbying organization supported by both secular and faith organizations. Related issues include peace/conscientious objection and religious/civil liberty.

PUBLICATION
Peace Tax Fund Update, staff editor (same address as above)

Native Mennonite Ministries
(Native Mennonite Ministries is the new combined organization; see below for former groups MILC and UNM)
Joint appointments:
Mennonite Church USA Intercultural Relations—Carol Roth
Mennonite Church USA Executive Board—Olivette McGhee

MENNONITE INDIAN LEADERS COUNCIL (MILC)
milc@mennonitemission.net
316-283-5100, fax 316-283-0454;
    722 Main St, Newton KS 67114-0347
or 574-523-3077, fax 574-294-8669;
    500 S Main St, PO Box 370,
    Elkhart IN 46515-0370
Call toll-free (both locations) 866-866-2872

INFORMATION
The Mennonite Indian Leaders Council (MILC) was formed in 1969 to help Indian churches in the United States and Hopi Mission School to decide goals and programs of Indian ministries. The Mennonite Mission Network is a partner with MILC and funds their program with budget monies. (Relates to Mennonite Mission Network.)
CLC rep: Lawrence Hart (ccctr@itlnet.net)

UNITED NATIVE MINISTRIES (UNM)
rrhorst@verizon.net
574-295-8530, fax 574-293-1892
2121 Hawthorne Dr, Elkhart IN 46517

STAFF
Ray E. Horst, executive secretary

INFORMATION
Founded 1987. United Native Ministries is an organization of representatives from Native American Mennonite congregations. The council meets semiannually for work on issues related to Native American Ministries, promotes leadership training, assists with congregational resources and serves as an advocate with conference and churchwide agencies. UNMC cosponsors the intertribal assembly every two years and is a channel of relationships with other churchwide programs.

BOARD
Olivette McGhee, president
(olivettemcghee@hotmail.com), 1675 Poarch Rd, Atmore AL 36502, 251-368-5938; Elizabeth Detweiler, vice president; Lena Willis, secretary; CLC rep: Steve Cheramie Risingsun

TRIBAL GROUPS, CONGREGATIONS AND COUNCIL MEMBERS
Choctaw: Nanih Waiya Mennonite Church, Bobbie Frazier; Pearl River Mennonite Church, Lena Willis. **Creek:** Poarch Community Church, Olivette McGhee; Gospel Light Church. **Ojibway:** Morson Community Bible Fellowship, Elizabeth Detweiler. **Navajo:** Upper Room Mennonite

Church, Frank James; Light of Life Mennonite Church, Priscilla Wero; Black Mountain Mennonite Church, Mary Mitchell Trejo. **Houma (Biloxi-Chitimacha):** Native Christian Fellowship, Steve Cheramie Risingsun. **Lakota Sioux:** Lakota Gospel Church, Vina Steele.

New Call to Peacemaking
—see Every Church a Peace Church

New York City Council of Mennonite Churches
NYCMennoCouncil1@aol.com
212-737-3700, fax 212-244-0476
216 East 70th St, New York NY 10021

STAFF
Ruth Yoder Wenger, administrator

INFORMATION
Founded 1980. The underlying purpose of this council is to promote a spirit of Christian unity and fellowship among the congregations and members of the council in fulfilling their mission. It includes 18 congregations of the Lancaster (12) and Atlantic Coast (6) conferences.

TRANSITION/EXECUTIVE COMMITTEE
Ruth Yoder Wenger, moderator, 3304 Steuben Ave, Bronx NY 10467, 718-882-8924; Peter Castle, vice moderator; Sandra Perez, secretary; Berhane Kifle, treasurer

PROGRAMS AND PROJECTS
Camp Deerpark, PO Box 394, Westbrookville NY 12785, 914-754-88669, Ken Bontrager, director
Heartease Home, 216 E 70th St, New York NY 10021, 212-249-3107 (ministry in transition)
Menno House, 314 E 19th St, New York NY 10003, 212-677-1611, sponsored by Manhattan Mennonite Fellowship

NISBCO
—see Center on Conscience & War

North American Vietnamese Mennonite Fellowship (NAVMF)
nhienp@hotmail.com
604-324-1200
7155 Sherbrooke St, Vancouver BC V5X 4E3, Canada

INFORMATION
Founded 1997. NAVMF promotes fellowship and cooperation among its members in the areas of leadership development and church planting. Members include Vietnamese Mennonite churches in North America. It currently has nine member churches.

EXECUTIVE COMMITTEE
Nhien Huu Pham, president (nhienp@hotmail.com), 13477 60 Ave Surrey BC V3X 2M4; Chau Hong Dang, vice president; Hoa Van Chau, treasurer; (Peter) Duc Phu Nguyen, secretary; Thanh Cong Pham, mission coordinator

P

Pandora Press U.S.
—see Cascadia Publishing House

Park View Federal Credit Union
info@pvfcu.org, www.pvfcu.org
888-900-6444 and 540-434-6444, fax 540-433-0108
1675 Virginia Ave, Harrisonburg VA 22802

STAFF
John Beiler, CEO (pvfcu@pvfcu.org)

OTHER AGENCIES

3

INFORMATION
Founded 1969. A full-service financial cooperative serving the Mennonite community in Harrisonburg/Rockingham County, Va., as well as students, alumni, residents, and employees of listed Mennonite-affiliated organizations.

Services include mortgage and home equity loans, vehicle and student loans, credit cards, savings, checking, money market, certificates, ATM/check cards, online banking and bill payment, IRAs and Coverdell ESAs. Member-owned. Volunteer board of directors is elected by membership.

Peace and Justice Support Network
leoh@mennonitemission.net,
www.peace.mennolink.org
717-399-8353, fax 717-391-6512
202 S Ann St, Lancaster PA 17602

STAFF
Leo Hartshorn, minister of peace and justice
    (leoh@mennonitemission.net)
Susan Mark Landis, peace advocate
    (susanml@mennoniteusa.org)
Lisa Amstutz, administrative assistant
    (lisaa@mennoniteusa.org)
Valerie A. Weidman, administrative assistant
    (valeriepjsn@comcast.net), 717-397-3855)

INFORMATION
Founded in 2003. Sponsored by Mennonite Church USA Executive Leadership and Mennonite Mission Network. PSJN is an inclusive group open to anyone who wants to support in a special way Mennonite Church USA's work of peace and justice.

Tasks of the network include: creating and focusing the vision of peace and justice in Mennonite Church USA, promoting the expansion of peace and justice through gatherings for inspiration, providing counsel to MC USA's agencies, sharing and publicizing resources for congregations, and communicating peace and justice work to the wider constituency.

REFERENCE COMMITTEE
Richard Davis, facilitator (Dick@PeaceMennonite.org), Peace Mennonite Church, PO Box 59926, Dallas TX 75229, 214-350-5244; Malinda Berry; Mark Frey; Yvonne Keeler; Andy Peifer Nissley; Titus Peachey; Jorge E. Vielman

PUBLICATION
PJSN has two printed publications, *Dove Tales* and *Olive Branches*, and an online magazine, *PeaceSigns*.

R

Retirement Centers
—see Mennonite Health Services Alliance

Retreat Centers
—see Mennonite Camping Association

S

Schools
—For elementary schools and secondary schools, see lists below.
For colleges, see individual listings for Bethel, Bluffton, Eastern Mennonite, Goshen, and Hesston earlier in this section.
For seminaries, see individual listings for Associated Mennonite Biblical Seminary and Eastern Mennonite Seminary earlier in this section.

ELEMENTARY AND SECONDARY SCHOOLS

The sponsoring body is noted with each school. Schools that are members of Mennonite Secondary Education Council (MSEC) are identified with an asterisk (*), of the Mennonite Elementary Education Council (MEEC) with a pound sign (#), and of the Lancaster Area Council of Mennonite Schools with a caret (^).

Other affiliations are indicated by the following abbreviations: Association of Christian Schools International (ACSI), Mid-Atlantic Christian School Association (MACSA), Middle States Association of Colleges and Schools (MSA), National Institute for Learning Disabilities (NILD), Northwest Association of Schools and Colleges (NASC), and Southern Association of Colleges and Schools (SACS).

Academia Menonita*
787-783-1295, fax 787-783-1280
1751 Asomante St, Summit Hills PR 00920
Founded: 1961. Sponsor: Summit Hills Mennonite Church (PRMC)
Margarita Kolthoff-Benners, principal. 2003-04 enrollment: 460 students, grades P-8; 189 students, grades 9-12. Mary Cotto, board chair.

Belleville Mennonite School *#
bmsinfo@pa.net,
akanagy@bellevillemennoniteschool.org
www.bellevillemennoniteschool.org
717-935-2184, fax 717-935-5641
4105 Front Mountain Rd, PO Box 847, Belleville PA 17004-0847
Founded: 1945. Sponsor: Patrons Association. R. Ann Kanagy, superintendent. 2003-04 enrollment: 78 students, grades 9-12; 175 students, grades P-8. Affiliated with MACSA. Lowell Peachey, board chair (717-483-6731).

Bethany Christian Schools *
info@bethanycs.net, www.bethanycs.net
574-534-2567, fax 574-533-0150
2904 S Main St, Goshen IN 46526-5499
Founded: 1954/1996. Sponsor: Indiana-Michigan Mennonite Conference (IM).
Allan Dueck, principal. 2003-04 enrollment: 207 students, grades 9-12; 109 students, grades 6-8. Accredited by Indiana Department of Education. Eldon Heatwole, board chair (574-875-8059), eldonheatwole@hotmail.com.

Calvary Christian Academy
www.calvarycommunity.org
757-825-1133, fax 757-825-8711
2311 Tower Pl, Hampton VA 23666
Sponsor: Calvary Community Church (V).
L. W. Francisco III, chief administrator. 2003-04 enrollment: 121 students, grades P-5. Accredited by Accrediting Commission International; affiliated with ACSI. L. W. Francisco III, board chair.

Calvary Christian School
Lvb5@juno.com
323-752-7594 or 323-752-7406, fax 323-752-1481
2400 W 85th St, Inglewood CA 90305
Founded: 1970. Sponsor: Calvary Christian Fellowship Church (PSMC).
Shirley Ollie, principal. 2003-04 enrollment: 238 students, grades P-8. Affiliated with ACSI. Alvin L. Isaacs, pastor/board chair (323-752-8552).

Central Christian School *
FredMiller@centralchristian.k12.oh.us,
www.centralchristian.k12.oh.us
330-857-7311, fax 330-857-7331
3970 Kidron Rd, PO Box 9, Kidron OH 44636-0009
Founded: 1961. Sponsor: Ohio Mennonite Conference (OH).
Frederic A. Miller, superintendent; Pam Matsos, high and middle school principal; Joyce Taylor, learning center principal. 2003-04 enrollment: 216 students, grades 9-12; 141 students, grades K-8.

Chicago Mennonite Learning Center
cmlc@infolaunch.com, www.cmlc.infolaunch.com
773-735-9304, fax 773-735-9832
4647 W 47th St, Chicago IL 60632
Founded: 1981. Sponsor: Illinois Menn Conf (IMC)/Central Dist Conf (CDC).
Ken Hawkley, principal; Sarah Sales, assistant principal. 2003-04 enrollment: 80 students, grades K-8. Serves children of diverse cultural, racial, and ethnic backgrounds. Leanne Schertz, board chair (309-383-2451).

Christopher Dock Mennonite High School *
cdock@christopherdock.org, www.christopherdock.org
215-362-2675, fax 215-362-2943
1000 Forty Foot Rd, Lansdale PA 19446
Founded: 1952. Sponsor: Franconia Mennonite Conference (F).
Elaine A. Moyer, principal. 2003-04 enrollment: 415 students, grades 9-12. Accredited by MSA. Lee Delp, board chair (215-368-8019).

Clinton Christian School
clinton@bnin.net
574-642-3940, fax 574-642-3674
61763 CR 35, Goshen IN 46528
Founded: 1950. Sponsor: Michiana area churches of the Conservative Mennonite Conference.
Robert Carroll, principal. 2003-04 enrollment: 111 students, grades K-12. Affiliated with ACSI. Dwayne Borkholder, board chair (574-633-4316).

Conestoga Christian School *^
info@conestogachristian.org
610-286-0353, fax 610-286-0350
2760 Main St, Morgantown PA 19543-9623
Founded: 1952. Sponsor: Rockville, Conestoga, and Hopewell congregations (AC).
Susan Yoder, administrator. 2003-04 enrollment: 90 students, grades 9-12; 177 students, grades K-8. Affiliated with ACSI, MACSA, NILD; accredited by ACSI and MSA.

OTHER AGENCIES

3

Eastern Mennonite High School *
emhs@emhs.net, www.emhs.net
540-432-4500, fax 540-432-4528
801 Parkwood Dr, Harrisonburg VA 22802
Founded: 1917. Sponsor: Virginia Mennonite
Conference (V).
    Paul G. Leaman, principal. 2003-04 enrollment: 223
students, grades 9-12; 113 students, grades 6-8.
Affiliated with MACSA and VAIS; accredited by SACS.
Jackie Hartman, board chair.

Ephrata Mennonite School #^
ems@ephms.com
717-738-4266, fax 717-738-4266
598 Stevens Rd, Ephrata PA 17522
Founded: 1946.
    David L. Sauder, principal. 2003-04 enrollment: 196
students, grades K-9. Affiliated with MSA and MACSA.
Lynn Zimmerman, board chair.

Freeman Academy *
www.freemanacademy.pvt.k12.sd.us
605-925-4237, fax 605-925-4271
748 S Main St, PO Box 1000, Freeman SD 57029
Founded: 1900. Sponsor: Independent.
    Marlan Kaufman, president, Nathan Epp, principal.
2003-04 enrollment: 37 students, grades 9-12. Stewart
Hofer, board chair (605-729-9487).

Gateway Christian School
gatewycs@hotmail.com
610-682-2748, fax 610-682-9670
245 Fredericksville Rd, Mertztown PA 19539
Founded: 1978. Sponsor: Patrons.
    Daniel Stringfellow, principal. 2003-04 enrollment:
105 students, grades K-12. Glenn Nissly, board chair
(304-789-6399)

Gehmans Mennonite School #^
gms@dejazzd.com
717-484-4222, fax 717-484-4222
650 Gehman School Rd, Denver PA 17517
Founded: 1952. Sponsor: Patrons.
    Melvin L. Weaver, administrator. 2003-04 enroll-
ment: 183 students, grades K-8. Affiliated with MACSA.
Irvin Weaver Jr., board chair (717-445-6791).

Greenwood Mennonite School
gms@dmv.com
302-349-4131, fax 302-349-5076
12802 Mennonite School Rd, Greenwood DE 19950
Founded: 1928. Sponsor: Cannon and Greenwood
Mennonite churches (CM).
    Larry J. Crossgrove, administrator. 2003-04 enroll-
ment: 91 students, grades 9-12; 193 students, grades
K-8. Affiliated with MACSA.

Hinkletown Mennonite School #^
office@hms.pvt.k12.pa.us, www.hms.pvt.k12.pa.us
717-354-6705, fax 717-354-8438
272 Wanner Rd, Ephrata PA 17522
Founded: 1981. Sponsor: Patron families.

Tom Burnett, administrator. 2003-04 enrollment:
184 students, grades K-8. Accredited by MSA. Roy
Hoover, board chair.

Hopi Mission School
HMS@hopimissionschool.org,
www.hopimissionschool.org
928-734-2453, fax 928-734-2453
PO Box 39, Kykotsmovi AZ 86039-0039
Founded: 1951. Sponsor: Mennonite and American
Baptist Churches USA.
    William R. Zuercher, administrator; 2003-04 enroll-
ment: 65 students, grades K-6. Staffed primarily by
MVS volunteers. Laverne Dallas, board president (928-
734-2302), ldallas83@hotmail.com.

Iowa Mennonite School *
ims@iamenno.pvt.k12.ia.us,
www.iamenno.pvt.k12.ia.us
319-656-2073 and 319-683-2586, fax 319-656-2073
1421 540th St SW, Kalona IA 52247
Founded: 1945. Sponsor: Central Plains Mennonite
Conference (CPMC).
    Wilbur D. Yoder, principal. 2003-04 enrollment: 155
students, grades 9-12. Mike Brenneman, board chair
(319-683-2661).

Juniata Mennonite School #^
jms@tricountyi.net
717-463-2898
PO Box 278, McAlisterville PA 17049
Founded: 1980. Sponsor: Juniata Mennonite School
Association.
    Andrew R. Meiser, principal. 2003-04 enrollment:
159 students, grades K-10. Affiliated with ACSI and
MACSA. Doug Brubaker, board chair (717-463-2280).

Kraybill Mennonite School #^
Kraybillmennonite.org
717-653-5236, fax 717-653-7334
598 Kraybill Church Rd, Mount Joy PA 17552
Founded: 1949.
    John S. Weber, principal. 2003-04 enrollment: 395
students, grades K-8. Affiliated with MACSA. Rose Baer,
board chair (717-361-0431).

Lake Center Christian School *#
lccsmmcmullen@yahoo.com
330-877-2049, fax 330-877-2040
12893 Kaufman Ave NW, Hartville OH 44632
Founded: 1947. Sponsor: Cornerstone, Hartville, Maple
Grove Menn churches.
    Matthew R. McMullen, Superintendent. 2003-04
enrollment: 510 students, grades K-10 (adding 11 in
2005 and 12 in 2006). Member of ACSI and NILD. Chip
Weisel, board chair (330-877-2732).

Lancaster Mennonite School *#^
thomasjr@lancastermennonite.org,
www.lancastermennonite.org
J. Richard Thomas, superintendent, 2003-04 enrollment:
1,449, grades K-12.

Lancaster Mennonite School consists of the following:

Lancaster Mennonite High School
yoderme@lancastermennonite.org
717-299-0436, fax 717-299-0823
2176 Lincoln Hwy E, Lancaster PA 17602
    Miles E. Yoder, principal. 2003-04 enrollment:
814 students, grades 9-12.

Lancaster Mennonite Middle School
kingda@lancastermennonite.org
717-299-0436, fax 717-299-0823
2176 Lincoln Hwy E, Lancaster PA 17602
    David A. King, principal. 2003-04 enrollment: 131
students, grades 6-8.

Lancaster Mennonite School—New Danville
mollenkofju@lancastermennonite.org
717-872-2506, fax 717-872-5201
393 Long Ln, Lancaster PA 17603
    Judi U. Mollenkof, principal. 2003-04 enrollment:
194 students, grades K-8.

Locust Grove Mennonite School—LMS
rothjl@lancastermennonite.org
717-394-7107, fax 717-394-4944
2257 Old Philadelphia Pk, Lancaster PA 17602
    Jay L. Roth, principal. 2003-04 enrollment: 310
students, grades K-8.
    Founded: 1942. Sponsor: Atlantic Coast (AC) and
Lancaster (L) conferences.
    Accredited by MSA. Connie F. Stauffer, board chair.

Linville Hill Mennonite School #^
linvillehill@juno.com
717-442-4447, fax 717-442-9283
295 S Kinzer Rd, Paradise PA 17562
Founded: 1944. Sponsor: Atlantic Coast (AC) and
Lancaster (L) conferences.
Dwilyn Beiler, administrator. 2003-04 enrollment: 169
students, grades K-8. Affiliated with MACSA. Dale Hess,
board chair (717-548-2573).

Lititz Area Mennonite School #^
lamsoff@dejazzd.com
717-626-9551, fax 717-626-0430
1050 E Newport Rd, Lititz PA 17543
Founded: 1978. Sponsor: LAMS patrons.
    Neal J. Eckert, administrator. 2003-04 enrollment:
291 students, grades K-8. Affiliated with MACSA;
accredited by MSA. Nelson Zimmerman, board chair
(717-738-0184).

Manheim Christian Day School #^
mcdschool@dejazzd.com, www.mcdsschool.com
717-665-4300 and 717-664-2638, fax 717-664-4253
686 Lebanon Rd, Manheim PA 17545
Founded: 1952. Sponsor: Manheim Mennonite District.
    Ray Kratz, administrator. 2003-04 enrollment: 115
students, grades K-8. Affiliated with MACSA. Julie
Good, board chair (717-664-4717).

Mount Pleasant Christian School
mpcs4kids@assure.net
757-482-9557, fax 757-482-3447
1613 Mount Pleasant Rd, Chesapeake VA 23322
Founded: 1941. Sponsor: Mount Pleasant Mennonite
Church (V).
    Carol Wenger, interim principal. 2003-04 enrollment:
125 students, grades K-8. Affiliated with ACSI, NILD,
and Hampton Roads Association of Christian Schools.
Lynn Keffer, board chair (757-482-2179).

New Covenant Christian School *#^
NCCS@nccspa.org, www.nccspa.org
717-274-2423, fax 717-274-9830
452 Ebenezer Rd, Lebanon PA 17046
Founded: 1982. Sponsor: Association school under
Lebanon District (L).
    Kathy Bauman, assistant administrator. 2003-04
enrollment: 261 students, grades P-12.

Penn View Christian School
brutt@pennview.org, www.pennview.org
215-723-1196, fax 215-723-0148
420 Godshall Rd, Souderton PA 18964
Founded: 1945. Sponsor: Franconia Menn Conference
(FCMC).
    Robert D. Rutt, executive director. 2003-04 enroll-
ment: 515 students, grades P-8. Affiliated with MACSA;
accredited by MSA. Ken Hochstetler, board chair (215-
723-5236).

Philadelphia Mennonite High School *
office@pmhsonline.org, www.pmhsonline.org
215-769-5363, fax 215-769-4063
860 N 24th St, Philadelphia PA 19130
Founded: 1996. Sponsor: Philadelphia Mennonite
Council.
    Dr. Barbara Moses, principal. 2003-04 enrollment:
82 students, grades 9-12. Affiliated with ACSI, PACS,
and MACSA. Dr. Mark Garis, board chair (215-769-
5363).

Quakertown Christian School
info@quakertownchristian.org;
www.quakertownchristian.org
215-536-6970, fax 215-536-2115
50 E Paletown Rd, Quakertown PA 18951
Founded: 1951. Sponsor: Franconia Menn Conference
(FCMC). Member: ACSI, MACSA
    Alma J. Geosits, administrator. 2003-04 enrollment:
284 students, grades P-8. Accredited by MSA. Mark
Swartley, board chair.

Sarasota Christian School *#
admissions@sarasotachristian.org,
www.sarasotachristian.org
941-371-6481, fax 941-371-0898
5415 Bahia Vista St, Sarasota FL 34232
Founded: 1958. Sponsor: Sarasota area Menn churches
(SE and CM).

Eugene Miller, superintendent; Jean Martin, elementary and middle school principal; Robert Hovde, high school principal. 2003-04 enrollment: 167 students, grades 9-12; 386 students, grades K-8. Accredited with Florida Council of Independent Schools.

Shalom Christian Academy *
shalom@shalomca.com, www.shalomca.com
717-375-2223, fax 717-375-2224
126 Social Island Rd, Chambersburg PA 17201
Founded: 1976. Sponsor: Shalom Christian Academy
Association.

Conrad Swartzentruber, administrator. 2003-04
enrollment: 151 students, grades 9-12; 269 students,
grades K-8. Affiliated with ACSI, MACSA, MSA, and
NILD. Darrell Baer, board chair (717-762-4041).

Warwick River Christian School #
GorZook@yahoo.com, www.wrcs.info
757-877-2941, fax 757-877-6510
252 Lucas Creek Rd, Newport News VA 23602-6251
Founded: 1942. Sponsor: Warwick River, Huntington,
Providence congs. (V).

Gordon D. Zook, administrator; Mabel R. Nelson,
principal. 2003-04 enrollment: 342 students, grades
P-8. Member of SACS and ACSI. Danni Clark, board
chair (757-988-8080).

West Fallowfield Christian School #^
WFCS279@epix.net, www.wfc.org
610-593-5011 and 610-593-7150, fax 610-593-6041
795 Fallowfield Rd, PO Box 279, Atglen PA 19310-0279
Founded: 1941.

Elvin Kennel, principal. 2003-04 enrollment: 196 students, grades K-8. Affiliated with NILD and MACSA.
Eric Nafziger, board chair.

Western Mennonite School *
wmsoffice@teleport.com, www.westernmennonite.org
503-363-2000, fax 503-370-9455
9045 Wallace Rd NW, Salem OR 97304-9716
Founded: 1945. Sponsor: Pacific Northwest Menn
Conference (PNMC).

Darrel White, executive director; principal. 2003-04
enrollment: 131 students, grades 9-12; 56 students,
grades 6-8. Accredited by NASC; affiliated with Oregon
Federation of Independent Schools, Salem Area
Association of Christian Schools, and National Honor
Society of Secondary Schools. David Detweiler, board
chair (541-258-5109).

Schowalter Foundation Inc.
316-283-3720, fax 316-283-2039
900 N Poplar St, Suite 200, Newton KS 67114

STAFF
Willis Harder, president and manager

INFORMATION
Founded 1954. Seeks to encourage and stimulate outreach and witness locally and through the two sponsoring Mennonite denominations: Mennonite Church USA and Church of God in Christ, Mennonite.

Seminaries
—see individual listings for Associated Mennonite Biblical Seminary and Eastern Mennonite Seminary.

Shalom Foundation Inc.
rbenner833@aol.com,
    www.churchoutreach.com
888-833-3333 and 540-433-5351,
    fax 540-434-0247
1251 Virginia Ave, Harrisonburg VA 22802

STAFF
Richard L. Benner, executive director
    (rbenner833@aol.com)
Melodie M. Davis, editor
    (melodie@mennomedia.org)

INFORMATION
Publishes three every-home, full-color, outreach-oriented quarterlies: *Together* and *NEIGHBORS* for congregations and *Living* for local communities. Subscribers to *Together* and *NEIGHBORS* (an upscale version of *Together*) are predominantly Mennonite, Church of the Brethren, and Brethren congregations, but the

publications are open to any congregation, affiliated or independent, with evangelism goals.

Shalom Foundation was founded in 1991 to advance Christian values and to cultivate the development of faith in Christ through the production and dissemination of quality, easy-to-use communication tools.

BOARD

Jonas Borntrager, chair (jborntrager@ldbinsurance.com), 205A S Liberty, Harrisonburg VA 22801, 540-433-2796; Robert Kettering (bobket@juno.com), vice chair, 1043 W Elizabethtown Rd, Manheim PA 17545, 717-664-2620; Peggy Landis, secretary; Philip C. Stone Jr., treasurer; Myron S. Augsburger; Jerry Engle; Rhoda Oberholtzer; James W. Moss Sr.; Steven E. Clapp

PUBLICATIONS

Together and *Living* and *NEIGHBORS*, Melodie M. Davis, editor (same address as above)

T

Ten Thousand Villages
—see Mennonite Central Committee

The Mennonite

editor@themennonite.org,
www.themennonite.org
800-790-2498 and 574-535-6051 (Goshen);
316-283-5155 (Newton); fax 574-535-6050
(Goshen); fax 316-283-0454 (Newton)
1700 S Main St, Goshen IN 46526 and 722 Main St, PO Box 347, Newton KS 67114

STAFF

Everett J. Thomas, editor
    (everett@themennonite.org)
Gordon Houser, associate editor
    (gordonh@themennonite.org)

Marla Cole, marketing and advertising coordinator (marlac@themennonite.org)
Kristene Miller, secretary and bookkeeper (kristenem@themennonite.org)
J. Lorne Peachey, editor emeritus (LornePeachey@mwc-cmm.org)

INFORMATION

The Mennonite is the official periodical of Mennonite Church USA. Its mission is to help readers glorify God, grow in faith, and become agents of healing and hope in the world.

The Mennonite was founded in 1998 as a merger of the General Conference Mennonite Church periodical, *The Mennonite*, and the Mennonite Church periodical, *Gospel Herald*.

BOARD

Joe Roos, chair, (jroos@verizon.net); Gerald Biesecker-Mast; Joe Manickam; Miriam Martin; Esther Martinez; Larry Miller; Susan Sommer; Everett J. Thomas (ex officio); Cindy Snider, Executive Board participant/observer

TourMagination

office@tourmagination.com,
www.tourmagination.com
Main office: 519-885-2522, fax 519-885-0941,
9 Willow St, Waterloo ON N2J 1V6
U.S. office: 215-723-8413, fax 215-723-8351,
1011 Cathill Rd, Sellersville PA 18960

STAFF

Wilmer Martin, president and managing partner (martin@tourmagination.com)

INFORMATION

TourMagination is owned and operated by Mennonites from Ontario and Pennsylvania who love to create educational travel experiences. TourMagination's mission statement is "Building bridges among Mennonites and other Christians around the world through custom-designed travel." Founded 1970.

TourMagination plans custom-designed tours for groups to their destination of choice. In addi-

tion to custom-designed tours, TourMagination also plans service tours for those who want to make a difference while they are on vacation. TourMagination also offers a roster of tours to many destinations, including the European Heritage Tour upon which TourMagination was founded, the Bible Lands, Alaska, South America, North American tours, etc.

BOARD

Henry D. Landes, chair (1011 Cathill Rd, Sellersville PA 18960, 215-723-8413); Wilmer Martin, president and managing partner

PUBLICATION

Discovery (quarterly), David Beckerson, editor, 9 Willow St, Waterloo, ON N2J 1V6, Canada, 800-565-0451 and 519-885-2522, fax 519-885-0941

U

United Native Ministries (UNM)
—see Native Mennonite Ministries

V

Virginia Mennonite Board of Missions (VMBM)

info@vmbm.org; www.vmbm.org
800-707-5535 and 540-434-9727,
   fax 540-434-7627
901 Parkwood Dr, Harrisonburg VA 22802

STAFF

Loren E. Horst, president
G. Edwin Bontrager, director of development & church relations
Joseph Bontrager, director USA ministries
Beth Brunk, human resources coordinator

Willard K. Eberly, Mediterranean regional director
Eva Eberly, Mediterranean assistant
Kenneth Horst, director of *Partners in Mission* and Mediterranean associate
Evelyn Kratz, director of finance
Galen Lehman, Caribbean regional director
Gloria Lehman, public relations director and Caribbean regional assistant
Lavonne Lehman, financial associate
Lois E. Maust, assistant to president
Laura Moyers, receptionist
Rachel Smith, communications associate

INFORMATION

Founded in 1919 as the mission agency of Virginia Mennonite Conference. International work began in 1949 in Sicily. VMBM works in collaboration with the districts of Virginia Mennonite Conference in USA ministries. Internationally, VMBM also works in collaboration with other Mennonite-affiliated churches and agencies in the countries of Albania, Italy, Jamaica, and Trinidad. Short-term teams serve through Partners in Mission. Constituent churches and individuals sponsor VMBM ministries through contributions, including estate bequests and endowments.

BOARD

Marvin Slabaugh, chair (mcslabaugh@aol.com); James Foster, vice chair; Milton Heatwole, treasurer; Carol Rhodes, secretary; Janet Blosser; Lori Green; Mark Hodge; Laurel Horst; Beth Jarrett; Ammeral Johnson; Janine Kanagy; Kenneth Kurtz; Barry Loop; Basil Marin; Lowell Miller; Phyllis Miller

PUBLICATION

Connections (monthly), Gloria Lehman, editor (gloria.lehman@vmbm.org); Rachel Smith, assistant editor (rachel.smith@vmbm.org); *Mission News* (monthly newsletter) to congregational mission communicators

OTHER AGENCIES

3

W

Washington DC Area Mennonite Workers Fellowship

STAFF

Steve Ramer, group facilitator
(rameregan@yahoo.com)

INFORMATION

Founded 1995. Meets monthly (except July, August, and December) at noon on the third Wednesday at Washington Community Fellowship (907 Maryland Ave NE, Washington DC) for fellowship, prayer, and a speaker. Includes pastors from Baltimore and Washington, MCC's Washington office, the International Guest House, MMN's VS unit, MCC's VS unit, and Washington Study Service Year.

West Coast Mennonite Men's Chorus

mrke@juno.com;
www.geocities.com/mmchorus
559-251-3345
267 S Armstrong Dr, Fresno CA 93727

INFORMATION

The West Coast Mennonite Men's Chorus is organized to minister through music, promote male singing, cultivate common bonds of the Mennonite tradition, and support the work of Mennonite Central Committee. It is supported by Mennonite Central Committee constituent churches in the San Joaquin Valley of California.

The West Coast Mennonite Men's Chorus was organized in 1977 to sing praise to God in Mennonite fashion and tradition. These 150 lay volunteers present three benefit concerts each year.

BOARD

Randy Toews, chair, 240 Elm, Shafter CA 93263, 661-746-2771; Ken Elrich (mrke@juno.com), contact person and financial officer; Bill Braun, secretary; Bob Buxman; Wink Farrand; Paul Flaming; Al Fleming; Walt Goertzen; Amos Kleinsasser; Arnold Liesch; Don Loewen; Lola Penner; Marvin Regier; Ben Warkentin

Mennonite World Conference

4

Mennonite World Conference (MWC) is a global community of Christian churches who trace their beginning to the 16th-century Radical Reformation in Europe, particularly to the Anabaptist movement. Today close to 1.3 million believers belong to this faith family. At least 60 percent of these believers are African, Asian, or Latin American. Mennonite Church USA is one of 95 Mennonite and Brethren in Christ (BIC) national churches from 52 countries on six continents that MWC represents.

Mennonite World Conference is called to be a communion *(Koinonia)* of Anabaptist-related churches linked to one another in a worldwide community of faith for fellowship, worship, service, and witness.

MWC exists to (1) be a global community of faith in the Anabaptist tradition, (2) facilitate community among Anabaptist-related churches worldwide, and (3) relate to other Christian world communions and organizations.

With MWC, Mennonite Church USA believes that the church is a worldwide body where people of different cultures and nations are "no longer strangers ... but members of God's household" (Ephesians 2:19).

Website
www.mwc-cmm.org

Strasbourg office
8 rue du Fossé des Treize, 67000 Strasbourg, France

tel (33) 3 88-15-27-50, fax (33) 3 88-15-27-51 (Strasbourg@mwc-cmm.org)

Kitchener office
50 Kent Ave, Kitchener, ON N2G 3R1, Canada

tel (1) 519-571-0060, fax (1) 519-571-1980 (Kitchener@mwc-cmm.org)

Fresno office
2529 Willow Ave, Clovis CA 93612, USA

tel (1) 559-291-2125, fax (1) 559-291-2065 (Fresno@mwc-cmm.org)

Executive staff
Larry Miller, executive secretary (LarryMiller@mwc-cmm.org), Strasbourg office

Pakisa Tshimika, associate executive secretary, Networks and Projects (PakisaTshimika@mwc-cmm.org), Fresno office

Ray Brubacher, associate executive secretary, Events and Administration (RayBrubacher@mwc-cmm.org), Kitchener office

EXECUTIVE COMMITTEE
Officers

Nancy Heisey, president (NancyHeisey@mwc-cmm.org), 556 Lee Ave, Harrisonburg VA 22802, USA

Danisa Ndlovu, vice-president (DanisaNdlovu@mwc-cmm.org), BICC Office, PO Box 711, Bulawayo, Zimbabwe

Larry Miller, executive secretary (LarryMiller@mwc-cmm.org), Conférence Mennonite Mondiale, 8, rue du Fossé des Treize, 67000 Strasbourg, France

Paul Quiring, treasurer (pquiring@quiring.com), 2207 W Spruce Ave, Fresno CA 93711-0456, USA

Members
Africa

Dieudonné Fimbo Ganvunze, B.P. 4081, Kinshasa II, Dem. Rep. of Congo (mcc@ecc-sn.org)

Joshua Okello Ouma, PO Box 39, Suna-Migori 40400, Kenya (bishopjouma@agape.westernet.co.ke)

Asia

Joren Basumata, A-9 C.I.T. Building, Christopher Road, Calcutta 700 014, India (umsindia@cal13.vsnl.net.in)

Eddy Sutjipto, Jl. Tosiga W E 7, Jakarta 11530, Indonesia (ed777dd@cbn.net.id)

Caribbean, Central and South America

Peter Stucky, Diagonal 31 #37-74, Bogotá, Colombia (imcol@latino.net.co)

David Villalta Benavides, Convención Menonita de C.R., Apartado Postal #116-3000, Heredia, Costa Rica (davillaltab@racsa.co.cr)

Europe

Markus Rediger, Alpenweg 8, 3110 Münsingen, Switzerland (rediger@lid.ch)

Katarina Thijink-van der Vlugt, Haaksbergerstraat 859, 7548 PB Enschede, Netherlands (thijnthijink@doopsgezind.nl)

North America

Naomi Unger, Box 127, Rabbit Lake SK S0M 2L0, Canada (dnunger@sasktel.net)

David Wiebe, 169 Riverton Ave, Winnipeg MB R2L 2E5, Canada (dwiebe@mbconf.ca)

COMMUNICATIONS, COUNCILS, AND PROJECTS STAFF

Rainer Burkart, secretary, Faith & Life Council, Torneystr. 90a, 56567 Neuwied, Germany (1114-631@online.de)

Ferne Burkhardt, news editor, copyeditor, regional editor—North America, 1895 Huron Rd, RR 2, Petersburg ON N0B 2H0, Canada (fburkhardt@golden.net)

Doris Dube, regional editor—Africa, 212-213 Lutheran House, Bulawayo, Zimbabwe, (mccz@mweb.co.zw)

Ricardo Esquivia Ballestas, central communicator, GAPJN, Av calle 32 No 14-42 Piso 1, Bogotá, Colombia (justapaz@colnodo.apc.org)

Sylvie Gudin, French editor, 7 rue Specklin, 67000 Strasbourg, France (SylvieGP@mwc-cmm.org)

John A. Lapp, coordinator, Global Mennonite History Project, 13 Knollwood Dr, Akron PA 17501, USA (jalapp@lancnews.infi.net)

Tim Lind, Global Gifts Sharing coordinator, 10418 Harder Rd, Three Rivers MI 49093, USA (TimLind@mwc-cmm.org)

Eleanor Miller, communications assistant, MWC Strasbourg office, France (EleanorMiller@mwc-cmm.org)

Lorne Peachey, *Courier* managing editor, 800 Walnut Ave, Scottdale PA 15683-1999, USA (LornePeachey@mwc-cmm.org)

Milka Rindzinski, *Courier* general editor and regional editor—Central and South America, 3 de Febrero 4381, 12900 Montevideo, Uruguay (MilkaRindzinski@mwc-cmm.org)

Liesa Unger, director, YAMEN!, Blumentorstrasse 12, 76227 Karlsruhe, Germany (liesaunger@mwc-cmm.org)

Paulus Widjaja, secretary, Peace Council, Fakultas Theologia, Universitas Kristen Duta Wacana, Jalan Dr. Wahidin 5-19, Jogjakarta, Indonesia (pauluswidjaja@ukwd.ac.id)

Judy Zimmerman Herr, associate secretary, Peace Council, Mennonite Central Committee, 21 South 12th St, PO Box 500, Akron PA 17501-0500, USA (jzh@mcc.org)

PUBLICATIONS

Courier/Correo/Courrier, a quarterly publication available in three languages (English, Spanish, French) that provides news, feature articles, essays, and testimonies as a means to promote community, communication, and cooperation in the worldwide Mennonite and Brethren in Christ faith family. Larry Miller, publisher; Milka Rindzinski, editor; J. Lorne Peachey, managing editor; Sylvie Gudin Poupaert, French edition editor.

Gift Sharing Newsletter, semi-annual newsletter produced by MWC Global Gifts Sharing staff, which provides a forum for news, ideas, thoughts, and stories about the sharing of gifts among members of the worldwide Mennonite/Brethren in Christ family.

All publications are available on the MWC website (www.mwc-cmm.org). Paper editions of *Courier, Correo,* or *Courrier* are available by request from MWC, 8, rue du Fossé des Treize, 67000 Strasbourg France; email: Strasbourg@mwc-cmm.org

MEMBERSHIP SUMMARY

The statistical information is based on the 2003 *Mennonite and Brethren in Christ Directory* or more recent data. * Membership statistics indicate baptized members in all Anabaptist-Mennonite churches worldwide, not only MWC member churches. Some statistics are estimates.

Africa
Members 452,209
Countries 17
Organized Bodies 26

Asia and Pacific
Members 208,155
Countries 11
Organized Bodies 24

Caribbean, Central and South America
Members 133,150
Countries 23
Organized Bodies 94

Europe
Members 53,272
Countries 13
Organized Bodies 22

North America
Members 451,180
Countries 2
Organized Bodies .35

World Total *
Members 1,297,966
Countries 66
Organized Bodies .201

MENNONITE WORLD CONFERENCE

4

MWC Member Churches

AFRICA

Angola
Igreja da Comunidade Menonita em Angola,
CX. P. N. 232-C, Luanda
fax (244) 2-39-37-46, e-mail icma@angonet.org

Igreja Evangélica dos Irmãos Mennonitas em Angola, 21 de Janeiro/Rocha Pinto, CP 20066, Luanda
tel (244) 2-330-415, fax (244) 2-393-746,
e-mail ieima@angonet.org

Igreja Evangélica Mennonitas em Angola,
CP 5120, Luanda
tel (244) 330-0558, fax (244) 396-875,
e-mail iema@angonet.org

Democratic Republic of Congo
Communauté des Eglises de Frères Mennonites au Congo, B.P. 81, Kikwit
e-mail mcc@ecc-sn.org

Communauté Evangélique Mennonite,
B.P. 440, Mbuji Mayi/Kasai Oriental
tel (243) 815064037
e-mail pmisakabu@hotmail.com

Communauté Mennonite au Congo,
B.P.18, Tshikapa, Kasai Occidental
tel MCC-Congo, fax MCC-Congo,
e-mail mcc@ecc-sn.org

Ethiopia
Meserete Kristos Church,
P.O. Box 24227, Addis Ababa
tel (251) 1-534-758, fax (251) 1-513-310,
e-mail meserete_kristos@telecom.net.et

Ghana
Ghana Mennonite Church,
P.O. Box 5485, Accra-North
tel (233) 21-310113, fax (233) 21-227125,
e-mail michaelkodzo@yahoo.com

Kenya
Kenya Mennonite Church,
P.O. Box 39, Suna-Migori

Malawi
**Brethren in Christ Church, Mpingo Wa Abale
Mwa Kristu,** PO Box 2544, Blantyre
tel (265) 9-01623841, fax (265) 623-193,
e-mail ejvbs@malawi.net

Nigeria
Mennonite Church Nigeria, P.O. Box 123, Uyo,
Akwa Ibom State
fax (234) 85-203840, e-mail mccnigeria@hisen.org

South Africa
Grace Community Church in South Africa,
5 Cachetstreet, 8795 Phillipstown
tel (27) 53-665-0051, fax (27) 53-665-0147

Tanzania
Kanisa la Mennonite Tanzania,
PO Box 1040, Musoma
tel (255) 28-620143, fax (255) 2-622826,
e-mail kmtbaraza@juansun.net

Zambia
Brethren in Christ Church (Zambia),
Box 630115, Choma
tel (260) 32-20127, fax (260) 32-20127,
e-mail biccz@zamtel.zm

Zimbabwe
Brethren in Christ Church, Ibandla Labazalwane ku
Kristu e Zimbabwe, PO Box 711, Bulawayo
tel (263) 9-62839, fax (263) 9-42193,
e-mail bicchu@mweb.co.zw

ASIA AND PACIFIC

Australia
**Australian Conference of Evangelical
Mennonites,** 9 Brougham Avenue,
Fennell Bay 2283 N.S.W.
tel (61) 2 4959 3847, fax (61) 2 4959 3847,
e-mail foppe-b@acay.com.au

India
**Bharatiya Jukta Christa Prachar Mandali
(United Missionary Church),** Hastings Chapel, 10
St. Georges Gate Rd, Calcutta 700 022
tel (91) 33-223 0609, e-mail umsindia@cal3.vsnl.net.in

Bhartiya General Conference Mennonite Church,
H.Q. at PO Jagdeeshpur, Dist. Mahasamund, CG 493 555

**Bihar Mennonite Mandli, Mennonite Mission
Compound,** PO Chandwa, Dist. Latehar,
Jharkhand 829 203

Brethren in Christ Church Orissa, Biju Pattnaik
Chhak, PO Tulsipur, Dist. Cuttack, Orissa 753 008
tel (91) 671-2300386, fax (91) 671-2300386,
e-mail roulbicctc@hotmail.com

Brethren in Christ Church Society, Bharatiya
Khristiya Mandali, Box 6, Purnea, Bihar 854 301
tel (91) 64-54-22926,
e-mail bicpurnea@rediffmail.com

**Conference of the Mennonite Brethren
Churches in India,** MB Medical Centre, Jadcherla,
A.P. 509 302
tel (91) 8544-32-488

**Mennonite Church in India (Bharatiya
Mennonite Church in India ki Pratinidhi Sabha),**
Mennonite Centre, Dhamtari, CG 493 773
tel (91) 7722-35809, fax (91) 7722-38226

Indonesia
Gereja Injili di Tanah Jawa, Jl. Diponegoro No. 33,
Pati 59112 Jateng
tel (62) 295-385337, e-mail hendrosp@telkom.net

**Persatuan Gereja-Gereja Kristen Muria
Indonesia,** Jl. Sompok Lama 60, Semarang 50249,
Jateng
tel (62) 24-312795, fax (62) 24-442644,
e-mail sinodemi@idola.net.id

Sinode Jemaat Kristen Indonesia, Jl. Permata
Hijau Blok BB-25A, Pondok Hasanudin, Semarang-
50176 Jawa Tengah
tel (62) 24-3557300, fax (62) 24-3557300,
e-mail jkiinjil@indosat.net.id

Japan
Nihon Kirisuto Keiteidan, 4-12-6 Hanakoganei,
Kodaira-shi, Tokyo 187-0002
tel (81) 424-63-7295, fax (81) 424-63-7295

Nihon Menonaito Kirisuto Kyokai Kaigi,
2-7-4 Yodogawa, Miyazaki-shi 880-0907
tel (81) 985-51-4009, fax (81) 985-51-4009

Nihon Menonaito Kirisuto Kyokai Kyogikai
(Japan Mennonite Christian Church Conference), c/o
Mennonite Fukuzumi Center,
2-3-6-1 Fukuzumi, Toyohira-ku, Sapporo 062-0042
tel (81) 11-836-2133, fax (81) 11-854-4470,
e-mail harada1@soleil.ocn.ne.jp

Tokyo Chiku Menonaito Kyokai Rengo, 2-1-17
Honan, Suginami, Tokyo 168-0062
  tel (81) 3-3311-4277, fax (81) 3-3313-1201,
  e-mail anabap@gol.com

Philippines
Integrated Mennonite Churches, Inc.,
177 Tabia St, Barangay Salac, Lumban, 4014 Laguna
  tel (63) 49-808-4363, fax (63) 49-810-0027,
  e-mail alporcin@mozcom.com

Taiwan
Fellowship of Mennonite Churches in Taiwan,
PO Box 27-50, Taipei 104
  tel (886) 2-2503-9618, fax (886) 2-2501-6497,
  e-mail fomcit@ms18.hinet.net

CARIBBEAN, CENTRAL AND SOUTH AMERICA

Argentina
Iglesia Evangélica Menonita Argentina,
Mercedes 149, Buenos Aires
  tel (54) 2946-443111, fax (54) 2946-443576,
  e-mail juansieber@mym.com.ar

Belize
Belize Evangelical Mennonite Church,
PO Box 30, Orange Walk Town
  tel (501) 322-2953, e-mail alcoser2000@yahoo.com

Bolivia
Iglesia Evangélica Menonita Boliviana,
Casilla 3086, Santa Cruz
  tel (591) 3-346-0401, fax (591) 3-337-0675,
  e-mail mcc.bolivia.ca@scbbs-bo.com

La Iglesia Evangélica Anabautista en Bolivia,
Cajón 2487, Santa Cruz
  tel (591) 3-356-1512, fax (591) 3-356-1512,
  e-mail seta@scbbs-bo.com

Brazil
Associação das Igrejas Menonitas do Brasil,
Rua Cristiano Strobel, 1630 - Xaxim, 81.720-140
Curitiba, Paraná
  tel (55) 41-376-7954, fax (55) 41-275-3477,
  e-mail aimb2@ig.com.br

Associação Evangélica Menonita, Q.N.N. 31- mód.
H Area Especial, N. Norte — Ceilandia 72225-310
  tel (55) 61-3747099, fax (55) 61-3448440,
  e-mail cldivino@ig.com.br

Colombia
Asociación de Iglesias Hermanos Menonitas de
Colombia, Apartado Aéreo 4172, Cali - Valle
  tel (57) 2-513-23-19, fax (57) 2-513-07-67,
  e-mail dihmeno@telesat.com.co

Iglesia Cristiana Menonita de Colombia,
Ave. 32#14-42 P.2, Bogotá
  tel (57) 1-287-2927, fax (57) 1-245-2182,
  e-mail imcol@aolpremium.com

Costa Rica
Convención de Iglesias Menonitas de Costa
Rica, Apartado 116-3000, Heredia
  tel (506) 237-7130, fax (506) 237-0520,
  e-mail menonitacr@vmm-costarica.org

Cuba
Sociedad Misionera Hermanos en Cristo,
Calle 102 No. 10307, Cuatro Caminos, Cotorro, La
Habana 19340
  tel (53) 6829-4052, e-mail curbelo_2001@yahoo.com

Dominican Republic
Concilio Nacional Menonita Faro Divino,
Avenida Libertad 128, Apartado 3, Bonao
  tel (1809) 525-3057, fax (1809) 525-2530,
  e-mail rjbarranco@hotmail.com

Conferencia Evangélica Menonita Dominicana,
Apartado 21408, Santo Domingo
  tel (1809) 689-9060, fax (1809) 684-9724,
  e-mail micro.ind.dom@codetel.net.do

Ecuador
Iglesia Evangélica Menonita de Ecuador,
Casilla 13-05-2744, Manta
  tel (593) 42-288141, fax (593) 42-776338,
  e-mail cavipo1@yahoo.com

Guatemala
Iglesia Evangélica Menonita de Guatemala,
Apartado 1779, 19 Avenida 5-94, Zona 11 Mirador I,
Ciudad de Guatemala
  tel (502) 471-89-87, fax (502) 471-89-87,
  e-mail iemg@intelnet.net.gt

Iglesia Nacional Evangélica Menonita
Guatemalteca, Apartado 1, 16909 San Pedro Carchá,
Alta Verapáz
  tel (502) 951-6385, fax (502) 951-6041,
  e-mail menonita@amigo.net.gt

Honduras
Iglesia Evangelica Menonita Hondureña,
Apartado Postal 77, La Ceiba Atlántida
  tel (504) 441-2663, fax (504) 441-2663,
  e-mail iemh@hondusoft.com; iemh@laceiba.com

Organización Cristiana Amor Viviente,
Apartado 2017, San Pedro Sula
  tel (504) 551-5511, fax (504) 551-5522,
  e-mail heredad@123.hn

Jamaica
Jamaica Mennonite Church,
28 Upper Waterloo Road, PO Box 358, Kingston 10
  tel (876) 92-50878

México
Conferencia de Iglesias Evangélicas
Anabautistas Menonitas de México,
Palmas Mz 23 Lote 3, Col. Alfredo del Mazo,
Ixtapaluca, Edo. de México, C.P. 56570
  tel (52) 55-59-76-75-77, fax (52) 55-59-76-75-77,
  e-mail cieamm@mx.inter.net

MENNONITE WORLD CONFERENCE

4

Conferencia Menonita de México, Campo 22, Apartado 518, Cuauhtémoc, Chih. 31500
tel (52) 625-581-0109, fax (52) 625-587-7001,
e-mail petstoesz@terra.com.mx

Nicaragua
Convención de Iglesias Evangélicas Menonitas de Nicaragua, Km. 8 Carr. sur, Apartado 3305, Managua
tel (505) 2-651-367, fax (505) 2-651-229,
e-mail mlorozco@ibw.com.ni

Fraternidad de Iglesias Evangélicas Menonitas de Nicaragua, Apartado 3163, Managua
tel (505) 266-30-78, fax (505) 266-30-78,
e-mail fiemn@ibw.com.ni

Misión Evangélica Hermanos en Cristo de Nicaragua, Bello Horizonte L-I-17, Managua
tel (505) 887-7597, e-mail empoe@ibw.com.ni

Panamá
Iglesia Evangélica Unida Hermanos Menonitas de Panamá, Apartado 812-0025, Zona 12, Panamá
tel (507) 220-6801, fax (507) 220-6801,
e-mail ieu@sinfo.net

Paraguay
Convención de las Iglesias Evangélicas Hermanos Menonitas Nivaclé, c/o Luz a los Indígenas, Filadelfia 40, c.d.c. 984, Asunción 9300
tel (595) 491-32231, fax (595) 491-32453,
e-mail miluz@telesurf.com.py

Convención de las Iglesias Evangélicas Unidas, c/o Menno Indianer Mission, Casilla 883, Loma Plata
tel (595) 918-301

Convención Evangélica de Iglesias Paraguayas Hermanos Menonitas, C.D. 1154, Juan Diaz de Solis 2150, Asunción
tel (595) 21-0423-891, fax (595) 21-0423-891,
e-mail conven@uninet.com.py

Convención Evangélica Menonita Lengua, c/o Luz a los Indígenas, Filadelfia 40, c.d.c. 984, Asunción 9300
tel (595) 491-32231, fax (595) 491-32453,
e-mail miluz@telesurf.com.py

Convención Evangélica Menonita Paraguaya, c.c. 2475, Av. Venezuela 1464, Asunción
tel (595) 21-296284, fax (595) 21-293054,
e-mail comenpar@rieder.net.py

Evangelische Mennonitische Bruderschaft, Filadelfia-Chaco, Pf. 119, c.d.c. 984, Asunción
tel (595) 91-2456

Vereinigung der Mennoniten Brüdergemeinden Paraguays, Filadelfia 40, Col Fernheim, c.d.c. 984, Asunción 9300
tel (595) 21-481-081, fax (595) 21-481-081,
e-mail mbverein@rieder.net.py

Vereinigung der Mennonitengemeinden von Paraguay, Loma Plata Colonia Menno, c.d.c. 883, Asunción
tel (595) 492-52301,
e-mail nmk@telesurf.com.py

Uruguay
Consejo de las Congregaciones de los Hermanos Menonitas, C. Correo 122, Código Postal 11.000, Montevideo
tel (598) 2-355-5675,
e-mail lydea@adinet.com.uy

Convención de Iglesias Evangélicas Menonitas en Uruguay, 3 de Febrero 4381, C.P. 12.900, Montevideo
tel (598) 2-359-0316, fax (598) 2-357-5275,
e-mail coutorbn@adinet.com.uy

Konferenz der Mennonitengemeinden in Uruguay, c.d.c. 400, Montevideo
tel (598) 2-600-5067,
e-mail woelke@adinet.com.uy

EUROPE

France
Association des Eglises Evangéliques Mennonites de France, 3 route de Grand-Charmont, 25200 Montbéliard
tel (33) 381-94-59-14, fax (33) 381-95-56-30,
e-mail editions.mennonites@wanadoo.fr

Germany
Arbeitsgemeinschaft Mennonitischer Gemeinden in Deutschland, Ringstrasse 3, 67677 Enkenbach
tel (49) 6303 3883, e-mail Rwrc.Funck@t-online.de

Italy
Chiesa Evangelica Mennonita Italiana, Via R. d'Aquino, 9, Palermo
tel (39) 91-213084, fax (39) 091-422498,
e-mail chiesa.mennonita@libero.it

Netherlands
Algemene Doopsgezinde Sociëteit, Singel 454, 1017 AW Amsterdam
tel (31) 20-6230914, fax (31) 20-6278919,
e-mail info@ads.nl

Switzerland
Konferenz der Mennoniten der Schweiz (Alttäufer), Conférence Mennonite Suisse (Anabaptiste), Bugnon 19, 2316 Les Ponts de Martel.
tel (41) 32 937 11 54,
e-mail thomas.gyger@bluewin.ch

NORTH AMERICA

Canada
Canadian Conference of Mennonite Brethren Churches, 3-169 Riverton Ave, Winnipeg MB R2L 2E5
tel (1) 204-669-6575, fax (1) 204-654-1865,
e-mail executivedirector@mbconf.ca

Evangelical Mennonite Conference (Canada),
Box 1268, Steinbach MB R0A 2A0
tel (1) 204-326-6401, fax (1) 204-326-1613

Evangelical Mennonite Missions Conference,
Box 52059, Niakwa PO, Winnipeg MB R3T 5L2
tel (1) 204-253-7929, fax (1) 204-256-7384,
e-mail info@emmc.ca

Mennonite Church Canada, 600 Shaftesbury Blvd,
Winnipeg MB R3P 0M4
tel (1) 204-888-6781, fax (1) 204-831-5675,
e-mail office@mennonitechurch.ca

CANADA/USA
Brethren in Christ General Conference (North America), 431 Grantham Rd, PO Box A,
Grantham PA 17027
tel (1) 717-697-2634, fax (1) 717-697-7714,
e-mail bic@messiah.edu

USA
Conservative Mennonite Conference, 9910
Rosedale-Milford Center Rd, Irwin OH 43029
tel (1) 740-857-1234, fax (1) 740-857-1605,
e-mail cmcrosedale@juno.com

Mennonite Church USA, Box 1245, 500 S Main St,
Elkhart IN 46515-1245
tel (1) 574-294-7523, fax (1) 574-293-1892,
e-mail info@MennoniteUSA.org

U.S. Conference of Mennonite Brethren Churches,
315 S Lincoln St, Box 220, Hillsboro KS 67063-0220
tel (1) 620-947-3151, fax (1) 620-947-3266,
e-mail usconf@southwind.net

Associate Member Churches

AFRICA

Burkina Faso
Eglise Evangélique Mennonite du Burkina Faso,
B.P. 85, Orodara
tel (226) 96-01-29

Eritrea
Meserete Kristos Church

ASIA AND PACIFIC

China
Conference of Mennonite Churches in Hong Kong, Hong Kong Mennonite Centre,
76 Waterloo Rd 1/F, Kowloon, Hong Kong
tel (852) 2-713-4271, fax (852) 2-714-2852,
e-mail conf@hkmenno.org

Republic of Korea
Jesus Village Church, 103-502 Greentown,
Toegye-dong, ChunCheon, Kangwon-do 200-752,
Republic of Korea
tel (82) 33-261-2895,
e-mail sunham@kangwon.ac.kr

CARIBBEAN, CENTRAL AND SOUTH AMERICA

Colombia
Hermandad en Cristo, Apartado Aéreo 100655,
Santa Fé de Bogotá
tel (57) 258-2586, fax (57) 1-623-5057,
e-mail the_books@cable.net.co

El Salvador
Iglesia Evangélica Menonita de El Salvador,
Apartado postal #20, Metapán Santa Ana
fax (503) 400-0564, e-mail iemes@saltel.net

México
Iglesia Evangélica Menonita del Noroeste de México, Apartado 38, Ahome, Sinaloa
tel (52) 686-30429, fax (52) 686-30429

Peru
Iglesia Evangélica de los Hermanos Menonitas del Perú, Apartado 200, Sullana, Región Grau
tel (51) 74-49-0148

Iglesia Evangélica Menonita del Perú, Apartado 708, Cusco
tel (51) 84-262849 or 264606,
e-mail rubencarrasco@latinmail.com

Trinidad and Tobago
Mennonite Church of Trinidad and Tobago,
PO Box 300, Port-of-Spain
tel (868) 662-3358, e-mail rawlin@tstt.net.tt

Venezuela
Concilio de Iglesias Evangélicas Menonitas en Venezuela, Calle Miranda 2-112 Charallave,Apartado 28, Edo. Miranda
tel (58) 2-578-22-06, fax (58) 2-578-22-06,
e-mail ciemv@terra.com.ve

Iglesia Evangélica Menonita 'Shalom', Apartado
Postal 120, Charallave C.P. 1210, Estado Miranda
tel (58) 239-2481912, fax (58) 239-2481912,
e-mail vivianasarmientoz@cantv.net

EUROPE

Austria/Germany
Bund der Europäisch-Mennonitischen Brüdergemeinden, Falkenstr. 24, D-32791 Lage
tel (49) 5232 61770, e-mail gemeinde@mbg-lag.de

Spain
Asociación de Menonitas y Hermanos en Cristo en España, C/ Estrella Polar, 10, 09197
Quintanadueñas (Burgos)
tel (34) 947-292-618, e-mail dbyler@menonitas.org

United Kingdom
British Conference of Mennonites, c/o London
Mennonite Centre, 14 Shepherds Hill, London N6 5AQ
tel (44) 208-340-8775, fax (44) 208-341-6807,
e-mail LMC@menno.org.uk

MENNONITE WORLD CONFERENCE

4

Sister Denominations

5

Canada

Mennonite Church Canada

office@mennonitechurch.ca,
www.mennonitechurch.ca
1-866-888-6785 or 204-888-6781,
fax 204-831-5675
600 Shaftesbury Blvd, Winnipeg MB R3P 0M4,
Canada

To e-mail any staff member, use first initial of
first name and last name @mennonitechurch.ca.

General Secretary Dan Nighswander
Witness (includes International Ministries,
National Ministries, and Congregational
Partnerships); Executive Secretary: Robert J.
Suderman
Formation (includes Publishing and
Resources, Youth and Young Adults,
Christian Education and Nurture, and
Ministerial and Congregational Leadership);
Executive Secretary: Dave Bergen
Support Services (includes Communications,
Resource Development, Human Resources,
and Finance); Executive Secretary: Pam
Peters-Pries
Denominational Minister Sven Eriksson

GENERAL BOARD

The General Board includes 18 members of
whom 5 are on the Executive Committee. Henry
Krause is the Mennonite Church Canada moderator (hkrause@uniserve.com). Other officers
are Esther Peters, assistant moderator
(j.peters@uwinnipeg.ca); Marlene Janzen, secretary (Marlene.Janzen@enerpro.ca); Clare
Schlegal, treasurer (clare@sugarfield.ca).

ANNUAL ASSEMBLY

An elected program committee, together with
staff, plans and coordinates annual assemblies.
Pam Peters-Pries, executive secretary, Support
Services, is the lead contact.

PUBLICATION

Canadian Mennonite
editor@canadianmennonite.org,
www.canadianmennonite.org
519-884-3810, fax 519-884-3331
490 Dutton Dr, Unit C5, Waterloo ON N2L 6H7,
Canada
Tim Dyck, editor/publisher

PROFILE

Mennonite Church Canada represents over
35,000 members in 232 congregations across
Canada. Five area conferences (Mennonite
Church British Columbia, Mennonite Church
Alberta, Mennonite Church Saskatchewan,
Mennonite Church Manitoba, and Mennonite

Church Eastern Canada) represent the regional bodies of Mennonite Church Canada.

Mennonite Church Canada Witness and Formation seek to lead, motivate, and offer resources to the church to participate in holistic witness to Jesus Christ in a broken world. MC Canada is a co-owner of Mennonite Publishing Network, Canadian Mennonite University, Associated Mennonite Biblical Seminary, and is affiliated with Conrad Grebel University College and Columbia Bible College. Resources are at work in 39 countries, supporting 90 workers.

Many more Canadian workers are actively ministering in North America. A Resource Centre, Ministerial and Congregational Leadership office, Congregational Partnerships office, Support Services office, and activities in Publishing and Resources, Youth and Young Adults, Christian Education and Nurture combine with National and International Ministries to form a vital and energized Mennonite Church Canada, striving to do together what we cannot do alone, from across the street to around the world.

United States

Brethren in Christ General Conference (North America)

bic@messiah.edu, www.bic-church.org
717-697-2634, fax 717-691-7714
431 Grantham Rd, PO Box A, Grantham PA
17027
Warren L. Hoffman, moderator; Darrell S. Winger, general secretary; Elizabeth Brown, general treasurer; John Allen Brubaker, executive director, Board for World Missions

MESSIAH COLLEGE
One College Ave
Grantham PA 17027
717-766-2511
Kim S. Phipps, interim president

PUBLICATION
Visitor
biccomm@messiah.edu
717-697-2634, fax 717-697-7714
431 Grantham Road, PO Box A, Grantham PA
17027
Ron Ross, editor

Church of the Brethren

GENERAL BOARD
generalboard@brethren.org,
www.brethren.org/genbd
800-323-8039 or 847-742-5100,
fax 847-742-6103
1451 Dundee Ave, Elgin IL 60120
Stan Noffsinger, general secretary

BRETHREN SERVICE CENTER
www.brethren.org/genbd/BSC/index.html
410-635-8710, fax 410-635-8789
500 Main St, PO Box 188, New Windsor MD
21776-0188

WASHINGTON OFFICE
washofc@aol.com,
www.brethren.org/genbd/washofc/index.htm
202-546-3202, fax 202-544-5852
337 North Carolina Ave SE, Washington DC 20003

ANNUAL CONFERENCE
annualconf@aol.com, www.brethren.org/ac
800-323-8039 or 847-742-5100,
fax 847-742-3998
1451 Dundee Ave, Elgin IL 60120
Lerry Fogle, executive director

ASSOCIATION OF BRETHREN CAREGIVERS
abc@brethren.org, www.brethren.org/abc
800-323-8039 or 847-742-5100,
  fax 847-742-5160
1451 Dundee Ave, Elgin IL 60120
Kathy G. Reid, executive director

BETHANY THEOLOGICAL SEMINARY
bethanysem@aol.com,
  www.brethren.org/bethany
765-983-1800, fax 765-983-1840
Main Campus, 615 National Rd W,
  Richmond IN 47374
Eugene F. Roop, president

BRETHREN BENEFIT TRUST
www.brethrenbenefittrust.org
800-746-1505 or 847-695-0200,
  fax 847-742-0135
1505 Dundee Ave, Elgin IL 60120-1619
Wilfred E. Nolen, president

ON EARTH PEACE
oepa_oepa@brethren.org,
  www.brethren.org/oepa/index.html
410-635-8704, fax 410-635-8707
500 Main St, PO Box 188, New Windsor MD
  21776-0188
Barbara Sayler and Bob Gross, co-executive
  directors

PUBLICATION
Messenger
wwiltschek_gb@brethren.org,
  www.brethren.org
847-742-5100, fax 847-742-6103
1451 Dundee Ave, Elgin IL 60120
Walt Wiltschek, editor; Wendy McFadden,
  publisher

PROFILE
The Church of the Brethren General Board is
the primary ministry arm of the Church of the
Brethren Annual Conference, the denomination's highest elected authority. The General
Board's ministries demonstrate Brethren beliefs
and values to the world through word and deed.

General Board ministries include congregational life ministries; Brethren Volunteer
Service; publishing and communications; youth
and young adult ministries; serving pastors and
districts; global partnerships in Brazil, the
Dominican Republic, Nigeria, and Sudan; and
peace, justice, and ecological advocacy.

The General Board maintains a Washington,
D.C., office; has a disaster response network of
coordinators, workers, and childcare providers
ready to respond at a moment's notice; offers
refugee resettlement services, and ships material aid for places in need abroad.

The Church of the Brethren is headquar-
tered in Elgin, Illinois, with offices and a conference and service center in New Windsor,
Maryland; an office in Geneva, Switzerland; and
field staff placed throughout the United States,
Brazil, the Dominican Republic, and Nigeria.

Conservative Mennonite Conference
office@cmcrosedale.org, www.cmcrosedale.org
740-857-1234, fax 740-857-1605
9910 Rosedale Milford Center Rd,
  Irwin OH 43029

Administration and contact: Steve Swartz,
  general secretary, at the above address.
Executive Board: Philip Stutzman, moderator;
  Ben Shirk, moderator-elect; Scott
  Hochstedler, recording secretary; Ken Miller,
  recording secretary-elect; Dale Keffer; Luke
  Yoder.
Treasurer: Lynford Schrock

Committees related to categories of procedure
or concern, which may be contacted at the
above address, are Nominating, Ministerial,
Music and Worship, Peace Witness, Publication
and Literature, Stewardship, and Youth.
Representatives serve on the boards of
Mennonite Central Committee (bi-national, U.S.,

and regional), Mennonite Disaster Service, Mennonite Stewardship Consortium, and Mennonite World Conference.

ROSEDALE BIBLE COLLEGE
An accredited junior Bible college
info@rosedale.edu, www.rosedale.edu
740-857-1311, fax 740-857-1577
2270 Rosedale Rd, Irwin OH 43029

Administration: Leon Zimmerman, president; Jon Showalter, academic dean; Tim Stauffer, dean of students; Alfred Yoder, business manager. Board of Trustees: Levi Sommers, chairman; Eli Gingerich, vice chairman; Sheldon Swartz, secretary; Joe Byler, treasurer; Lowell Bender; Lester Diller; Roger Hazen

ROSEDALE MENNONITE MISSIONS
info@rmmoffice.org,
   www.rosedalemennonitemissions.org.
740-857-1366, fax 740-857-1605
9920 Rosedale Milford Center Rd,
   Irwin OH 43029

Administration: Joseph Showalter, president; Paul Kurt, director of global missions; Mim Musser, director of human resources; Keith Scheffel, chief financial officer. Board of Directors: Adin Miller, chairman; David Slabaugh, vice chairman; Tom Beachy, recording secretary; Harold Delegrange; Elmer Miller; Edward Roggie; Max Zook.

PUBLICATION
Brotherhood Beacon
beaconsubscriptions@cmcrosedale.org,
   www.cmcrosedale.org
740-857-1234, fax 740-857-1605
9910 Rosedale Milford Center Rd,
   Irwin OH 43029
Conrad Showalter, editor, beacon@bnin.net

ANNUAL EVENTS
The annual conference is held from Thursday to Sunday of the weekend of the first Sunday of August (with possible shifts to a week earlier or a week later when necessitated by local circumstances). Projected locations: Beaver Falls NY, 2004; Greenwood DE, 2005; Rosedale OH, 2006; Goshen IN, 2007.

Ministers' Fellowship, planned especially for ministers, is conducted annually in February. Projected locations and dates: Kalona IA, February 14-18, 2005; Goshen IN, February 13-17, 2006; Phoenix AZ, February 2007.

Mennonite Brethren Churches, U.S. Conference

U.S. CONFERENCE OFFICE
offices@usmb.org, www.usmb.org
620-947-3151, fax 620-947-3266
315 S Lincoln, PO Box 220,
   Hillsboro KS 67063-0220

PUBLICATION
Christian Leader
christianleader@usmb.org
620-947-5543, fax 620-947-3266
315 S Lincoln, PO Box 220,
   Hillsboro KS 67063-0220
Connie Faber, editor

EXECUTIVE DIRECTOR
chuckusmb@hotmail.com
office/fax 559-738-8829
cell 559-799-8964
1013 W Center Ave, Visalia CA 93291-5914
Chuck Buller

DIRECTOR OF MISSION USA
dmorris77@hotmail.com
620-947-3151, fax 620-947-3266
315 S Lincoln, PO Box 220,
   Hillsboro KS 67063-0220
Don Morris

MENNONITE BRETHREN BIBLICAL SEMINARY

mbseminary@aol.com, www.mbseminary.com
559-251-8628, fax 559-251-7212
4824 E Butler Ave, Fresno CA 93727-5097
Jim Holm, president

TABOR COLLEGE

www.tabor.edu
620-947-3121, fax 620-947-2607
400 S Jefferson, Hillsboro KS 67063
Larry Nikkel, president

FRESNO PACIFIC UNIVERSITY

admissions@fresno.edu, www.fresno.edu
559-453-2000, fax 559-453-2007
1717 S Chestnut Ave, Fresno CA 93702
D. Merrill Ewert, president

MENNONITE BRETHREN FOUNDATION

info@mbfoundation.com
800-551-1547 or 620-947-3151,
   fax 620-947-3266
315 S Lincoln, PO Box 220, Hillsboro KS
   67063-0220
Jon C. Wiebe, president/CEO

MBMS INTERNATIONAL

mission agency
mbmsi@mbmsinternational.org,
   www.mbmsinternational.org
1-888-866-6267 or 559-4546-4600,
   fax 559-251-1432
4867 E Townsend, Fresno CA 93727-5006
Randy Friensen, general director
604-859-6267
Abbotsford office: 302-32025 Dahlstrom Ave,
   Abbotsford BC V2T 2K7

PROFILE

The Mennonite Brethren are a people of faith, history and mission. In 1860, spiritual renewal among Russian Mennonites resulted in groups of believers meeting together for fellowship and Bible study. A close spiritual kinship resulted, and the group became known as "brethren," and eventually, "Mennonite Brethren." Mennonite Brethren are now found in more than 20 countries around the world.

The U.S. Conference of Mennonite Brethren Churches is made up of five district conferences that serve more than 200 churches in the United States. The Conference consists of ministries, including National Youth Commission, Peace Commission, cross-cultural ministries, church planting, discipleship, evangelism, mission both at home and abroad, education (Christian schools, two four-year liberal arts colleges, and a seminary), a denominational magazine, and stewardship resources and education. The Mennonite Brethren also participate in the relief and caring ministries of Mennonite Central Committee.

The national headquarters is located in Hillsboro, Kansas, which is also home to Tabor College. On the west coast, Fresno Pacific University, Mennonite Brethren Biblical Seminary, and the headquarters for the mission agency, MBMS International, all are located in Fresno, California.

SISTER DENOMINATIONS

5

I have great hope for our young church ...

MINISTERS

6

Ministers

Ministerial information for this section is provided by the Congregational and Ministerial Leadership staff of Mennonite Church USA in cooperation with area conferences. Ministerial names included are those who have been credentialed by Mennonite Church USA area conferences. The records that follow are complete as of July 2004. Updated ministerial information is available in the online directory at www.MennoniteUSA.org

SAMPLE LISTING

Name (name of spouse, if applicable)
Leatherman, Andrew H. (Dorothy)

Home (or preferred) address
1551 Valley Rd, Coatesville PA 19320

Telephone, e-mail address
610-384-3678, dotandy@yahoo.com

[Area conference holding credential], ministerial role, [credential status]
[ACC] IIB3a [AC] (conference codes on page 10; ministerial role and credential status codes below)

Title, congregation/organization served, location
Chaplain, Einstein Medical Center, Coatesville PA

FOR EXAMPLE
Leatherman, Andrew H. (Dorothy) 1551 Valley Rd, Coatesville PA 19320, 610-384-3678, dotandy@yahoo.com [ACC] IIB3a [AC] Chaplain, Einstein Medical Center, Coatesville PA

Credential status
AC—Active
AW—Active without charge
RE—Retired

Ministerial role
I—Oversight ministries
IA—Licensed toward ordination for oversight ministry
IB1—Ordained and serving in a denominational ministerial leadership office
IB2—Ordained and serving as a conference minister
IB3—Ordained and serving as an overseer or bishop
IC—Licensed/commissioned for a specific ministry within oversight

II—Church and pastoral ministries
IIA—Licensed toward ordination
IIB1—Ordained and serving as a lead pastor or co-pastor in a congregation
IIB2—Ordained and serving as an associate/assistant pastor, youth minister
IIB3a—Ordained and serving as a chaplain/pastoral counselor
IIB3b—Ordained and serving in a missions or service assignment
IIB3c—Ordained and serving as a conference or church administrator, conference youth minister
IIB3d—Ordained and serving as a teacher in a church educational institution
IIC—Licensed/commissioned for a specific ministry

III—Lay ministries
III—Elders, deacons, lay ministers

MINISTERS

6

A

Acosta, Eusebio, Colonia Union, Tijuana, Baja CA, Mexico, 619-232-1385 [PSW] IIB1 [AC] Pastor, Casa de Oración Menonita, San Diego CA

Adams, Jesse U. (Martha Elizabeth) 145 Dover Chester Rd, Randolph NJ 07869, 201-927-1362 [FRC] IIB1 [AC] Pastor, Garden Chapel, Dover NJ

Adams, Ronald W. (Marilou) 320 Abbeyville Rd, Lancaster PA 17603, 717-397-9882 [LAN] IIB1 [AC] Pastor, E Chestnut St Menn Ch, Lancaster PA

Adi, Sutanto, 2472 White Dove Ln, Chino Hills CA 91709, 909-465-9211 [PSW] IIB1 [AC] Pastor, Jemaat Kristen Indonesia Bethel, Chino CA

Aeschliman, Quinn Anthony, 1664 Mt Pleasant Rd, Chesapeake VA 23322 [VA] IIA [AC]

Aguado, Gamaliel, 1312 Ridgeland Ave, Berwyn IL 60402, 708-795-4738, gamalielaguado@ccvidaabundante.com [IL] IIB2 [AC] Associate Pastor, Centro Cristiano Vida Abundante, Cicero IL

Aguilar, Guadalupe, 6711 Tallowood Cr, Brownsville TX 78521, 956-831-7193 [SC] IIA [AC] Pastor, Iglesia Menonita Rey de Gloria, Brownsville TX

Aguilera, Euclides, Shalom Mennonite (Spanish), Venezuela [LAN] IIA [AC] Associate Pastor, Shalom Mennonite, Venezuela

Ahanonu, George, 3939 Ursula Ave #4, Los Angeles CA 90008, 310-921-8233, aebere@earthlink.net [PSW] IIA [AC] Pastor, Great Commission Deliverance Ch, Los Angeles CA

Ahlgrim, Ryan Jeffrey (Laurie Ann Silver) 4831 Manning, Indianapolis IN 46228, 317-299-8368, ahlgrim@juno.com [IM] IIB1 [AC] Pastor, First Menn Ch, Indianapolis IN

Albrecht, Wayne L. (Annette) 1010 Cardinal Ln, Richardson TX 75080-4707, 214-235-8449 [WDC] IIB3a [AC] Executive Director, Pastoral Counseling & Ed Center, Dallas, TX

Alger, John Paul (Retha) 512 Bird Song Ln, Broadway VA 22815, 540-896-5909 [VA] [RE]

Allaby, Gordon K. (Leslie Ann) PO Box 167, 800 S Randall Ave, Moundridge KS 67107, 620-345-2566, goles@midusa.net [WDC] IIB1 [AC] Pastor, Osler Menn Ch, Osler SK

Allgyer, Michael D. (Debra) 4005 Conrad Weiser Pkwy, Womelsdorf PA 19567, 610-589-4458, mike@allequipmentrentals.com [LAN] IIC [AC] Minister of Evangelism, Hammer Creek Menn Ch, Lititz PA

Almodovar, Felipe (Iris) 1101 Arnold Dr, Corpus Christi TX 78412, 512-985-2790 [SC] IIB1 [AC] Pastor, Prince of Peace Menn Ch, Corpus Christi TX

Althouse, Daniel P. (Linda) 67 Wild Cherry Ln, Marietta PA 17547, 717-426-4871, mariettachapel@juno.com [LAN] IIB1 [AC] Pastor, Marietta Community Chapel, Marietta PA

Alwine, Clarence (Turie) 24 Apple House Rd, Belleville PA 17004, 717-935-2720 [ALL] [RE]

Amador, Victor S. (Carolina) 616 Jamaica Ave, Brooklyn NY 11208, 718-235-7249, victoramador2001@aol.com [LAN] IIA [AC] Pastor, International Christian Community Ch, Brooklyn NY

Amstutz, Anita F. (Kenneth Couch) 410 Morningside Dr SE, Albuquerque NM 87108, 505-255-4387, pastor@abqmennonite.org [RM] IIA [AC] Pastor,

Albuquerque Menn Ch, Albuquerque NM

Amstutz, James S. (Lorraine J.) 1135 Main St, Akron PA 17501-1615, amstutz@ptd.net [ACC] IIB1 [AC] Pastor, Akron Menn Ch, Akron PA

Amstutz, Myron J., 13887 Jericho Rd, Dalton OH 44618, 330-857-1293 [OH] [RE]

Amstutz, Neil B. (Janette) 520 S Maple, McPherson KS 67460, 620-241-0652, neilafmc@earthlink.net [WDC] IIB1 [AC] Pastor, First Menn Ch, McPherson KS

Amstutz, Vilas, 4195 Old Delphos Rd, Elida OH 45807, 419-339-6807 [OH] [RE]

Anders Jr., Earl N. (Elaine Lewis Anders) 91 Allentown Rd, Elroy PA 18964, 215-799-0864, eanders12@juno.com [FRC] IIB1 [AC] Pastor, Providence Menn Ch, Collegeville PA; Pastor, Hersteins Menn Ch, Schwenksville PA

Andres, Karen (David) 14919 NW 160th St, Newton KS 67114, kandres@tabormennonite.org [WDC] IIA [AC] Associate Pastor, Tabor Menn Ch, Newton KS

Andrew, Dennis W. (Cindy) 214 N Charlotte St, Manheim PA 17545, 717-664-4820, cdandrew@supernet.com [LAN] IIC [AC] Pastor, Grace Community Fell, Manheim PA

Angerman, Rob L., 34816 Spicer Dr SE, Albany OR 97321, 541-924-0679, pastorrob@plainview.org [PNW] IIB1 [AC] Pastor, Plainview Menn Ch, Albany OR

Angstadt Sr., Paul D., 85 E College Ave, Wernersville PA 19565, 610-678-3812 [LAN] [RE]

Angustia, Nicolas (Carolina) 1346 Dekalb Ave #1, Brooklyn NY 11221, 718-456-9401, pangustia@aol.com [LAN] IB3, IIB1 [AC] Pastor, Iglesia Unida de Avivamiento, Brooklyn NY; Bishop/Overseer/Supervisor, LMC New York City District, New York City, NY

Arana, Salvador, 3119 Liberty Blvd, Southgate CA 90280, 323-569-2029 [PSW] IIB1 [AC] Pastor, Iglesia Monte Sinai, South Gate CA

Araujo, David (Sonia) 506 Liberty St, E Chicago IN 46312, 219-397-9936 [IL] IIB1 [AC] Pastor, Iglesia Menonita Getsemani, E Chicago IL

Araujo, Sonia N. (David) 506 Liberty St, E Chicago IN 46312, 219-397-9936 [IL] IIA [AC] Co-Pastor, Iglesia Menonita Getsemani, E Chicago IL

Araya, Mario E. (Yanette) 237 Locust St, New Holland PA 17557, 717-354-2366, marioearaya@hotmail.com [LAN] IB3, IIB1 [AC] Pastor, New Holland Spanish Menn, New Holland PA; Bishop/Overseer/Supervisor, Spanish District, W Supervisor, New Holland, PA

Arbaugh II, John Joseph (Sharon Rose) 286 Cider Barn Ln, Stuarts Draft VA 24477, 540-337-1975, joearbaugh@juno.com [VA] IIB2 [AC] Minister of Missions, Waynesboro Menn Ch, Waynesboro VA

Arevalo, Jesus Antonio (Elsa Marlen) 4215 Rockford Dr, Dallas TX 75211-8438, 214-337-2200 [SC, WDC] [RE]

Argueta, Jorge, PO Box 338, Upland CA 91785, 909-987-9594 [PSW] IIA [AC] Pastor, Iglesia Fuente de Vida, Upland CA

Arias, Salomon (Betty) 9 Kew Gardens Apt 102, Jamaica NY 11415, 718-261-4752 [ACC] IIB1 [AC] Pastor, Ephesians Menn Ch, Queens NY

Armstrong, James R., 3603 Engel Dr, Valparaiso IN 46383, 219-464-8101, larmstro@niia.net [IM] IB3, IIB3a [AC] Overseer, Burr Oak Menn Ch, Rensselaer IN

Arn Jr., John Willard (Sarah E.) 102 Highland Ave,

Lansdale PA 19446-3207, 215-855-4584, twinoaks7@juno.com [EDC] [RE]

Asante, Albert, 1243 W 46th St, Los Angeles CA 90037, 323-292-8139 [PSW] IIB1 [AC] Pastor, Labor for Christ Ministry, Los Angeles CA

Assefa, Dagne (Carol Sue Weaver) 2613 Astro Ct, Indianapolis IN 46229, 317-895-6756, dcassefa@sprynet.com [IM] IIB1 [AC] Pastor, Shalom Menn Ch, Indianapolis IN

Assis, Nilson (Mary Jane) 105 Eric Ave, Shillington PA 19607-2811, 610-796-2776, nilson.assis@verizon.net [ACC] IIB1 [AC] Interim/Transitional Pastor, Maple Grove Menn Ch of Atglen, Atglen PA

Augsburger, A. Don (Martha Kling Augsburger) 3901 Bahia Vista, Lot 128, Sarasota FL 24232, mdaugs@aol.com [FRK] IIB1 [AC]

Augsburger, David, 135 N Oakland Ave, Pasadena CA 91101, 909-621-1126 [PSW] IIB3d [AW]

Augsburger, Fred E., 32035 SR 643, Fresno OH 43824, 216-897-1075 [OH] [RE]

Augsburger, Larry (Jeananne Joy) 848 Runkle St, West Liberty OH 43357, 937-465-4314, augsburg@bright.net [OH] IIB1 [AC]

Augsburger, Myron S. (Esther) 1549 Hillcrest Dr, Harrisonburg VA 22802, 540-433-2151 [VA] IB3 [AC]

Aukamp, James Arnold (Jean) 2212 Bald Eagle Rd, Drumore PA 17518, 717-548-3477 [LAN] IIB2 [AC] Associate Pastor, Living Stones Fell, Peach Bottom PA; Chaplain, Evangelism & Prison Ministry, PA; Evangelist, Living Stones Fell, Peach Bottom PA

B

Baccam, Ha (La) 121 SE Emma Ave, Des Moines IA 50315, 515-285-7057, HaBaccam@aol.com [CP] IIB2 [AC] Associate Pastor, Des Moines Menn Ch, Des Moines IA

Baer, Dale T. (Susan E.) 207 Sherwood Dr, Lexington OH 44904, 419-884-1128 [EDC] III [AC]

Baer, Darrell (Sharon) 3715 Clay Hill Rd, Waynesboro PA 17268, 717-762-4041 [FRK] IB2 [AC] Conference Minister, Franklin Mennonite Conference, Chambersburg, PA

Baer, Harold J. (Gail M.) 5347 Acre, Mapleton IL 61547, 309-697-0715, norwoodchurch@mail2.myexcel.com [IL] IIC [AC] Pastor, First Norwood Menn Ch, Peoria IL

Bair, Ray, 937 Oxford St, Elkhart IN 46516, 574-522-3743 [IM] [RE]

Baker, Ronald, 7200 Briar Spring Farm, Schuyler VA 22969, 804-831-2593, rrbak@juno.com [VA] IIB3a [AC]

Bal, Joan C. (Martin L.) PO Box 749, Point Blank TX 77364-0749, 713-460-2338, jbal@houston.rr.com [WDC] IIB3a [AC] Chaplain, Houston, TX

Baldwin, Robert B. (Edea Anne) PO Box 508, Quitman MS 39355, 601-776-6407 [GS] IIC [AC]

Ball, Kelly J., 865 Rt 113, Harleysville PA 19438, 610-584-5721 [EDC] IIA [AC] Youth Pastor, West Swamp Menn Ch, Quakertown PA

Ball, Torrey D., 13 Detroit Dr, So Hutchinson KS 67505, 620-669-8979, tball@ourtownusa.net [SC] IIB2 [AC] Maintenance Coordinator, Camp Mennoscah, Murdock, KS

Baluyot, Benjamin C. (Evangeline) 4224 J St, Philadelphia PA 19124, 215-743-4341, bengiebaluyot@msn.com [LAN] IIB2 [AC] Associate

Pastor, Kapatiran Christian Ch, Havertown PA

Banks, Michael E. (Addie) 1114 Sherman Ave, Bronx NY 10456, 718-538-6570, kgtbronx@localnet.com [LAN] IB3, IIB1 [AC] Pastor, King of Glory Tabernacle, Bronx NY; Bishop/Overseer, LMC New York City District, New York, NY

Banks, Otis M. (Carlett) 1606 Ivy Hill Rd, Philadelphia PA 19150, 215-247-8825, revitalization@juno.com [LAN] IIB1 [AC] Pastor, Diamond St Menn Ch, Philadelphia PA

Bapst, Rodney, 13249 SR 104, Lucasville OH 45648, 740-259-5712, rjbapst@zoomnet.net [OH] IIB1 [AC] Pastor, Owl Creek Menn Ch, Lucasville OH

Barahona, Rafael E. (Maria del Pilar Lillo) 1314 S 11th St, Goshen IN 46526, 574-534-4569, rafaeleb@goshen.edu [IM] IIB3d [AC] Congregational Development Resource person, Iglesia Menonita Hispana, USA & Canada; Director, Hispanic Ed in Theology & Leadership/Goshen Coll, Goshen IN

Bardell, Larry (Linda L.) 1708 Springhill Dr NW, Albany OR 97321, 541-928-0747, lbdesigns@attbi.com [PNW] IIA [AC]

Bare, Donald (Arlene) 12467 Millertown Rd, Fulks Run VA 22830, 540-896-1149 [VA] IIB1 [AC] Pastor, Hebron Menn Ch, Fulks Run VA

Barkema, David M. (Regina) 5067 Indian Mound St, Sarasota FL 34232, 941-378-3999 [SE] IIC [AC] Youth Pastor, Bay Shore Menn Ch, Sarasota FL

Barker, Nate (Denise) 460 Hartman Dr, Harrisonburg VA 22802 [VA] IIA, IIB2 [AC]

Barnhart, Matthew Emerson, 640 Brisban Rd, Baltimore MD 21229, 410-646-3243 [LAN] IIA [AC] Pastor, Wilkens Ave Menn Ch, Baltimore MD

Barrett, Lois Yvonne (Thomas Bruce Mierau) 1508 Fairview, Wichita KS 67203-2634, 316-264-3686, mierau@onemain.com [WDC] IIB3c [AC] Director, AMBS-Great Plains Extension, North Newton, KS

Barrett, Richard (Mary J.) 1525 Mennonite Church Rd, West Liberty OH 43357, 937-465-4749, oakgrove@bright.net [OH] IIA [AC] Associate Pastor, Oak Grove Menn Ch, W Liberty OH

Bartel, Floyd G. (Justina Neufeld) 2916 Wildwood Way, North Newton KS 67117, 316-283-7890, floydb@mennowdc.org [WDC] [RE]

Bartholomew, James E., 733 W Maple St, North Canton OH 44720, 330-499-9708, jpbart@juno.com [OH] IIB1 [AC] Pastor, Dayspring Christian Fell, North Canton OH

Bartholomew, Maxine (Richard Carl Sr.) 12759 Blosser Rd, North Lima OH 44452, 330-549-3389, rbarth1@zoominternet.net [OH] IIB1 [AC] Co-Pastor, Maple Grove Menn Ch, New Castle PA

Bartholomew, Rebecca J., 1508 Lincoln, Columbus OH 43212, 614-488-4377, questions@agoraministries.org [CDC, OH] IIB1 [AC] Co-Pastor, Agora Christian Fell, Columbus OH

Bartholomew, Richard (Maxine Fay) 12759 Blosser Rd, North Lima OH 44452, 330-549-3389, rbarth1@zoominternet.net [OH] IIB1 [AC] Co-Pastor, Maple Grove Menn Ch, New Castle PA

Bartholomew Jr., Richard, 1508 Lincoln Rd, Columbus OH 43212-2722, 614-488-4377, questions @agoraministries.org [CDC, OH] IIB1 [AC] Co-Pastor, Agora Christian Fell, Columbus OH

Bartow, David W. (Rebecca J.) Box 115, Zionsville PA

18092-0115, DaveWinB@aol.com [EDC] IIB1 [AC] Interim Pastor, First Menn Ch, Allentown PA; Associate Chaplain, Frederick Mennonite Community, Frederick PA

Bartsch, Mark (Stephanie) 5743 Pinecroft Dr, Toledo OH 43615, 419-539-6944 [OH] IIA [AC] Co-Pastor, Toledo Menn Ch, Toledo OH

Bartsch, Stephanie (Mark) 5743 Pinecroft, Toledo OH 43615, 419-539-6944 [OH] IIA [AC] Co-Pastor, Toledo Menn Ch, Toledo OH

Bates, Karl Michael, 41109 E 291st St, Garden City MO 64747 [SC] IIA [AC] Co-Pastor, Sycamore Grove Menn Ch, Garden City MO

Bauer, Royal H., 1440 Greencroft Dr, Goshen IN 46526, 574-533-6931, RoEvBauer@juno.com [IM] [RE]

Bauman, Harold E. (Carolyn Hertzler) 1418 Hampton Cr, Goshen IN 46526, 574-533-6526, hbauman@maplenet.net [IM] IB3 [AC] Overseer, Yellow Creek Mennonite, Goshen IN; Overseer, Faith Mennonite, Goshen IN; Overseer, Olive Mennonite, Elkhart IN

Bauman, John (Susan E. Ebersole) 50 Maple Ave, Hastings Hdsn NY 10706, 212-665-3577 [LAN] IIB1 [AC]

Baumgartner, Beverly, 200 W Cedar St, Hesston KS 67062-8100 [WDC] IIB3a [AC] Chaplain

Beachey, Duane, 424 Addax Dr, San Antonio TX 78213, 210-341-3967, dbeachey@earthlink.net [SC, WDC] IIB1 [AC] Lead Pastor, San Antonio Menn Ch, San Antonio TX

Beachy, Daniel (Emma) 4040 Main St, Conestoga PA 17516, 717-871-0320, dan@goldrule.net [LAN] IIC [AC] Staff, Life Ministries, Conestoga PA

Beachy, Edward R. (Louise) 35 Country Ln, Honey Brook PA 19344, 610-273-2555 [LAN] IIB2 [AC] Associate Pastor, Cambridge Menn Ch, Gordonville PA

Beachy, Eleanor Jeanette (Perry J.) 353 W Cedar St, Hesston KS 67062, 620-327-4211 [WDC] [RE]

Beachy, James K. (Pamela Annette) 134 Kutz Rd, Fleetwood PA 19522, pastorjim@hopecomm.org [ACC] IIB1 [AC] Pastor, Hope Community Ch, Fleetwood PA

Beachy, John E., 1739 Wildwood Ct, Goshen IN 46526, 574-533-6198 [IM] [RE]

Beachy, Marvin J. (Dorothy) 815 Cloverleaf Rd, Elizabethtown PA 17022, 717-367-6267 [LAN] [RE]

Beachy, Moses, 716 E Jackson, Goshen IN 46526, 574-533-5832 [IM] [RE]

Beachy, Perry J. (Eleanor J.) 353 W Cedar St, Hesston KS 67062, 620-327-4211 [WDC] [RE]

Bean, Heather Ann Ackley, 8404 Frankfort Ave, Fontana CA 92335-4113, 909-822-8715, heathrbean@aol.com [PSW] IIB1, IIB3d [AC] Associate Professor, Azusa Pacific University, Azusa CA

Bechler, Leroy (Irene) 1213 Camden Ct, Goshen IN 46526, 574-537-8698, ibechler@juno.com [IM] IB3 [AC] Overseer, Mennonite Church of Warsaw, Warsaw IN

Bechtel, Lowell B. (Peggy) RD 3 Box 49D, Greenwood DE 19950, 410-896-3451 [ALL] IIB1 [AC] Pastor, Tressler Menn Ch, Greenwood DE

Bechtold, J. Nelson (Connie) 2563 Bainbridge Rd, Bainbridge PA 17502, 717-367-1938, jnbechtold@dejazzd.com [LAN] IIB1 [AC] Pastor, Goods Menn Ch, Bainbridge PA

Beck, Bill (Sherry) 589 S 300 WPO Box 316, Hebron IN 46341, 219-477-4776, billsherrykids@juno.com [IM] IIB1 [AC] Co-Pastor, Hopewell Menn Ch, Kouts IN

Beck, Carl, Akishma Shi, Tokyo 196, Japan [OH] [RE]

Beck, Duane E. (Lois A.) 56939 Pearl Ann Dr, Elkhart IN 46516, 574-294-3016, duaneb@maplenet.net [IM] IIB1 [AC] Pastor, Belmont Menn Ch, Elkhart IN

Becker, Kenneth Duane (Anne) 68 Horning Rd, Mohnton PA 19540, 610-777-8905 [LAN] IIC [AC] Youth Pastor, Bowmansville Menn Ch, E Earl PA

Becker, Palmer Joseph (Ardys) 221 Kingsway, Hesston KS 67062-9267, 620-327-4355, palmerb@southwind.net [SC, WDC] IIB3c [AC] Director of Pastor Ministries Program, Hesston College, Hesston KS

Beidler, Luke (Dorothy) 606 Swede St, Norristown PA 19401, 610-270-0636, Lukdot@juno.com [FRC] IIB1 [AC] Pastor, Methacton Menn Ch, Norristown PA; Associate Pastor, Norristown New Life Menn Ch, Norristown PA

Beidler, S. Ken (Elaine M. Shenk) 608 Walnut St, Iowa City IA 52240, 319-338-2318, kbeidler@avalon.net [CP] IIA [AC] Pastor, First Menn Ch of Iowa City, Iowa City IA

Beiler, Keith L. (Cheryl) 2185 Smyrna Rd, Paradise PA 17562, 717-442-8085, kcbeiler@juno.com [LAN] IIB2 [AC] Associate Pastor, Millwood Menn Ch, Bird In Hand PA

Beitzel, Leroy P. (Mary) 51 Hossler Rd, Manheim PA 17545, 717-664-4000, beitzel@desupernet.net [LAN] IIC [AC] Licensed Deacon, Kauffman Menn Ch, Manheim PA

Bender, John A. (Jean) 134 E Mohler Church Rd, Ephrata PA 17522, 717-733-4258 [LAN] III [AC] Ordained Deacon, Millport Menn Ch, Leola PA

Bender, John Paul (Marilyn Handrich) 640 Melbourne St, Pittsburgh PA 15217 [VA] IIB1 [AC] Pastor, Pittsburgh Menn Ch, Pittsburgh PA

Bender, L. Roy (Connie Kreider) 808 E Jefferson Ct, Lancaster PA 17602, 717-293-1513, whmc2270@aol.com [LAN] IIB1 [AC] Pastor, Witmer Heights Menn Ch, Lancaster PA

Bender, Marilyn Handrich (John Paul) 640 Melbourne St, Pittsburgh PA 15217, jbender770@aol.com [VA] IIB1 [AC]

Bender, Merle L., 215 Lake Vista Cr, Hesston KS 67062, 620-327-4227 [SC] [RE]

Bender, Paul E. (Leona) 3464 W Main St, Belleville PA 17004, 717-935-2598 [ALL] IB3 [AC]

Bender, Ralph N., PO Box 123, Morris Run PA 16939, 717-638-2453 [LAN] IIB1 [AC] Associate Pastor, Calvary Menn Fell, Morris Run PA

Bender, Ross T., 1444 Hampton Cr, Goshen IN 46526, 574-534-9010 [IM] [RE]

Benner, David K. (Priscilla) PO Box 216, Pennsburg PA 18073, 215-679-6590 [FRC] [RE]

Benner, Kenneth, 2285 N Kemp Rd, Elida OH 45807, 419-339-8505 [OH] IIB2 [AC] Associate Pastor, Kalida Family Outreach Center, Kalida OH

Benner, Mary Elizabeth (Darin S.) 704 Quail Cr, Hatfield PA 19440, 215-721-6466 [FRC] [AW]

Benner, Millard (Lura) RR 3 Box 51C, Greenwood DE 19950, 302-349-4734 [ALL] IB3 [AC]

Benner, Paul K. (Faith) PO Box 288, Morris PA 16938, 717-353-2019, pbmorris@epix.net [FRC] [RE]

Benner, Robert H. (Betsy) 506 Meeting House Rd, Gap PA 17527, 717-768-7612, bbbenner@wjtl.net [LAN] IIB1 [AC] Pastor, Old Rd Menn Ch, Gap PA

Benner, Scott Springer (Angela B.) 17B Franklin Ave, Souderton PA 18964, 215-723-6918, socialmisfits@enter.net [EDC] IIB1 [AC] Associate Pastor-Youth, Zion Menn Ch, Souderton PA

Bentzinger, Richard Alvin (Marian Ruth) 504 University, Box 83, Donnellson IA 52625, 319-835-9124 [CP] IIB1 [AC] Pastor, Zion Menn Ch, Donnellson IA

Bergey, Curtis L. (Esther) 207 W Summit Apt A365, Souderton PA 18964, 215-723-4924 [FRC] [RE]

Bergey, J. Harold (Rose) 2041 Mount Pleasant Rd, Chesapeake VA 23322, 757-482-4379, bergey@arilion.com [VA] IIB1 [AC] Pastor, Mount Pleasant Menn Ch, Chesapeake VA

Bergey, James H. (Mary) 405 Maxwell St, Chesapeake VA 23322, 757-482-4711, 10777s.474@compuserve.com [VA] [RE]

Bergey, Philip C. (Evon Swartzentruber) 2527 Peachtree Dr, Perkasie PA 18944, 215-453-7454 [FRC] IIC [AC] Conference Coordinator, Franconia Mennonite Conference, Souderton PA

Bergstresser, Deron Brill (Annette) 1838 Manor Haus Ct Apt 3, Goshen IN 46526, 574-533-9702 [CDC, IM] IIA [AC] Pastor, Faith Menn Ch, Goshen IN

Bernhard, Carlos (Karl) Enrique (Marlene S.) 3500 Edenborn St Apt 209, Metairie LA 70002, 504-780-0663, ceb.05@gnofn.org [GS] IIB1 [AC] Pastor, Iglesia Amor Viviente, Metairie LA

Berthold, Josef V. (Brenda Wert) 516 S Queen St, Lancaster PA 17603, 717-299-3228, berthojos@cs.com [LAN] IIB1 [AC] Pastor, W End Menn Fell, Lancaster PA

Bertsche, Jim, 57770 Roys Ave, Elkhart IN 46517, 574-522-7916 [CDC] [RE]

Beyer, E. Eugene (Linda) 3924 Oregon Pk, Leola PA 17540, 717-859-5626, eebeyer@dejazzd.com [LAN] IIB1 [AC] Pastor, Millport Menn Ch, Leola PA

Bianchi, Tony (Zenobia Sowell) PO Box 6357, Chicago IL 60680, 312-922-5333 [IL] IIB1 [AC] Pastor, Bethel Menn Community Ch, Chicago IL

Biandudi, Celestin Hill (Brenda J.) 2701 13th St S, Saint Petersburg FL 33705, 727-823-0346 [SE] IIC [AC] Pastor, New Beginning Community Ch, St Petersburg FL

Binder, Neil (Anna Margaret) 321 Broad St, Port Allegany PA 16743, 814-642-9275, bindluse@penn.com [ACC] IIB1 [AC] Pastor, Birch Grove Menn Ch, Port Allegany PA

Birkey, Marlin Keith (Cherie Lynn) 3701 Aster Dr, Sarasota FL 34233, 941-926-4615, MBirkey@comcast.net [SE] IB3, IIB1 [AC] Pastor, Ashton Menn Ch, Sarasota FL; District Minister, SE Mennonite Conference, Sarasota FL; Moderator, SE Mennonite Conference, Sarasota FL

Birky, Chris (Melissa) 527 E SR 8, Kouts IN 46347, 219-766-3270, birky@netnitco.net [IM] IIB1 [AC] Co-Pastor, Hopewell Menn Ch, Kouts IN

Birky, Glen I. (Erma) 35272 State Hwy 34, Detroit Lakes MN 56501-8000, 218-847-4988, dgbari@tekstar.com [NC] IB3 [AC]

Birky, Mervin R. (Venita King) 1015 Bowser Dr, Colorado Spring CO 80909, 719-596-5776, mervenita@juno.com [RM] IIB1 [AC] Pastor, Beth-El Menn Ch, Colorado Springs CO

Bishop, H. Earl (Esther) 1001 Weston Andover Rd, Andover VT 05143, 802-875-2769 [FRC] [RE]

Bishop, Michael Scott (Brenda Lee) 2 Woodlawn Dr, Blooming Glen PA 18911 [FRC] IIA [AC]

Bitkofer, Phares (Helen) 5535 Patton Rd, Greencastle

PA 17225, 717-597-9566 [FRK] IIC [AC] Licensed Minister

Bixler, Sarah, 3260 Zion Church Rd, Broadway VA 22815, gehmans@emu.edu [VA] IIB2 [AC]

Blackburn, Jeffrey D. (Lori) 310 W Pennsylvania St, Greensburg KS 67054, 620-723-2478 [SC] IIB1 [AC] Pastor, Greensburg Menn Ch, Greensburg KS

Blackburn, Richard G. (Arlee) 101 W Washington, Lombard IL 60148, 630-627-2597, Admin@LMPeaceCenter.org [IL] IIB3c [AC] Director, Lombard Mennonite Peace Center, Lombard IL

Blank, Bill D. (Glenda) 160 McHenry Rd, Parkesburg PA 19365, 610-593-7315, wdb@epix.net [ACC] IIB1 [AC] Associate Pastor, Maple Grove Menn Ch of Atglen, Atglen PA

Blank, Keith W., 49 Brandt Blvd, Landisville PA 17538, 717-892-1047 [LAN] IIC [AC] Director of Discipleship Ministries, Eastern Mennonite Missions, Salunga PA

Blank, Lester A. (Mary Lou Lauver) 126 N Christiana Ave, Gap PA 17527, 610-593-5790, lablank@epix.net [LAN] [RE]

Blosser, Donald W. (Carolyn Brooks) 65241 CR 27, Goshen IN 46526, 574-533-8147 [IM] IIB3d [AC] President and Director of Education, Oakwood Academy, Syracuse IN

Blosser, Eugene (Elsie) 510 14th St, Wellman IA 52356, 319-646-2615 [CP] [RE]

Blosser, Floyd G. (Janet Keller) 1281 Mt Clinton Pk, Harrisonburg VA 22802, 540-434-8474, FJBlosser@aol.com [VA] [AW]

Blosser, Gary S. (Judith Marie Brunk) 725 Ann Ave, Wauseon OH 43567, 419-446-7457 [OH] IIB1 [AC] Lead Pastor, North Clinton Menn Ch, Wauseon OH

Blosser, Glendon L. (Dorothy) 1513 Mount Clinton Pk, Harrisonburg VA 22802, 540-434-0657, gblosser@aol.com [VA] IB3 [AC]

Blosser, Janet, 1281 Mt Clinton Pk, Harrisonburg VA 22802 [VA] IIC [AC]

Blough, Ronald L. (Rhoda M.) 6977 Paris Ave NE, Louisville OH 44641, 330-875-4953, bloughr@juno.com [OH] IIB1 [AC] Pastor, Beech Menn Ch, Louisville OH

Bodem, Bob (Paulette Munsell) 1267 SW Pine Chapel Dr, Arcadia FL 34266, 863-494-9166, rebodem@earthlink.net [SE] IIA [AC] Pastor, Pine Creek Chapel, Arcadia FL

Boers, Arthur Paul (Lorna Jean McDougall) AMBS, 3003 Benham Ave, Elkhart IN 46517, 574-295-3726 [IM] IIB3d [AC]

Bogard, Marlene (Michael) 7732 NW 12th St, Newton KS 67114, 316-284-2183 [WDC] IIA [AC] Minister of Christian Nurture, Western District Conference, North Newton, KS

Bohn, Ernest Stanley (Anita Pannabecker) 333 E 9th, Newton KS 67114, fmc@wwwebservice.net [WDC] [RE] Interim Pastor, First Menn Ch, Hillsboro KS

Bolanos Sr., Israel (Alma Marina) 2020 Baker Dr, Allentown PA 18103, 610-791-1469 [FRC] [RE]

Boll, John E. (Anna Lois) 96 Olive St, Bolivar NY 14715, 716-928-2380 [LAN] IIB1 [AC] Pastor, Kossuth Community Chapel, Bolivar NY

Boll, Mark B. (Roseanna E.) 823 Pine Hill Rd, Lititz PA 17543, 717-626-8685, bollmbre@lycos.com [LAN] IIB1 [AC] Pastor, Derry Menn Ch, Manheim PA

Bonham, Rusty (Mary Lou) 2526 N Webb Rd, Newton

MINISTERS

6

KS 67114, 620-837-5673, Rbonham@southwind.net [WDC] IIB2 [AC]

Bontrager, Brent (Diana) 1381 E Phelps, Kalkaska MI 49646, 616-258-2339, bbontrager@hotmail.com [IM] IIB1 [AC] Pastor, Coldsprings Christian Fell, Kalkaska MI

Bontrager, Eugene, 11846 CR 16, Middlebury IN 46540, 574-825-9284 [IM] [AW]

Bontrager, G. Edwin (Edith) 2 E Spur Ct, Hampton VA 23666, eebontrag@aol.com [VA] IIB3c [AC]

Bontrager, Jonas, 1707 E Longview Rd, Hutchinson KS 67501-8411, 620-662-2500 [SC] [AW]

Bontrager, Joseph E. (Gloria B.) 6521 Gateridge Dr Apt 202, Raleigh NC 27613, 919-783-0492 [VA] IIB3c [AC] Interim/Transition Pastor, Raleigh Menn Ch, Raleigh NC

Bontrager, Marion (Buetta) PO Box 3000, Hesston KS 67062, 620-327-4472 [SC] IIB3d [AC] Professor, Hesston College Bible Department, Hesston, KS

Bontrager, Orvan, 1945 S 600 W, Topeka IN 46571, 260-593-2060 [IM] [RE]

Bontrager, Willard L., 7517 CR 751 NE, Mancelona MI 49659, 616-587-8190 [IM] [RE]

Bontreger, Kenneth, 1006 E Kercher Rd, Goshen IN 46526, 574-533-3671, kenb@maplenet.net [CDC] IIB1 [AC] Senior Pastor, Silverwood Menn Ch, Goshen IN

Bontreger, Vernon E., 1420-6 Kentfield Way, Goshen IN 46526, 574-533-7068 [IM] [RE]

Bontreger, Wes J. (Cheryl) 63630 CR 111, Goshen IN 46526-8101, 574-862-2849 [IM] IIB1 [AC] Pastor, Yellow Creek Menn Ch, Goshen IN; Overseer, Sunnyside Mennonite, Elkhart IN

Book, David (Martha) 16692 CH 29, Frazee MN 56544, 218-847-3914, mmbook@i29.net [NC] IIB1 [AC] Pastor, Lake Region Menn Ch, Frazee MN

Book, Miriam F. (James M. Lapp) 443 Penn Oak Ct, Harleysville PA 19438, 215-513-4115, miriamfbook@juno.com [FRC] IIB2 [AC] Pastor, Salford Menn Ch, Harleysville PA

Borg, Jeffrey A., 219 W St, Ft Collins CO 80521, 970-416-1687, revborg@juno.com [RM, WDC] IIB1 [AC] Pastor, Fort Collins Menn Fell, Fort Collins CO

Borjas, Jose Franscico (Irma) 7810 Clark Rd C-2, Jessup MD 20794, 410-799-1461 [VA] IIB2 [AC] Associate Pastor, Iglesia del Evangelio Completo Alpha y O, Germantown DC

Borkholder, CarolSue Hostetler, 10713 E U Ave, Vicksburg MI 49097, 616-649-4348, borker@concentric.net [CDC] IIB3a [AC] Chaplain, Battle Creek Health Systems, Battle Creek MI

Born, Floyd E. (Bertha Toews) 308 Normandy Rd, Newton KS 67114, fborn@iwichita.com [WDC] IIB1 [RE]

Boshart, David W. (Shana) 3382 305th St, Parnell IA 52325, 319-646-2842, dboshart@netins.net [CP] IIB1 [AC] Pastor, W Union Menn Ch, Parnell IA

Boshart, Shana Peachey (David W.) 3382 305th St, Parnell IA 52325, 319-646-2842, shana@netins.net [CP] IIA [AC]

Bowman, Edwin S. (Minerva) 106 Sunset Rd, New Holland PA 17557-9618, 717-354-9478 [LAN] [RE]

Bowman, James C. (Lois) 433 Linden Rd, East Earl PA 17519, 717-445-5339 [LAN] IIB2 [AC] Associate Pastor, Lichty Menn Ch, New Holland PA

Bowman, Leroy H. (Lydia Ann) 3001 Lititz Pk, PO Box 5093, Lancaster PA 17606-5093, 717-560-4747 [LAN] [RE]

Bowman, Nelson L. (Mary Ann) 658 Wentzel Rd, East Earl PA 17519, 717-445-7790 [LAN] IB3 [AC]

Bowman, Paul K., 1520 Harrisburg Pk, Lancaster PA 17601-2632, 717-392-6596 [LAN] [RE]

Bowman, R. Todd (Maria) 201 Church St, Landisville PA 17538, faiththinker@hotmail.com [LAN] IIA [AC] Associate Pastor, Chestnut Hill Menn Ch, Columbia PA

Bowman, Richard L. (Elsie C.) 937 College Ave, Harrisonburg VA 22802, 540-434-0892, rbowman@bridgewater.edu [VA] IB3 [AC]

Boyer, Claude F. (Mary M.) 205 Diller St, Pandora OH 45877-9709, 419-384-3508, boyer@wcoil.com [CDC] [RE]

Boyer, H. Wesley (Lois A.) 2153 E Cedarville Rd, Pottstown PA 19465, 610-705-8836, vincentmennonite@juno.com [FRC] IIB1 [AC] Pastor, Vincent Menn Ch, Spring City PA

Boyer, Joan (Carl John) 429 E 1st, PO Box 291, Newton KS 67114, 316-283-0273, fstmenno@southwind.net [WDC] IIA [AC] Minister of Outreach, First Menn Ch, Newton KS

Brandenberger, Martin, 6925 Black Rd, New Haven IN 46774, 260-749-9045 [IM] [RE]

Brandt, LeRoy (Linda) 40 Cadbury St, Pottsville PA 17901-3921, 570-628-4992 [LAN] [AW]

Breckbill, Willis L. (Ina Ruth) 1521 Kentfield Way #7, Goshen IN 46526, 574-534-8370, 105060.2416@compuserve.com [CDC, IM] [RE]

Breeden, Diana (Marty) 10709 Indian Trail Rd, Harrisonburg VA 22802, 540-574-4007 [VA] IIC [AC] Associate Pastor, Grace Menn Fell, Linville VA

Breeden, Marlon W. (Diana J.) 10709 Indian Trail Rd, Harrisonburg VA 22802, 540-574-4007 [VA] IIC [AC] Associate Pastor, Grace Menn Fell, Linville VA

Breeze, Cynthia Massanari (Clark Alan) 1310 Old Farm Rd, Champaign IL 61821, 217-356-2471, cbreeze4@aol.com [CDC, IL] IIB2 [AC] Associate Pastor, First Menn Ch of Champaign-Urbana, Urbana IL

Breneman, Janet M., Apartado 11, Periferico, Zona 11, Cd Guatemala, Guatemala, janetb@intelnet.net.gt [LAN] IIC [AC] Overseas Mission Worker, EMM, Belize, South America

Breneman, Robert A. (Mabel) 620 Sandstone Rd, Strasburg PA 17579, 717-786-3823 [LAN] [RE]

Brenneman, Diane Zaerr (Douglas Joseph) 1061 480th St SW, Parnell IA 52325, 319-646-5636 (work), dianezb@mennoniteusa.org [CP] IB1 [AC] Denominational Minister, Congregational & Ministerial Leadership Team, Mennonite Church USA, Parnell IA

Brenneman, Donald L. (Marilyn) 4899 Chaucer Dr, Greensboro NC 27407, 919-299-1369 [VA] [RE]

Brenneman, James E. (Terri J. Plank) 1915 Mill Rd, South Pasadena CA 91030, 626-799-6340, JEBrenneman@aol.com [PSW] IIB1 [AC] Pastor, Pasadena Menn Ch, Pasadena CA; Professor of OT, Episcopal Theological School at Claremont, Claremont CA

Brenneman, John K. (Lois) 258 Brenneman Rd, Lancaster PA 17603, 717-872-5183 [LAN] [RE]

Brenneman, Todd (Chelsea) 113 Maple Springs Rd, Hollsopple PA 15935, 814-479-2670 [ALL] IIA [AC] Pastor, Carpenter Park Menn Ch, Davidsville PA

Brenneman, Virgil J. (Helen Good) 516 E Waverly Ave, Goshen IN 46526-4726, 574-534-3345,

MINISTERS

6

vjbren@bnin.net [CDC, IM] [RE]

Brewer, Douglas W. (Marla) RR 1 Box 30A, Birch Tree MO 65438-9606, 573-292-3553, menno_9@hotmail.com [SC] [AW]

Brock, William, PO Box 150777, Cape Coral FL 33915-0777, 239-772-5683, RBrock@capechristian.com [SE] IIA [AC] Associate Pastor, Cape Christian Fell, Cape Coral FL

Brooks, Dennis R. (Sheri) 4550 Leaman Ave, Millersville PA 17551 [LAN] [AC]

Brown, Cora L. (Jonathan) 56564 Woodbine Ln, Elkhart IN 46516, 574-522-1832, coralbrown@juno.com [IM] IIB1 [AC] Co-Pastor, Ch Without Walls, Elkhart IN

Brown, Jonathan (Cora L.) 56564 Woodbine Ln, Elkhart IN 46516, 574-522-1832, jonbrown@juno.com [IM] IIB1 [AC] Pastor, Ch Without Walls, Elkhart IN

Brown, Lena H. (Michael R.) PO Box 112, Grantham PA 17027, 717-766-3985 [LAN] IIC [AC] Associate Pastor, Slate Hill Menn Ch, Camp Hill PA

Brown, Mitchell C. (Deborah) 1334 Elmwood Ave, Wilmette IL 60091, 847-256-3985, mcb9476@ameritech.net [CDC, IL] IIB1 [AC] Pastor, Evanston Menn Ch, Evanston IL

Brown, Steven Lavonne, 81 Michaels Woods Dr, Hampton VA 23666-5614, 757-826-9140, minsbrown@aol.com [VA] IIB2 [AC]

Brubacker, John S. (Rachel) Laborie PO, St Georges Granada, West Indies [LAN] IIC [AC] Missionary/Church Worker, St. Georges, Granada, West Indies

Brubaker, Cliff, 11794 Clark Rd, Hillsdale MI 49242, 517-254-4643, cbrubaker@frontiernet.net [OH] IIB1 [AC] Interim Pastor, Pine Grove Menn Ch, Stryker OH

Brubaker, Dean M., 1801 Greencroft Blvd, Goshen IN 46526, 574-534-4955 [IM] [RE]

Brubaker, Doane (Sharon) 212 S Baltimore, Morton IL 61550, 309-263-7306, fmmorton@mtco.com [IL] IIB1 [AC] Pastor, First Menn Ch of Morton, Morton IL

Brubaker, Donald L. (Lyndell) 634 Lincoln Rd, Lititz PA 17543, 717-626-4833 [LAN] III [AC] Ordained Deacon, Crossroads Community Fell, Lititz PA

Brubaker, Greggory Lynn (Sharon Louise), Klaipeda, Lithuania, gsbrubaker@emm.org [LAN] IIC [AC]

Brubaker, J. Donald (Marian) 460 Stony Battery Rd, Landisville PA 17538-1032, 717-898-2517, donmarb@juno.com [LAN] III [AC] Ordained Deacon, Chestnut Hill Menn Ch, Columbia PA

Brubaker, James C. (Naomi) 269 Meetinghouse Ln, Lewisburg PA 17837, 717-524-2838, jnbru@sunlink.net [ALL] IB3, IIB3a [AC] Elder, contact person, Boyer Menn Ch, Middleburg PA

Brubaker, Roy L. (Anita Hope) RR 1 Box 209, Mifflintown PA 17059, 717-436-9477, hoperoy@pa.net [LAN] [RE]

Brubaker, Sharon L. (Gregg) Lithuania Christian College, Kretingos gatve 36, Klaipeda LT 5808, Lithuania, gsbrubaker@emm.org [LAN] IIC [AC] Chaplain, EMM, Klaipeda, Lithuania

Brubaker, Shirley Yoder (Kenton K.) 1222 Parkway Dr, Harrisonburg VA 22802, 540-434-0473, kkbrubaker@juno.com [VA] [AW]

Brubaker, Verle Alden (Maralee Ann) 30550 Brannigan Dr, Princess Anne MD 21853, 410-621-0578, verleb@dmv.com [ACC] IIB1 [AC] Pastor, Holly Grove Menn Ch, Wover MD

Brunk III, George R., 983 Summit Ave, Harrisonburg VA 22802, 540-434-1583 [VA] IB3, IIB3d [AC]

Brunk, Kenneth S. (Twila Yoder) 5420 Riverview Rd, Williamsburg VA 23188, 757-566-1619 [VA] [RE]

Brunk, Lawrence (Dorothy Metzler) 41 Hausman Rd, Lenhartsville PA 19534, 610-756-3601 [ACC] [RE]

Brunk, Nathan W. (Diane) 107 Garris Rd, Dowingtown PA 19335, 610-269-9602, NWBrunk@safeplace.net [LAN] IIB1 [AC] Pastor, Downing Hills Christian Fell, Downingtown PA

Brunk Jr., Truman H. (Betty) 909 Summit Ave, Harrisonburg VA 22802, 540-801-0918, btrubet@aol.com [VA] IB3, IIB2 [AC]

Brunk, William A. (Nancy) 8568 Shupps Ln, Coopersburg PA 18036, 610-965-8849 [FRC] IIB1 [AC] Pastor, Swamp Menn Ch, Quakertown PA

Brunner, David D. (Jo Ann) 2219 15th Ave NW, Rochester MN 55901-1569, 507-529-7910, brunnerd@prodigy.net [CP] IIB1 [AC] Pastor, Rochester Menn Ch, Rochester MN

Brunner, Grace (Paul) 441 S Main St, Hesston KS 67062, 620-327-2157 [SC] [RE]

Brunner, Paul D. (Grace) 441 S Main St, Hesston KS 67062, 620-327-2157 [SC] [RE]

Brunstetter, Charles E. (Miriam) 736 Centre St, Eon PA 18042, 610-252-5351, charb@entermail.net [FRC] [AW]

Brutus, Dieudonne (Lunie) PO Box 380386, Miami FL 33238, 305-756-5101 [SE] IIC [AC] Pastor, Tabernacle of Bethlehem, Miami-Dade FL

Bryant, B. Elaine (Clarence C.) 8636 S Wolcott, Chicago IL 60620-4730, 773-779-6566, elainebryant@ameritech.net [IL] IIB1 [AC] Pastor, Englewood Menn Ch, Chicago IL

Buch, Richard E. (Kathryn) 120 S 10th St, Akron PA 17501, 717-859-2660, rbuch@dejazzd.com [LAN] IIB1 [AC] Pastor, Metzler Menn Ch, Akron PA

Buchen, Curvin R. (Lois) 178 Forest Hill Rd, Leola PA 17540, 717-656-6905 [LAN] [RE]

Bucher, Kenneth A. (Evelyn) 2474 Wisgarver Rd, Manheim PA 17545, 717-665-6411, kebucher@juno.com [LAN] IIB1 [AC] Pastor, Manheim Menn Ch, E Petersburg PA

Bucher, Richard Wayne (Carol A.) 113 W Columbia, Box 22, Danvers IL 61732, 309-963-6323, rbucher@frontiernet.net [CDC] IIB1 [AC] Pastor, North Danvers Menn Ch, Danvers IL

Bucher, Roy C. (Betty Jane Ruppert) 1001 E Oregon Rd, Lititz PA 17543, 717-519-2658, roybucher@juno.com [ACC] [RE]

Buckwalter, A. David (Marian) 1957 Drexel Ave, Lancaster PA 17602-3363, 717-397-3605 [LAN] [RE]

Buckwalter, Dale L. (Rosalie) 5519 Division Hwy, Narvon PA 17555, 717-354-4974, drbuckwalter@paonline.com [LAN] III [AC] Licensed Deacon, Goodville Menn Ch, Goodville PA

Buckwalter, J. Harold (Twila) 453 Wenger Rd, Chesapeake VA 23322-1612, 804-482-4918 [VA] IIB3c [AC]

Buckwalter, Kyle D. (Rachelle) 98 Pebble Creek Dr, Lititz PA 17543, 717-626-7559, skarbucks4@netzero.com [LAN] IIA [AC] Associate Pastor, Crossroads Community Fell, Lititz PA

Buckwalter, Richard B. (Sara) 433 S Kinzer Ave Apt #339, New Holland PA 17557, 717-355-6844 [LAN] [RE]

MINISTERS

6

Buckwalter, Richard L. (Deborah) 124 Skyline Dr, New Holland PA 17557, 717-355-2725, rlbuck@frontiernet.net [LAN] IB3 [AC] Bishop/Overseer, LMC Pequea Valley, PA; Bishop/Overseer, LMC Manor District, PA

Bulford, Charles (Nadine G. Smith-Bulford) 3015 Midvale Ave, PO Box 43174, Philadelphia PA 19129-3306, 215-438-0293, cmercies@aol.com [LAN] IIB1 [AC] Pastor, New Mercies Menn Ch, Philadelphia PA

Bulford, Nadine G. Smith (Charles) 3015 Midvale Ave, PO Box 43174, Philadelphia PA 19129-3306, 215-438-0293, cmercies@aol.com [LAN] IIC [AC] Associate Pastor, New Mercies Menn Ch, Philadelphia PA

Buller, Charles (Tracy Marble) 405 N Constitution Ave, Goshen IN 46526-1464, 574-534-4714, cbuller@communionfellowship.org [IM] IIB1 [AC] Pastor, Communion Fell, Goshen IN

Buller, Eric, Rt 1 Box 69, Ransom KS 67572, 785-731-2283, buller@gbta.net [WDC] IIB1 [AC] Pastor, First Menn Ch, Ransom KS

Buller, Harold W. (Anne W.) 1108 Monroe St, Beatrice NE 68310, 402-228-3004 [WDC] [RE]

Buller, Jane Stoltzfus (Jim) 2711 S Main St, Goshen IN 46526, 574-533-1353, jsb53@hotmail.com [IM] IIB2 [AC] Pastor, Walnut Hill Menn Ch, Goshen IN

Buller, Jeannette, 3018 W Rose Ln, Phoenix AZ 85017-1641, 602-246-7237, JBuller@CoachNet.org [IM] IIB3b [AC] Missionary-Coach, Strategic Ministries Inc, Phoenix AZ; Coach-Consultant, CoachNet, Phoenix AZ

Buller, Peter (Gladys E.) 15 Fairfield Park, Goshen IN 46526, 574-534-4158, pwbuller@juno.com [CDC, IM] [RE]

Burdette, Rob (Patty) 17827 Carson Rd, Butler OH 44822-9427, 740-694-1759 [OH] IIA [AC]

Burke, John H. (Mamie R.) 9435 S Green St, Chicago IL 60620-2715, 312-233-2892 [CDC] IIB1 [AC] Pastor, First Menn Ch, Chicago IL

Burkhalter, Sheldon Wayne (Janis Sprunger) 19532 NE Glisan St , Portland OR 97321, 503-492-4216, sburkhalter@pnmc.org [PNW] IIB2 [AC] Regional Conference Minister, Pacific NW Mennonite Conference, Woodburn, OR

Burkhart, Gina L. (Dan) 512 W High St, Manheim PA 17545, 717-665-3423, burkhartdg@onemain.com [LAN] IIC [AC]

Burkhart, Larry E. (Carol J.) 277 Black Rd, Quarryville PA 17566, 717-529-2227, MTHLRTL@juno.com [LAN] IIB1 [AC] Associate Pastor, Living Stones Fell, Peach Bottom PA

Burkholder, Brian Martin, 1200 Park Rd, Harrisonburg VA 22802 [VA] IIB3a, IIB3c [AC]

Burkholder, David A. (Lorraine) 853 Clay Hill Rd, Chambersburg PA 17201, 717-597-2276 [FRK] [RE]

Burkholder, David H. (Edna) 803 Burky Ln, Ephrata PA 17522, 717-733-3210 [LAN] IIB3a [AC] Evangelist, Carpenter Community Ch, Talmage PA

Burkholder, Galen E. (Marie) 165 Cooper Ave, Salunga PA 17538, 717-898-0335 [LAN] IIB3c [AC]

Burkholder, Isaac R. (Rosanna) 745 Twin Bridge Rd, Chambersburg PA 17201, 717-369-4185 [FRK] IIB3a [AC] Chaplain, Franklin County Prison, Chambersburg PA

Burkholder, James A. (Marian G.) 13 Montadale Dr, Dillsburg PA 17019, 717-502-1216, jimburk@supernet.com [LAN] [RE]

Burkholder, John Richard (Susan Elizabeth) 1508 S 14th St, Goshen IN 46526-4546, 574-533-1326 [CDC, IM] [RE]

Burkholder, Leonard G. (Anna Mary) 7332 Bunting Pl, Philadelphia PA 19153, 215-365-0670 [LAN] IIB2 [AC] Associate Pastor, Indonesian Fell, Philadelphia PA

Burkholder Jr., Lewis (Helen) 1125 Rocky Ford Rd, Powhatan VA 23139, 804-598-3643 [VA] IIB3a [AC]

Burkholder, Marlin S. (Katie) 254 Morris Rd, Harleysville PA 19438 [LAN] [RE]

Burkholder, Nelson D. (Dorothy) 234 Lakewood Park Dr, Newport News VA 23602, 757-877-4606 [VA] [RE]

Burkholder, Owen E. (Ruth Ann Augsburger) 1585 College, Harrisonburg VA 22802-5550, 540-433-2138, oweneb@juno.com [VA] IB2 [AC] Conference Minister, Virginia Mennonite Conference, Harrisonburg VA

Burkholder, Paul G. (Miriam) 1001 E Oregon Rd, Lititz PA 17543, 717-581-3964, pburkholder@juno.com [ACC] [RE]

Burkholder, Raymond (Naomi) Grand Anse Valley PO, St George's, Grenada, 473-444-4762, rayburkholder@anabaptist.org [LAN] IIB1 [AC]

Burkholder, Samuel S. (Naomi) 112 Apple Blossom Cr, Lititz PA 17543, 717-627-2222 [LAN] IIB1 [AC] Associate Pastor, Hammer Creek Menn Ch, Lititz PA

Burrus, Rennie W. (Kathlyn B.) 6442 Rd R, Columbus Grove OH 45830, 419-384-3131, rennie@wcoil.com [CDC] IIB1 [AC] Pastor, St John Menn Ch, Pandora OH

Busenitz, Willis Herman (Nadine Faye) PO Box 50, Busby MT 59016-0050, 406-592-3643 [CP] IIB1 [AC] Pastor, White River Cheyenne Menn Ch, Busby MT

Bustos, Mario (Shirley A.) 5406 4th Ave, Valparaiso IN 46383, 219-462-0526, mario_bustos@comcast.net [IM] IIB1 [AC] Pastor, Valparaiso Menn Ch, Valparaiso IN

Byler, J. (Jesse) Daryl (Cynthia Ann Lehman) 1104 E St NE, Washington DC 20002, 202-543-7542, J._Daryl_Byler@mcc.org [GS] IIB3c [AC] Director, Washington Office, Mennonite Central Committee, Washington DC

Byler, Jayne M., 338 Haven, Barberton OH 44203, 330-753-9737, jkejbyler@juno.com [OH] IIB1 [AC] Pastor, First Menn Ch, Sugarcreek OH

Byler, Jonathan Jesse (Loice N.) Box 3431, Thika, Kenya, East Africa, JonByler@maf.org [GS] IIB3b [AC] Director, Centre for Christian Discipleship, Thika, Kenya, East Africa

C

Caceros, S. Antonio, 2636 Lock Hurt Ave, Dallas TX 75228, 214-321-9062, caceros@sbcglobal.net [WDC] IIA [AC] Pastor, Iglesia Menonita Monte Horeb, Dallas TX

Caes, Elizabeth Werenfels, 3562 E Kerckhoff, Fresno CA 93702, 559-495-1731, libbycaes@juno.com [PSW] [AW]

Cahill, Robert D. (Tara Jean) c/o FUNDAMENO, Apartado 1, 16909 San Pedro Carcha, Av, GUATEMALA, rtcahill@yahoo.com [ACC] IIB3b [AC] Missionary, MCC, San Pedro Carcha, Guatemala

Calderon, Armando J. (Sara) RR 4 Box 64L, Mathis TX 78368, 512-547-3727 [SC] IIB1 [AC] Pastor, Calvary Menn Ch, Mathis TX

Caldwell, G. Darrell (Susan) 1315 Southern Rd, Norwich OH 43767, 614-872-4111 [LAN] IIB3b [AC]

Callahan, Charles W. (Linda) 212 A Hibiscus St, Honolulu HI 96818, 808-836-5651 [LAN] IIA [AC] Associate Pastor, New Life Christian Fell, Honolulu HI

Campbell Jr., Walter A. (Ester Arline) 5085 Jack Springs Rd, Atmore AL 36502, wacamp@juno.com [OH] [AW]

Campoz, Jose, 763 18th St NE, Salem OR 97301, 503-363-8687, mom1963@aol.com [PNW] IIB1 [AC] Pastor, Jerusalem Iglesia, Salem OR

Cañon, Angel M. (Elcira) 2520 S Lawndale Ave, Chicago IL 60623, 773-277-6665 [IL] IIB1 [AC] Pastor, Lawndale Menn Ch, Chicago IL

Cantu, Felipe (Maria) 1208 14½ St, Rock Island IL 61201, 309-788-2941 [CP] IIB1 [AC] Pastor, Templo Alabanza Menonita, Moline IL

Carlson, Robert Joel (Phyllis Hershey) 9730 Reeder, Overland Park KS 66214-2577, 913-894-9408, grandpa1@ix.netcom.com [WDC] [RE]

Carmona, Juan C. (Sonia) 2151 N Howard St #2NDFL, Philadelphia PA 19122-1712, 215-455-0263 [LAN] IIB1 [AC] Pastor, Arca de Salvación, Philadelphia PA

Carpenter, James J. (Faith) 25894 Whitetail Rd, Sturgis MI 49091 [IM] IIB2 [AC] Minister of Nurture, Locust Grove Menn Ch, Burr Oak MI

Carrasco, Ruben Duenas (Haydee) Apartado 708, Cusco, Peru [LAN] IIB3b [AC] Missionary/Church Worker, Cusco, Peru

Carrion, Daniel (Albilda) 2997 Wilson School Ln, Sinking Springs PA 19608, 610-670-9743 [LAN] IIA [AC] Pastor, Luz Verdadera, Reading PA

Carson, Kelly, 1517 South Clinton, Berwyn IL 60402, 708-749-2683, kelcarson@earthlink.net [CDC, IL] IIA [AC]

Chapman, Christine Fowle (Daniel E.) 112 Main St, North Springfield VT 05150, 802-886-2142, cfnier@hotmail.com [FRC] IIA [AC] Assistant Pastor, Andover Community Church, Chester VT

Chapman, Daniel Ernest (Christine) 112 Main St, North Springfield VT 05150, 802-886-2142, creekbird@hotmail.com [FRC] IIA [AC] Pastor, Andover Community Church, Chester VT

Charles, Abram H. (Ruth) 449 S Centerville Rd, Lancaster PA 17603, 717-872-7478, abecharles@juno.com [LAN] [RE]

Charles, Mervin (Laurel F.) 546 Leaman Ave, Millersville PA 17551, 717-626-4716 [LAN] IIB1 [AC]

Charles, Paul K. (Dorothy) 125 S Donerville Rd, Lancaster PA 17603, 717-285-4251 [LAN] [RE]

Charles, Sylvia Shirk (J. Robert) 904 College Ave, Goshen IN 46526, 574-534-0142 [IM] IIB3a [AC] Campus Minister, Goshen College, Goshen IN

Chen, Mark (Susan Chuang) 30129 Third Place S, Federal Way WA 98003-3139, 253-946-9553 [PNW] [RE]

Chenlo, Mauricio Walter (Sara) 3012 Arrowwood Dr, Raleigh NC 27604, mchenlo@nc.rr.com [VA] IIC [AC] Peace Director and Youth Pastor, Raleigh Menn Ch, Raleigh NC

Cheramie Risingsun, Steve W., 6210 Jack Springs Rd, Atmore AL 36502, 251-368-0280 [GS] IIB1 [AC] Pastor, Native Christian Fell, Atmore AL; Pastor, Poarch Community Ch, Atmore AL

Cheung, Paul (Alice) 14 Leland St, Malden MA 02148, 781-397-109 [LAN] IIB1 [AC] Pastor, Chinese Christian Ch of Malden, Malden MA

Chigoji, Nehemiah James, 382 N 6th Ave, Upland CA 91786, 909-946-7453, chigoji@verizon.net [PSW] IIA [AC] Assistant Pastor, First Menn Ch of Upland, Upland CA

Childs, Evelyn E., 18948 Monte Vista, Detroit MI 48221, 313-345-5615 [IM] IIB1 [AC] Pastor, Peace Community Menn Ch, Detroit MI

Chiles, Lawrence F. (Nereida) 150 City Mill Rd, Lancaster PA 17602-3808, 717-393-2654, lawrencech@juno.com [LAN] IIB3c [AC] Global Ministries Representative to USA, Eastern Mennonite Missions, Salunga PA

Chitchalerntham, Tong Barnabas (Kathy Khith) 5112 Cedar Ave S, Minneapolis MN 55417, 612-721-6544, chitchalerntham@msn.com [CP] [AW] Vice President, Lao Mennonite Conference, Mountain Lake MN

Choi, Bong-Gi (Young-Hee) 16205 Redland Rd, Rockville MD 20855 [VA] IIB1 [AC]

Choi, Sang Jin (Jin Son Park) 40-1 Hearthstone Ct, Annapolis MD 21403, 410-295-7059, appasc@aol.com [VA] IIB2 [AC]

Christophel, James L., 1702 S MacGregor Rd, South Bend IN 46614, 574-291-4228 [IM] [RE]

Chupp, Harvey (Carolyn) 1310 Orchard Ln, Shipshewana IN 46565, 260-768-7017 [IM] IB3 [AC] Overseer, Hopewell Mennonite, Kouts IN

Chupp, Ruben (Idella) 1002 Beechwood Dr, Nappanee IN 46550, 574-773-2963, rubenc@juno.com [IM] IIB1 [AC] Pastor, North Main St Menn Ch, Nappanee IN

Cius, David (Theanard) PO Box 255532, Dorchester MA 02125, 781-396-6009 [LAN] IIA [AC] Pastor, Boston Bethel Missionary Ch, Dorchester MA

Claassen, Arlin G. (Helen) 1229 Camden Ct, Goshen IN 46526, 574-534-0407 [IM] [RE]

Claassen, Curt Albert (Olga Rose) 284-1350 W Main St, Berne IN 46711, 260-589-8148 [CDC] [RE]

Clark, Benjamin L. (Mary Esther) 43 S Kinzer Rd, Kinzers PA 17535, 717-442-4865, bmeclark@juno.com [LAN] III [AC] Ordained Deacon, Kinzer Menn Ch, Kinzer PA

Clark, Kevin A. (Susan) 3484 Mt Clinton Pk, Harrisonburg VA 22802, 540-867-0409, clarkka@emu.edu [VA] IIB1 [AC] Pastor, Big Spring Menn Ch, Luray VA

Clark, Paul L. (Faye) 2552 S Cherry Ln, Ronks PA 17572, 717-687-8870, paul.clark@fandm.edu [LAN] IIB2 [AC] Associate Pastor, Kinzer Menn Ch, Kinzer PA

Claudio Sr., Samuel (Ana) 240 Tenth Ave, Bethlehem PA 18018, 610-865-5602, samclaudio@fast.net [EDC] IIB1 [AC] Pastor, Spanish Cong., Grace Menn Ch, Lansdale PA

Clemens, Donella M. (R. Wayne) 401 Leidy Rd, PO Box 439, Souderton PA 18964, 215-723-2223, DonellaC@FMC-online.org [FRC] IC [AC] Conference Minister, Franconia Mennonite Conference, Souderton PA

Clemens, Philip K. (Nancy M.) 11716 Rte 89, Corry PA 16407, 814-664-9102, clemens@worldconnx.net [OH] IIB1 [AC]

Clements, Ryan, 2465 Monterey, Wooster OH 44691, 330-264-0093, ryanc@sssnet.com [OH] IIA [AC] Youth Pastor, Wooster Menn Ch, Wooster OH

Clemmer, Gerald A. (Lydia M.) 59 W Chestnut St, Souderton PA 18964, 215-721-0356 [FRC] IIB1 [AC] Senior Executive Pastor, Souderton Menn Ch, Souderton PA

Clemmer, Paul M. (Ronda) PO Box 237, Marion MD

17235, 717-375-2434 [FRK] IIB1 [AC] Pastor, Community Menn Ch, Marion MD

Clugston, Dale Eugene (Ethel) 6072 Olde Scotland Rd, Shippensburg PA 17257, 717-263-1518, dandeclugston@clugstons.com [FRK] III [AC] Ordained Deacon, Cedar St Menn Ch, Chambersburg PA

Coblentz, Glenn Dale (Viola Elaine) 16329 Harrison Rd, Navarre OH 44662, 330-359-7181, revc@sssnet.com [OH] IIB1 [AC] Pastor, Longenecker Menn Ch, Winesburg OH

Coblentz, Randy, 9301 Barnes Rd, Toano VA 23168, rscoblentz@tni.net [VA] IIB1 [AC] Pastor, Williamsburg Menn Ch, Williamsburg VA

Collins, Ronald C. (Betty Lou) 1504 S 13th St, Goshen IN 46536, 574-533-5269, roncoll@juno.com [IM] [RE]

Colliver, Kathy, 607 3rd St, Fort Wayne IN 46808, 260-422-1649, kathycolliver@hotmail.com [IM] IIB1 [AC] Pastor, First Menn Ch, Fort Wayne IN

Combs, Jeff (Joyce) 1555 S Limestone St, Springfield OH 45505, 937-322-9130, jeffcombs@mics.net [OH] IIB1 [AC] Co-Pastor, Southside Menn Ch, Springfield OH

Combs, Joyce (Jeff) 1555 S Limestone St, Springfield OH 45505, 937-322-9130, jeffcombs@mics.net [OH] IIB1 [AC] Co-Pastor, Southside Menn Ch, Springfield OH

Conn, Jay, 5325 PR 382, Millersburg OH 44654, 330-893-8109 [OH] IIB2 [AC] Associate Pastor, Martins Creek Menn Ch, Millersburg OH

Conrad, Paul E. (S. Ann Burkholder) 820 Bellows Dr, New Carlisle OH 45344, 937-849-9778 [OH] [RE]

Conrad, Paul G. (Rhonda Rae) 2826 Fillmore Dr, Chambersburg PA 17201, 717-977-6207 [FRK] IIB1 [AC] Pastor, Cedar St Menn Ch, Chambersburg PA

Conrad, Willard D. (Hettie M.) 359 W Cedar, Hesston KS 67062, 620-327-2782 [SC] [RE]

Coon, Robert Russell (Catherine Helen) 214 Morrow Ave #503, Topeka IN 46571, 260-593-3443 [CDC] IIB3a [RE]

Cooper, Robert D., 398 Geigel Hill Rd, Upper Black Eddy PA 18972, bjcooper@epix.net [FRC] IIB2 [AC] Associate Pastor, Rocky Ridge Menn Ch, Quakertown PA

Corbin, Jonathan, 1725B Graceland Ct, Goshen IN 46526, 574-534-1738, jonc@maplenet.net [CDC] IIA [AC] Associate Pastor, Silverwood Menn Ch, Goshen IN

Cordell, Irvin E. (Margaret) 1222 Arbor Ridge, Chambersburg PA 17201 [FRK] [RE]

Cordell, Merle G. (Beulah) 8979 Grindstone Hill Rd, Chambersburg PA 17201, 717-597-7415 [FRK] [RE]

Cosden, Charlotte (David) 1552 Virginia Ave, Folcroft PA 19032, 610-237-8937, teachingtruthministries@juno.com [LAN] IIC [AC] Minister, Teaching Truth Ministries to Women, Folcraft PA

Cosden, David T. (Charlotte) 1552 Virginia Ave, Folcroft PA 19032, teachingtruthministries@juno.com [LAN] IIB1 [AC] Pastor, Delaware County Fell, Folcraft PA

Coss, Lewis M. (Mary) 13505 Olde Mystic Cr, Hagerstown MD 21742, 301-733-2147 [FRK] IIB1 [AC] Pastor Emeritus, Community Menn Ch, Marion MD

Cotchen, Joy (Patrick James) 178 Maplebrook Ln, Johnstown PA 15905, pjcotch@aol.com [ALL] IIC [AC] Minister of Children and Youth, Allegheny Mennonite Conference, Somerset PA; Youth Pastor, Stahl Menn Ch, Johnstown PA

Crable, David (Betty) 23 S Water St, Masontown PA 15461, 724-583-7464 [ALL] IIA [AC]

Cragan, Daniel J., 1070 A CR 411, Westerloo NY 12193 [LAN] IIB3a [AC]

Crawford, Walter Lewis (Hattie) 8910 Blue Ridge Dr, Tampa FL 33619, 813-623-6010 [SE] IIB1 [AC] Pastor, Newtown Gospel Chapel, Sarasota FL

Cretsinger, Lewis (Irma Jane) PO Box 130, Morris Run PA 16939, 570-638-3110 [EDC] [RE]

Crockett, Maria (Robert) 1704 DeCamp, Elkhart IN 46516, 574-293-5118 [IM] IIA [AC] Co-Pastor, House of Power, Elkhart IN

Crockett, Robert (Maria) 1704 DeCamp, Elkhart IN 46516, 574-293-5118 [IM] IIB1 [AC] Pastor, House of Power, Elkhart IN

Croegaert, James Charles (Janalee) 827 Monroe St, Evanston IL 60202, 847-475-2749, jcroegaert2@attbi.com [IL] IIB3a [AC] Chaplain, Resurrection Medical Center, Chicago IL

Croyle, Ellis B. (R. Charlotte) 1112 Spring Brooke Dr, Goshen IN 46528, 574-533-2248 [IM] [RE]

Cruz, Justiniano (Mabel) 5327 16th St NW, Washington DC 20011, 202-726-8161 [VA] IIB1 [AC] Pastor, Iglesia del Evangelio Completo Alpha y O, Germantown DC

Cruz, Miriam R. (Jesus) 441 Surrey Dr, Lancaster PA 17601, 717-581-7816, jcruz1225@aol.com [LAN] IIC [AC] Chaplain, Mennonite Home, Lancaster PA

Cubbage, R. Matthew (Glenda) 6101 Monaco Ct, Hickory NC 28601, 828-267-5754 [VA] III [AC]

Custar, Deanna (Daniel Lamar) 11261 US Rte 127, West Unity OH 43570, 419-924-5158, dandeecust@cs.com [OH] IIB1 [AC] Preaching Minister, Salem Menn Ch, Waldron MI

Cutipa, Celestino Santa Cruz (Inez) Apartado 708, Cusco Peru [LAN] IIA [AC] Missionary/Church Worker, Cusco Peru

Cyster, Graham James (Dorcas) 15 Savo Ave, Lancaster PA 17601, 717-519-0315 [LAN] [AW]

D

Dagen, Paul L. (Lois) 1001 E Oregon Rd, Lititz PA 17543, 717-581-3965 [LAN] [RE]

Dalke, Herbert M. (Bertha) 33 6th Ave SE, Oelwein IA 50662, 319-283-9211 [CDC, IL] [RE]

Dalke, Robert Eugene (Flauretta Faye) 645 N Wall, PO Box 38, Buhler KS 67522-0038, 620-543-6623, bmcpastor@2buhlerks.net [WDC] IIB1 [AC] Pastor, Buhler Menn Ch, Buhler KS

Danner, Michael (Melissa) 1001 E Partridge St, Metamora IL 61548, 309-367-6042, mikemmc@mtco.com [IL] IIB1 [AC] Lead Pastor, Metamora Menn Ch, Metamora IL

Darling, Timothy E. (Dawn M.) 177 Almond Rd, Pittsgrove NJ 08318, 856-692-7441, nmpastor@juno.com [LAN] IIB1 [AC] Pastor, Norma Menn Ch, Norma NJ

Daught, Gary (Mary Beth) 925 N Desert Ave Apt C, Tucson AZ 85711-2044, 520-881-8834, gfdaught@cox.net [PSW] IIB1 [AC]

Daux, Simon, 281 NW 79th St, Miami FL 33150-2961, 305-687-3949 [SE] IIC [AC] Pastor, Eglise du Nouveau Testament, Miami FL

Davis, Richard Douglas (Marla Janice) 10007 Dale Crest Dr, Dallas TX 75229-5841, 214-350-5244, Dick@PeaceMennonite.org [WDC] IIB1 [AC] Pastor, Peace Menn Ch, Dallas TX

MINISTERS

6

Dawson, Daryl (Sandy) 176 Chalybeate Rd, Bedford PA 15522-9801, 814-623-7792 [ALL] IB3, IIB1 [AC] Pastor, Canan Station Menn Ch, Altoona PA

Dayton, Philip, RR 2 Box 647, Ridgeley WV 26753, 304-726-4380 [ALL] IIB1 [AC] Pastor, Pinto Menn Ch, Pinto MD

De Jesus, Artemio, 13411 Misti Loop, Lakeland FL 33809-9709 [SE] IIC [AC] Pastor, Luz y Verdad, Lakeland FL

De Leon, Nestalis Robles (Xiomara) 130 3rd Ave Apt 18G, Brooklyn NY 11207, 718-522-5029 [LAN] IIA [AC] Pastor, Menn Evangelical Tabernacle, Brooklyn NY

de Leon-Hartshorn, Iris (C. Leo Hartshorn) 202 S Ann, Lancaster PA 17602-4315, 717-391-6512, idh@mccus.org [EDC] IIB3c [AC]

Deal, Michael (Christine) 12 N Fourth St, Hughesville PA 17737, 717-584-3881, mcdeal@chilitech.net [LAN] IIB1 [AC] Pastor, Agape Fell, Williamsport PA

Dean, Michael Richard (Tonya) PO Box 520, Fisher IL 61843, 217-897-1365 [IL] IIB1 [AC] Pastor, East Bend Menn Ch, Fisher IL

Deckert, Eric R., Freeman SD 57029, 605-925-7024 [CP] IIA [AW]

DeHoogh, Arthur T. (Doris) 504 Lincoln Ave SE, Orange City IA 51041-1827 [WDC] [RE]

Deiter, Raymond L. (Elizabeth) 595 Cinder Rd, New Providence PA 17560, 717-786-3890, rldaed@juno.com [LAN] IIB1 [AC] Pastor, Living Stones Fell, Peach Bottom PA

DeLeon, Seferina Garcia, 712 S 12th St, Goshen IN 46526, 574-534-0362, seferina.deleon@lacasagoshen.org [IM] IIB1 [AC] Pastor, Iglesia Menonita del Buen Pastor, Goshen IN

Dellinger, Janet B. (William E.) 3250 Winn Rd, Sturgeon MO 65284, 573-696-3604, jfisher@tranquility.net [SC] IIA [AC] Hospice Chaplain, MidMissouri HomeCare and Hospice, Moberly MO

Delp, Earl R. (Emma Catherine) 1309 Woodland Dr, Harrisonburg VA 22802, 540-564-3778 [VA] [RE]

Delp, James S. (B. Jane) 115 Green Hill Ln, Churchville VA 24421-2521, 540-337-8883, jdelp@surfbest.net [VA] IIB1 [AC] Pastor, Staunton Menn Ch, Staunton VA

Delp, Lowell H. (Brenda) 2828 Woodview Dr, Hatfield PA 19440, 215-822-0235 [FRC] IIB1 [AC] Pastor, Line Lexington Menn Ch, Line Lexington PA

Delp, Melvin B. (Elma) 1007 Haverhill Rd, Baltimore MD 21229, 410-644-8343 [LAN] IB3 [AC] Bishop/Overseer, LMC Washington-Baltimore District, MD

Delp, R. Lee (Ruth) 840 Keeler Rd, Lansdale PA 19446, 215-368-8019, ldelp@voicenet.com [EDC] III [AC] Lay Minister, Grace Menn Ch, Lansdale PA

Delp, Willard B. (Arlene) 7186 Iron Stone Hill Rd, Dallastown PA 17313, 717-428-1709 [LAN] [RE]

Dengler, Lee (Susan) 611 S 8th St, Goshen IN 46526, 574-534-7552, lee@collegemennonite.org [IM] IIC [AC] Pastor, College Menn Ch, Goshen IN

Dengler, Susan (Lee) 611 S 8th St, Goshen IN 46526, 574-534-7552, susan@collegemennonite.org [IM] IIC [AC] Pastor, College Menn Ch, Goshen IN

Denlinger, Garry L. (Ruth Helen) Box 3703, 31036 Haifa, Israel, garuden@aol.com [LAN] IIB3b [AC]

Denlinger, Glen M. (Marilyn J.) 2475 E Burr Oak Ct, Sarasota FL 34232, 941-371-7550 [SE] IIC [AC] Counselor/Director, Charis Center, Sarasota FL

Denlinger, Jason J. (Ann) RR 3 Box 250, Canton PA 17724, 717-243-9983 [LAN] IIB1 [AC]

Denlinger, John H. (Deborah) 2062 Millstream Rd, Lancaster PA 17602, 717-396-0031, jhdenlinger@paonline.com [ACC] IIB1 [AC] Pastor, Ridgeview Menn Ch, Gordonville PA

Denlinger, Lester K. (Marian) 388 Baumgardner Rd, Willow Street PA 17584, 717-464-4317, lesmarian@juno.com [LAN] IIB1 [AC] Pastor, Rossmere Menn Ch, Lancaster PA

Denlinger, Wilmer B. (Bertie) 400 Park Ave, Quakertown PA 18951-1638, 215-536-2900 [EDC] [RE]

Dennis, James (Kathleen) 2045 N Carlisle St, Philadelphia PA 19121, 215-765-2911 [LAN] IIB1 [AC] Pastor, Christian Life Menn Fell, Philadelphia PA

Derstine Jr., David F. (Maxine) 215 Dock Dr, Lansdale PA 19446, 215-362-6410 [FRC] [RE]

Derstine, Kenton Trost (Rhoda Trost) 146 Belmont Dr, Harrisonburg VA 22801, derstine@emu.edu [VA] IIB3a [AC] Staff, Eastern Mennonite Seminary, Harrisonburg VA

Derstine, Lorene B., 332 Homestead Dr, Harleysville PA 19438, 215-256-8320, 104105.3575@compuserve.com [FRC] IIA [AC] Chaplain, Dock Woods Community, Lansdale PA

Derstine, Michael L. (Dawn Frankenfield) 130 S Main St, Telford PA 18969, 215-723-8511, mikedawn@juno.com [FRC] IIB1 [AC] Pastor, Plains Menn Ch, Hatfield PA

Derstine, Norman (Virginia) 1285 Shank Dr Apt 220, Harrisonburg VA 22802, 540-433-1193 [VA] [RE]

Derstine, Samuel N., 112 8th St, Souderton PA 18964, 215-723-3151 [FRC] [RE]

Desalegn, Sisay (Yodit Alemu) 4048 South 148th St, Seattle WA 98168, 206-244-4892, sisayd@msn.com [PNW] IIB3b [AC] Pastor, Seattle African Ministries, Seattle WA

Detweiler, Alvin F. (Kass) 285 Mill St, Boyertown PA 19512, 610-367-0602 [FRC] [RE]

Detweiler, Bill, PO Box 11, Kidron OH 44636, 330-857-3151 [OH] [RE]

Detweiler, Dennis M. (Dorothy F.) 1341A W Campbell Rd, Green Ln PA 18054, 215-679-2468, dddetweiler@juno.com [FRC] IIA [AC] Associate Pastor, Perkiomenville Menn Ch, Perkiomenville PA

Detweiler, Randy (Joy) 4763 N 700 E, Kokomo IN 46901, 765-628-2865, pastor-randy@juno.com [IM] IIB1 [AC] Pastor, Howard-Miami Menn Ch, Kokomo IN

Detweiler, Rudy, 9652 Akron Rd, Rittman OH 44270, 330-927-3613 [OH] [RE]

Detweiler, Russell M. (Evelyn) 224 Detweiler Rd, Sellersville PA 18960, 215-257-7021 [FRC] IIB2 [AC] Assistant Pastor, Towamencin Menn Ch, Kulpsville PA

Detweiler, Timothy R. (Carol) 2675 230th St, Washington IA 52353, 319-653-4109, tdetweiler@hotmail.com [CP] IB2, IIB1 [AC] Pastor, Washington Menn Ch, Washington IA; East Regional Minister, Central Plains Mennonite Conference, Washington IA

Detweiler, Wally (Liz) RR 1, Sleeman ON P0W 1M0, Canada, 807-488-5620, debwhetz@jam21.net [NC] IIB1 [AC] Pastor, Morson Community Bible Fell, Sleeman ON

Detweiler, Wilton (Delores) PO Box 165, Shickley NE

MINISTERS

6

68436, 402-627-4155, wdd@inebraska.com [CP] IIB1
[AC] Pastor, Salem Menn Ch, Shickley NE

Detwiler, R. Blaine (Connie) RR 1 Box 55, Susquehanna
PA 18847, 717-756-2793 [FRC] IIB1 [AC] Pastor,
Lakeview Menn Ch, Susquehanna PA

Dey, John Michael (Susan Elizabeth) 504 E Main St , PO
Box 387, Pandora OH 45877, 419-384-3421,
deyjs@bluffton.edu [CDC] IIB1 [AC] Pastor, Grace Menn
Ch, Pandora OH

Dick, Jane (Mervin) 6195 Needlegrass Green, Frederick
CO 80530, 559-497-0198, janeldick@juno.com [RM]
IIB1 [AC] Interim Pastor, Boulder Menn Ch, Boulder CO;
Regional Conference Minister, Western District
Conference, Frederick CO

Dick, Mervin (Jane) 6195 Needlegrass Green, Frederick
CO 80530, 559-497-0198, mervdick@juno.net [RM]
IIB1 [AC] Interim Pastor, Boulder Menn Ch, Boulder CO;
Regional Conference Minister, Western District
Conference, Frederick CO

Diener Jr., Andrew S. (Jean Marie) 2464 Creek Hill Rd,
Lancaster PA 17601, 717-656-8341, ajdiener@juno.com
[LAN] III [AC] Deacon, Stumptown Menn Ch, Bird In
Hand PA

Diener, Edward, 3252 CR 19, Archbold OH 43502, 419-
445-5796 [OH] [RE]

Diener, Joe (Elizabeth (Liz)) 13580N CR 300E, Humboldt
IL 61931, 217-234-8709 [IL] [RE]

Diener, Larry (Doris L.) 1528 Springwood Dr, Sarasota FL
34232, 941-377-9085, lddiener@juno.com [SE] IIC [AC]
Minister of Music and Worship, Bahia Vista Menn Ch,
Sarasota FL

Diener, Ronald (Marilee) 58794 CR 19 N, Goshen IN
46528, 574-875-3594, rdiener@maplenet.net [IM] IIB1
[AC] Pastor, Pleasant View Menn Ch, Goshen IN

Diener, Terry L. (Julie) 14411 CR 28, Goshen IN 46528,
574-825-3222, diener2@juno.com [IM] IIB2 [AC]
Interim Pastor, Clinton Frame Menn Ch, Goshen IN

Diller, Aden K. (Ruth) 910A Menno Village,
Chambersburg PA 17201, 717-267-0282 [FRK] [RE]

Diller, Donavin Wayne (June Elizabeth) 1812 Jefferson,
Beatrice NE 68310, 402-223-2340 [WDC] [RE]

Diller, Dwight H. (Mary Elaine) PO Box 148, Hillsboro
WV 24946, 304-653-4397 [VA] IIB3b [AC]

Dintaman, Pamela R. (Larry Gingrich) 116 Swarthmore
Dr, Lititz PA 17543, 717-627-3649,
pamlarry@dejazzd.com [ACC] IIB1 [AC] Pastor,
Community Menn Ch of Lancaster, Lancaster PA

Dintaman, Steve F. (Betsy) 1190 Parkway Dr,
Harrisonburg VA 22802, 540-434-5148 [VA] IIB3b [AC]

Dombach, James (Donna) Azuolu 2-4, Staniunai,
Panevezio Raj 5368, Lithuania Air [LAN] IIC [AC]
Missionary/Church Worker, Eastern Mennonite
Missions, Panevezio Raj. 5368, Lithuania

Dominguez, Mario, 4148 NW 45 Terrace, Lauderdale
Lakes FL 33319, 954-739-8449,
Evangelical_Garifuna_Church@yahoo.com [SE] IIC [AC]
Pastor, Evangelical Garifuna Ch, Lauderdale Lakes FL

Dove, Otis W. (Lottie) 7081 Porch Swing Ln, Dayton VA
22821, 540-828-4864 [VA] [RE]

Dow, Leonard M. (Rosalie Rolon) 19 W Phil-Ellena St,
Philadelphia PA 19119, 215-991-5805,
pastorlen@verizon.net [LAN] IIB1 [AC] Pastor, Oxford
Cr Menn Ch, Philadelphia PA

Drescher, John M., 2265 Esten Rd, Quakertown PA
18951, 215-804-0248, jmdrescher@juno.com [FRC]

IIB3b [AC]

Drescher-Lehman, Sandra, 1900 Twin Lows Rd, Green
Lane PA 18054, 215-453-1624,
sdlehman@soudertonmennonite.org [FRC] IIA [AC]
Pastor of Worship and Congregational Care, Souderton
Menn Ch, Souderton PA

Duenas, Julio, 208 Hurst Cr, Ferris TX 76125 [WDC] [AC]

Duerksen, Carol M. (Maynard Knepp) 1582 Falcon,
Hillsboro KS 67063, cduerksen@tabormennonite.org
[WDC] IIC [AC]

Duerksen, Norma B. (Philip K.) 2595 Paradise Rd,
Orrville OH 44667-9161, 216-682-1465,
ogsmthvll@aol.com [CDC, OH] IIB1 [AC] Pastor, Oak
Grove Menn Ch, Smithville OH

Dula, Mary Ellen (Mamo) 47 W Roseville Rd, Lancaster
PA 17601, 717-519-2495, dulamm@supernet.com
[LAN] IIC [AC] Chaplain, Community Hospital of
Lancaster, Lancaster PA; Pastoral Care, Blossom Hill
Mennonite Church, Lancaster PA

Dunigans, Jesse (Portia) 2932 Wintergreen Dr, Florissant
MO 63033, 314-385-5877, dunigans4444@aol.com [IL]
IIB1 [AC] Pastor, Bethesda Menn Ch, St Louis MO

Dunn, George B., 13735 Equestrian Dr, Burton OH
44021, 440-834-9317 [OH] IIB3a [AC]

Dunn, James L. (Ann Suderman Dunn) 8611 N Hesston
Rd, Hesston KS 67062, 620-327-2185 [WDC] IIB1 [AW]

Dunn, Kathy Neufeld (Michael J. Dunn) 1204 Oread
Ave, Lawrence KS 66044, 734-930-0176,
dunfeld@juno.com [CDC] IIB3a [AC] Interim, Peace
Mennonite, Lawrence KS

Dupuy, George R. (Abbey Davis Dupuy) 316 2nd St,
Luray VA 22835, 540-843-0271,
vacaredeo@hotmail.com [VA] IIB1 [AC] Associate
Pastor, Big Spring Menn Ch, Luray VA

Dutchersmith, Teresa (Kent) 515 S 5th St, Goshen IN
46526, 574-535-1103 [CDC, IM] [AW]

Dutt, Krista Diane, PO Box 448, La Jara CO 81140, 719-
274-4145, kddutt@hotmail.com [RM] IIC [AC]

Dyck, Arthur P. (Suzanne Ruth Nix) 914 Pinetree Way,
Lancaster PA 17601-6608, 717-285-7678,
artdyck@msn.com [ACC] IIB2 [AC] Minister of Music &
Worship, Neffsville Menn Ch, Lancaster PA

Dyck, Cornelius John (Wilma Louise Regier) 1252
Westbrooke Ct, Goshen IN 46528-5065, 574-533-2677
[CDC] [RE]

Dyck, Edna Margaret (George) PO Box 293, Walhalla
ND 58282-0293, gdyck@kscable.com [WDC] [RE]

Dyck, Gordon R. (Judy Beechy) 2212 Wakefield Rd,
Goshen IN 46528, 574-533-5909, grdjab@aol.com [IM]
IB3 [AC] Overseer, Parkview Mennonite, Kokomo IN;
Overseer, Bonneyville Mennonite, Bristol IN; Overseer,
Southside Fell, Elkhart IN

Dyck, Peter Henry (Sheryl June) 202 W Clark St, PO Box
354, Thomasboro IL 61878-0354, 217-643-2789,
peterhenrydyck@juno.com [CDC, IL] IIB3a [AC]
Chaplain, Provena Covenant Medical Center, Urbana IL

Dyck, Peter J. (Elfrieda Klassen) 1 Woodcrest Cr #209,
Scottdale PA 15683-9500, 724-887-3924 [ALL] [RE]

E

Eads, John, 115 W 27th St, North Newton KS 67117,
316-281-9513, eadsjp@bethelks.edu [WDC] IIC [AC]

Early, Richard K. (Kay G) 5379 Klines Mill Rd, Linville VA
22834, 540-896-3423 [VA] IIB1 [AC] Pastor, Grace

Menn Fell, Linville VA

Eash, Brent (Heidi) 15485 CR 4, Bristol IN 46507, 574-848-4589, brenteash@netscape.net [IM] IIB2 [AC] Pastor, Shore Menn Ch, Shipshewana IN

Eash, Theodore M., 16038 CR 4, Bristol IN 46507, 260-848-7089 [IM] [RE]

Eberly, Ben (Martha) 5923 Corinth Dr, Colorado Springs CO 80918, 719-265-9478, beneberly@juno.com [RM] [AW]

Eberly, Harold B. (Ruth Ann) 616 Sawmill Rd, East Earl PA 17519, 717-445-5543 [LAN] III [AC] Ordained Deacon, Bowmansville Menn Ch, E Earl PA

Eberly, Kenneth B. (Betty Lou) 816 N 13th St, Reading PA 19604, 610-378-1017, servantken@juno.com [LAN] IIB1 [AC] Associate Pastor, Hampden Menn Ch, Reading PA

Eberly, Peter (Natalie Fawne) 1280 Greystone St, Harrisonburg VA 22802, 540-574-3284 [VA] IIC [AC]

Ebersole, Lee E. (Connie Joy) 951 Chestnut Dr, Harrisonburg VA 22801, 540-434-6065, leencon@rica.net [VA] IIB2 [AC]

Ebersole, Marlin E. (Doris) 6495 Olde Pine Dr, Chambersburg PA 17201, 717-352-2135, mdebersole@pa.net [FRK] IIB1 [AC] Pastor, Pond Bank Menn Ch, Chambersburg PA

Ebersole, Myron L. (Geraldine Ann Hartman) 2001 Harrisburg Pk, Apt B 407, Lancaster PA 17601, 717-735-2564, mgebersole@aol.com [ACC] [RE]

Ebersole, Phil (Gail Merrick) 13833 E Bellewood Dr, Aurora CO 80015, 303-766-5008, philebersole@yahoo.com [WDC] [AW] Pastor, Peace Menn Community Ch, Aurora CO

Eby, J. Herbert (Marian) RR 3 Box 332, Canton PA 17724-9317, 570-924-3260 [LAN] IIC [AC] Associate Pastor, Mountain View Fell, Trout Run PA

Eby, J. Wilmer (Anna) 24 Creekside Dr, Millersville PA 17551, 717-872-5924, wilann62@juno.com [LAN] IIB1 [AC] Pastor, Masonville Menn Ch, Washington Boro PA

Eby, Kathryn Weaver (J. Harold) 198 Delp Rd, Lancaster PA 17601, 717-569-1290, hakat@juno.com [LAN] IIC [AC] Chaplain, Prison and Landis Homes, Lititz PA

Eby, Paul H. (Barbara) 12 Mary Dr, Gap PA 17527, 717-442-9050 [LAN] [RE]

Ediger, Darrell Lee (Deadra J.) 225 N Wenger Rd, Dalton OH 44618, 330-828-8186, d_ediger@bigfoot.com [CDC] IIB1 [AC] Pastor, Salem Menn Ch, Kidron OH

Ediger, George Roland (Margaret Irene) 426 W Ave, Kelowna BC V1Y 4Z2, Canada, 250-712-9383, Mediger@silk.net [WDC] [RE]

Ediger, Margaret I. (George Roland) 426 W Ave, Kelowna BC V1Y 4Z2, Canada, 250-712-9383, miediger@aol.com [WDC] [RE]

Edwards, Dennis Robert (Susan Steele) 636 Lexington Place NE, Washington DC 20002 [VA] IB1 [AW]

Egli, Marian, 406 2nd St, PO Box 411, Hopedale IL 61747, 309-449-5475, Egli_2@hotmail.com [IL] IIC [AC] Chaplain, St. Joseph's Hospice Program, Bloomington IL

Eglinton-Woods, Bruce (Nancy) 307 4th St, East Greenville PA 18041, 215-679-3380, salempastor@netcarrier.com [FRC] IIB1 [AC] Pastor, Salem Menn Ch, Quakertown PA

Egwuonwu, John, 411 E 157th St, Gardena CA 90248,

310-329-7460, pastorjohn_richesofchrist@juno.com [PSW] IIA, IIB1 [AC] Pastor, Riches of Christ Fell, Los Angeles CA

Ehst, Abram M., HC Box 11, Bally PA 19503, 610-845-2529 [FRC] [RE]

Ehst, John M. (Beverly Meyers) 507 Schoolhouse Rd, Harleysville PA 19438, 215-721-7498 [FRC] IIB1 [AC] Lead Pastor, Franconia Menn Ch, Telford PA

Eisele, Randy (Karen E) 115 Judd Rd, Siletz OR 97380, 541-444-9063 [PNW] IIA [AC] Pastor, Logsden Neighborhood Ch, Logsden OR

Elias, Jacob W. (Lillian E.) 602 W Hively Ave, Elkhart IN 46517, 574-293-6657, jelias@ambs.edu [IM] IIB1 [AC] Co-Pastor, Parkview Menn Ch, Kokomo IN

Elias, Lillian (Jacob) 602 W Hively Ave, Elkhart IN 46517, 574-293-6657, lillianelias@juno.com [IM] IIB1 [AC] Co-Pastor, Parkview Menn Ch, Kokomo IN

Emerson-Pierce, Jonathan, PO Box 17564, Atlanta GA 30316-0564, 404-244-0289, BereaMennonite@juno.com [SE] IIA [AC] Pastor, Berea Menn Ch, Atlanta GA

Encarnacion, Ambrosio (Jennie) 2591 Apache St, Sarasota FL 34231, 941-926-0843 [SE] IIB1 [AC] Pastor, Iglesia Evangelica Nueva Vida, Sarasota FL

Engbrecht, Robert L. (Joan) 618 E 7th St, Box 67, Freeman SD 57029, 605-925-7410 [CP] IIB1 [AC] Pastor, Salem-Zion Menn Ch, Freeman SD

Engel, Harold R. (Anna Mae) 145 Doe Run Rd, East Fallowfield PA 19320, 610-593-6464 [LAN] IIB1 [AC] Pastor, Newlinville Menn Ch, Coatesville PA

Engle, George W. (Betty) RR 1 Box 1690, Pineville MO 64856, 501-636-1645, gengle@leru.net [SC] III [AC] Elder, Rogers Menn/Ch of the Brethren, Pea Ridge AR

Engle, Jesse, 8973 Wiencek Rd, Streetsboro OH 44241, 330-422-0829, jpastorbigjess@juno.com [OH] IIA [AC] Pastor, Aurora Menn Ch, Aurora OH

Engle, Naomi, 8973 Wiencek Rd, Streetsboro OH 44241, 330-442-0829, pastornaomiengle@juno.com [OH] IIA [AC] Associate Pastor, Aurora Menn Ch, Aurora OH

Epp, Arlen, 51892 CR 11, Elkhart IN 46514-8558, 574-293-8100, repp@juno.com [CDC] IIB3a [AC]

Epp, Charlene, 1292 NW Fall Ave, Beaverton OR 97006-4031, 503-533-5654, charlene.epp@providence.org [PNW] IIB3a [AC] Chaplain, Providence St Vincent Medical Center, Portland OR

Epp, Eldon John, 710 Mission, Manhattan KS 66502, 785-587-8256 [WDC] IIB3a [AC] Chaplain, Community Hospital, Manhattan KS

Epp, Rosella E. (Raymond Reimer) 3916 E Ronning Dr, Sioux Falls SD 57103 [CP] IIB1 [AC] Pastor, Good Shepherd Community Ch, Sioux Falls SD; Pastor, Sermon on the Mount Menn Ch, Sioux Falls SD

Erb, Leroy H. (Rachel) 925 Strick Rd, Milton PA 17847, 570-437-3773 [LAN] IIC [AC] Associate Pastor, Derry Menn Ch, Manheim PA

Erb, Ross (Cathy Smeltzer) 251 Comfort Ct, Harrisonburg VA 22802 [VA] IIA, IIB2 [AC] Associate Pastor, Park View Menn Ch, Harrisonburg VA

Ernest, Dennis Wayne (Rosalind Dawn) 165 E Front St, Lititz PA 17543, 717-626-8237, lmchurch@dejazzd.com [LAN] [AW]

Esau, John A. (Bernice A.) Box 117, 9 Emerald Ct, North Newton KS 67117-0117, 316-283-4624, jae@southwind.net [WDC] [RE]

MINISTERS

6

Esbenshade, Adam (Alta) 626 S Kinzer Ave, New Holland PA 17557, 717-354-9509 [LAN] [RE]

Esh, Glenn (Jennifer L.) 52 Evergreen St, Gordonville PA 17529, 717-768-0532, jenglenn@frontiernet.net [LAN] IIA [AC] Pastor, Cambridge Menn Ch, Gordonville PA

Esh, Robert E., 45565 Erie County Line Rd, Corry PA 16407, 814-664-7892, ree0817@aol.com [OH] IIA [AC] Pastor, Valley View Menn Ch, Spartansburg PA

Esh, Stephen S., 2655 Valley View Rd, Morgantown PA 19543, 610-286-8892 [LAN] [RE]

Eshleman, Allen R. (Mary Ellen) 13239 Buchanan Trail W, Mercersburg PA 17236, 717-328-0058 [FRK] IIB1 [AC] Pastor, Mercersburg Menn Ch, Mercersburg PA

Eshleman, D. Rohrer (Mabel) 46 Country Ln, Landisville PA 17538, 717-898-2593 [LAN] [RE]

Eshleman, J. David (Helen) 8806 Ebourne Ln, Laurel MD 20708, 301-725-5692, eshlemanjd@capitalchristian.org [LAN] IIB1 [AC] Pastor, Capital Christian Fell, Laurel MD

Eshleman, J. Leon (Melba) 570 Fruitville Pk, Manheim PA 17545, 717-665-6690, leon17545@aol.com [LAN] III [AC] Ordained Deacon, Chestnut Hill Menn Ch, Columbia PA

Eshleman, J. Lester (Lois) 1001 E Oregon Rd, Lititz PA 17543, 717-581-3968 [LAN] [RE]

Eshleman, Mahlon D. (Mary) 450C Menno Village, Chambersburg PA 17201, 717-263-1082 [FRK] [RE]

Estrada, Gilberto, 1765 Tomlin Ave, Woodburn OR 97071, 503-982-5731 [PNW] IIA [AC] Pastor, Comunidad Cristiana de Vida Nueva, Woodburn OR

Evans, Faith (David) 4500 Mass Ave, NW Box 150, Washington DC 20016, faith_evans73Wyahoo.com [VA] IIB2 [AC] Associate Pastor for Youth, Washington Community Fell, Washington DC

Evers, Larry (Elva M.) 1628 N 26th St, Ft Dodge IA 50501, 515-573-3048, elevers@frontiernet.net [CP] IIA [AC] Pastor, Evangelical Menn Ch, Fort Dodge IA

Ewert, David Darrel (Karen Lou) 2111 E Luther Rd, Janesville WI 53545, 608-754-6942, loudarew@juno.com [CDC, IL] [RE]

Ewert, Linda (Morris Earl) 346 N Parkridge, Wichita KS 67212, 316-773-4349 [WDC] IIA [AC] Associate Pastor, Hope Menn Ch, Wichita KS

Ewert, Marvin H. (Alma L.) 1328 W 9th St, Newton KS 67114-1620, 316-283-8520 [WDC] [RE]

F

Fahnestock, James R. (Nancy) 7 Audubon Cr, Stevens PA 17578, 717-336-8263, jnfahnestock@dejazzd.com [LAN] IIB1 [AC] Pastor, Blainsport Menn Ch, Stevens PA

Fahrer, Walfred J. (Susan R.) 16 Despard Rd, Upper Holloway, London N195 NW Great Britain [IM] IIB3b [AC] Counselor, Cholmeley Evangelical Church, London, England

Faler, Brad (Vivian Elaine) 21636 US Hwy 20A, Archbold OH 43502, 419-445-4408, brad.faler@northclinton.org [OH] IIB2 [AC] Associate Pastor, North Clinton Menn Ch, Wauseon OH

Falla, Amanda (Gamaliel) Apartado 24226, Cali, Colombia, 011-572-3331 ext 521, cindy@colombianet.net [SE] IIB3b [AC] Mission Service, Encuentro de Renovación, Colombia, South America

Falla, Gamaliel (Amanda) Apartado 24226, Cali, Colombia, 011-572-3331 ext 521, cindy@colombianet.net [SE] IIB3b [AC] Mission Service,

Encuentro de Renovación, Colombia, South America

Farmer, Roger Alan (Mary Lou Swartzendruber) 2830 Coppock Rd, Washington IA 52353, 319-653-2547, rfarmer1@juno.com [CP] [AW]

Farmwald, Kevin Dale (Susie Kay) 607 S 3rd St, Goshen IN 45626, 574-533-8739, kfarmwald@bnin.net [CDC] IIB1 [AC] Pastor, Eighth St Menn Ch, Goshen IN

Farrell, William (Bonnie) 182 Ark Ln, Schoharie NY 12157, 518-295-7891, wfarrell@midtel.net [NY] IIB1 [AC] Pastor, Grace Fell, Schoharie NY

Farrow, Frank E. (Susan B.) 115 Bunker Hill Rd, Rogersville TN 37857-6049, 423-345-3503, w4us@arrl.net [VA] [RE]

Farsaci, Steven, PO Box 1785, Americus GA 31709, 229-924-0603, threehermits@earthlink.net [SE] IIA [AC] Pastor, Americus Menn Fell, Americus GA

Fatunmbi, Olwfemi A., 6503/6505 S Normandie Ave, Los Angeles CA 90043, 323-779-4363 [PSW] IIB1 [AC] Mission Associate, Center for Anabaptist Leadership; Founding Pastor, Royal Dominion Family Chapel, Los Angeles CA

Felgar, Muzet D., 170 Hall School Rd, Waynesboro VA 22980, 540-949-8945, muzet@ntelos.net [VA] IIC [AC] Youth Pastor, Springdale Menn Ch, Waynesboro VA

Feliciano, Rogelio, 1116 Kittatinny St, Harrisburg PA 17014 [LAN] [AW]

Feliz, Jose, 426 Highlawn Ave, Elizabethtown PA 17022, 717-367-3966 [LAN] IIB2 [AC]

Fellenbaum, Robert E. (May) 508 N Plum St, Mount Joy PA 17552, 717-653-1278 [LAN] III [AC] Ordained Deacon, Elizabethtown Menn Ch, Elizabethtown PA

Ferreras, Juan (Maritza) PO Box 50870, Cicerio IL 60804, 708-652-3145, admin@sonidodealabanza.com [IL] IIB1 [AC] Pastor, Sonido de Alabanza, Cicero IL

Fetterly, Tim (Candy) PO Box 368, Grantsville MD 21536, 301-895-4054, tcfetterly@earthlink.net [ALL] IIB1 [AC] Pastor, Oak Grove Menn Ch, Grantsville MD

Fisher, J. Herbert (Ruth) 117 Weaver Rd, Lancaster PA 17603, 717-394-8159 [LAN] [RE]

Fisher Jr., Menno B. (Sallie) 2523 Old Philadelphia Pk, Bird In Hand PA 17505-9797, salliestamper@supernet.com [LAN] IIB2 [AC] Associate Pastor, Millwood Menn Ch, Bird In Hand PA

Fisher, Orlo J. (Dorothy M.) 9365 Vest-Talcum Rd, Talcum KY 41722, 606-251-3303, dabdo@hotmail.com [IM] IIB1 [AC] Pastor, Talcum Menn Ch, Talcum KY

Fisher, Rachel S. (Robert) 1724 S 12th St, Goshen IN 46526, 574-533-0669, fisher915@bnin.net [IM] [RE]

Flaming, Ron (Patrice Stucky) 125 Broad St, Akron PA 17501 [WDC] IIB3c [AC] Director of International Programs, Mennonite Central Committee, Akron PA

Flinner, Matt, 5337 PR 382, Millersburg OH 44654, 330-893-3923 [OH] IIB2 [AC] Associate Pastor, Martins Creek Menn Ch, Millersburg OH

Flores, Gilberto, PO Box 347, 722 Main, Newton KS 67114-0347, 316-283-5100, GilbertoF@MennoniteUSA.org [WDC] IIB3c [AC] Director of Leadership Development, Mennonite Mission Network, Newton KS

Flowers, Claude, 10634 Navajo Rd, Apple Valley CA 92308, 760-247-5713 [PSW] IIB1 [AC] Pastor, Family Menn Ch, Los Angeles CA

Foncannon, David (Brenda) 408 Morrison, Pueblo CO 81005, 719-561-1609, blindpossum@juno.com [RM]

IIB1 [AC] Pastor, Pueblo Menn Ch, Pueblo CO

Foote, Ralph Wayne (Eloise Christine) PO Box 337, Carlock IL 61725-0337, 309-376-4014, ralphfoote@mac.com [CDC] IIC [AC] Pastor, Carlock Menn Ch, Carlock IL

Forestal, Ducois, 801 NW 111th St, Miami FL 33168-2144, 305-953-9703, D.Forestal@juno.com [SE] IIC [AC] Pastor, Unity Pentecostal Ch of God, Miami FL

Forrey, K. Eugene (Nancy) 312 Druid Hill Dr, Mountville PA 17554, 717-285-4046 [LAN] IIB2 [AC] Associate Pastor, East Petersburg Menn Ch, East Petersburg PA

Forry, Nevin (Fanny) 3500 Oxford Rd, New Oxford PA 17350, 717-624-4263 [LAN] IIA [AC] Associate Pastor, Life Menn Fell, Conestoga PA

Foss, Richard Gordon (Sarah Genet) RR 2 Box 2A, Tiskilwa IL 61368, 815-646-4264, richfoss@plowcreek.org [CDC, IL] IIC [AC] Lay Minister, Plow Creek Menn Ch, Tiskilwa IL

Foster, Brent Edwin (Sandra Louise) 2710 W Kansas, Peoria IL 61604, 309-685-0213 [CDC, IL] [AW]

Foster, Sandra S. (James Larry) 204 Busbee Rd, Knoxville TN 37920, 865-573-4089 (h) 865-541-8256 (w), sfoster@etch.com [VA] IIB3a [AC]

Fountain, Brian Eric, 126 E Lemon St Apt 3, Lancaster PA 17602, 717-393-7232 [LAN] IIA [AC] Pastor, Peace Chapel, Harrisburg PA

Fox, Gerald W. (Tracey) 210 S Windy Mansion Rd, Denver PA 17517 [LAN] IIA [AC] Associate Pastor, Hinkletown Menn Ch, Ephrata PA

Fox, Randy (Arlene) 15 S Ridge Rd, Reinholds PA 17569-9692, 717-336-2471, randyfox@dejazzd.com [LAN] III [AC] Ordained Deacon, Red Run Menn Ch, Denver PA

Francisco, Karla (Steven) 4507 Lear Close, Chesapeake VA 23321, 757-686-0049 [VA] IIB2 [AC]

Francisco III, Leslie W. (Natalie) 4505 McRae Close, Chespeake VA 23321, 757-483-3784, pastor@calvarycommunity.org [VA] IB3, IIB1, IIB3c [AC] Pastor, Calvary Community Ch, Hampton VA

Francisco, Natalie A. (Leslie W. III) 4505 McRae Close, Chesapeake VA 23321, 757-483-3784 [VA] IIB2 [AC] Associate Pastor, Calvary Community Ch, Hampton VA

Franco, Eliseo, 6226 Colfax Ave, North Hollywood CA 91606, 818-508-6467 [PSW] IIB1, IIB3b [AC] Pastor, Iglesia Evangelica Bethel, Sun Valley CA

Frank, Richard H. (Naomi) 3104 Bossler Rd, Elizabethtown PA 17022, 717-367-3242 [LAN] IIB3a [AC] Chaplain, Mennonite Home, Lancaster PA

Frankenfield, Marlene F., 428 Turnberry Way, Souderton PA 18964, 215-723-5857, MarleneF@FMC-Online.org [FRC] IC [AC] Conference Youth Minister, Franconia Conference, Souderton, PA; Campus Pastor, Christopher Dock Mennonite High School, Lansdale PA

Franz, Delton W. (Marian C.) 6151 3lst St NW, Washington DC 20015-1515, 202-966-5271 [ALL] [RE]

Frederick, Duane, 1034 O'Brien Rd, Swanton MD 21561, 301-387-2763, revfrederick@hotmail.com [ALL] IB3, IIB1 [AC] Pastor, Meadow Mountain Menn Ch, Swanton MD

Frederick, Elmer S., 37 E 8th St, Pennsburg PA 18073, 215-679-9368 [FRC] IIB1 [AC] Pastor, Covenant Community Fell, Lansdale PA

Frederick, Emma (J. Mark) 341 Franklin St, Quakertown PA 18951, 215-536-0710 [FRC] IIA [AC] Interim Pastor

of Pastoral Care, Deep Run Menn Ch East, Perkasie PA

Frederick, Franklin M. (Naomi) 778 Morwood Rd, Telford PA 18969, 215-723-7351 [FRC] [RE]

Frederick Jr., J. Mark (Emma) 341 Franklin St, Quakertown PA 18951-1725, 215-536-0710, jmemfred@hotmail.com [FRC] IIB1 [AC] Interim Pastor, Deep Run Menn Ch East, Perkasie PA

Frederick, Jacob W. (Anna) 906 Pine Hill Rd, Lititz PA 17543, 717-626-7464 [LAN] [RE]

Freed, Floyd W., Box 109, Putnam Station NY 12861 [FRC] [RE]

Freed, Glenn W. (Ella Mae Jones) 3312 Pruss Hill Rd, Pottstown PA 19464, 610-326-5478 [FRC] IIB2 [AC] Assistant Pastor, Hersteins Menn Ch, Schwenksville PA

Freed, Richard L. (Georgina) 2178 Mixsell Ave, Bethlehem PA 18015, 610-867-9023, RLFreed34@aol.com [LAN] III [AC] Ordained Deacon, Bethlehem Community Fell, Bethlehem PA

Fretz, J. Herbert (Helen Habegger) 625 South 7th St, Goshen IN 46526, 574-533-1961 [CDC] [RE]

Fretz, Stephen P. 102 E Hykes Rd, Greencastle PA 17225, 717-597-3785, stevef@pa.net, [ACC] IIB1 [AC] Pastor, Cedar Grove Menn Ch, Greencastle PA

Frey, Adin L. (Janet) 1838 Falling Spring Rd, Chambersburg PA 17201, 717-267-3654 [FRK] [RE]

Frey, Harold R. (Ruth) 1930 Colebrook Rd, Lebanon PA 17042, 717-274-3394 [LAN] [RE]

Frey, Preston M. (Lorraine) 3492 Glen Eagles Dr, Chambersburg PA 17201-8190, 717-352-3600 [FRK] [RE] Pastor Emeritus, Chambersburg Menn Ch, Chambersburg PA

Frey, Vincent J. (Marcella) 890 Blind Brook Dr, Columbus OH 43235, 614-436-9615, freyv@juno.com [ACC] [RE]

Friesen, Ben K. (RaeVella) 1004 Old Farm Est, Hutchinson KS 67502, 620-665-9868 [WDC] [RE]

Friesen, Delores (Stanley) 3014 N 8th St, Fresno CA 93703, 559-229-3645 [PSW] [AW] Associate, Mennonite Board of Missions, Fresno CA

Friesen, Dorothy Nickel (Richard Allen) 1100 Grandview Ave, Newton KS 67114, 316-281-9364, dorothynf@cox.net [WDC] IB2 [AC] Conference Minister, Western District Conference, Newton, KS

Friesen, Elmer R. (Lois M.) 11003 SE Home, Milwaukie OR 97222, 503-786-0289 [PNW] [RE]

Friesen, Ivan D. (Rachel Hilty) PO Box 30, Freeman SD 57029, 605-925-7186, irfriegwtc.net [CP] IIB1 [AC] Co-Pastor, Hutterthal Menn Ch, Freeman SD

Friesen, J. Stanley (Delores) 3014 N 8th St, Fresno CA 93703, 559-229-3645 [PSW] [AW] Teacher, Fresno College, Fresno, CA; Ministry Team, First Menn Ch of Paso Robles, Paso Robles CA

Friesen, Jacob Toews (Lola M.) Box 133, North Newton KS 67117, 316-283-8064 [WDC] IIB3a [RE]

Friesen, John A., 1558 Greencroft Dr, Goshen IN 46526, 574-537-4392 [IM] [RE]

Friesen, Matthew Charles (Terisa Lyn) 2480 Boston St, Albany OR 97322, 541-791-9604, amcpastor@proaxis.com [PNW] IIB1 [AC] Pastor, Albany Menn Ch, Albany OR

Friesen, Patty Jo (Patrick Charles Preheim) 2211 28th Ave S, Minneapolis MN 55406, 612-724-0733, faithmc@juno.com [CP] IIB1 [AC] Pastor, Faith Menn Ch, Minneapolis MN

Friesen, Philip E. (Kim Vu) 2012 Como Ave SE #2,

Minneapolis MN 55414, 612-378-9114, fries009@umn.edu [CP] IIB3a [AC] Partner, Galilean Center, Minneapolis MN; Chaplain, International Student & Family Center, Minneapolis MN; International Student Outreach, Stadium Village Church, Minneapolis MN

Friesen, Rachel (Ivan Dan) PO Box 30, Freeman SD 57029, 605-925-7186, irfriegwtc.net [CP] IIB1 [AC] Co-Pastor, Hutterthal Menn Ch, Freeman SD

Friesen, Todd K. (Dennette Alwine) 536 E Madison St, Lombard IL 60148, 630-627-5310, tkfriesen@aol.com [IL] IIB1 [AC] Lead Pastor, Lombard Menn Ch, Lombard IL

Friesen, Walter S. (Carol M.) 2009 Clover Ln, Newton KS 67114, 316-283-5250 [WDC] IIB3a [AC] Chaplain, Bethesda Home, Goessel KS; Interim Pastor, Zion Menn Ch, Elbing KS

Friesen, Wilbert (Will) James (Glenna Ruth Wahl) 3643 E Kerckhoff Ave, Fresno CA 93702-2809, 559-255-4185 [PSW] IIC [AW]

Fry, Donald William (Katherine P.) 5 Audubohn Cr, Stevens PA 17578, 717-336-6849, rdonfry@juno.com [EDC] IIB3b [AC] Pastor, New Eden Fell, Schwenksville PA

Funk, Melvin F. (Frances J.) 118 Mallard Ln, Goshen IN 46526, 574-537-1991 [CDC] [RE]

Fyffe, Direl (Polly) 52 Fyffe Ct, West Liberty KY 41472, 606-743-4389 [VA] [RE]

G

Gaeddert, John W. (Mary Lou) Box 186, 108 W 24th St, North Newton KS 67117-0186, 316-283-7660 [WDC] [RE]

Gaiotti, Michael C., RR 3 Box 255, Canton PA 17724-9771 [LAN] IIB1 [AC] Pastor, Faith Mountain Fell, Canton PA

Galati, Jr., Mauro A. (Maryann) 3233 Maplecrest Terrace, Lancaster PA 17601, 717-285-3991, maurojr@earthlink.net [LAN] IIC [AC] Pastor of Evangelism, Rohrerstown Menn Ch, Lancaster PA

Gallardo, Andres (Lilia) 1323 S Austin Blvd, Cicero IL 60804-1026, 708-863-6495, CCVIDA@aol.com [IL] IIB1 [AC] Pastor, Centro Cristiano Vida Abundante, Cicero IL

Garber, Derrick (Jen) 6601 Hollow Dr, East Petersburg PA 17520, 717-560-2263 [LAN] IIC [AC] Youth Pastor, East Petersburg Menn Ch, East Petersburg PA

Garber, Fred M., 1614 Bossler Rd, Elizabethtown PA 17022, 717-367-5215, fgarb@juno.com [LAN] IIB1 [AC] Pastor, Bossler Menn Ch, Elizabethtown PA

Garber, Gerald B. (Jewel) 208 Long Rifle Rd, Willow Street PA 17584, 717-464-0640, gjgarber@juno.com [LAN] IIB1 [AC] Associate Pastor, Willow Street Menn Ch, Willow St PA

Garber, Jay C. (Lois) 2275 New Danville Pk, Lancaster PA 17603-9667, 717-872-6298, garberlj@juno.com [LAN] [RE]

Garber, Joe C. (Yvonne) 242 Stoney Ln, Lancaster PA 17603, 717-872-6922, jygarber@juno.com [LAN] IIA [AC] Pastor, Byerland Menn Ch, Willow Street PA

Garber, Leonard (Veva Roine Hershberger) 1301 Somerset Ct, Goshen IN 46528, 574-534-9622, lvgarber@peoplepc.com [IM] [RE]

Garber, Robert E., 17500 Northside Blvd, Nampa ID 83687, 208-466-5081 [PNW] [RE]

Garber, Robert H. (Alta Mae) 1001 W Oregon Rd, Lititz PA 17543, 717-581-1623 [LAN] [RE]

Garber, S. David, 300 S High St, Scottdale PA 15683, 724-887-9407 [ALL] IB3 [AC]

Garber, Shirley Kay (David) 2271 New Danville Pk, Lancaster PA 17603, 717-872-7599, garberds@juno.com [LAN] IIC [AC] Deaconess, New Danville Menn Ch, Lancaster PA

Garcia, Hugo E. (Ivania) 1035 N 27th St, Camden NJ 08105-3952, 609-365-9236, pastorhugo@netzero.com [LAN] IB3, IIB1 [AC] Pastor, Iglesia Evangelical Menonita Manantial de Vida, Camden NJ; Supervisor, Spanish District, Camden NJ

Garrett, Millard P. (Priscilla) 1145 Kenneth Dr, Lancaster PA 17601, 717-397-4593, millardg@emm.org [LAN] IIB3c [AC] Director of Finance, Eastern Mennonite Missions, Salunga PA

Gary, Joe (Lucy) 731 Wagner Ave, Elkhart IN 46516, 574-293-0776 [IM] IIB1 [AC] Other, Ch Without Walls, Elkhart IN

Gascho, Harry (Elva) 1425 Greencroft #265, Goshen IN 46526, 574-534-2190 [IM] [RE]

Gaskins, Paul (Belinda) PO Box 60923, Washington DC 20039, 301-868-1519, powell.dottie@starpower.net [VA] IIB1 [AC] Pastor, Christian Conquest Fell, Washington DC

Gatlin, Joe (Nancy) 1700 Morrow, Waco TX 76707, 254-754-5942, jngatlin@grandecom.net [SC, WDC] IIB1 [AC] Co-Pastor, Hope Fell, Waco TX

Gatlin, Nancy (Joe) 1700 Morrow, Waco TX 76707, 817-754-5942, jngatlin@grandecom.net [SC, WDC] IIB1 [AC] Co-Pastor, Hope Fell, Waco TX

Gautsche, Charles H. (Marjorie Ann) 820 Ringenberg Dr, Archbold OH 43502-3248, 419-445-6451, cmgautsc@fulton-net.com [OH] IIB3a [AC]

Gaytan, Gilberto (Gloria) 1322 Kingston Ln, Schaumburg IL 60193, 847-534-7242 [CDC] IIB1 [AC] Pastor, Comunidad de Fe, Schaumburg IL

Gehman, Brooke L. (Dana) 122 Garris Rd, Downingtown PA 19335, 610-873-5429, gehmanpottery@characterlink.net [LAN] IIA [AC] Associate Pastor, Downing Hills Christian Fell, Downingtown PA

Gehman, Dale Lee (Brenda) 314 Millway Rd, Ephrata PA 17522, 717-859-4246 [LAN] [AW]

Gehman, David L. (Lois W.) 562 Octorara Trl, Parkesburg PA 19365, 610-857-1641, dlgehman@chesco.com [LAN] IIB1 [AC] Pastor, Parkesburg Menn Ch, Parkesburg PA

Gehman, John W. (Susan Marie) RR2 Box 1435, Mcalisterville PA 17049-9716, 717-463-9378, johnwg@nmax.net [LAN] IIB1 [AC] Pastor, Lauver Menn Ch, Richfield PA

Gehman Jr., Lester W. (Ruth Ann) 565-A Schoeneck Rd, Ephrata PA 17522, 717-738-1235 [LAN] IIB2 [AC] Youth Pastor, Village Chapel Menn Ch, New Holland PA

Gehman, Paul H. (Edith) 351 E Farmersville Rd, Ephrata PA 17522, 717-354-9725 [LAN] [RE]

Gehring, Barbara Krehbiel (Richard) 221 S 8th, Manhattan KS 66502, 785-770-8816, rbgehring@juno.com [SC, WDC] IIB1 [AC] Co-Pastor, Manhattan Menn Ch, Manhattan KS

Gehring, Richard L. (Barbara Krehbiel) 221 S 8th, Manhattan KS 66502, 785-770-8816, rbgehring@juno.com [SC, WDC] IIB1 [AC] Co-Pastor,

Manhattan Menn Ch, Manhattan KS

Geib, Daniel R. (Cheryl) 73 Sun Ln, Millersville PA 17551, 717-871-8775, dcgeib@juno.com [LAN] IIC [AC] Licensed Deacon, Lyndon Menn Ch, Lancaster PA

Geib, David (Linda) 112 Longfellow Rd, Dagmar MT 59219, 406-483-5307 [NC] IIB1 [AC] Pastor, Coalridge Menn Ch, Dagmar MT

Geigley, Ray M. (Dorothy) 3459 Church St, Chambersburg PA 17201, 717-264-9490 [FRK] IIB3a [AC] Chaplain, Menno Haven Retirement, Chambersburg PA

Geiser, Elmer, 16306 SR 160, Vinton OH 45686, 614-388-9809 [OH] [RE]

Geissinger, Carl (Sherry) 1329 Ertley Rd, McClure PA 17841, 717-543-5130 [ALL] IB3 [AC]

Geissinger, Norman A. (Mianna) 460B Menno Village, Chambersburg PA 17201, 717-267-1050 [EDC] [RE]

Gerber, James (Barbara) PO Box 526, Brutus MI 49716, 616-529-6276, bjgerber@freeway.net [IM] IB3 [AC] Overseer, Rexton Mennonite, Naubinway MI; Overseer, Wildwood Mennonite, Engadine MI; Overseer, Naubinway Mennonite, Naubinway MI

Gerber, Lowell Keith (Lois Shank) 511 N Water St, Lititz PA 17543, 717-626-1557, shankgerber@aol.com [LAN] IIB1, IIB3a [AC] Pastor, Lititz Menn Ch, Lititz PA

Gerber, Robert (Fran) 5373 W Summy, Leesburg IN 46538-9253 [IM] IIB3b [AC] Assistant to the Director, China Educational Exchange, Harrisonburg VA

Gerber, Shawn (Rachel Springer) 104A Pennie Ln, Bridgewater VA 22812, 540-828-0167, rsgerber@yahoo.com [VA] IIA, IIB3a [AC] Resident Chaplain, University of Virginia Medical Center, Charlottesville VA

Gerbrandt, David (Marilyn) 200 Rawlings Dr, Clinton OK 73601, 580-323-6304 [WDC] IIB1 [AC] Pastor, First Menn Ch, Clinton OK

Gerig, Virgil M. (Mary K. Ramseyer) 1801 Greencroft Blvd #214, Goshen IN 46526, 574-537-4577 [CDC] [RE]

Gerig Unruh, Pamela, 1114 Franklin Ave, Wayland IA 45572 [CP] IIC [AC] Co-Pastor, Wayland Menn Ch, Wayland IA

Gering, William M. (Lucille E.) 624 W Mishawaka Ave, Mishawaka IN 46545-6013, 574-255-3296 [CDC] [RE]

Gibbs, Elizabeth Anne (Stephen) 250 Lucas Creek Rd, Newport News VA 23602, 757-874-0794, stevebethgibbs@juno.com [VA] IIA [AC] Associate Pastor of Youth and Worship, Warwick River Menn Ch, Newport News VA

Gibbs, Stephen H. (Elizabeth) 118 Binnacle Dr, Newport News VA 23602-6239, stevebethgibbs2@juno.com [VA] IIB1 [AC] Pastor, Warwick River Menn Ch, Newport News VA

Giersch, William E. (Carol Tobin) 1400 E King St, Lancaster PA 17602, 717-396-8928, wgiersch@yahoo.com [LAN] IIA [AC] Pastor, Beaver Run Menn Ch, Watsontown PA

Gilot, Marie, 1707 6th Ave, Immokalee FL 34142 [SE] IIC [AC] Associate Pastor, Assemblee de la Grace, Immokalee FL

Ginder, Larry Eugene (Sharon) 2940 Sunnyside Rd, Manheim PA 17545, 717-653-5337 [LAN] IIC [AC] Associate Pastor, Risser Menn Ch, Elizabethtown PA

Ginder, Ralph G. (Margaret) 1958 Cloverleaf Rd, Mount Joy PA 17552, 717-653-5042 [LAN] [RE]

Gingerich, Dennis D. (Linda) 502 SE 17th Ave, Cape Coral FL 33990, 239-574-8382, DGingerich@capechristian.com [SE] IIB1 [AC] Senior Pastor, Cape Christian Fell, Cape Coral FL

Gingerich, Emanuel (Margaret M.) 7185 Chases Lake Rd, Glenfield NY 13343, 315-376-7126, usadatanet.net [NY] IIC [AC] Overseer, Northern District of the NY Conference, Glenfield NY

Gingerich, Firman (Susan) 64542 Orchard Dr, Goshen IN 46526, 574-534-7365, gingeric@verizon.net [IM] IIB1 [AC] Pastor, College Menn Ch, Goshen IN

Gingerich, James Daniel (Roberta S.) PO Box 48, Moundridge KS 67107-0048, 620-345-2130 [WDC] [RE] Director, Mennonite Men of MCUSA, Newton KS

Gingerich, Jana, 6124 S Whiskey Hill Rd, Hubbard OR 97032, 503-651-2274, zionmc@canby.com [PNW] IIC [AC] Associate/Youth Pastor, Zion Menn Ch, Hubbard OR

Gingerich, Michael A. (Gail) 422 S 13th St, Harrisburg PA 17104-1774, mikeg@emm.org [LAN] IIC [AC] Discipleship Ministries Staff, Eastern Mennonite Missions, Salunga PA

Gingerich, Ray C. (Wilma) 1018 Waterman Dr, Harrisonburg VA 22802, 540-434-4465 [VA] IIB3d [AC]

Gingrich, Beth, 100 S Strong Dr, Gallup NM 87301 [IM] IIB3a [AC] Chaplain, Rehobeth McKinnley Hospital, Gallup NM

Gingrich, Byron, 7857 Lavender Ln, Turner OR 97392, 541-363-2662 [PNW] IIB3a [AC]

Gingrich, Lloyd W. (Rachel) 12357 Orchard Cr, Mercersburg PA 17236, 717-328-5389, lorae@southpenn.net [FRK] IIB2 [AC] Minister of Visitation, Mercersburg Menn Ch, Mercersburg PA

Gingrich, Mervin M. (Janet) 1 Valley View Ct, Lititz PA 17543, 717-626-6111 [LAN] III [AC] Ordained Deacon, Hammer Creek Menn Ch, Lititz PA

Gingrich, Paul M. (Ann) 1903 Maywood Ct, Goshen IN 46526, 574-534-9762, gingrichp@juno.com [IM] IB3 [AC] Overseer, College Mennonite, Goshen IN; Overseer, Prairie St Mennonite, Elkhart IN

Glanzer, Paul J. (Eva Gay) 1820 Glanzer Ct, Harrisonburg VA 22801, 540-433-8234 [VA] [RE]

Glick, Del, 1126 G St, NE, Washington DC 20002, 202-398-7234, delglick@yahoo.com [VA] IB3, IIB3c [AC] Director of Church Partnerships, Eastern Mennonite Seminary, Washington DC

Glick, Elam H., 234 Hartzler Dr, Belleville PA 17004, 717-935-5495 [ALL] [RE]

Glick, Herman N. (Mary) 1603 Swan Rd, Atglen PA 19310, 610-593-5757 [ACC] [RE]

Glick, Jesse B., 464 Ball Fall Rd, Middletown CT 06457-2331, 860-344-0864 [IM] IIB3b [AC] Service Assignment, Church World Service, Colchester CT

Glick, Karl G. (Charlotte) 2724 W Philadelphia Ave, Oley PA 19547, 610-987-0429, kglick@juno.com [ACC] IIB1 [AC] Pastor, Ark Bible Chapel, Boyertown PA

Gochnauer, David L. (Rebecca) 367 Long Ln, Lancaster PA 17603, drgochnauer@paonline.com [LAN] IIA [AC] Pastor, River Corner Menn Ch, Conestoga PA

Gochnauer, Paul H. (Jean) 720 Centerville Rd, Lancaster PA 17601, 717-898-8361 [LAN] [RE]

Godoy, Filemon B. (Tammy) 529A Analu St, Honolulu HI 96817, 808-595-6906 [LAN] IIA [AC] Associate Pastor, New Life Christian Fell, Honolulu HI

Godshall, Edward M. (Evelyn Pauline) 3733 Hickory-

MINISTERS

6

Lincolnton Hwy, Newton NC 28658, 704-462-1707, edwardgo@aol.com [VA] IB3 [AC]

Godshall, Ernest M. (Martha) 14 Elowro Dr, Newport News VA 23602, 757-877-2007 [VA] [RE]

Godshall, Leroy G., Souderton Mennonite Homes, 207 W Summit St, Rm S137, Souderton PA 18964 [FRC] [RE]

Godshall, Paul (Catherine) 3203 Hursey St, Durham NC 27703, 919-598-7533, p.godshall@verizon.net [VA] IIB1 [AC] Pastor, Durham Menn Ch, Durham NC

Godshall, Stanley G., 5132 McLean Station Rd, Green Ln PA 18054, 215-679-2834 [FRC] [RE]

Godshall, Susan E. (Dr. Stanley M.) 1891 Mt Pleasant Rd, Mount Joy PA 17552, 717-653-6191 [LAN] IIC [AC] Associate Pastor, EMM Africa, Africa

Goering, Paul Louis (Wilda M.) 505 Carter Rd, Goshen IN 46526-5209, 574-533-3762 [CDC] [RE]

Goering, Steven William (Susan Ortman) 1339 Ashland Ave, Grandview Heights OH 43212, 614-486-3245, swgoering@columbusmennonite.org [CDC] IB2, IIB1 [AC] Co-Pastor, Columbus Menn Ch, Columbus OH

Goering, Susan Ortman (Steven William) 1339 Ashland Ave, Grandview Heights OH 43212, 614-486-3245, sogoering@columbusmennonite.org [CDC] IIB1 [AC] Co-Pastor, Columbus Menn Ch, Columbus OH

Goertz, Charles G. (Beverly) 966 S Bluebird Ln, Homestead FL 33035, 305-242-4543, Goertz@Bellsouth.net [SE] IB3, IIB1 [AC] Pastor, Homestead Menn Ch, Homestead FL; Urban Minister Director, SE Mennonite Conference, Miami FL

Goertzen, Kevin T. (Denise F.) PO Box 368, Goessel KS 67053, goesselchurch@juno.com [WDC] IIB1 [AC] Pastor, Goessel Menn Ch, Goessel KS

Goldfus, Ross H. (Ruth) 580 HiView Dr, Lititz PA 17543, 717-664-4613, rgoldfus@aol.com [ACC] [RE] Minister of Visitation, Neffsville Mennonite Church, Lancaster PA

Gonsman, Elsie M. (John A.) 1022 Queen Rd, Claysburg PA 16625, 814-239-2566, JGNLC2@wmconnect.com [EDC] IIA [AC] Pastor, Roaring Spring Menn Ch, Duncansville PA

Gonzalez, Jose A., 546 Reading Rd, East Earl PA 17519, 717-445-9752 [LAN] IIB1 [AC]

Gonzalez, Juan (Mercedes) 625 Harrison St, Lancaster PA 17602, 717-396-0346 [LAN] IIB1 [AC] Pastor, El Buen Pastor, Lancaster PA

Good, Charles E. (Susie) 1001 E Oregon Rd K13, Lititz PA 17543-9205, 717-687-6714 [LAN] [RE]

Good, Clair Bennett (Geraldine) 992 Dry Tavern Rd, Denver PA 17517, 717-445-4107 [LAN] IIB1 [AC] Pastor, Churchtown Menn Ch, East Earl PA

Good, Clair E. (Beth) 3004 Hossler Rd, Manheim PA 17545, 717-653-6728, clairg@emm.org [LAN] IIB2, IIB3c [AC] Associate Pastor, Bossler Menn Ch, Elizabethtown PA; Staff Representative to Africa, Eastern Mennonite Missions, Salunga PA

Good, Claude, 215 Wile Ave, Souderton PA 18964, 215-723-0904 [FRC] [RE]

Good, Daniel D. (Lois E.) 1334 N 14th St, Reading PA 19604-1936, 610-375-0208, dan.lois@juno.com [LAN] IIB2 [AC] Associate Pastor, Alsace Christian Fell, Temple PA

Good, Dennis M. (Dorcas Lady) 4724 Sieria St, Riverside CA 92506 [WDC] IIB3c [RE]

Good, Donald W. (Phebe) 3713 Nolt Rd, Landisville PA 17538, 717-898-2500, bsktmore@dejazzd.com [LAN]

IIB2 [AC] Chaplain, Landis Homes, Lititz PA

Good, E. Richard (Wanda) 317 Weavers Rd, Harrisonburg VA 22802, 540-434-4086 [VA] [RE]

Good, Ethan Joseph (Shirley) 4651 Hwy 490, Preston MS 39341-9345, 662-726-5577 [GS] IIB1 [AC] Retiring Pastor, Nanih Waiya Indian Menn Ch, Philadelphia MS

Good, Harley D. (Irene) 1813 Park Rd, Harrisonburg VA 22802, 540-434-0896 [VA] IIB3a [AC]

Good, Harold, 6135 Billymack Rd, Elida OH 45807, 419-339-1906 [OH] [RE]

Good, Harry S. (Alta Mae) 336 W BRd St, New Holland PA 17557-1239, 717-354-2219 [LAN] [RE]

Good, Jacob K. (Elaine) 424 S 7th St, Reading PA 19602, 610-375-9223 [LAN] [RE]

Good, John W. (Phoebe) 1415 Lime Valley Rd, Lancaster PA 17602-1815, 717-687-6360, pgood@desupernet.net [LAN] III [AC] Ordained Deacon, Strasburg Menn Ch, Strasburg PA

Good Jr., Lewis C. (Helen) 9326 Dubarry Ave, Lanham MD 20706-3108, 301-577-3554, lewgood@pressroom.com [LAN] IB3 [AC] Bishop/Overseer, Capital Christian Fell (Wash.-Baltimore), Laurel MD

Good, Linford L. (Velma) 1690 Wheatland School Rd, Lancaster PA 17602, 717-687-0704, Illgood@aol.com [LAN] III [AC] Licensed Deacon, Mellinger Menn Ch, Lancaster PA

Good, Linford W. (Teresa) 424 Park Ave, Milton PA 17847, 570-742-4485, gfamily@ptd.net [LAN] IB3 [AC] Bishop/Overseer, Juniata District/LMC, PA; Bishop/Overseer, LAN-Williamsport-Milton, PA

Good, Melvin S. (Irene) 3004 Hossler Rd, Manheim PA 17545, 717-653-6728, clairg@emm.org [LAN] IIC [AC] Chaplain, Prison Ministry, PA

Good, Merlin, 3535 N Grubb Rd, Elida OH 45807, 419-339-1998 [OH] [RE]

Good, Randy (Carolyn) RR 1 Box 218, Woodstock VT 05091, 802-457-5838, jrccgood@valley.net [FRC] IIA [AC] Pastor, Taftsville Chapel Menn Fell, Taftsville VT

Good, Roy F. (Kathryn Louise) 16 Grandview Dr, Harrisonburg VA 22802, 540-433-8584 [VA] [AC] Interim Pastor, Gospel Hill Menn Ch, Harrisonburg VA

Good, Stephen J. (Carol) 347 S 7th St, Reading PA 19602-2442, 610-374-8590, scjjgood@juno.com [LAN] IIC [AC] Licensed Deacon, South 7th St Menn Ch, Reading PA

Good, Steven Joe (Pamela Liby) 2738 E Charleston Ave, Phoenix AZ 85032, 602-923-7362, sunny_good@juno.com [PSW] IIB1 [AC] Pastor, Sunnyslope Menn Ch, Phoenix AZ

Good, Warren S., 1884 Division Hwy, Ephrata PA 17522-9803, 717-354-9113 [LAN] [RE]

Good, Wilmer Z. (Barbara) 6010 Carters Ln, Riverdale MD 20737, 301-864-8798, wilgood@capitalchristian.org [LAN] IIB2 [AC] Associate Pastor, Capital Christian Fell, Laurel MD

Goossen, Henry William (Edna Marie) Box 372, North Newton KS 67117-0372, 316-283-5963 [WDC] [RE]

Goossen, Paul Franz (Hildegard Marie) 6434 Pine Dr, Rhinelander WI 54501-8735 [CDC] [RE]

Gordon, Andrew T (Randi) 9 Jefferson Ave, Marlton NJ 08053, 609-988-9419, atgoodnews@aol.com [LAN] IIB1 [AC] Pastor, CrossRds Christian Community, Marlton NJ

Gorno, Timothy M. (Phyllis) 13 Silver Creek Rd, Lititz PA 17543, 717-738-2918 [LAN] [AW]

Goshow, Henry, 207 W Summit St Apt 180, Souderton PA 18964, 215-721-3011 [FRC] [RE]

Graber, Dan (Rose Elaine) 3069 Mill Rd, Norristown PA 19403, 610-222-3973, danrose70s@enter.net [EDC] IIB1 [AC] Interim/Transitional Pastor, Zion Menn Ch, Souderton PA

Graber, Daniel J. (Mary M.) 29129 Johnston Rd Apt 2619, Dade City FL 33523-6128, 352-588-4865 [CDC] [RE] Interim Pastor, Deep Run W Menn Ch, Perkasie PA

Graber, David J., PO Box 117, Montgomery IN 47558, 812-486-3451 [IM] [RE]

Graber, Donovan Roy (Jill Rae) 724 Park Ln, RR 1 Box 172, Moundridge KS 67107, 620-345-6424 [WDC] [AW]

Graber, Eddie, RR 3 Box 317, Loogootee IN 47553, 812-636-4181 [IM] IIB1 [AC] Pastor, Berea Menn Ch, Loogootee IN

Graber, Glen D., 1225 Greencroft Dr #223, Goshen IN 46526-5102, 574-537-3527 [CDC] [RE]

Graber, Larry E. (Bonnie) 1653 Lestercove, Springdale AR 72764, 501-631-3904 [SC] III [AC] Minister, Rogers Menn/Ch of the Brethren, Pea Ridge AR

Graber, Melvin Lynn, 311 Wollmann St, Box 894, Moundridge KS 67107 [WDC] IIC [AC]

Graber, Rose Elaine (Dan) 3069 Mill Rd, Norristown PA 19403, 610-222-3973, danrose70s@aol.com [EDC] IIB1 [AC] Pastor, Upper Milford Menn Ch, Zionsville PA

Graham, Reginald C. (Andrea Lynette) 822 E 14th St, Chester PA 19013 [LAN] III [AC] Pastor, Jesus Power and Love Ministries, Claymont DE; Ordained Deacon, Way Thru Christ Ministry, Chester PA

Gray, Albert (June) RD 2, Box 110, Mifflintown PA 17059, 717-436-8585, lighthouse@tricountyi.net [EDC] IIC [AC] Pastor, Cornerstone Community Ch, Mifflintown PA

Gray, John, 20191 Kentville Rd, Tiskilwa IL 61368, 815-646-4620, grayone74@hotmail.com [IL] IIB2 [AC] Associate Pastor, Willow Springs Menn Ch, Tiskilwa IL

Graybill, Carl E. (Sharon) HC 63 Box 38, Cocolamus PA 17014, 717-694-3725 [LAN] [AW]

Graybill, Douglas C. (Leona) RR 1 Box 178A, Granville Summit PA 16926, 570-673-3418, dgraybil@sosbbs.com [LAN] IIB1 [AC] Pastor, Canton Menn Ch, Canton PA

Graybill, Earl R. (Miriam) 5841 Zook Ln, Gap PA 17527-9650 [LAN] [RE]

Graybill, J. Lester (Eileen) 324 Hilltop Dr, Leola PA 17540, 717-656-8267, lgraybil@mindspring.com [ACC] [RE]

Greaser, Lawrence, 1411-7 Kentfield Way, Goshen IN 46526, 574-534-3934 [IM] [RE]

Green, Stanley W., 203 Mount Vernon Dr, Goshen IN 46526, 574-533-4251 [IM] IIB3c [AC] Executive Director, Mennonite Mission Network, Elkhart IN

Green, Tim (Karen) 2502 Ridgedale Rd, Harrisonburg VA 22801, 540-433-1566 [VA] [AW]

Greenawalt, Kimberlee (Tedd) 3306 Harpine Hwy, Harrisonburg VA 22802, 540-833-8043, GKimberlee@aol.com [VA] IIA [AC] Conference Youth Minister, Virginia Mennonite Conference, Harrisonburg VA

Greene, William F. (Cynthia) 475 Northglen Ln, Harrisonburg VA 22802, 540-434-5696 [VA] IIB1 [AC]

Pastor, Crossroads Menn Ch, Broadway VA

Greer, Doris J., 5400 S 11th Ave, Los Angeles CA 90043, 323-292-8503, faithnlovecc@aol.com [PSW] IIB1 [AC]

Greiser, David (Anita Nussbaum) 116 W Chestnut St, Souderton PA 18964, 215-723-7490 [FRC] IIB1 [AC] Senior Teaching Pastor, Souderton Menn Ch, Souderton PA

Grimsrud, Theodore Glenn (Kathleen Janet Temple) 1150 Lincolnshire Dr, Harrisonburg VA 22802, 540-574-4311, grimsrud@emu.edu [VA] IIB3d [AC] Professor of Theology, Eastern Mennonite University, Harrisonburg VA

Groff, Dwight L., 35 S Kinzer Rd, Kinzers PA 17535, 717-442-4901 [LAN] IIB1 [AC] Pastor, Kinzer Menn Ch, Kinzer PA

Groff, Elias H. (Elizabeth) 1520 Harrisburg Pk, Lancaster PA 17601, 717-295-7464 [LAN] [RE]

Groff, Galen (Phyllis) Fray Bartolome de Las Casas, Alta Verapaz 16015, Guatemala, gpgroff@ns.intelnet.net.gt [LAN] IIC [AC] Minister, EMM, Alta Verapaz, Guatemala

Groff, Gwendolyn M. (Robert) Box 145, Bridgewater VT 05035, 802-672-2140, bethanym@sover.net [FRC] IIB1 [AC] Pastor, Bethany Menn Ch, Bridgewater Corners VT

Groff, J. Wesley (Wanda) RR1 Box 131-G, Mt Pleasant Mills PA 17853, 570-539-2575, wgroff@chilitech.net [LAN] IIB2 [AC] Pastor, Susquehanna Menn Ch, Mt Pleasant Mills PA

Groff, Leonard L. (Anna Mary) 756 Bellevue Ave, Gap PA 17527, 717-442-8394, lgroff1460@copper.net [LAN] IIB1 [AC] Pastor, Coatesville Menn Ch, Coatesville PA

Groff, Philip M. (Sharon) 1640 S Cocalico Rd, Denver PA 17517, 717-336-0198 [LAN] IIC [AC] Youth Pastor, Churchtown Menn Ch, East Earl PA

Groff, Weyburn W., 1432 Bradford CT, Goshen IN 46528-5052, 574-533-8554 [IM] [RE]

Groh, David (Mary) PO Box 55, Kalona IA 52247, 319-656-5221 [CP] [RE]

Grosh, Jeffrey A. (Christine Ann) 52 Main St, Yorkanna PA 17402, 717-755-8756, jcgrosh@juno.com [LAN] IIB1 [AC] Pastor, Stony Brook Menn Ch, York PA

Grove, Mary (Stan) 20063 CR 46, New Paris IN 46553-9210, 574-831-2266, stanng@goshen.edu [IM] IIC [AC] Chaplain, Greencroft, Inc., Goshen, IN

Guengerich, Owen, PO Box 198, Springs PA 15562, 814-662-2884 [ALL] [RE]

Guengerich, Ronald D., 1100 Lindau St, Archbold OH 43502, 419-446-1002, rgueng1@bnnorth.net [OH] IIB1 [AC] Pastor, Zion Menn Ch, Archbold OH

Guengerich, Vernard E. (Florence) 25231 SR 119, Goshen IN 46526, 574-862-2521 [IM] IIB2 [AC] Associate Pastor, Holdeman Menn Ch, Wakarusa IN

Guete, Marco A. (Sandra L.) 815 Parkside Dr, Cedar Hill TX 75104-3147, 972-293-2761, marcoguete@aol.com [WDC] IB2 [AC] Associate Conference Minister, Western District Conference, Dallas TX

Gullman, David J. (Deborah) 2336 Mayland Rd, Broadway VA 22815, 540-896-7529, gullman4@juno.com [VA] IIB3a [AC]

Gundy, James Ralph (Marjorie Ann) Box 227, Burrton KS 67020-0237, 620-463-3415, mgundy1@cox.net [WDC] IIB1 [AC] Pastor, Burrton Menn Ch, Burrton KS

Gustafson-Zook, Gwen Ann (Les) 1608 S 8th St, Goshen IN 46526-4704, 574-534-1173, gustazook@aol.com [CDC, IM] IIB1 [AC] Pastor, Faith Menn Ch, Goshen IN

MINISTERS

6

Gutierrez, Luis (Nancy Salazar) Tio Ave: Jorge Chavez M-1-1, san francisco 138 interior, Cusco 708, Peru, 239905, luisgu@latinmail.com [LAN] IIA [AC]

Guyton, Cynthia A. (Glen) 3510 Mallow Ct, Chesapeake VA 23321, 757-722-0238 [VA] IIB2 [AC]

Guyton, Glen A. (Cynthia) 3510 Mallow Ct, Chesapeake VA 23321, 757-722-0238 [VA] IIB2 [AC]

H

Haarer, Charles, 605 Woodbridge Ct, Middlebury IN 46540, 574-825-5339 [IM] [RE]

Haarer, Lowell W. (Miriam) 8997 Mt Zion Rd, Linville VA 22834, 540-833-4753, lowellhaarer@juno.com [VA] IIB1 [AC] Pastor, Zion Hill Menn Ch, Singers Glen VA

Haarer, Verlin (Doris) 16901 Hand Rd, Huntertown IN 46748, 260-637-2309, dove9@juno.com [IM] IIB1 [AC] Pastor, Carroll Community Worship Center, Fort Wayne IN

Habegger, David Luther (LaVeta) 219 Sutton Dr, Newton KS 67114, 316-283-1061 [WDC] [RE]

Habegger, Howard J. (Marlene J.) 613 S Main, Hesston KS 67062, 620-327-5092 [WDC] [RE]

Habegger, Loris A. (Evelyn J.) 86 22nd Ave, Moundridge KS 67107-7005 [WDC] [RE]

Hadtasunsern, Chaiya (Aranya Khoklasutchai) Village Ridge 3, 18th St NW Apt 124, Hickory NC 28601 [VA] IIA [AC] Associate Pastor, Hickory Menn Ch, Hickory NC

Haines, Elaine (Joseph M.) 5225 Harris Hill Rd, Williamsville NY 14221, 716-688-6867, joselahai@aol.com [NY] IIC [AC] Co-Pastor, Harris Hill Menn Ch, Williamsville NY

Haines, Joseph M. (Elaine) 112 Huntleigh Cr, Amherst NY 14226, 716-725-9581, joselahai@aol.com [NY] IIB1 [AC] Co-Pastor, Harris Hill Menn Ch, Williamsville NY

Hall, David L. (Carol A.) 1322 Edison St NW, Hartville OH 44632, 330-877-4385 [OH] IIB1 [AC] Pastor, Hartville Menn Ch, Hartville OH

Hallman, Willis (Kathryn) 11305 Norton, Kansas City MO 64137, 816-763-4637; 816-942-1441 (office) [WDC] [RE]

Hampton, Timothy S. (Chris) 9506 Highlander Cr, Walkersville MD 21793, timh98@juno.com [FRK] IIC [AC] Pastor, Faith Community Menn Ch, Walkersville MD; Church Planter, Franklin Mennonite Conference

Hamsher, Bruce Allen (Jocelyn Marie) PO Box 93, Berlin OH 44610, 330-893-0418, brujoc@aol.com [OH] IIB2 [AC] Associate Pastor, Berlin Menn Ch, Berlin OH

Hamsher, Don, 169 N Walnut, Davidsville PA 15928, 814-479-2702, hamsher@valkyrie.net [ALL] IIB1 [AC] Pastor, Kaufman Menn Ch, Davidsville PA

Hamsher, Matthew W. (Kristina Zendt) 850 Geneva St, Sugarcreek OH 44681, 330-852-1086 [OH] [AW]

Handoyo, Virgo, 1632 Locust St, Pasadena CA 91106, 626-564-9869, vhandojo@calbaptist.edu [PSW] IIB1 [AC] Pastor, Jemaat Kristen Indonesia Anugrah, Pasadena CA

Handrich, Bruce, PO Box 25, Germfask MI 49836, 906-586-9738 [IM] [RE]

Handrich, Ellsworth, PO Box 215, Fairview MI 48621, 517-848-2322 [IM] [RE]

Handrich, Willard D., PO Box 271, Grand Marais MI 49839, 906-494-2547 [IM] [RE]

Hang, Tong (Pai K) 7827 Rimbley Rd, Woodbury, MN 55125, 651-501-0836 [CP] [AW]

Hange, Maren Tyedmers (Roy) 102 Linda Ct, Charlottesville VA 22901, 434-296-5289, pastorcmc@earthlink.net [VA] IIB1 [AC] Co-Pastor, Charlottesville Menn Ch, Charlottesville VA

Hange, Roy (Maren Tyedmers) 102 Linda Ct, Charlottesville VA 22901, 434-296-5289, pastorcmc@earthlink.net [VA] IIB1 [AC] Co-Pastor, Charlottesville Menn Ch, Charlottesville VA

Hanger, T. Kirk, 6572 Yadkin Ct, Alexandria VA 22310 [FRC] IIB1 [AC] Church Planter, New Hope Fell of Alexandria, Alexandria VA

Hankee, Bruce W. (Janet Louise) c/o Greenmonte Mennonite Church, 1661 Cold Springs Rd, Stuarts Draft VA 24477, brucehankee@hotmail.com [VA] IIB1 [AC] Pastor, Greenmonte Menn Ch, Stuarts Draft VA

Hannanoto, Buddy, 1419 S 3rd St, Alhambra CA 91803, 626-588-2102, bususy@netzero.com [PSW] IIA [AC] Pastor, Indonesian Worship Ch, Alhambra CA

Harder, Keith R. (Judy) 951 190th, Hillsboro KS 67063-8019, 620-947-2510 [WDC] IB1 [AC] Director of Congregational & Ministerial Leadership Team, Mennonite Church USA, Newton KS

Harder, Leland David (Bertha F.) PO Box 363, North Newton KS 67117-0363, 316-283-0186 [WDC] [RE]

Harder, Lois, 868 Vandalia Rd, Morgantown WV 26505, 304-328-5510 [ALL] IIB3a [AC]

Harder, Lois M. (Thomas Lee) 654 S Chautauqua, Wichita KS 67211, 316-687-4151, tlharder@juno.com [WDC] IIB1 [AC] Co-Pastor, Lorraine Ave Menn Ch, Wichita KS

Harder, Milton J. (Katharine Moyer) RR 1 Box 66, Deer Creek OK 74636, 580-267-3544 [WDC] [RE]

Harder, Thomas L. (Lois M.) 654 S Chautauqua, Wichita KS 67211, tlharder@juno.com [WDC] IIB1 [AC] Co-Pastor, Lorraine Ave Menn Ch, Wichita KS

Harder, Willmar Toews, 47 13th Ave, Inman KS 67546, wtharder@hotmail.com [WDC] IIB1 [AC] Pastor, Hoffnungsau Menn Ch, Inman KS

Harding, Dorothy, 5218 Goldcrest Trace, Stone Mountain GA 30088 [SE] IIC [AC] Minister of Urban Evangelism, Berea Menn Ch, Atlanta GA

Harms, Dawn Yoder (Douglas Paul) 226 W Main St, Ephrata PA 17522, 717-733-4522 [ACC] IIB2 [AC] Pastor, Akron Menn Ch, Akron PA

Harms, Loanne (Len) 811 N Main St, Goshen IN 46528, 574-533-9983 [IM] IIA [AC] Minister to Youth, Waterford Menn Ch, Goshen IN

Harnish, Sr., John H. (Ruth) 156 Victoria Rd, Millersville PA 17551-9762, 717-872-8680 [LAN] [RE]

Harnish Jr., John Henry (Judy) 3731 Blue Rock Rd, Washington Boro PA 17582, 717-872-4450, jhh1346@aol.com [LAN] III [AC] Ordained Deacon, Millersville Menn Ch, Millersville PA

Harnish, Marion Elaine (Marvin) 327 N Reservoir St, Lancaster PA 17602, 717-399-8830, meharnishx2@cs.com [LAN] IIC [AC] Chaplain, Evergreen Estates, Lancaster PA

Harnish, Paul K. (Anna) 2000 Franklin Rd, Washington Boro PA 17582, 717-684-8691 [LAN] [RE]

Harnish, Robert A. (Marian N.) 2179 Beaver Valley Pk, New Providence PA 17560-9605, 717-872-6704, bobharnish@epix.net [LAN] IIB1 [AC] Pastor, New Providence Menn Ch, New Providence PA

Harnish, Robert Brunk (Carol) 1609 Carnavon Pl, Colorado Springs CO 80919, 719-277-7086 [RM] [AW]

Harnish, Robert L. (Ruth) 611 E Center St, Eureka IL 61530, 309-467-4452, Bob@Maple-Lawn.com [IL] IIB3a [RE]

Harnly, Lester M. (Mary) 7 Central Pk Dr Ste 110, Manheim PA 17545, 717-665-3104 [LAN] [RE]

Harris, Doug, PO Box 403, Montezuma KS 67867, 620-846-2663, erdwko@yahoo.com [SC, WDC] IIA [AC] Pastor, Gospel Fell Ch, Montezuma KS

Harrison, Daniel, Leadership Development International, PO Box 4152, Evergreen CO 80437 [IM] IIB3b [AC] President, Leadership Development International, PO Box 4152, Evergreen CO

Hart, Lawrence H. (Betty E.) 2501 E Modelle Ave, Clinton OK 73601-9358, 580-323-5320 [WDC] [AC] Pastor, Koinonia Menn Ch, Clinton OK

Hartman, Darwin, 1324 Linwood, Weatherford OK 73096 [SC] [AC] Pastor, Pleasant View Menn Ch, Hydro OK

Hartman, Gene A. (Cynthia A.) PO Box 502, Topeka IN 46573, 260-593-3726, genhart@maplenet.net [IM] IIB1 [AC] Pastor, Emma Menn Ch, Topeka IN

Hartman, Peter E. (Marilyn) 706 Wheat Ln, Hesston KS 67062 [SC] [RE]

Hartman, Wilmer J. (Lois) 1013 Olds Ln, Archbold OH 43502, 419-445-6329, whartman@juno.com [OH] [AW]

Hartshorn, C. Leo (Iris DeLeon-Hartshorn) 202 S Ann St, Lancaster PA 17602-4315, 717-391-6512, cleohart@aol.com [EDC] IIB3c [AC] Minister of Peace and Justice, Mennonite Mission Network, Elkhart IN

Hartwell, Bill, 3105 Maplewood Blvd #73, Omaha NE 68134, 402-573-5601 [CP] IIB3a [AC] Chaplain, Nebraska Prisons, Omaha NE

Hartzler, Robert Lee (Phyllis Jean) 605 Northridge Ct, Wayland IA 52654, 319-256-4494, rhartz@farmtel.net [CP] IIB1 [AC]

Harwood, Bret (Leonora) 34 Cottage Ave, Lancaster PA 17602-3212, 717-295-4555, mednetbrett@juno.com [LAN] IIC [AC]

Haryono, Petrus, 7707 White Oak Ave, Reseda CA 91335, 818-342-6777, haryono@juno.com [PSW] IIB1 [AC] Pastor, Jemaat Kristen Indonesia Maranatha, Reseda CA

Hatfield, Maria (Jason) 2810 N Rustic Ridge Dr, Peoria IL 61604, 309-685-0094, pastoramariah@sbcglobal.net [CDC, IL] IIA [AC] Pastor, Living Love Ministries, Peoria IL

Hathaway, Melvin R. (Dottie B.) 3935 Allentown Rd, Elida OH 45807, 419-331-4971, hathaway@wcoil.com [OH] IIB1 [AC] Pastor, Salem Menn Ch, Elida OH

Hauder, Larry (Rebecca S.) 2102 N 20th St, Boise ID 83702-0831, 208-344-3331, lhauder@earthlink.net [PNW] [AW]

Haupert, Stephen Andrew (Phoebe) 239 Slacks Run Rd, Trout Run PA 17771, 570-995-5620, prov356@uplink.net [LAN] IB3 [AC] Bishop/Overseer, North Penn District, PA

Hayes, Benjamin R. (Christine) 119 Vista Dr, Mifflinburg PA 17844, 570-966-9636, bhayes@sunlink.net [LAN] IIB2 [AC] Co-Pastor, Buffalo Menn Ch, Lewisburg PA

Heacock, Randy E. (Nancy J.) 2193 Winterberry Ct, Warrington PA 18976, 215-343-7099, randy.heacock@doylestownmc.org [FRC] IIB1 [AC] Pastor, Doylestown Menn Ch, Doylestown PA

Headrick, Don, 2202 Chatalet Ln, Pueblo CO 81005, 717-564-0649 [RM] IIB3a [AC] Prison Chaplain, Colorado State Prison, Canon City CO

Heatwole, Edwin M. (Eileen K.) 8735 Union Springs Rd, Dayton VA 22821, 540-867-5216, eheatwole@yahoo.com [VA] IIB1 [AC] Pastor, New Beginnings Ch, Bridgewater VA

Heatwole, Steven Jay (Bonnie) PO Box 127, Springs PA 15562, 814-662-2507 [ALL] IB3, IIB1 [AC] Pastor, Springs Menn Ch, Springs PA

Hedrick, Merlin, 605 Rte 113, Sellersville PA 18960, 215-723-6878 [FRC] IIB3a [AC] Chaplain, Dock Woods Community, Lansdale PA

Hege, Nathan B. (Arlene) 655 Church St, Landisville PA 17538, 717-898-0463 [LAN] [RE]

Heimbach, Albert W. (Mary) 521 Mill Rd, Selinsgrove PA 17870, 570-374-1713 [LAN] IIB2 [AC] Associate Pastor, Susquehanna Menn Ch, Mt Pleasant Mills PA

Heinlein, Chris (Carol) RR 2 Box 147, Mount Union PA 17066, 814-543-7269 [ALL] IIB1 [AC]

Heiser, Don J. (Betty L.) 19093 Rock Rd, New Paris IN 46553, 574-831-3427 [CDC] [RE]

Heisey, Dean (Tacy) 13060 Jackson Rd, Mishawaka IN 46544, 574-254-1554 [IM] IIB3c [AC] Dir Ch Rel & Partnership Formation, Mennonite Church USA, Elkhart IN

Heistand, Gerald M., 329 Trail Rd S, Elizabethtown PA 17022, 717-367-8587, g-heistand@juno.com [LAN] IIB1 [AC] Pastor, Risser Menn Ch, Elizabethtown PA

Heller, Fred G. (Julie) 250 Keener Rd, Lititz PA 17543-9604, 717-626-2649 [LAN] IIB1 [AC] Associate Pastor, Hammer Creek Menn Ch, Lititz PA

Heller, Parke M. (Charity) 228 Keener Rd, Lititz PA 17543, 717-626-5146 [LAN] [RE]

Helmus, Linda S. (David) 540 Eastside Dr, Lancaster PA 17601, lindah.lmc@verizon.net [LAN] IIC [AC] Minister of Pastoral Care, Landisville Menn Ch, Landisville PA

Helmuth, David (Naomi) 1118 S 7th St, Goshen IN 46526, 574-534-2576, helmuthdavid@hotmail.com [CDC, IM] [RE] Overseer, Iglesia Menonita del Buen Pastor, Goshen IN

Helmuth, Noah B. (Edna) 711 14th St, Kalona IA 52247, 319-656-4467 [VA] [RE]

Helmuth, Phillip N. (Loretta) 1141 Shenandoah St, Harrisonburg VA 22801, 540-433-5622 [VA] IIB3c [AC]

Helton Jr., Ova, 8753 Daly Rd, Cincinnati OH 45231, 513-522-1882, ohelton@fuse.net [OH] IIB1 [AC] Pastor, Springdale Chapel, Cincinnati OH

Henderson, Eric B. (Marilyn) 467 S Erisman Rd, Manheim PA 17545, 717-653-8316 [LAN] [AW]

Henderson, Richard, 16205 Glendale Ave, Cleveland OH 44128, 216-561-0637 [OH] IIC [AC] Associate Pastor, Lee Heights Community Ch, Cleveland OH

Henderson, Scott Anthony (Melissa Dawne) 212 Faith St, Jefferson OR 97352, 541-327-3554, pastorscott@plainview.org [PNW] IIA [AC] Youth Pastor, Plainview Menn Ch, Albany OR

Hendricks, Melvin E., Box 197, Carlock IL 61725, 309-376-7281 [CDC] [RE]

Hernández Jr., José R. (Rinna E.) 16130 SW 304 Terrace, Homestead FL 33033, 305-248-1279, Joseram@bellsouth.net [SE] IC, IIC [AC] Associate Pastor, Homestead Menn Ch, Homestead FL; Hispanic Advocate, SE Mennonite Conference, Homestead FL

Hernández, Luis (Diana) 19 Clarendon, Lancaster PA

17603, 717-394-7007 [LAN] IIA [AC] Pastor, Luz de Salvación, Lebanon PA

Hernández, Martha (Ramiro) 29725 SW Rose Ln #139, Wilsonville OR 97070, 503-682-9116 [PNW] IIA [AW]

Hernández, Ramiro (Martha Corpus) 746 S 10th Ave, Washington IA 52353, 319-653-6540 [CP] IIB1 [AC] Pastor, Iglesia Roca de Salvación, Washington IA

Herr, H. Eugene (Mary) 708 Normandy Rd, Newton KS 67114-1257 [SC] [RE]

Herr, Mary (H. Eugene) 708 Normandy Rd, Newton KS 67114-1257 [SC] [RE]

Herrera, Gerardo (Sandra) 12028 Bluhill Rd, Wheaton MD 20902, 301-933-8929 [VA] [AW]

Hershberger, Cheryl, 22 Pheasant Run Rd, Hesston KS 67062-9123, 620-327-4768, cherylh@dtnspeed.net [SC] IIB2 [AC] Associate Pastor, Hesston Menn Ch, Hesston KS

Hershberger, Delvin (Michele) 300 S Main St, Hesston KS 67062, 620-327-0579, Dmhersh@aol.com [SC] IIB3c [AC]

Hershberger, Duane (Ruth Ann) 403 E Third St, Boyertown PA 19512, 610-367-2879, DHershberger@hfhi.org [FRC] IIB1 [AC] Pastor, Shalom Christian Fell, East Greenville PA

Hershberger, Ernest, PO Box 214, Berlin OH 44610, 330-893-2098 [OH] IIB1 [AC] Pastor, Berlin Menn Ch, Berlin OH

Hershberger, Gregory L. (Lois I.) 524 S 16th St, Columbia PA 17512, 717-684-5935, ghershberg@aol.com [LAN] IIB1 [AC] Pastor, Columbia Menn Ch, Columbia PA

Hershberger, James L., 5647 Wengers Mill Rd, Linville VA 22834, 540-833-8033, hershberg1@aol.com [VA] IIB1 [AC] Pastor, Beldor Menn Ch, Linville VA

Hershberger, John K. (Diana) 1706 S 13th St, Goshen IN 46526, 574-533-9982 [IM] IIB3a [AC] Counselor, Oaklawn, Inc, Goshen IN

Hershberger, Marc (Jennifer) 1472 260th St, Mount Pleasant IA 52641, 319-986-6162 [CP] IIB1 [AC] Pastor, Pleasant View Menn Ch, Mount Pleasant IA

Hershberger, Mervin (Judith) 3711 Metropolitan Ave, Kansas City KS 66106, 913-677-0249, ArgentineMenn@aol.com [SC] IIB1 [AC] Pastor, Argentine Menn Ch, Kansas City KS

Hershberger, Virgil S. (Margaret) 1549 N Abbe Rd Box 100, Fairview MI 48621, 517-848-2417 [IM] [RE]

Hershey, Carl E. (Doris) 25 Main St, Landisville PA 17538, 717-898-1737, dhersh48@aol.com [LAN] IIB1 [AC] Pastor, Chestnut Hill Menn Ch, Columbia PA

Hershey, Clair J. (Dorothy) 2090 Jarvis Rd, Lancaster PA 17601, 717-393-7077 [LAN] [RE]

Hershey, Glenn C. (Helen) 121A N New Holland Rd, Gordonville PA 17529, 717-354-9951, glennhelen@juno.com [LAN] [AW]

Hershey, J. Kenneth (Joanne Campbell) 24 Hawthorne Cr, Willow Street PA 17584, 717-284-3841, JFCH29@aol.com [LAN] IIB2 [AC] Associate Pastor, New Providence Menn Ch, New Providence PA

Hershey, John O. (Dorothy) 1001 E Oregon Rd, Lititz PA 17543 [LAN] [RE]

Hershey, Kurt Eugene (Rachel) 5264 Lincoln Hwy, Gap PA 17527, 717-442-0804 [LAN] IIA [AC] Associate Pastor, Parkesburg Menn Ch, Parkesburg PA

Hershey, Lester T., PO Box 1160, Fort Ashby WV 26719,

304-298-4452, lthersh1@prodigy.net [ALL] IIB1 [AC] Associate Pastor, Pinto Menn Ch, Pinto MD

Hershey, Melvin L. (Anna) 152 Iris Dr, Lancaster PA 17602, 717-392-1558 [LAN] [RE]

Hershey, Nelson H. (Thelma) 420 Rohrer Rd, Mountville PA 17554-1818, 717-285-5030 [LAN] [RE]

Hershey, Noah L. (Alta Mary Metzler) 8875 N Moscow Rd, Parkesburg PA 19365-9802, 717-442-4629 [LAN] [RE]

Hershey, Phoebe, 27877 Old Valley Pk, Toms Brook VA 22660, 540-436-9481 [VA] IIB3a [AC]

Hershey, Sanford E. (Mae) 3728 Ridge Rd, Gordonville PA 17529, 717-768-8602 [LAN] [RE]

Hershey, William E. (Diane) 26 Ferncrest Rd, Quarryville PA 17566, 717-548-3757 [LAN] IIC [AC] Associate Pastor, Mechanic Grove Menn Ch, Peach Bottom PA

Hertzler, Daniel (Mary) RR 1 Box 576, Scottdale PA 15683, 724-887-7598 [ALL] IB3 [AC]

Hertzler, Joseph, 2731 Pleasant Plain Ave, Elkhart IN 46517, 574-293-8358 [IM] [RE]

Hess, Donald W. (Diane) 27 Cherokee Rd, Willow Street PA 17584, 717-464-4506, ddhess71@juno.com [LAN] IIC, III [AC] Licensed Deacon, New Danville Menn Ch, Lancaster PA

Hess, Ernest M. (Lois) 1709 Newport Dr, Lancaster PA 17602-1309, 717-464-3505, elhess@infionline.net [LAN] IB3 [AC] Bishop/Overseer, LMC New Danville District, PA

Hess, J. Brent (Julie) 1068 Central Manor Rd, Lancaster PA 17603-9484, brenthess@onemain.com [LAN] [AW]

Hess, James R. (Beatrice) 77 Highland Dr, Lancaster PA 17602-3336, 717-393-7348, hessjb@aol.com [LAN] [RE]

Hess, James R. (Helen Keener) 445 Yeagley Rd, Meyerstown PA 17067-1786, 717-933-8470, helen-jimhess@juno.lcom [LAN] [RE]

Hess, John C. (Anna Mary) 5834 Country Rd 2B, Belmont NY 14813, 716-268-7415 [LAN] III [AC] Ordained Deacon, Kossuth Community Chapel, Bolivar NY

Hess, Mahlon M. (Mary Harnish) 1001 E Oregon Rd, Lititz PA 17543, 717-509-5883, mahlonhess@juno.com [LAN] [RE]

Hess, Marshall (Karen) 2317 Conley Ln, Lancaster PA 17603, 717-872-9749 [LAN] IIC, III [AC] Licensed Deacon, New Danville Menn Ch, Lancaster PA

Hess, Thomas A. (Janice) 9310 Old 22, Bethel PA 19507, 717-933-8434, phess@ptd.net [LAN] IIB1 [AC] Pastor, Schubert Menn Ch, Bethel PA

Heusinkveld, David Scott (Gail Patricia) 1107 S 7th St, Goshen IN 46526, 574-537-8442, dagaheu@earthlink.net [IM] [AW]

Heyerly, John Ernest (Jeanne C.) 24955 Church St, Chenoa IL 61726-9391, 309-747-3256, heyerly@gridcom.net [CDC] IIB1 [AC] Pastor, Meadows Menn Ch, Chenoa IL

Hicks, Richard Douglas (Elaine K.) 5101 Georgetown Rd, Washington IL 61571, 309-444-2999, doug@maple-lawn.com [IL] IIC [AC] Pastor, Maple Lawn Fell, Eureka IL

Hickson, Mark C. (De Anna) 625 Walnut St, Coatesville PA 19320, 610-383-1921 [LAN] IIB1 [AC] Pastor, Coatesville Menn Ch, Coatesville PA

Higgins, William S. (Stacey) 19510 NE Glisan, Portland OR 97230, 503-667-9115, peacemennonite@juno.com [PNW] IIB1 [AC] Pastor, Peace Menn Ch, Portland OR

High Jr., David F. (Rebecca) 995 N Penryn Rd, Manheim

PA 17545-8515, 717-665-7967 [LAN] IIC [AC] Licensed Deacon, Erb Menn Ch, Lititz PA

High, Jeffery L. (Janet) 705 Hopeland Rd, PO Box 142, Hopeland PA 17533, 717-733-4390, jhigh5@juno.com [LAN] IIC [AC] Leadership Team, Ephrata Menn Ch, Ephrata PA

High, Levi G. (Elizabeth) 3454 Bimini St, Sarasota FL 34239-7421 [LAN] [RE]

Himes, Kevin S. (Jennifer Janene) 982 Marilyn Dr, Wooster OH 44691, 330-262-8369, himesks@hotmail.com [CDC] IIA [AC] Minister of Music, Salem Menn Ch, Kidron OH

Hinojosa, Conrado (Esther) 2408 Fern Dr, San Juan TX 78589-3879, conrado_hinojosa@hotmail.com [SC] IB3 [AC] Pastor, Iglesia Menonita Buenas Nuevas, San Juan TX

Hochstedler, Jarvis (Ruby Lee) RR 2 Box 445, Montgomery IN 47558, 812-486-2443 [IM] IIB1 [AC] Interim Pastor, Providence Menn Ch, Montgomery IN

Hochstedler, Kathryn J. (Wayne) 2440 Ebersole Rd, Harrisonburg VA 22802, 540-438-9454, kjhoch@aol.com [VA] IIB2 [AC] Associate Pastor, Harrisonburg Menn Ch, Harrisonburg VA

Hochstetler, David (Anna) W1216 CR B, Stone Lake WI 54876, 715-865-5403, davanna@centurytel.net [NC] IIB1 [AC] Pastor, Sand Lake Menn Chapel, Stone Lake WI

Hochstetler, Dean, 13684 N SR 19, Nappanee IN 46550, 574-773-4915 [IM] IIB3b [AC] Bondage & Deliverance Committee, IN-MI Mennonite Conference, Goshen IN

Hochstetler, Emery (Audry) 755 Elliott Ct, Iowa City IA 52246, 319-628-4174 [CP] [RE]

Hochstetler, Harold (Lydia) 4721 Becker Cr SE, Albany OR 97321, 541-928-9474, harold@transport.com [PNW] [RE]

Hochstetler, Lois (Wayne C.) 1324 E Vernon Ave, Normal IL 61761-3266, 309-862-9061, lohoch@mindspring.com [CDC, IL] IIB3a [AC] Pastoral Counselor, BroMenn Counseling Center, Bloomington IL

Hochstetler, M. Clair (Carole Anne Stanton) 603 Gra-Roy Dr Apt 4, Goshen IN 46526, 574-537-1907, clair@freewheeling.com [CDC] IIB3a [AC]

Hochstetler, Marc, 4725 Township Rd 354, Millersburg OH 44654, 330-674-0963, wallykyt@yahoo.com [OH] IIA [AC] Pastor, Moorhead Menn Ch, Millersburg OH

Hochstetler, Noah, Box 34, Dangriga, Belize [IM] IIB3b [AC] Missionary, Mennonite Mission Agency, Belize, Central America

Hochstetler, Ritch (Char) 104 E Lincoln, Hesston KS 67062, 620-327-3052 [IM] IIB3d [AC] Director of Education, Oakwood Academy IN

Hochstetler, Roger L. (Glennis.) 6173 W 75th Ave, Arvada CO 80003, 303-403-4280 [RM] [RE]

Hochstetler, Wayne C. (Lois King) 1324 E Vernon Ave, Normal IL 61761-3266, 309-268-9268, ilconmin@mindspring.com [CDC, IL] IB2 [AC] Conference Minister, Illinois churches—Central District, Bloomington IL

Hockman, John Edward (Joan Lattimore) 425 S Hillcrest Ct, PO Box 297, Topeka IN 46571, 260-593-3701, hockman@kuntrynet.com [CDC] IIB1 [AC] Pastor, Topeka Menn Ch, Topeka IN

Hoffer, Jeffrey W. (Jan) 340 N George St, Millersville PA 17551, 717-872-5540, Jjhoffer@aol.com [LAN] [AW]

Hoffman, Philip (Edna) RR 1 Box 136, Gulliver MI 49840, 906-283-3117 [IM] IIB1 [AC] Pastor, Maple Grove Menn Ch, Gulliver MI

Hoffman, Verle, 23675 River Manor Blvd, Elkhart IN 46516, 574-875-7715 [IM] [RE]

Hollinger, Aaron H. (Marian) 219 Clematis Ct, New Holland PA 17557, 717-354-7572 [LAN] [RE]

Hollinger, Clyde M. (Elaine) 34 Twin Brook Rd, Lititz PA 17543, 717-626-0427, cedel@supernet.com [LAN] IIA [AC] Associate Pastor, Millport Menn Ch, Leola PA

Hollinger, Dennis P. (Mary Ann) 441 N 25th St, Camp Hill PA 17011-2102, dphmah@aol.com [LAN] [AW]

Hollinger, J. Clair (Lois) 265 E Noble St, Lititz PA 17543, 717-626-0517 [LAN] [RE]

Hollinger, Jeryl (Mary) 127 Browns Gulch Rd, Kalispell MT 59901, 406-755-3920, jhollinger@montana.com [PNW] IIB1 [AC] Pastor, Mountain View Menn Ch, Kalispell MT

Hollinger, L. Kenneth (Rosene) 4 Crestview Dr, Akron PA 17501, 717-859-4593 [LAN] III [AC] Ordained Deacon, Ephrata Menn Ch, Ephrata PA

Hollinger, Lloyd L. (Edith Marie) 1001 E Oregon Rd, Lititz PA 17543 [LAN] [RE]

Hollinger, Philip R. (Linda) 1732 Weaverland Rd, East Earl PA 17519, 717-445-5486 [LAN] III [AC] Ordained Deacon, Churchtown Menn Ch, East Earl PA

Holsopple, Elvin (Rena) 648 Sugar Maple Ave, Hollsopple PA 15935, 814-479-4638 [ALL] [RE]

Hoober, Kristen, 916 S 7th St, Goshen IN 46526, 574-535-0610, kristen@collegemennonite.org [IM] IIB2 [AC] Youth Pastor, College Menn Ch, Goshen IN

Hook, Andrew, PO Box 271, Dalton OH 44618, andyhookedonjesus@yahoo.com [OH] IIA [AC] Youth Pastor, Martins Menn Ch, Orrville OH

Hooley, Daniel, 1939 3rd St SE, Canton OH 44707, 330-453-1015, danhooley@sbcglobal.net [OH] IIB1 [AC] Pastor, First Menn Ch of Canton, Canton OH

Hooley, Gary Dean (Miriam Jean) 945 Catalpa St, Sweet Home OR 97386, 541-367-5657, rol@centurytel.net [PNW] IIB1 [AC] Pastor, River of Life Fell, Sweet Home OR

Hooley, William D. (Edith) 68080 CR 29, New Paris IN 46553, 574-831-4708 [IM] IB3 [AC] Overseer, Shore Mennonite, Shipshewana IN; Overseer, College Mennonite, Goshen IN; Overseer, Emma Mennonite, Topeka IN

Hoopert, Daniel, 6220 Townsend Ln, Waxhaw NC 28173 [VA] IIB3b [AW]

Hoover, Abram N. (Jean) 710 Horseshoe Pk, Lebanon PA 17042-4842, 717-867-4495 [LAN] [RE]

Hoover, Daryl L. (Jenn) 106 S Sixth St, Akron PA 17501, 717-951-6133, dnjhoover@juno.com [LAN] IIC [AC] Elder of Worship, Carpenter Community Ch, Talmage PA

Hoover, Glenn A. (Virginia) 78 N Church St SW, Ephrata PA 17522, 717-859-2347, glennhoo@juno.com [LAN] IIB1 [AC] Pastor, Carpenter Community Ch, Talmage PA

Hoover, Jon R. (Jacqueline Y.) jonhoover@hotmail.com [ACC] IIB3b [AC] Mission Worker, Near East School of Theology, Beirut PO Box 13-5780 Chouran, Beirut 1102 2070 Lebanon

Hoover, Lester M. (Anna) 1001 E Oregon Rd, Lititz PA 17543-9205, 717-560-3506, hoover_lm@juno.com [LAN] [RE]

Hoover, Lloyd E. (Elaine) 30 Hoover Ln, Leola PA 17540,

717-656-3464 [LAN] IB3 [AC]

Hoover, Pearl Ann, 3918 Penderview Dr #432, Fairfax VA 22033-4797, 703-246-9124, nvmc1@juno.com [VA] IIB1 [AC] Pastor, Northern Virginia Menn Ch, Fairfax VA

Hoover, Saralee M. (Thomas R.) 915 Washington St, Reading PA 90601, 610-374-7842, smartinhoover@aol.com [LAN] IIC [AC] Associate Pastor, South 7th St Menn Ch, Reading PA

Hoover, Thomas R. (Saralee M.) 915 Washington St, Reading PA 19601, 610-374-7842, TomRHoover@aol.com [LAN] IIC [AC] Associate Pastor, South 7th St Menn Ch, Reading PA

Hopson, Helen M., 561 Rockhurst St, Buda TX 78610, 512-295-5410, hm.hopson@lycos.com [WDC] IIB3a [AC] Associate Director, Dept. of Pastoral Care, Austin State Hospital, Austin TX

Horiuchi, Paul Tadashi, 1720 Huna Apt 205, Honolulu HI 96817, 808-521-4838 [LAN] IIA [AC] Associate Pastor, New Life Christian Fell, Honolulu HI

Horner, Carl (Stephanie R.) 29484 CR 36, Wakarusa IN 46573, 574-862-1403, carlhorner@juno.com [IM] IIB1 [AC] Pastor, Shore Menn Ch, Shipshewana IN

Horner, Glen A. (Thelma Elaine) 510 Redbud Ln, Middlebury IN 46540, 574-825-3985, gthorner@prodigy.net [IM] [RE]

Horner, Thelma (Glen A.) 510 Redbud Ln, Middlebury IN 46540, g2horner@aol.com [IM] [RE]

Horning, Alvin B. (Roberta) 2680 Conestoga Creek Rd, Morgantown PA 19543, 610-286-9851, alvin107@juno.com [ACC] IIB1 [AC] Pastor, Conestoga Menn Ch, Morgantown PA

Horning, Carl E. (Erma) 595 Wedgewood Dr, Lebanon PA 17042-8832, 717-202-0400, chorning@comcast.net [LAN] IB3 [AC] Interim Bishop, Ephrata District/LMC, PA; Assistant Moderator, Lancaster Mennonite Conference, Lancaster PA; Bishop/Overseer, LMC Lebanon District, PA

Horning, J. Ronald (Karen) 1727 Bowmansville Rd, Mohnton PA 19540, 717-445-4348, karon@dejazzd.com [LAN] IIC [AC] Youth Pastor, Weaverland Menn Ch, East Earl PA

Horning, James S. (Jean) 842 Ballstown Rd, Lititz PA 17543-8550, 717-625-0297, jimhorning@juno.com [LAN] III [AC] Ordained Deacon, Carpenter Community Ch, Talmage PA

Horning Sr., Kenneth L. (Selena) 5 St Paulia Ln, Oley PA 19547, 610-987-9833, kshorning@enter.net [ACC] [RE]

Horning, Kevin E. (Melanie) 219 Country Ln, Denver PA 17517, 717-445-5548, nlfephrata@juno.com [LAN] IIB2 [AC] Pastor, New Life Fell, Ephrata PA

Horsch, James E. (Ruth A. Emerson) 1404 Pembroke Cr Apt 3, Goshen IN 46526, 574-534-4609, jrhorsch@Maplenet.net [IM] IIB3c [AC] Editor, Faith & Life Resources/MPN, Goshen IN

Horst, Aaron M., Garden Spot Village Apt 338, 433 S Kinzer Ave, New Holland PA 17557, 717-355-6843 [LAN] [RE]

Horst, Aaron Z. (Loretta) 270 Panorama Dr, Denver PA 17517, 717-445-4189 [LAN] III [AC] Ordained Deacon, Lichty Menn Ch, New Holland PA

Horst, Aden, 56864 Pinecrest Dr, Elkhart IN 46516, 574-293-2199 [IM] [RE]

Horst, Eric E., 1453 W Broad St, Quakertown PA 18951, 215-538-9061, Ehorst@juno.com [FRC] IIB2 [AC]

Associate Pastor, Swamp Menn Ch, Quakertown PA

Horst, Frank Kenneth (LaVerne Marie) 408 E 8th St, Warden WA 98857, 509-349-2001 [PNW] [RE]

Horst, Glenn R. (Velma) 511 Lester St, Christiansburg VA 24073, 540-381-2486, glenn.horst@juno.com [VA] [RE]

Horst, J. Alton (Dorothy) 629 Hubbard Holl Ln, Elkhart IN 46517, adhorst51@msn.com [IM] [RE]

Horst, Jeffrey S. (Julia) 3720 Yost Rd, Gordonville PA 17529, 717-354-6075, jsjshorst@juno.com [LAN] IIB1 [AC] Pastor, Village Chapel Menn Ch, New Holland PA

Horst, Jere A. (Doreen) 4290 Black Gap Rd, Chambersburg PA 17201, 717-263-0561 [FRK] IIB2 [AC] Associate Pastor, Chambersburg Menn Ch, Chambersburg PA

Horst, John A. (Linda) 13526 Big Pool Rd, Clear Spring MD 21722, 301-842-3282, horstjl@copper.net [FRK] III [AC] Ordained Deacon, Mercersburg Menn Ch, Mercersburg PA

Horst, Kenneth R. (Sue) 1037 Smith Ave, Harrisonburg VA 22802, 540-433-6584 [VA] IIB1 [AC]

Horst, Kenny L. (Sheldene) 120 Whitetail Pass, Morgantown PA 19543, 610-913-6003 [LAN] IIB2 [AC] Associate Pastor, Churchtown Menn Ch, East Earl PA

Horst, Kurt M. (Elaine Kauffman) 327 W Race St, Somerset PA 15501, 814-445-9006, KurtHorst@Compuserve.com [ALL] IB2, IB3 [AC] Conference Minister, Allegheny Mennonite Conference, Somerset PA

Horst, Lauren B. (Betty) 3920 Scar Hill Rd, Greencastle PA 17225, 717-597-4681 [FRK] [RE]

Horst, Laurence, 1414 Greencroft Dr 4D, Goshen IN 46526, 574-537-4371 [IM] [RE]

Horst, Lloyd R. (Elverta) 72 Hillside Dr, Maurertown VA 22644-0161, 540-436-8012 [VA] [RE]

Horst, Loren (Earlene) 845 College Ave, Harrisonburg VA 22802, 540-432-1038 [VA] IIB3c [AC] President, Virginia Mennonite Board of Missions, Harrisonburg VA

Horst, Luke L. (Ruth) 1001 E Oregon Rd, Lititz PA 17543-9205, 717-509-5849 [LAN] [RE]

Horst, Nevin L. (Blanche) 360 E Church St, Stevens PA 17578, 717-721-3413, bhnh@juno.com [LAN] [RE]

Horst, Reuben W. (Ruth Ann) 224 Northview Dr, Dayton VA 22821, 549-879-3822, reuben@horst.net [VA] IIB2 [AC] Associate Pastor, New Beginnings Ch, Bridgewater VA

Horst, Thomas A. (Thelma) 110 Savo Ave, Lancaster PA 17601, 717-560-3999, tomhorst@peoplepc.com [LAN] IIB1 [AC] Pastor, Landis Valley Menn Ch, Lancaster PA

Horst, Thomas E. (Nancy L.) 17803 Alpine Dr, Maugansville MD 21767, 301-797-0746, thorst@juno.com [ACC] IIC [AC] Chaplain, Manor Care, Chambersburg PA

Horst, Tina Stoltzfus (Gary) 59900 CR 21, Goshen IN 46528, 574-534-1953, GTSHorst@juno.com [IM] IIC [AC] Counselor, Communion Fell, Goshen IN

Hosler, Glenn D. (Judy) RR1 Box 65H, Thompsontown PA 17094-9713, 717-463-3468, geehoss@juno.com [LAN] IIB1 [AC] Pastor, Delaware Menn Ch, Thompsontown PA

Hostetler, Darrel M. (Marian) 627 S 3rd St, Goshen IN 46526, 574-533-9456 [IM] [RE]

Hostetler, David E. (Rose) 209 Newcomer Dr, Scottdale PA 15683-9510, 724-887-4401 [ALL] [RE]

Hostetler, Dennis, 384 N Jackson, Brewster OH 44613 [OH] IIA [AC] Youth Pastor, Longenecker Menn Ch,

Winesburg OH

Hostetler, Donnita J. Payne (Marvin D.) 1666 N Womer Ave, Wichita KS 67203, 316-943-4102 [CP] IIB3a [AC] Chaplain, Hospice Care of Kansas, Wichita KS

Hostetler, John H. (Ann) 172 Skyview Ln, Evensville TN 37332, 423-775-5737 [OH] IIB3b [RE]

Hostetler, Joseph B. (Dorothy) 1001 E Oregon Rd, Lititz PA 17543-9205, 717-519-2686 [LAN] [RE]

Hostetler, Marvin Dean (Donita J. Payne) PO Box 987, Kalona IA 52247-0987, 319-656-3790, marvinhostetler@netins.net [CP] IIB1 [AC] Pastor, Wellman Menn Ch, Wellman IA

Hostetler, Marvin E., 333 E Sassafras Apt 503, Orrville OH 44667, 330-683-5445 [OH] [RE]

Hostetler, Merle (Mary) 2041 Nathan Ln, Goshen IN 46528, 574-533-5540, merle@Egoshenmc.org [IM] IIB1 [AC] Pastor, East Goshen Menn Ch, Goshen IN

Hostetler, Michael (Virginia A.) PO Box 11 16100, Nazareth, Israel [ALL] IIC [AC]

Hostetler, Richard, 1307 Wilson Ave, Goshen IN 46526, 574-533-7343 [IM] [RE]

Hostetler, Samuel, 1401 S 13th St, Goshen IN 46526, 574-534-4548 [IM] [RE]

Hostetler, Sheri, 2825 Kingsland, Oakland CA 94619, 415-695-2812, sherihoss@aol.com [PSW] IIA [AC] Pastor, First Menn Ch of San Francisco, San Francisco CA

Hostetler, Tony (Ada T. Troyer) 3326 SE 15th Pl, Cape Coral FL 33904, 941-549-4894 [SE] IIB2 [AC] Pastor of Visitation, Cape Christian Fell, Cape Coral FL

Hostetler, Virginia A. (Michael) PO Box 11 16100, Nazareth, Israel [ALL] IIC [AC]

Hostetter Jr., B. Charles (Joyce) 4208 Hickory Lincolnton Rd, Newton NC 28658-8691, bchjoyce@twave.net [VA] IIB1 [AC] Pastor, Mountain View Menn Ch, Hickory NC

Hostetter, Darrel M. (Sherill Louise King) 735 Emerald Dr, Lancaster PA 17603-5823, 717-672-0655, growinjc@aol.com [LAN] IIB3c [AC] Co-Director Human Resources, Eastern Mennonite Missions, Salunga PA

Hostetter, Doug (Barbara E. Smolow) 731 South Blvd, Evanston IL 60202, 847-864-5470, doughostetter@earthlink.net [CDC, IL] IIA [AC] Peace Pastor, Evanston Menn Ch, Evanston IL

Hostetter, G. Hershey (Evelyn) 220 Millwood Rd, Gap PA 17527, 717-442-4569 [LAN] IIB1 [AC]

Hostetter, Isaac E. (Elizabeth) 2540 Noble Rd, Kirkwood PA 17536, 717-529-2852 [LAN] III [AC] Ordained Deacon, Mechanic Grove Menn Ch, Peach Bottom PA

Hostetter, J. Martin (Lena) 720 Wide Hollow Rd, East Earl PA 17519, 717-445-4775, mlhost@pto.net [LAN] III [AC] Ordained Deacon, Martindale Menn Ch, Ephrata PA

Hostetter, Sherill Louise King (Darrel) 735 Emerald Dr, Lancaster PA 17603, 717-672-0655, growinjc@aol.com [LAN] IIC [AC] Co-Director Human Resources, Eastern Mennonite Missions, Salunga PA

Howe, Allan H. (Jeanne C.) 723 Seward St, Evanston IL 60202, 708-475-5041, ahhowe@aol.com [IL] [AW] Mission and Service Director, Illinois Mennonite Conference, Evanston IL

Hoy, Edmond (Kay) 507 Wentworth Dr, Winchester VA 22601, 540-662-1981 [VA] [AW]

Huber, B. Landis (Anna) 1001 E Oregon Rd, Lititz PA 17543, 717-509-5859 [LAN] [RE]

Hudgens, Ric (Helen) 716 Monroe St, Evanston IL 60202,

847-328-7827 (h), richudgens@yahoo.com [IL] IIA [AC] Pastor, Reba Place Ch, Evanston IL

Huerta, Ismael, 201 E Mechanic St, Archbold OH 43502, 419-446-7458, mileyhuerta@hotmail.com [OH] IIA [AC] Associate Pastor, Iglesia Menonita del Buen Pastor, Archbold OH

Hunsberger, Paul A., 1804 S 13th St, Goshen IN 46526, 574-533-2843 [IM] [RE]

Hunsberger, Walter I., PO Box 214, Worcester PA 19490, 610-584-9385 [FRC] [RE]

Hunsberger, Willis G. (Mary Ellen) PO Box 12308, Knoxville TN 37912, 865-558-8305, Wgmeh@wmconnect.com [VA] IIA [AC] Pastor, Knoxville Menn Ch, Knoxville TN

Hunsecker, Wilmer A. (Dorothy) 7 Kenneth Dr, Walkersville MD 21793, 301-845-2280 [LAN] [RE]

Hunsicker, Ronald Jay (Kendall Keech-Hunsicker) 501 Randolph Dr, Lititz PA 17543, 717-560-3553 [ACC] IIB3a [AC] President/CEO, National Association of Addiction Treatment Providers, Inc, Lancaster PA

Hunt, Dion, 2895 B Ashton Rd, Sarasota FL 34231 [SE] IIA [AC] Minister of Youth, Ashton Menn Ch, Sarasota FL

Hurst, George M., 2870 Oregon Pk, Lititz PA 17543, 717-656-7305, gmchurst@yahoo.com [LAN] IIB1 [AC] Pastor, Hernley Menn Ch, Manheim PA

Hurst, Leon R. (Rosella) 570 Snapper Dr, Ephrata PA 17522, 717-656-3224 [LAN] IIB2 [AC] Associate Pastor, Weaverland Menn Ch, East Earl PA

Hurst, Noah S., 1026 Pinehill Rd, Lititz PA 17543, 717-626-8773 [LAN] [RE]

Hurst, Ray N. (Brenda Martin) 1591 Dinkel Ave, Bridgewater VA 22812-9803, 540-828-6578, raynhurst@ntelos.net [VA] IIB2 [AC] Co-Pastor, Community Menn Ch, Harrisonburg VA

Hurst, Raymond S. (Ruth) 1089 Rock Rd Apt 1, Schuylkill Haven PA 17972 [LAN] [RE]

Hutchings, Michael D. (Roxanne L.) 1901 S 4th St, Morton IL 61550, mrhutch81@juno.com [IL] IIC [AC] Pastor, Trinity Menn Ch, Morton IL

Huyard, Alvin M. (Rose) 103 Cherry Ave, Grottoes VA 24441, 540-249-0331 [VA] IIB1 [AC] Co-Pastor, Mount Vernon Menn Ch, Grottoes VA

Huyard, David S. (Anna Mary) 541 New York Ave, Harrisonburg VA 22801, 540-433-9481 [VA] [RE]

Huyard, Elvin R. (Linda) 46 Meadow View Dr, Leola PA 17540, 717-656-2505, erh.nh.pa@juno.com [LAN] IIB1 [AC] Pastor, Crossroads Community Fell, Lititz PA

Huyard, Rose (Alvin) 103 Cherry Ave, Grottoes VA 24441, 540-249-0331 [VA] IIB2 [AC] Co-Pastor, Mount Vernon Menn Ch, Grottoes VA

Imchen, Ramoktoshi (Beth Rice) 1096A Rettew Mill Rd, Ephrata PA 17522, 717-733-1784, rimchen@hydrosoft.net [LAN] IIB1 [AC] Pastor, Hershey Menn Ch, Kinzers PA

Intagliata, Stephen, 7727 N 34th Dr, Phoenix AZ 85051, tig7@juno.com [PSW] IIB2 [AC] Associate Pastor, Trinity Menn Ch, Glendale AZ

Isaac, Dewayn (Marilyn Irene Classen) PO Box 1088, Chouteau OK 74337 [WDC] IIB1 [AC] Pastor, Eden Menn Ch, Inola OK

Isaac, Gary Orrin (Jean Elizabeth) 307 Sutton, Newton KS 67114 [WDC] IIB3b [AC]

MINISTERS

6

Isaacs, Alvin, 718 E 121st St, Los Angeles CA 90059, 213-754-7376 [PSW] IIB1 [AC] Pastor, Calvary Christian Fell, Inglewood CA

Isaacs, Brenda, 9711 Rancho Verde Dr, Bakersfield CA 93311-3018 [PSW] IIB3b [AW] Co-Pastor, Bakersfield Anabaptist Ministries, Bakersfield CA

Isaacs, James M. (Brenda D.) 9711 Rancho Verde Dr, Bakersfield CA 93311-3018 [PSW] IIB3b [AC] Co-Pastor, Bakersfield Anabaptist Ministries, Bakersfield CA

Isaak, Paul J. (Beryl Berdeen) PO Box 187, Inman KS 67546, 620-585-2425, pji201@aol.com [WDC] IIB1 [RE]

Isner, Vernon D. (Gail) 24 Clover Cr, Chambersburg PA 17201, 717-267-0870 [FRK] IIB3a [AC] Chaplain, Menno Haven, Chambersburg, PA

Ivy, Clifford Dale (Diane) PO Box 916, Blountstown FL 32424, 850-674-4516, twodivys@gtcom.net [SE] IB3, IIB1 [AC] Pastor, Oak Terrace Menn Ch, Blountstown FL; Assistant Moderator, SE Mennonite Conference, FL

Jachin, Stephen M. (Cathrine June) 3360 Punta Del Este Dr, Hacienda Heights CA 91745, 626-333-2033, stevejachin@juno.com [PSW] IIB1 [AC] Pastor, Jemaat Kristen Indonesia Imanuel, Downey CA

Jackson, Warner, 24580 Ridgeline Dr, Bedford Heights OH 44146, 440-232-2519 [OH] IIB1 [AC] Pastor, University Euclid Christ New Testament, Bedford Heights OH

Jacobs, Donald R. (Anna Ruth) 2118 Lyndell Dr, Lancaster PA 17601, 717-391-9604, drarjacobs@comcast.net [LAN] [RE]

Jaime, Celso C. (Zulma) 1419 Zerega Ave A, Bronx NY 10462, 718-792-5455, jaime4ever@aol.com [LAN] IIB1 [AC] Pastor, Evangelical Garifuna, Bronx NY

James, Frank, PO Box 2401, Chinle AZ 86503, 520-674-3402 [PSW] IIA, IIC [AC] Pastor, Upper Room Menn Ch, Chinle AZ

Jantz, Wallace (Sylvia) 736 Random Rd, Hesston KS 67062, 620-327-2059 [SC] [RE]

Jantzen, Lubin W. (Matilda M.) 217 Vista Cr, Hesston KS 67062 [WDC] [RE]

Jantzi, Beryl M. (Margo M.) 825 Sugar Maple Ln, Harrisonburg VA 22801, 540-574-4348, bjantzi@aol.com [VA] IIB1 [AC] Pastor, Harrisonburg Menn Ch, Harrisonburg VA

Jantzi, Denton R. (Kathleen M.) 918 N 12th St, Beatrice NE 68310, 402-228-6997, bm84101@alltel.net [WDC] IIB1 [AC] Pastor, Beatrice Menn Ch, Beatrice NE

Janzen, Anna S. (Milton) 318 Lucas Creek Rd, Newport News VA 23602, 757-988-1797, MiltonAnna@aol.com [VA] IIB2 [AW] Interim Pastor, Huntington Menn Ch, Newport News VA

Janzen, Dorothea Marie (Heinz Daniel) Box 529, 3004 Ivy Dr, North Newton KS 67117, 316-283-4729, dorheinz@mennonite.net [WDC] [RE]

Janzen, Harold Henry (Margie Lois) 714 Highland, Newton KS 73703, 316-282-2123 [WDC] [RE]

Janzen, Heinz Daniel (Dorothea Marie) Box 529, 3004 Ivy Dr, North Newton KS 67117, 316-283-4729, dorheinz@mennonite.net [WDC] [RE]

Janzen, J. Melvin, 1929 Mt Vernon St, Waynesboro VA 22980-2240, 540-942-2471 [VA] IIB3a [AC]

Janzen, Samuel R. (Lila Mae) 1256 Shank Dr, Harrisonburg VA 22802, 540-732-7241 [VA] [RE]

Janzen, Susan E., 2116 Clay St, Cedar Falls IA 50613, 319-277-3262, sejanzen@msn.com [CP] IIB1 [AC]

Pastor, Cedar Falls Menn Ch, Cedar Falls IA

Jarrett, Harry (Mary Elizabeth) 1672 Sunny Slope Ln, Harrisonburg VA 22801, 540-442-8089, hjarrett7@adelphia.net [VA] IIB2 [AC] Associate Pastor, Harrisonburg Menn Ch, Harrisonburg VA

Jefferson, Nathaniel L. (Pamela) 2108 Briarcliff Rd, Richmond VA 23225, 804-232-9987 [VA] IIB3b [AC]

Jewell, Gary Lee (Janice Elizabeth Yoder) 210 South F St, Spokane WA 99204, 509-456-4973, mrglj@juno.com [PNW] IIB1 [AW]

Johns, Galen (Edith M.) 18166 CR 48, New Paris IN 46553, 574-831-4019, gijohns@maplenet.net [IM] [RE]

Johns, Loren L. (Rachel Ann Leaman) 514 N Greene Rd, Goshen IN 46526-1310, 574-535-0410, llj215@yahoo.com [CDC] IIB3d [AC] Academic Dean, AMBS, Elkhart IN

Johnson, Arlee (JoAnn) 1313 N College, Cordell OK 73632, 580-832-3435, arleejohnson@sbcglobal.net [WDC] IIB1 [AC] Pastor, Herold Menn Ch, Cordell OK

Johnson, Janeen Bertsche (Barry Lee) 64382 Limberlost Dr, Goshen IN 46526, 574-533-3608, jbjohnson@ambs.edu [CDC] IIB3d [AC]

Johnson Jr., Joseph, 830 Keefer Rd, Girard OH 44420, 330-539-2059 [OH] [RE]

Johnson, Morton H. (Katherine) 1533 Siegfried St, Bethlehem PA 18017, 610-868-1241, adriene3@aol.com [LAN] IIC [AC] Chaplain, Prison Ministry, Bethlehem PA

Johnson, Norma J. (Vern Preheim) 127 S Main, Newton KS 67114, 316-283-4018, normaj@southwind.net [WDC] IIB1 [AC] Associate Pastor, Bethel College Menn Ch, North Newton KS

Johnston, Daniel R. (Michelle) 15606 L St, Omaha NE 68135, 402-896-4132 [CP] IIB3a [AC] Healthy Ministries Coordinator, Methodist Health System, Omaha NE

Johnston, Ruth Marie (Shuji Moriichi) 2704 41st Ave S, Minneapolis MN 55406, 612-721-7068, shujiruth@juno.com [CP] IIB3a [AC] Staff Chaplain, Methodist hospital, St Louis Park MN

Jones, Jeff J. (Christianna L.) 24 Devon Dr, Hollidaysburg PA 16648, 814-695-8935, Revjjj@aol.com [ALL] IIB1 [AC] Pastor, Cornerstone Fell of Mill Run, Altoona PA

Jones, Rick, 402 W St, Archbold OH 43502, 419-445-2612, yfcjones@hotmail.com [OH] IIB1 [AC] Pastor, Inlet Menn Ch, Wauseon OH

K

Kahila, Chris C. (Kerri Ann) 23723 M 86, Centreville MI 49032-9796, ckahila@prairieinet.net [IM] IIB3c [AC] Service Adventure Administrator, Mennonite Mission Network, Elkhart IN

Kaiser, Jerry Lee (Allene Grace) 305 S Walnut, PO Box 236, Inman KS 67546, 620-585-2333, akaiser@southwind.net [WDC] IIB1 [AC] Pastor, Inman Menn Ch, Inman KS

Kalous, Charles, 3775 Susanna Dr, Cincinnati OH 45251, 513-385-8462 [OH] [RE]

Kampen, John I., 507 Greding St, Bluffton OH 45817, 419-358-0033, kampenj@bluffton.edu [CDC] IIB3c [AC]

Kanagy, Conrad L. (Heidi) 423 S Spruce St, Elizabethtown PA 17022-2549, ckanagy@earthlink.net [LAN] IIB1 [AC] Pastor, Elizabethtown Menn Ch, Elizabethtown PA

Kanagy, Curtiss Lee (Robin L.) 2106 S 5th Ave, Lebanon PA 17042, 717-295-7359, cr_kanagy@juno.com [LAN] IIB1 [AC] Pastor, New Danville Menn Ch, Lancaster PA

Kanagy, Fred (Lila) 753 Rd 523, Bloomfield MT 59315, 406-583-7782, KanagyF@miDrrs.com [NC] IIB1 [AC] Pastor, Red Top Menn Ch, Bloomfield MT

Kanagy, Irene, 5838 E 19th St, Indianapolis IN 46218 [IM] IIC [AC] Chaplain/Pastoral Counselor, Community Hospital, Indianapolis IN

Kanagy, Philip C. (Janine) 17091 Timberview Rd, Timberville VA 22853, 540-896-4439, pjkanagy@shentel.net [VA] IIB1 [AC] Pastor, Trissels Menn Ch, Broadway VA

Kanagy, Robert L. (Audrey) 292 Bender Rd, Millersville PA 17551, 717-872-4203, rakanagy@juno.com [LAN] IIA [AC] Pastor, Masonville Menn Ch, Washington Boro PA

Kanagy, Wilfred (Charleen) 18872 CR 40, Goshen IN 46526, 574-534-4878, willie@collegemennonite.org [IM] IIC [AC] Pastor, College Menn Ch, Goshen IN

Kandel, Homer, PO Box 198, Berlin OH 44610, 330-893-2622 [OH] [RE]

Kanski, David K. (Linda) 84 Hill St, Jersey Shore PA 17740, 570-398-3455, PastorDavid@suscom.net [LAN] IIB1 [AC] Pastor, Emmanuel Community Ch, Jersey Shore PA

Kao, Nelson Kuang-Daw, 60 Grant, Irvine CA 92620, 949-653-2785, jtancpa@aol.com [PSW] IIB1 [AC] Pastor, Trinity Chinese Menn Ch, Irvine CA

Kauffman, Aaron W. (Anna) 651 Steelville Rd, Cochranville PA 19330, 610-593-5665 [LAN] [RE]

Kauffman, Allen L. (Susie) RR 1 Box 295-A, Loysville PA 17047-9767, 717-789-9671 [LAN] [RE]

Kauffman, Alvin, 1801 Greencroft Blvd, Goshen IN 46526, 574-537-4638 [IM] [RE]

Kauffman, Daniel, 200 Sunnydell Cr #39, South Hutchinson KS 67505-1724, 620-665-7180 [SC] [RE] Mentoring Pastor, Yoder Menn Ch, Haven KS

Kauffman, E. Elaine, 315 N 7th St, PO Box 473, Mountain Lake MN 56159, 507-427-2212, seekfrst@rconnect.com [CP] IIB1 [AC] Pastor, First Menn Ch, Mountain Lake MN

Kauffman, Earnest (Lois) 544 E Park, W Point NE 68788, 402-372-5027 [CP] [RE]

Kauffman, Edward John (Gay Lee) 2204 E Edgewood Rd, Sioux Falls SD 57103, 605-334-2778, egkauff@sio.midco.net [CP] IB2 [AC] Conference Minister, Central Plains Mennonite Conference, Freeman SD

Kauffman, Galen E. (Betty Jean) PO Box 190, Surrey ND 58785-0236, 701-852-4957, galenkauffman@hotmail.com [NC] IIB1 [AC] Pastor, Prairie Peace Fell, Surrey ND

Kauffman, Glenn R. (June Louise) 76 Waterloo Rd, Kowoloon, Hong Kong [LAN] IIB3b [AC]

Kauffman, J. Brent (Debra Ann) 3020 Oak Terrace Dr, Lebanon OR 97355, 541-259-2127, kauffmanjb@cs.com [PNW] IIB1 [AC] Pastor, Lebanon Menn Ch, Lebanon OR

Kauffman, J. Fred, 816 S 48th St, Philadelphia PA 19143, 215-727-8136, JFKauffman@wpmf.com [FRC] IIB1 [AC] Pastor, W Philadelphia Menn Fell, Philadelphia PA

Kauffman, J. Robert (Mary Etta) 686 Meetinghouse Rd, New Holland PA 17557, 717-354-2533, caltechdad@yahoo.com [LAN] IIA [AC] Pastor, Welsh Mountain Menn Ch, New Holland PA

Kauffman, Jeffery Lane (Jan), Harrisonburg VA, jkauffman@mennonite.net [VA] IIB1 [AC] Pastor, Weavers Menn Ch, Harrisonburg VA

Kauffman, Melvin L. (Erma) 1001 E Oregon Rd, Lititz PA 17543-9205, 717-519-2681 [LAN] [RE]

Kauffman, Norman D., 420 Bachelor Grade Rd, Kalispell MT 59901, 406-755-2902 [PNW] [RE]

Kauffman, Richard Alan (Nancy Jane) 4902 Front Mountain Rd, Belleville PA 17004, 717-935-9965, ank@pa.net [ALL] IIB1 [AC] Pastor, Maple Grove Menn Ch, Belleville PA

Kauffman, Ron, 850 Burr Rd, Wauseon OH 43567, 419-335-3212 [OH] IIC [AC]

Kauffman, Sherman W. (Betty L.) 2420 S Main, Goshen IN 46526, 574-533-2461, sherm@im.mennonite.net [IM] IB2 [AC] Executive Conference Minister, IN-MI Mennonite Conference, Goshen IN

Kauffman, Stanlee D. (Marcia) 1703 Goose Creek Rd, Waynesboro VA 22980, 540-943-1324, pastork@ntelos.net [VA] IIB1 [AC] Senior Pastor, Waynesboro Menn Ch, Waynesboro VA

Kauffman, Thomas E. (Julia Gerber) 981-A Summit Ave, Harrisonburg VA 22802, 540-801-8920 [VA] [RE]

Kauffman, Tom (Amy Gerber) 2303 Maryann Pl, Toledo OH 43614-2113, 419-382-3816, tekauffman@sev.org [OH] IB2 [AC] Conference Minister, Ohio Conference of the Mennonite Church, Toledo OH

Kauffmann, Ivan J., 1725 Wildwood Ct, Goshen IN 46526, 574-534-0232 [IM] [RE]

Kauffmann, Nancy Lee (Joel Dean) 111 Carter Rd, Goshen IN 46526, 574-533-7252, nancy@im.mennonite.net [IM] IB2 [AC] Conference Regional Minister, Indiana-Michigan Mennonite Conference, Goshen IN

Kaufman, Calvin R. (Loretta) 901 Mervin Ave, Goshen IN 46526, 574-537-8002 [IM] [RE]

Kaufman, Donald David (Eleanor Wismer) 609 Central, Newton KS 67114, 316-283-7421, dekaufman@juno.com [WDC] [RE]

Kaufman, Douglas D. H. (Jill Hostetler) 1101 S 8th St, Goshen IN 46526, 574-533-7625, kaufman@bnin.net [IM] IIB1 [AC] Pastor, Benton Menn Ch, Goshen IN

Kaufman, George K. (Naomi Marie Esau) PO Box 130, Henderson NE 68371-0130, gkaufman@mainstaycomm.net [CP] IIB2 [AC] Associate Pastor, Bethesda Menn Ch, Henderson NE

Kaufman, Gordon D., 6 Longfellow Rd, Cambridge MA 02138, 617-491-1771 [EDC] [RE] Pastor, Menn Congregation of Boston, Cambridge MA

Kaufman, Marvin L. (Ruth) 2968 Carpenter Park Rd, Davidsville PA 15928, 814-288-2167, kaufmanrm@hotmail.com [ALL] IIB1 [AC]

Kaufman, Orlo N. (Edna G.) c/o Eugene Kaufman, 415 W 4th, Valley Center KS 67147 [WDC] [RE]

Kaufman, Robert (Krista) 7702 Garnett, Lenxa KS 66214, 913-248-0642 [WDC] IIB1 [AC] Pastor, Rainbow Menn Ch, Kansas City KS

Kaufman, S. Roy (Lorretta) 28103 443rd Ave, Freeman SD 57029, 605-925-7106, lorokauf@gwtc.net [CP] IIB1 [AC] Pastor, Salem Menn Ch, Freeman SD

Kaufman-Frey, Cameron Blake (Dawn Renae) 501 Center St, Morgantown WV 26505, 304-296-1822, cameronkf@mail2-mennonite.net [ALL] IB3, IIB1 [AC]

MINISTERS

6

Pastor, Morgantown Ch of the Brethren, Morgantown WV

Kaufmann, Lois Johns (H. James) 18166 CR 48, New Paris IN 46553, 574-831-2072, loisjk@juno.com [CDC, IM] IIB1 [AC] Co-Pastor, Assembly Menn Ch, Goshen IN

Kautz, Delbert L. (Mary Ann Hosler) 475 Letort Rd, Millersville PA 17551, 717-872-2695, dellamark@prodigy.net [LAN] IIB1 [AC] Pastor, Millersville Menn Ch, Millersville PA

Kebede, Berhanu (Yenewopk) 382 Dohner Dr, Lancaster PA 17602, 717-293-0983 [LAN] IIA [AC] Pastor, Tinsae Kristos Evangelical Ch, Lancaster PA

Keeler, Kendall Ray (Barbara Elizabeth) 379 Scotland Rd, Quarryville PA 17566, 717-786-8130, kendallbarb@juno.com [LAN] IIA [AC] Associate Pastor, Mt Vernon Menn Ch, Kirkwood PA

Keeler, Randall S. (Karen Joan) 55 Crystal Pl, Bluffton OH 45817, 419-358-1932, keelerr@bluffton.edu [CDC] IIB3a [AC] Pastor, Bluffton College, Bluffton OH

Keeler, Richard Freed (Margaret) 6 Darcy Ave, Central Park, Balmain Village, Couva TRINIDAD, Trinidad, 868-679-7258, keeler2@att.net.tt [VA] IB3, IIB3b [AC]

Keener, Gerald (Donna Zehr) 731 Hempfield Hill Rd, Columbia PA 17512, 212-234-9539 [LAN] IIB3b [AC] Overseas Worker, Eastern Mennonite Missions, Ho Chi Minh City, Vietnam

Keener, Robert E. (Rhoda) 5207 Heisey Rd, Shippensburg PA 17257, 717-532-9723 [FRK] IIB3a [AC] Chaplain, Menno Haven, Chambersburg PA

Keener, Walter L. (Martha) 2001 Harrisburg Pk, Apt 227, Lancaster PA 17601, 717-390-4176 [LAN] [RE]

Keeney, William Echard (Willadene Hartzler) 140 North Lawn Ave, Bluffton OH 45817-1275, 419-358-6017 [CDC] [RE]

Kehr, Anita Yoder (Bryan) 65719 SR 15, Goshen IN 46526, 574-535-1014, anitakehr@juno.com [IM] IIB1 [AC] Pastor, Berkey Ave Menn Fell, Goshen IN

Keidel, Levi (Eudene) 14409 Sunrise Ct #124, Leo IN 46765-9515 [IM] [RE]

Keim, Howard (Tami) 209 N Weaver, Hesston KS 67062 [SC] IIB3d [AC] Professor, Tabor College, Hillsboro KS

Keim, Ray, 920 Chalet Dr Apt 309, Berne IN 46711, 260-589-8596, craykeim@juno.com [CDC] IIB2 [AC] Pastor of Congregational Care, First Menn Ch, Berne IN

Keller, Frank Reller (Lorraine H.) 603 Bluestem St, PO Box 476, North Newton KS 67117, fkeller@alltel.net [WDC] [RE]

Keller, Lloyd B. (Eunice) 535 Fruitville Pk, Manheim PA 17545, 717-665-3137 [LAN] [RE]

Keller, Mark Haven (Darlene) 1018 Taliaferro Dr, Harrisonburg VA 22802, 540-434-4535, mkeller123@aol.com [VA] IIB2 [AC] Associate Pastor, Harrisonburg Menn Ch, Harrisonburg VA

Kelly, John, 16975 SR 93, Pedro OH 45659, 740-643-2731, shauna@bright.net [OH] IIC [AC] Pastor, Wayside Chapel, Pedro OH

Kennel, Leroy Eldon (Pauline) 888 S Roselle Rd, Schaumburg IL 60193-3965, 847-895-3654, lpkennel@msn.com [CDC, IL] IIB1, IIB3a [AC] Minister of the Word, Christ Community Menn Ch, Schaumburg IL

Kennel, Pauline (LeRoy Eldon) 888 S Roselle Rd, Schaumburg IL 60193-3965, 847-895-3654, lpkennel@msn.com [CDC, IL] IIB1 [AC] Pastor, Christ Community Menn Ch, Schaumburg IL

Kennel, Ronald L. (Judy) 2714 Evergreen Ln, Goshen IN 46526, 574-534-1385, rkennel@npcc.net [IM] IB3, IIB1 [AC] Pastor, Clinton Brick Menn Ch, Goshen IN; Overseer, Benton Mennonite, Goshen IN

Kennel, Sharon, 1017 Rd V, Strang NE 68444-3027, 402-627-4375, sharondkennel@yahoo.com [CP] IB2 [AC] W Regional Minister, Central Plains Mennonite Conference

Kennell, Dennis (Nelda) RR 2 Box 39, Roanoke IL 61561, 309-923-6621, kennells@mtco.com [IL] IIB1 [AC] Pastor, Cazenovia Menn Ch, Roanoke IL

Kennell, Eldon W. (Mary Alice Ulrich) PO Box 801, Roanoke IL 61561, 309-923-7172 [IL] IIB3a [AC] Chaplain, Pontiac Correctional Center, Pontiac IL

Kennell, Timothy D. (Beverly Ann) 3250 Pineview Dr, Powhatan VA 23139, 804-598-9355, timbev2@yahoo.com [VA] IIB1 [AC] Pastor, Powhatan Menn Ch, Powhatan VA

Kern, Marilyn Ruth, 704 Charles Ave, Findley OH 45840-4515, 419-420-9927, kernmom@aol.com [CDC] [RE]

Kerner, David (Diane Sue O'Leary) PO Box 11, Highland Park IL 60035, 847-204-5746, dckerner@trimedia.net [CDC, IL] IIB1 [AC] Pastor, North Suburban Menn Ch, Mundelein IL

Kiblinger, John D. (Catherine Anne) 1860 Glanzer Court, Harrisonburg VA 22802, 540-433-6612 [VA] [RE]

Kimes, Steve (Diane) 17734 NE Glisan, Portland OR 97230, 503-492-1149, stevekimes@aol.com [PNW] IIA [AC] Pastor, Anawim Christian Community, Portland OR

Kindy, David (Merna Jo) 2701 Griffith Rd, Winston Salem NC 27103, 910-760-4294 [VA] [AW]

Kindy, Erie, 1325 E Gordonville Rd, Midland MI 48640, 517-631-4637 [IM] [RE]

King, Aaron (Betty) 5975 Whippoorwill Ln, Harrisonburg VA 22802, 540-833-5135 [VA] IIB3a [AC]

King, Betty (Aaron) 5975 Whippoorwill Ln, Harrisonburg VA 22802, 540-833-5135 [VA] IIB3a [AC]

King, Calvin J. (Ardis J.) 17713 Hartman St, South Bend IN 46614-3619, 574-299-0351, Caljk@comcast.net [IM] IIB3c [AC] Constituent Information Manager, Mennonite Mission Network, Elkhart IN

King, Clifford E. (Mona Bebe) 7512 Los Banos Ct, Colorado Spring CO 80920, 719-260-7024, cliffmona@juno.com [RM] [RE]

King, Daniel L., PO Box 128, Kidron OH 44636, 330-857-0305, djking@bright.net [OH] IIB1 [AC] Pastor, Dover Christian Fell, Dover OH

King, Donald G. (Barbara) 413 Alana Dr, Goshen IN 46526, 574-534-3778 [IM] [RE]

King, Douglas D. (Paula M.) 509 S Jackson St, PO Box 594, Flanagan IL 61740, 815-796-4298, dpking@frontiernet.net [CDC, IL] IIB1 [AC] Pastor, Prairieview Menn Ch, Flanagan IL

King, Eldon (Dorothy P.) 551 Tionesta Dr, Dalton OH 44618, 330-828-1004, eldor@sssnet.com [OH] IIB3a [AC]

King, John C., 1727 S 13th St, Goshen IN 46526, 574-533-1052, john@waterfordchurch.org [IM] IB3, IIB2 [AC] Overseer, Pleasant View Mennonite, Goshen IN; Minister to Older Adults, Waterford Menn Ch, Goshen IN

King, Linford D. (Mary Etta) 311 N Lime St, Lancaster PA 17602-2334, 717-391-6445, leking@supernet.com [LAN] IB3, IIB3c [AC] Overseer-Bishop, Lancaster City District, Lancaster Mennonite Conference, Lancaster

PA; Asst Co-Director, MC USA Office of Congregational Life, Elkhart IN

King, Michael A. (Joan) 126 Klingerman Rd, Telford PA 18969, 215-721-7967, mking@netreach.net [FRC] IIB1 [AC] Pastor, Spring Mount Menn Ch, Schwenksville PA

King, Nicholas James (Ronda Suderman) 1558 Fairview, Wichita KS 67203, 316-265-8568, Rondask@Juno.com [WDC] IIB2, IIB3b [AC]

King, Wayne D. (Clara) 418 N Elm, Arthur IL 61911, 217-543-3352, wcking@net.care-il.com [IL] [RE]

Klaassen, Glendon J. (Reitha J.) 19 EMS D22C Ln, Syracuse IN 46567-9068, 574-658-3222, glendon.klaassen@gte.net [WDC] [RE]

Kleinsasser, Alvin D., PO Box 143, Mt Lake MN 56159, 507-427-2219 [WDC] [RE]

Klemm, Ulli M. (Theda Siegrist) 7241 Princeton Pl, Pittsburgh PA 15218, 412-241-5149 [ALL] IIB3a [AC]

Kliewer, Tim (Myrna) 301 S Main St, Hillsboro KS 67063, 620-947-2984, tkliewer@southwind.net [WDC] IIB1 [AC] Pastor, Trinity Menn Ch, Hillsboro KS

Klingensmith, Jr., David P., 435 Beechdale Rd, Bird in Hand PA 17505, 717-656-7206 (h) 717-656-2451 (w) [ACC] IIA [AC] Associate Pastor, Sandy Hill Menn Ch, Coatesville PA

Klopfenstein, Gerry, 209 S Washington, Wayland IA 52654 [CP] IIC [AC] Co-Pastor, Wayland Menn Ch, Wayland IA

Kniss, Carl D. (Rochelle) 878 S College Ave, Harrisonburg PA 17522, 540-574-2779, crkniss@aol.com [LAN] IIC [AC] Pastor, Marion Menn Ch, Chambersburg PA

Kniss, David L. (Esther Leaman) 4454 NW Dunn Dr, Arcadia FL 34266-5373, dkniss@aol.com [SE] [RE]

Kniss, Paul G., 1549 Hillcrest Dr, Harrisonburg VA 22801, 540-432-0286 [OH] [RE]

Kniss, Philip L. (Irene Hershberger) 889 College Ave, Harrisonburg VA 22802, 540-564-1231, phil@pvmchurch.org [VA] IIB1 [AC] Pastor, Park View Menn Ch, Harrisonburg VA

Knowles, Michael (June) 12883 NW Hwy 225, Reddick FL 32686, 352-591-4140, mjknowles@peoplepc.com [WDC] IIB1 [AW]

Koch, Roy, 204 S 6th St, Goshen IN 46526, 574-533-1798 [IM] [RE]

Kochsmeier, David K. (Bev Goshow) 1775 Creek Rd, Bethlehem PA 18015, 610-758-8156 [FRC] IIB1 [AC] Pastor, Steel City Menn Ch, Bethlehem PA; Radio Pastor/Producer, Life with God Radio Broadcast, Souderton PA

Koehn, Clifford E. (Anna Ruth) 111 NE 2nd St, Geary OK 73040-2005, 405-884-2705 [WDC] [AW]

Koehn, Melvin J. (Dolora M.) 200 Deerview Ave, Tea SD 57064, 605-368-2245 [CP] [AW] Pastor, Eicher Emmanuel Menn Ch, Wayland IA

Koehn, Orlan, 2275 N Cable Rd, Apt 181, Lima OH 45807, 419-221-3605 [OH] IIA [AC] Interim Pastor, Pk Menn Ch, Elida OH

Koeshadi, Mathilda, 794 N Calaveras Dr, Walnut CA 91789, 626-913-3366 [PSW] IIA, IIB2 [AC] Associate Pastor, Gereja Kristus Injili, Pasadena CA

Kolb, Elmer G., 207 W Summit St, Souderton PA 18964, 215-721-0599 [FRC] [RE]

Kolb, Joseph M. (Lorraine) 1 Fisherman Dr, Berlin MD 21811, josephkolb@msn.com [ACC] IIB1 [AC] Pastor, Ocean City Menn Christian Fell, Ocean City MD

Kolb, Matthew G., 592 Mennonite Rd, Royersford PA 19468, 610-948-6094 [FRC] [RE]

Kolb, Noah S. (Sara Jane) 631 Melvins Rd, Telford PA 18969-2121, 215-723-7399, NoahK@FMC-online.org [FRC] IB2 [AC] Conference Minister, Franconia Conference, Souderton PA

Kolb, Norman G., 1191 Peiffer Hill Rd, Stevens PA 17578 [FRC] [RE]

Kolb-Wyckoff, Martha (Ron) 257 W Reliance Rd, Souderton PA 18964, 215-799-2374, mkolbwyckoff@rmcomm.org [FRC] IIB3a [AC]

Koop, Cleo H. (Faye A.) 1800 N Spencer Rd, Newton KS 67114, 316-283-2536 [WDC] IIB1 [AC] Pastor, First Menn Ch, Halstead KS

Kotva Jr., Joseph J. (Carol S.) 56893 Pinecrest Dr, Elkhart IN 46516, 574-294-1777, kotva@verizon.net [EDC] IIB3c [AC] Executive Director, Anabaptist Center for Health Care Ethics, Elkhart IN

Kouttjie, Frederik Jan, 14732 Dunnet Ave, La Mirada CA 90638, 714-521-5742, janasria@aol.com [PSW] IIB1 [AC] Pastor, Gereja Kristen Injili Indonesia Zion, LaMirada CA

Krabill, James R., 500 S Main, Box 370, Elkhart IN 46515-0370, 574-294-7523 [IM] IIB3c [AC] Staff, Mennonite Mission Network, Elkhart IN

Krabill, Murray, 7348 Perry Twp Rd 95, Fredericktown OH 43019, 419-768-3278 [OH] [RE]

Krabill, Russell, 26221 Vista Ln, Elkhart IN 46517, 574-522-6869 [IM] [RE]

Kratz, Clarice (Lawrence M.) N31 W28 795 Lakeside Rd, Pewaukee WI 53072, 262-691-0304, clariKra@aol.com [CDC, IL] IIB1 [AC] Co-Pastor, Maple Ave Menn Ch, Waukesha WI

Kratz, Clyde G. (Eunice A.) 264 Gap Place, Broadway VA 22815, 540-896-0378, cgkratz@adelphia.net [VA] IIB1 [AC] Pastor, Zion Menn Ch, Broadway VA

Kratz, Dorothy (James D.) 54269 Old Mill Dr, Elkhart IN 46514, 574-266-5277 [IM] IIB2 [AC] Minister of Pastoral Care and Visitation, Sunnyside Menn Ch, Elkhart IN

Kratz, Lawrence M. (Clarice B.) N31 W28 795 Lakeside Rd, Pewaukee WI 53072, 262-691-0340, clariKra@aol.com [CDC, IL] IIB1 [AC] Co-Pastor, Maple Ave Menn Ch, Waukesha WI

Kratz, Paul Leonard (Evelyn W.) 3226 Old Thirty-three Rd, Harrisonburg VA 22801, 540-432-9050 [VA] IB3 [AC]

Kratzer, Amy (Amos M.) 210-C S Silverwood Ln, Goshen IN 46526, amykratzer@yahoo.com [IM] IIA [AC] Pastor of Youth/Worship, Sunnyside Menn Ch, Elkhart IN

Kraus, C. Norman (Rhoda Hess) 1210 Harmony Dr, Harrisonburg VA 22802, 540-432-0828 [VA] [RE]

Kraybill, J. Nelson (Ellen Graber) 26103 Vista Ln, Elkhart IN 46517, 574-293-2391, nkraybill@aol.com [IM] IIB3c [AC] President, Associated Mennonite Biblical Seminary, Elkhart IN

Kraybill, John H. (Thelma) Harvest View 220, 1001 E Oregon Rd, Lititz PA 17543, 717-509-5861, johnkraybill@yahoo.com [LAN] [RE]

Kraybill, Simon P. (Mary Jean) 860 Maytown Rd, Elizabethtown PA 17022-9765, 717-367-2060, spkmaryjk@aol.com [LAN] [RE]

Krehbiel, Ronald Allen (Cynthia) 212 Kingsway, Hesston KS 67062, 620-327-4437 [WDC] [RE]

Krehbiel, Val R. (Consuelo) 713 Carl Ave, Salina KS

67401-6660 [WDC] IIB1 [AC] Pastor, Salina Menn Ch, Salina KS

Kreider, Alan (Eleanor) 215 W Dinehart, Elkhart IN 46526 [IM] [AC] Mission Educator, Mennonite Mission Network, Elkhart IN

Kreider, Andrew (Katie) 1726 Roys Ave, Elkhart IN 46516, 574-293-7354, psmcak@aol.com [IM] IIB1 [AC] Pastor, Prairie St Menn Ch, Elkhart IN

Kreider, Barry R. (Erika Landes) 908 Grandview Rd, Akron PA 17501, 717-859-4596, berika@ptd.net [LAN] IIA [AC] Pastor, Pilgrims Menn Ch, Akron PA

Kreider, Ellis D. (Amy) 171 Black Bear Rd, Quarryville PA 17566, 717-786-2626 [LAN] [RE]

Kreider, Harold, 24B Green Top Rd, Sellersville PA 18960, 215-257-7322 [FRC] [RE]

Kreider, Heidi Regier (David J.) PO Box 116, North Newton KS 67117, 316-284-0448, hkreider@southwind.net [WDC] IIB1 [AC] Pastor, Bethel College Menn Ch, North Newton KS

Kreider, J. Robert, 1408-5 Kentfield Way, Goshen IN 46526, 574-533-5726 [IM] [RE]

Kreider, John T., 105 Hertzler Rd, Newport News VA 23602, 757-877-1204, johnT2125@juno.com [VA] [RE]

Kreider, Philip (Lois) PO Box 447, Harrisonburg VA 22801, 540-433-8243 [VA] [AW]

Kreider, Wayne E. (Carla JoAnn) 1207 River Rd, Quarryville PA 17566, 717-548-2466, wkreider@epix.net [LAN] IIB2 [AC] Associate Pastor, Mechanic Grove Menn Ch, Peach Bottom PA

Kriss III, Stephen F., 1324 W Sycamore St, Pittsburgh PA 15211, 412-481-9614, Kriss1633@duq.edu [ALL] IIB3b [AC]

Kropf, Marlene Y. (Stanley E.) 337 E Beardsley Ave, Elkhart IN 46514, 574-262-8880 [IM] IIB3c [AC] Professor, Associated Mennonite Biblical Seminary, Elkhart IN

Kropf, Paul L. (June Louise) L Beslidhja P86 Ap 40, Lezhe, Albania, 001-355-0-26-22677 [LAN] IIC [AC] Minister, EMM, Lezhe, Albania

Kuhns, Curtis (Carol) PO Box 627, Manson IA 50563, 712-469-2014, curtkuhns@juno.com [CP] IIB1 [AC] Pastor, Manson Menn Ch, Manson IA

Kulp, Henry D., 161 W Cherry Ln, Souderton PA 18964, 215-723-3047 [FRC] [RE]

Kuniholm, Jason (Joanne) 53 Maple Linden Ln, Frazer PA 19355, 610-640-4075, jasonholm9@aol.com [LAN] IIB1 [AC] Pastor, Frazer Menn Ch, Frazer PA

Kunkle, Albert B. (Vera Mae) 1297 Earl Ave, East Earl PA 17519, 717-354-5563 [LAN] III [AC] Ordained Deacon, Hinkletown Menn Ch, Ephrata PA

Kurtz, Calvin (Esther) 334 S Twin Valley Rd, Elverson PA 19520, 610-286-9574 [ACC] IIB3c [AC] Executive Director, Berks Co. Conference of Churches, Reading PA

Kurtz, Ira A. (Evelyn) 724 E End Ave, Lancaster PA 17602-3714, 717-293-0001, iekurtz2@juno.com [LAN] IIB1 [AC] Pastor, Sunnyside Menn Ch, Lancaster PA

Kurtz, Kathleen Weaver (Wayne David) 8914 Grant Ave, Manasses VA 22110, 703-361-7796 [VA] IIB3a [AC] Pastoral Counselor, Center for Pastoral Counseling of Virginia, McLean VA

Kurtz, Marilyn E. (Mervin) 655 Rawlinsville Rd, Willow St PA 17584, 717-464-4427, kurtzme@juno.com [LAN] IIC [AC] Associate Pastor, Rossmere Menn Ch, Lancaster PA

Kurtz, Omar A. (Emily) 32 Furnace Rd, Birdsboro PA 19508, 610-286-0159 [ACC] [RE]

Kusuma, Rina (Yusak) 1408 Forest Glen Dr #77, Hacienda Heights CA 91745 [PSW] IIB1 [AC] Co-Pastor, Gereja Kristus Injili, Pasadena CA

Kusuma, Yusak (Rina) 1408 Forest Glen Dr #77, Hacienda Heights CA 91745 [PSW] IIB1 [AC] Co-Pastor, Gereja Kristus Injili, Pasadena CA

Kuttab, George M. (Frosina) 8131 Washington Ln Apt 156, Wyncote PA 19095, 215-884-4839 [LAN] IIB1 [AC] Pastor, Salam Menn Fell, Wyncote PA

Kym, Marlin (Betta Ruth) 621 South D St, Milford NE 68405, 402-761-3202, bell606@juno.com [CP] IIB1 [AC] Pastor, Bellwood Menn Ch, Milford NE

L

La Rue, Robin, 57019 Westlake Dr, Middlebury IN 46540, 574-825-1958, randrlarue@juno.com [CDC] IIB1 [AC] Pastor, Pleasant Oaks Menn Ch, Middlebury IN

Lahman, Harold H. (Evelyn M.) 14983 Model Rd, Elkton VA 22827, 540-298-8229 [VA] [RE]

Lanctot, Nina Bartelt (Donald) 1828 Roys Ave, Elkhart IN 46516, 574-295-6427, ninal@maplenet.net [IM] IIB1 [AC] Associate Pastor, Belmont Menn Ch, Elkhart IN

Landes, Craig Pelkey (Fortana May) 35 S Main St, Perkasie PA 18944-1910, 215-453-6743 [FRC] IIB3b, IIB3c [AC]

Landes, R. Scott (Wendy Hange) 436 C Swamp Pk, Schwenksville PA 19473, 610-754-8865 [FRC] IIB1 [AC] Pastor, Frederick Menn Ch, Frederick PA

Landis, Abram K., Apt 272, Sellersville PA 18960, 215-453-9443 [FRC] [RE]

Landis, Betty (Elias) 1820 Rothsville Rd, Lititz PA 17543, 717-626-5741 [LAN] IIC [AC] Chaplain, Ephrata Community Hospital, Ephrata PA

Landis, Ira B. (Ruth) 2421 Camp Rd, Manheim PA 17545-8001, 717-664-2026 [LAN] [RE]

Landis, John G. (Eileen M. Hart) 1805 Thompson Ave, Lebanon PA 17046, 717-867-1517, jgl@mbcomp.com [LAN] IIB1 [AC] Pastor, Gingrichs Menn Ch, Lebanon PA

Landis, Keith L. (Brenda K.) 9150 Hite Rd, W Liberty OH 43357, 937-465-0312, kblandis@2access.net [OH] IIB1 [AC] Pastor, South Union Menn Ch, West Liberty OH

Landis, Mark (Elizabeth) 845 Quince Dr, Harrisonburg VA 22801, 540-801-8020 [VA] IIB2 [AC] Associate Pastor, Grace Menn Fell, Linville VA

Landis, Mark G. (Alma) 881 Louser Rd, Annville PA 17003, 717-867-2028 [LAN] [RE]

Landis, Merrill B. (Betty Godshall) 1009 Pine Cr, Telford PA 18969, 215-721-0152 [FRC] [RE]

Landis, Mervin L. (Rachel) 1045 Hunscker Rd, Lancaster PA 17601, 717-569-1334 [LAN] [RE]

Landis, Paul R. (Evelyn) 1160 Broadway Rd, Milton PA 17847-9506, 570-742-4110, paulyns@uplink.net [LAN] [RE]

Landis, Paul S. (Joanne) 12 Church Landing Rd, Pennsville NJ 08070, 856-678-3926, mojodnl@aol.com [LAN] IIB2 [AC] Visitation Pastor, Friendship Menn Ch, Carney's Point NJ

Landis, Steven E. (Rosemary K.) 201 Maple Ave, Harleysville PA 19438, 215-513-0926 [FRC] IIB2 [AC] Minister of Pastoral Care, Franconia Menn Ch, Telford PA

Lange, Shawn (Leandrea) 2803 Burr Oak Ave, Elkhart IN 46517 [IM] IIA [AC] Minister of Outreach, House of

Power, Elkhart IN

Lanting, Esther, 410 S Washington, Wakarusa IN 46573, 574-862-1910, elanting@maplenet.net [IM] IIB1 [AC] Pastor, Hudson Lake Menn Ch, New Carlisle IN

Lantz, Paul, 1804 College Manor, Goshen IN 46526, 574-533-1949 [IM] [RE]

Lapp, Ben F. (Geraldine D.) 2846 Little Rd, Perkiomenville PA 18074, 610-754-7258 [FRC] [RE]

Lapp, Cynthia, 3102 Webster St, Mt Rainier MD 20712, 301-927-2983 [ALL] IIB1 [AC] Pastor, Hyattsville Menn Ch, Hyattsville MD

Lapp, Dan L. (Anna Ruth) 11 Benjamin Green Rd, Pedricktown NJ 08067, 856-299-6589 [LAN] IIB2 [AC] Associate Pastor, Friendship Menn Ch, Carney's Point NJ

Lapp, James M. (Miriam F. Book) 443 Penn Oak Ct, Harleysville PA 19438, 215-513-4115, jamesl@FMC-online.org [FRC] IB2 [AC] Conference Pastor, Franconia Mennonite Conference, Souderton PA

Lapp, John H. (Floy) RD 2 Box 243, Port Allegany PA 16743, 814-642-9401, jflapp@usachoice.net [ACC] [RE] Minister of Visitation, Birch Grove Menn Ch, Port Allegany PA

Lapp, M. Eugene (Marie) 53 Pequea Valley Rd, Kinzers PA 17535, 717-768-7550 [LAN] III [AC] Licensed Deacon, Millwood Menn Ch, Bird In Hand PA

Lapp, Ray (Edna) 109 Hershey Church Rd, Kinzers PA 17535, 717-768-3314, ridgeviewchurch@juno.com [ACC] [RE]

Larson, Jonathan (Mary Kay) 2108 Kodiak Dr NE, Atlanta GA 30345-4150, 404-636-7915, jonathan_larson@earthlink.net [SE] IB3 [AC] District Minister, SE Mennonite Conference, GA/SC, GA

Lasure, D. Wayne (Katie) 252 Keyser Rd, Boswell PA 15531, 814-629-7216 [ALL] IIB1 [AC] Pastor, Thomas Menn Ch, Hollsopple PA

Laureano, Juan (Amarillys) 5731 S Tripp Apt 1, Chicago IL 60629, 773-582-6785 [IL] IIA [AC] Pastor, Iglesia Cristiana Peniel, Chicago IL

Lauver, J. Paul, 3910 N 760 W, Shipshewana IN 46565, 260-768-7073 [IM] [RE]

Lawton, Wayne D. (Mary Lou) 624 Groff Ave, Elizabethtown PA 17022, 717-361-8990, lawtonwd@pngusa.net [LAN] IIB1, IIB3a [AC] Pastor, Cedar Hill Community Ch, Elizabethtown PA

Lay, Sarin (Hun) 2421 S 5th, Philadelphia PA 19148-3907, 610-986-3253 [LAN] IIA [AC] Pastor, Philadelphia Cambodian Menn Ch, Philadelphia PA

Le, Can Ngoc (Lisa Pham) 105 Landale Dr, Sterrett AL 35147, 205-678-9090, mscanle@hotmail.com [VA] [AW]

Le Blanc, Marvin (Shirley Champagne) PO Box 144E, Des Allemands LA 70030, 504-758-2929 [GS] [AW]

Leaman, Daniel G. (Miriam) 2259 Seitz Dr, Lancaster PA 17601, 717-392-5950 [LAN] [RE]

Leaman, George W., 1001 E Oregon Rd, Lititz PA 17543, 717-569-0689 [LAN] [RE]

Leaman, James R. (Elizabeth Ann Kling [Beth]) 157 Conestoga Blvd, Lancaster PA 17602-3811, 717-672-0970, jiml@groffdale.com [LAN] IIB1 [AC] Pastor, Groffdale Menn Ch, Leola PA

Leaman, John M. (Nancy L. Gehman) 159 Glenbrook Rd, Bird In Hand PA 17505-9748, 717-656-6612, johnleaman@juno.com [LAN] IIB2 [AC] Minister of Mission, Stumptown Menn Ch, Bird In Hand PA

Leaman, Mark M. (Brenda) 1284 Edgewood Dr, East

Earl PA 17519, 717-354-8227 [LAN] IB3 [RE] Interim Bishop/Overseer, LAN 2 churches, PA

Leaman, Paul G. (Erma L.) 3907 Lemonwood Dr, Sarasota FL 34232, 941-378-2793 [SE] [RE]

Leaman, Paul M. (Lillian) 1329 Union Grove Rd, Terre Hill PA 17581, 717-445-4431 [LAN] III [AC] Ordained Deacon, Welsh Mountain Menn Ch, New Holland PA

Leaman, Ray K. (Carol) 484 Willow Rd, Lancaster PA 17601-6022, 717-392-7745, rleaman@epix.net [LAN] III [AC] Licensed Deacon, Mellinger Menn Ch, Lancaster PA

Leaman, Wilmer W. (Marie) 1342 Reading Rd, Denver PA 17517-9726, 717-445-4792 [LAN] [RE]

Leatherman, Andrew H. (Dorothy) 1551 Valley Rd, Coatesville PA 19320, 610-384-3678, dotandy@yahoo.com [ACC] IIB3a [AC] Chaplain, Einstein Medical Center, Coatesville PA

Lebron, Rodney, 3408 Lindale Rd, Linville VA 22834 [VA] IIC [AC] Pastor, Woodland Menn Ch, Linville VA

Lechlitner, Michael, 203 W Wilden Ave, Goshen IN 46526, 574-533-6532 [IM] IIB1 [AC] Pastor, Praise Chapel Christian Fell, Goshen IN

Lederach, John M. (Naomi) 1326 Pebble Ct, Goshen IN 46528, 574-534-8395 [IM] [RE] Overseer, Waterford Mennonite Church, Goshen IN

Lederach, Paul M. (Mary Slagell) 203 Woods Dr, Lansdale PA 19446, 215-393-8396 [FRC] [RE]

Ledford, Monty Dell (Elaine Joyce) PO Box 246, Aberdeen ID 83210-0246, 208-397-4202, mepluseight@juno.com [PNW] IIB1 [AC] Pastor, First Menn Ch, Aberdeen ID

Lefever, Harold H. (Mary) 16 S Mountain Rd, Harrisburg PA 17112, 717-545-1858 [LAN] IIB1 [AC] Pastor, Herr St Menn Ch, Harrisburg PA

Lefever, Paul B. (Ellene) 714 W Brubaker Valley Rd, Lititz PA 17543, 717-626-5885 [LAN] [RE]

Lehman, Barbara Moyer (John Paul) 1023 Stuart St, Harrisonburg VA 22802, 540-432-6310, barbara@pvmchurch.org [VA] IIB2 [AC] Associate Pastor, Park View Menn Ch, Harrisonburg VA

Lehman, Dale E. (Ruby) 498 Cedar Flat Rd, Warfordsburg PA 17267, 717-294-3896, dlehman@pa.net [FRK] IB2 [AC] Associate Pastor, Bethel Community Ch, Warfordsburg PA

Lehman, David Jan (Lavonne Weaver) 1051 College Ave, Harrisonburg VA 22802, 540-434-8448 [VA] [AW]

Lehman, Dean M. (Brenda) 4819 Guitner Rd, Chambersburg PA 17201, 717-375-4586 [FRK] III [AC] Ordained Deacon, Pleasant View Menn Ch, Chambersburg PA

Lehman, Dorcas Miller (Glenn M.) 34 W Eby Rd, Leola PA 17540, 717-656-6226, lehmangd@hydrosoft.net [LAN] IIC [AC] Campus Pastor, Lancaster Mennonite School, Lancaster PA

Lehman, G. Irvin (Verna) 1592 Park Rd, Harrisonburg VA 22801, 540-434-3161 [LAN] [RE]

Lehman, Gerald D. (Joyce) 3729 Edenville Rd, Chambersburg PA 17201, 717-264-1576, gjlehman@yellowbananas.com [FRK] III [AC] Ordained Deacon, Marion Menn Ch, Chambersburg PA

Lehman, J. Allen (Laura) 1633 Elizabeth Dr, Chambersburg PA 17201, 717-263-3308 [FRK] IIB1 [AC] Pastor, Pleasant View Menn Ch, Chambersburg PA

Lehman, John Paul (Barbara Moyer) 1023 Stuart St, Harrisonburg VA 22802, 540-432-6310, jplomc@aol.com [OH] [AW]

Lehman, Larry (Helen) 750 Tallow Hill Rd, Chambersburg PA 17201, tallowhill@juno.com [FRK] IIB1 [AC] Pastor, Mount Zion Menn Ch, Boonsboro MD

Lehman, Mark N. (Pauline) 330 Kelley St, Harrisonburg VA 22802, 540-433-0020 [VA] IIB3a [AC]

Lehman, Maurice E., 1001 E Oregon Rd, Lititz PA 17543-9205 [LAN] [RE]

Lehman, Tim (Susan Marie Gotwals) 1345 Twp Rd 181, Bellefontaine OH 43311-2751, 937-592-8101, jubilee@2access.net [OH] IIB1 [AC] Pastor, Jubilee Menn Ch, Bellefontaine OH

Lehman, Todd (Dawn) 30821 S Meridian Rd, Hubbard OR 97032, 503-266-6994, zionpastor@canby.com [PNW] IIA [AC] Pastor, Zion Menn Ch, Hubbard OR

Lehman, Todd A., 526 N Streeter, Hesston KS 67062, 620-327-2904, toddlehman@hotmail.com [WDC] IIA [AC] Youth Pastor, First Menn Ch, Hillsboro KS

Lehman, Verl, 66124 CR 27, Goshen IN 46526, 574-533-7943 [IM] [RE]

Lehman, Wilmer R. (Mary Louise) 1570 College Ave, Harrisonburg VA 22802, 540-438-9569, wmlehman@rica.net [VA] [RE]

Leichty, Paul D. (Nancy J.) 1417 S Main St, Goshen IN 46526-4348, 574-535-0067, paul@firstmennonite.net [IM] IIB2 [AC] Associate Pastor, Music, First Menn Ch, Middlebury IN

Leichty, Philip D. (Virginia) 502 Jefferson St, Rensselaer IN 47978, 219-866-8404, bomc@netnitco.net [IM] IIB1 [AC] Pastor, Burr Oak Menn Ch, Rensselaer IN

Leidig, Melvin, 3212 7th St SW, Canton OH 44710, 330-455-5502 [OH] [AW]

Leinbach, Alan E. (Helen K.) 5417 N 900 E, North Webster IN 46555, 574-834-4137, leinbaae@grace.edu [IM] IIB1 [AC] Pastor, Menn Ch of Warsaw, Warsaw IN

Leinbach, Etril J., 1801 Greencroft Blvd, Goshen IN 46526, 574-533-6550 [IM] [RE]

Leman, Robert, 2619 Coronado Dr, Fullerton CA 92635, 714-870-5766 [PSW] IIB2 [AC]

Lemon, J. Robert, 58 Gravel Hill Rd, Beaver OH 45613, 614-226-7635 [OH] [RE]

Lentz, Wilbur A., 1001 E Oregon Rd, Lititz PA 17543-9205, 717-509-5823 [LAN] [RE]

Lepard, Alan, 516 N Duncan, Newton KS 67114, 316-284-9871, alepard@sbcglobal.net [WDC] IIA [AW]

Leppert, George Earl (Yvonne Grace) 226 North St, Filer ID 83328, 208-326-3288, gleppert@filertel.com [PNW] IIB1 [AW]

Lever, Lawrence Lee (Terri Lea) 201 N Wedel, PO Box 378, Moundridge KS 67107, 620-345-2629, leelever@hotmail.com [WDC] IIB1 [AC] Pastor, Eden Menn Ch, Moundridge KS

Lewman, Richard (Collene Mae) 420 Thousand Acre Rd, Sellersville PA 18960, 215-257-5365, pastorrich@netcarrier.com [FRC] IIB1 [AC] Pastor, Finland Menn Ch, Pennsburg PA

Lichti, Tim (Carolyn) 1234 Westbrooke Ct, Goshen IN 46528-5065, 574-537-8826, tim@im.mennonite.net [IM] IB2 [AC] Conference Regional Minister, Indiana-Michigan Mennonite Conference, Goshen IN

Lilliston, Brenda Glanzer (Cecil Douglas Jr.) 2200 S Rock Rd Apt 1308, Wichita KS 67207, 316-685-3951 [WDC] IIB3a [AC] Staff Chaplain, Via Christi-St. Joseph, Wichita KS

Lind, Millard (Mariam) 1123 S 8th St, Goshen IN 46526, 574-533-6098 [IM] [RE]

Lind, Ralph Irvin (Brenda Janzen) 304 Spruce NE #1, Albuquerque NM 87106, 505-247-9753, rlind@flash.net [RM] IIB3a [AC]

Lind, Wilbert G. (Rhoda Hess) 1001 E Oregon Rd, Lititz PA 17543, 717-560-2922 [LAN] [RE]

Linsenmeyer, Dean A. (Rebecca K.) 644 Elridge St , Golden CO 80401, 303-238-5097, glmenno.dean@att.net [RM] IIB1 [AC] Pastor, Glennon Heights Menn Ch, Lakewood CO

Linsenmeyer, Rebecca (Dean) 644 Elridge, Golden CO 80403, 303-238-5097, BDLinsenmeyer@aol.com [RM] [AW]

Littman, Elsa, 122 Fern Dr, Walkerton IN 46574, 219-369-9292 [IM] IIB3a [AC] Resource Chaplain, LaPorte Hospital, LaPorte IN

Litwiller, Kenneth (Laura Dewey) 27 Kristi Ln, Lewistown PA 17044, 717-242-2439, kleml@verizon.net [LAN] IIA [AC] Pastor, Lost Creek Menn Ch, Mifflintown PA

Litwiller, Kurt, 326 Madison St, Hopedale IL 61747, 309-449-3447, kurtlitwiller@hotmail.com [CDC] IIB1 [AC] Pastor, Boynton Menn Ch, Hopedale IL

Liu, Adam Chu-Tsun (Mei-Ying Tsai) 10084 Adriana, Cupertino CA 95014, 408-253-3638 [PSW] IIB1 [AC]

Livengood, Dwain D., 124 Herr Ave, Lancaster PA 17602, 717-390-8790, dwainl@juno.com [LAN] IIC [AC] Associate Pastor, Lyndon Menn Ch, Lancaster PA

Livengood, Paul T., RR 6 Box 6640, Keyser WV 26726, 304-788-1882 [ALL] IIC [AC] Associate Pastor, Pinto Menn Ch, Pinto MD

Livermore Jr., J. D. (Debra K.) RR 1 Box 215 Co Line Rd, Germfask MI 49836, 906-586-9978, dlivermore@portup.com [IM] IIB1 [AC] Pastor, Germfask Menn Ch, Germfask MI

Lloyd, Gary E. (Nancy) 419 E Vine St, Stowe PA 19464, 610-327-3109, clloyd98@juno.com [ACC] IIB1 [AC] Pastor, Hope Community Fell of Phoenixville, Phoenixville PA

Logan, Peter L. (Tamalyn) 125 Meadow View Ln, Bainbridge PA 17502, 717-367-4091, ptlogan4@aol.com [LAN] IIA [AC] Pastor, Fountain of Life Ch, Middletown PA

Lohrentz, Vernon P. (Luella Mae) 205 Beverly, Newton KS 67114, 316-284-2095 [WDC] [RE]

Long, Clair R. (Barbara) 5334 Southview Dr, New Holland PA 17557, 717-355-2031 [LAN] IIB1 [AC] Pastor, Lichty Menn Ch, New Holland PA

Long, Paul W. (Esther) 250 N Spring Garden St, Ambler PA 19002 [FRC] IIC [AC] Chaplain, Liberty Ministries, Montgomery Co Correctional Facility, Eagleville PA.

Longacre, James C. (Ellen) 1387 Rte 100, Barto PA 19504, 610-845-7686 [FRC] IIB1 [AC] Pastor, Salford Menn Ch, Harleysville PA

Longenecker, Alvin (Ada) 2702 Crossroads Dr, Lewisburg PA 17837-9737, 717-568-4832 [LAN] III [AC] Ordained Deacon, Buffalo Menn Ch, Lewisburg PA

Longenecker, Catherine S. (Daniel) 1580 College Ave, Harrisonburg VA 22802, 540-432-5549 [VA] [RE]

Longenecker, Daniel M. (Catherine S.) 1580 College Ave, Harrisonburg VA 22802, 540-432-5549 [VA] IIB3a [AC]

Longenecker, William P. (Rhoda), Morson ON P0W 1J0,

Canada, 807-488-5411 [NC] IIB3b [AC]

Loop, Barry W. (Sue) 2350 Staples Mill Rd, Richmond VA 23230, 804-355-4922, sloop@gardener.com [VA] IIB1 [AC] Pastor, First Menn Ch of Richmond, Richmond VA

Lopez Jr., Joselino (Carman A.) 723 S Marshall St, Lancaster PA 17602, 717-390-1835 [LAN] IIA [AC] Missionary/Church Worker, Cusco, Peru

Lopez, Samuel M. (Soledad) 573B E Main St, New Holland PA 17557-1406, 717-354-8867, slopezCIMH@aol.com [LAN] IB3 [AC] Administrator, Spanish Mennonite Council of Churches, New Holland PA; Spanish Supervisor (Overseer), LAN Spanish District, PA

Louis, Laurent (Jasimine) 3511 22nd St SW, Lehigh Acres FL 33971, 941-369-7158 [SE] IIC [AC] Pastor, Assemblee de la Grace, Immokalee FL

Louis II, Peter K. (Debra) 1521 A Kam IV Rd, Honolulu HI 96819, 808-847-6308 [LAN] IIA [AC] Pastor, New Life Christian Fell, Honolulu HI

Louis Jean, Hilaire, 1115 NW 126th St, North Miami FL 33168, 305-688-8245, PastorH56@aol.com [SE] IC, IIA [AC] Pastor, Ch of God Prince of Peace, Miami FL; Haitian Advocate, SE Mennonite Conference, Miami FL

Lowery, Lee A. (Leona) 11624 S Hale St, Chicago IL 60643, 773-233-9699 [IL] [RE]

Ludwig, Jeffery A. (Maietta A.) 790 Mimosa Ln, Reading PA 19606, 610-404-7348, jludwig@enter.net [ACC] [AW]

Luginbill, Douglas Ray (Paula Jean) 1947 N Smarsh St, Wichita KS 67212, 316-722-7190, dpluginbill@netzero.net [WDC] IIB1 [AC] Pastor, Hope Menn Ch, Wichita KS

Luitjens, Nathan (Rachelle Anne Patmore) 1230 Graham Ave, Wayland IA 52654, 319-256-8812, luitjens@farmtel.net [CP] IIA [AC] Pastor, Sugar Creek Menn Ch, Wayland IA

Luu, Paul Quoccuong (Na) 1536 Pohaku St #306, Honolulu HI 96817-2854, 808-545-8318, pjhonuluu@juno.com [LAN] IIA [AC] Pastor, Vietnamese Christian Fell, Honolulu HI

Lyndaker, Carolyn Z. (Milford E.) 154 Furnace Rd, Wardensville WV 26851 [VA] IIA [AC] Associate Pastor, Crest Hill Community Ch, Wardensville WV

Lyndaker, Milford E. (Carolyn June) 154 Furnace Rd, Wardensville WV 26851, 504-874-4247, mclyndaker@citlink.net [VA] IIB1 [AC] Pastor, Crest Hill Community Ch, Wardensville WV

M

Mack, Ellis L., 487 Smokepipe Rd, Souderton PA 18964, 215-256-8422 [FRC] [RE]

Maclin, Janace (Rick) 13208 Matador, St Louis MO 63141, 314-542-2123 [IL] [AW]

Maclin, Phillip, 2918 W Montana St, Peoria IL 61605, 309-674-0529 [CDC, IL] IIC [AC] Pastor, Joy Fell Menn Ch, Peoria IL

Maclin, Rick (Janace) 13208 Matador, Saint Louis MO 63141, 314-542-2123 [IL] [AW]

MacMaster, Eve B. (Richard Kerwin) 4130 NW 19th Pl, Gainesville FL 32605, gnvmenno@bellsouth.net [SE] IIB1 [AC] Pastor, Emmanuel Menn Ch, Gainesville FL

Maenza, Philip James, 123 S Main St, Athens PA 18810, 570-882-9366 [FRC] IIA [AC] Pastor, New Life Menn Ch, Athens PA

Maina, Gladys (Simon Mungai) 2104 W Bryden Dr, Muncie IN 47304, 317-289-5436, smungai@regenstrief.org [CDC, IM] IIB1 [AC] Pastor, Morning Star Ch, Muncie IN

Maldonado, Carlos M. (Adelaida) PO Box 1171, Lancaster PA 17608-1171, cmaldonado@pa.freei.net [LAN] IIB1 [AC]

Maldonado, David (Madaline) Iglesia Arca de Salvación, 126 Catalina, Fort Meyers FL 33916, 941-332-7556 [SE] IIB1 [AC] Pastor, Iglesia Menonita Arca de Salvación, Fort Myers FL

Maldonado, Madeline, 3225 4th St W, Lehigh Acres FL 33971 [SE] IIA [AC] Associate Pastor, Iglesia Menonita Arca de Salvación, Fort Myers FL

Malin, C. Ralph, 11 Sycamore Dr, Malvern PA 19355, 610-644-6726 [FRC] [RE]

Mamo, Mesfin (Lily Girma) 115 Old Short Hills Rd, Apt 350, W Orange NJ 07052, Mesfinm@att.net [LAN] IIB1 [AC] Associate Pastor, Emmanuel Worship Center, Bronx NY

Maniglia, Joseph (Rebecca) 1524 W Schreiber Ave 32, Chicago IL 60626, 773-262-4107, manigabyte@ameritech.net [IL] IIA [AC] Youth Pastor, Living Water Community Ch, Chicago IL

Marchand, James C. (Donna) 732 Ashby Dr, Waynesboro VA 22980, 219-261-3401, marchand@ntelos.net [VA] IIB1 [AC] Pastor, Lynside Menn Ch, Lyndhurst VA

Margono, Harjono (Maria Ong) 12051 Havelock Ave, Culver City CA 90230, 310-745-0335, margono@juno.com [PSW] IIB2, IIB3b [AW]

Marin, Basil (Diane) 446 E Rock St, Harrisonburg VA 22802, 540-574-3344, basil@rica.net [VA] IIB1 [AC] Pastor, Immanuel Menn Ch, Harrisonburg VA

Marshall, Eric P. (Cheryl) 53 E Main St , Reinholds PA 17569, 717-336-0392, cemarshall@dejazzd.com [LAN] IIB2 [AC] Youth Pastor, Blainsport Menn Ch, Stevens PA

Martens, John, PO Box 113, Chester VT 05143, 802-875-3057 [FRC] [RE]

Martens, Rudolph (Elvina Neufeld) 2114 Ln Ave, Elkhart IN 46517, 574-293-8612 [CDC] [RE]

Martens, Weldon R. (Jenny Harms) 1151 18th St , Henderson NE 68371-8910, 402-723-4878 [CP] IIB1 [AC] Pastor, Bethesda Menn Ch, Henderson NE

Martin, Alvin G. (Elva) 201 Wheat Ridge Dr, Ephrata PA 17522-8554, 717-445-6813 [LAN] [RE]

Martin, Brenda North (Stanley) 1616 Glengarry Dr, Cary NC 27561, 919-932-5206 [VA] IIB3a [AC]

Martin, Brian E. (Shirley) 5559 Division Hwy, Narvon PA 17555, 717-354-0784, bemartin@ptd.net [LAN] III [AC] Ordained Deacon, Weaverland Menn Ch, East Earl PA

Martin, Bruce (Jewell) 1423 Calihan NE, Bemidji MI 56601 [VA] [AW]

Martin, C. Kenneth (Lois) 238 Reading Rd, East Earl PA 17519, 717-445-5736, kenc@epix.net [LAN] IB3 [AC] Bishop, Weaverland Menn Ch, East Earl PA; Bishop, Weaverland-NE District, East Earl PA

Martin, Carl W. (Margaret) 106 Furlow Rd, Reinholds PA 17569-9057, 717-484-4239 [LAN] [RE]

Martin, Chester L. (Linda) 1200 Kramer Mill Rd, Denver PA 17517, 717-445-7563, clmartin@epix.net [LAN] IIB2 [AC] Associate Pastor, Village Chapel Menn Ch, New Holland PA

Martin, Clifford L. (Carol) 83 S Reamstown Rd, Stevens

PA 17578, 717-336-8239, ccmarfam@juno.com [LAN]
IIC [AC] Camp Administrator, Woodcrest Retreat Center,
Ephrata PA; Leadership Team, Ephrata Menn Ch,
Ephrata PA

Martin, Curvin (Mary Ann) 77 Rideout Ave Apt 10-3,
Lewiston ME 04240-3469 [LAN] [AW]

Martin, D. David (Robin) 603 Lititz Rd, Manheim PA
17545, 717-626-5295, ddavidmartin@juno.com [LAN]
IIB2 [AC] Associate Pastor, Manheim Menn Ch, East
Petersburg PA

Martin, Daryl G. (Doris) 16 Cherry St, Pine Grove PA
17963, 570-345-2552, dmartin@phfa.org [LAN] IIC
[AC] Pastor, Roedersville Menn Ch, Pine Grove PA

Martin, David Henry (Janet) 85 Dogwood Ct,
Shippensburg PA 17257, 717-264-8633 [FRK] III [AC]
Ordained Deacon, Chambersburg Menn Ch,
Chambersburg PA

Martin, Donald, 591 W Broad St, New Holland PA
17557, 717-354-8705 [LAN] [RE]

Martin, Edwin Ray (Janet) 105 S Blainsport Rd,
Reinholds PA 17569-9714, 717-336-3596 [LAN] III [AC]
Ordained Deacon, Blainsport Menn Ch, Stevens PA

Martin, Elmer E. (Grace) 105 New St PO Box 267, Blue
Ball PA 17506-0267, 717-354-4000 [LAN] [RE]

Martin, Elmer M. (Joanne) 795 Durlach Rd, Stevens PA
17578, 717-738-0589 [LAN] III [AC] Ordained Deacon,
Hershey Menn Ch, Kinzers PA

Martin, Emanuel (Lois Mumaw) 1921A Ty-Way
Crossing, Harrisonburg VA 22802, 540-434-3923,
manlois57@cs.com [ACC] [RE]

Martin, Enos D. (Ruth) 595 Old Hershey Rd,
Elizabethtown PA 17022-9409, 717-367-2628,
enosd@supernet.net [LAN] IB3 [AC] Bishop/Overseer,
LAN Elizabethtown District, PA

Martin, Ernest D. (Rosetta M.) 3005 Renkenberger Rd,
Columbiana OH 44408, 330-482-3139 [OH] [RE]

Martin, Ernest W. (Nancy) 49 Hillside Rd, Pottsville PA
17901, 570-622-8743, enmartin@losch.net [LAN] IIB2
[AC] Associate Pastor, Palo Alto Menn Ch, Pottsville PA

Martin, Erwin G. (M. Arlene) 323 Hartings Park Rd,
Denver PA 17517, 717-445-6546 [LAN] [RE]

Martin, Ezra M., 1415 Pleasant View Rd, Ephrata PA
17522, 717-733-4517 [LAN] [RE]

Martin, G. Joseph (Ruth Ann) 1539 Choxes Chase,
Greencastle PA 17225, 717-593-0060,
gjoemartin@earthlink.net [FRK] IIB1 [AC] Pastor, Salem
Ridge Menn Ch, Greencastle PA

Martin, Gary E. (Patricia Mierau) 1545 W Pratt #203,
Chicago IL 60626-4215, gmartin1545@sbcglobal.net
[IL] IIB1 [AC] Minister of Discipling, Arthur Menn Ch,
Arthur IL

Martin, Gary E. (Krista) 3911 Oregon Pk, Leola PA
17540, 717-661-7058, gkmartin6@yahoo.com [LAN]
IIA [AC] Associate Pastor, Landis Valley Menn Ch,
Lancaster PA

Martin, Glen D. (Mary) 119 Furlow Rd, Reinholds PA
17569-9143, 717-484-2162,
glenmarymartin@juno.com [LAN] IIB1 [AC] Associate
Pastor, Gehman Menn Ch, Adamstown PA

Martin, Glenn H. (Carolyn J.) 600 W Aberdeen Dr,
Trenton OH 45067-1008, 513-988-1355 [CDC] IIB1 [AC]
Pastor, Trenton Menn Ch, Trenton OH

Martin, Harold L. (Ellen) 3336 Teak Cr, Harrisonburg VA
22801, 540-432-0839 [VA] [RE]

Martin, Harold W. (Twila) 76 Reinholds Rd, Reinholds
PA 17569, 717-336-5418 [LAN] [RE]

Martin, Irvin L., 1788 Bowmansville Rd, Mohnton PA
19540, 717-484-4439, IrvinM3@juno.com [LAN] IB3,
IIB1 [AC] Pastor, Gehman Menn Ch, Adamstown PA

Martin, J. Daniel (Cynthia) 14 W Main St PO Box 441,
Richland PA 17087, 717-866-7911,
martinfam@dejazzd.com [LAN] III [AC] Ordained
Deacon, Meckville Menn Ch, Bethel PA

Martin Jr., J. Donald (Yvonne) 334 Pershing Ave,
Lebanon PA 17042, 717-270-9918,
donymartin@juno.com [LAN] IIB2 [AC] Pastor,
Lebanon Christian Fell, Lebanon PA

Martin Sr., J. Donald (Mary Ann) 697 Prescott Dr,
Lebanon PA 17042, 717-273-8797,
donaldmartin@paonline.com [LAN] IIB1 [AC] Pastor,
Meckville Menn Ch, Bethel PA; Chaplain, Lebanon
County Prison, Lebanon PA

Martin, J. Elvin (Laverne) 100 Main St, Akron PA 17501,
717-859-3960 [LAN] [RE]

Martin, J. Leon (Katherine S.) 1725 Juniper Pl Apt 105,
Goshen IN 46526, 574-537-3732 [EDC] [RE]

Martin, J. Nevin (Ruth Ann) 326 Broad St, PO Box 274,
Terre Hill PA 17581, 717-445-5618,
jnrmartin@juno.com [LAN] III [AC] Ordained Deacon,
Weaverland Menn Ch, East Earl PA

Martin, James R. (Betty) 1642 Reading Rd, Mohnton PA
19540, 717-445-4313 [LAN] IIB3c [AC]

Martin, Jason S. (Mary) 1801 Greencroft Blvd #316,
Goshen IN 46526-5173, 574-633-4605 [IM] [RE]

Martin, Jerold R., 200 Speedwell Forge Rd, Lititz PA
17543, 717-626-9148 [LAN] IIB2 [AC] Associate Pastor,
Hinkletown Menn Ch, Ephrata PA

Martin, Jewel (Bruce) 1423 Calihan NE, Bemidji MI
56601 [VA] [AW]

Martin, John R. (Marian) 1504 Hawthorn Cr,
Harrisonburg VA 22802, 540-432-7253 [VA] [RE]

Martin, Kelly G. (Sherry) 496 Weaverland Valley Rd, East
Earl PA 17519, 717-445-0930 [LAN] IIC [AC]

Martin, Kenneth (Dawn) 622 Front St, PO Box 463, New
Berlin PA 17855-0463, 717-966-0003,
kdmartins@chilitech.net [LAN] IIC [AC] Chaplain,
Prison Ministry, PA

Martin, Kerry D. (Marlene) 40 N Church St SW, Ephrata
PA 17522, 717-859-5626 or 717-859-2322,
kermar34@juno.com [LAN] IIA [AC] Associate Pastor,
Millport Menn Ch, Leola PA

Martin, Lauren R. (Kimberly) 2401 Blake Ave, Glenwood
Springs CO 81601-4326, 970-945-8851,
llkmsplace@juno.com [RM] IIB1 [AC] Pastor, Glenwood
Menn Ch, Glenwood Springs CO

Martin, Lee (Margaret) 4697 Mount Clinton Pk,
Harrisonburg VA 22802, mcmchurch@juno.com [VA]
IIB1 [AC] Pastor, Mount Clinton Menn Ch, Harrisonburg
VA

Martin, Lee Roy M. (Ann) 53 Maple Farm Rd, Ephrata
PA 17522-9582, 717-859-1526, lemars3@aol.com
[LAN] III [AC] Ordained Deacon, Metzler Menn Ch,
Akron PA

Martin, Lew K. (Kayleen) 30 S Whisper Ln, New Holland
PA 17557, 717-354-3126,
LewKayleenMartin@Paonline.com [LAN] IIC [AC] Youth
Pastor, Meadville Menn Ch, Kinzers PA

Martin, Linford (Elaine Carol) 12401 CR 20, Middlebury

IN 46540, 574-825-3572, linford@firstmennonite.net [IM] IB3, IIB1 [AC] Pastor, First Menn Ch, Middlebury IN; Overseer, Forks Mennonite Ch, Middlebury IN

Martin, Louis H. (Lois) 3795 Beagle Rd, Middletown PA 17057-4056, 717-944-5677 [LAN] III [AC] Ordained Deacon, Herr St Menn Ch, Harrisburg PA

Martin, Luke S. (Mary Kauffman) 29 S Madison St, Allentown PA 18102, 610-434-9031, LSMKM@Enter.net [FRC] [RE]

Martin, Marlin E. (Linda) PO Box 202, Terre Hill PA 17581, 717-445-6697 [LAN] IIC [AC] Pastor, Cedar Ln Chapel, Terre Hill PA

Martin, Nelson L. (Janet) 90A Menno Village, Chambersburg PA 17201, 717-263-4502 [ACC] [RE]

Martin, Nelson R. (Carol) 6229 Mount Pleasant Rd, Honey Brook PA 19344, 610-273-3381, nrcdmartin@onemain.com [LAN] IIB1 [AC] Associate Pastor, Goodville Menn Ch, Goodville PA

Martin, Nelson W. (Anna Mae) 7 Cindy Cr, Lititz PA 17543, 717-626-6301 [LAN] IB3 [AC]

Martin, Paul H. (Dorothy) 939 Main St Apt C-2, Akron PA 17501-1480, 717-859-1599, phdhmartin@aol.com [ACC] [RE]

Martin, Philip (Luann) 11588 Gebhard Ln, Alden NY 14004, 716-937-0412 [NY] IIB1 [AC] Pastor, Alden Menn Ch, Alden NY

Martin, Randall J., 3204 Hostetter Rd, Washington Boro PA 17582, 717-872-5910, giveitall@juno.com [LAN] IIB1 [AC] Pastor, Habecker Menn Ch, Lancaster PA

Martin, Raymond M. (Alice Good) 1212 Springwell Place, Newport News VA 23608-7709, ralmar@worldnet.att.net [VA] IB3 [AC] Overseer, Virginia Mennonite Conference, Newport News VA

Martin, Rebecca, 303 Wertz Ave, Dalton OH 44618, 330-828-2928, tbex303@netzero.net [OH] IIB2 [AC] Youth Pastor, Pleasant View Menn Ch, North Lawrence OH

Martin, Richard B., RR 1 Box 248A2, Monroeton PA 18832-9622, 717-364-3974 [LAN] IIB1 [AC] Pastor, W Franklin Menn Ch, Monroeton PA

Martin, Richard E. (Beverly) 2030 S 050 W, LaGrange IN 46761, 260-463-2231 [IM] [RE]

Martin, Robert A. (Sarah) 1460 Main St, East Earl PA 17519, 717-445-5101 [LAN] IIB1 [AC] Associate Pastor, River Corner Menn Ch, Conestoga PA

Martin, Robert K. (Sandra) PO Box 212, Morris Run PA 16939, 570-638-2274, rkmartin@ptdprolog.net [LAN] IIB1 [AC] Pastor, Calvary Menn Fell, Morris Run PA

Martin, Robert S. (Mary) 2510 S 5th Ave, Lebanon PA 17042, 717-949-3586 [LAN] [RE]

Martin, Rodney A. (Angie) 63 Robinhill Dr, Lititz PA 17543-7301, 717-625-1706, rodmarmis@aol.com [LAN] IIB1 [AC] Associate Pastor, Lititz Menn Ch, Lititz PA

Martin, Roger I. (Dorothy) 117 S Valley Dr, Hagerstown MD 21740, 301-790-3843 [FRK] [AW]

Martin, Roy B. (Grace) 17 Hilltop Dr, Ephrata PA 17522, 717-733-6351 [LAN] IIB2 [AC] Associate Pastor, Metzler Menn Ch, Akron PA

Martin, Roy D. (Ruth) RR 4 Box 236M, Waynesboro VA 22980, 540-943-8102 [VA] [RE]

Martin, Stephen L. (Betty) 875 Lincoln Garden Rd, Ephrata PA 17522, 717-733-3150, slm875@dejazzd.com [LAN] IIB1 [AC] Pastor, Indiantown Menn Ch, Ephrata PA

Martin, Todd, 303 Wertz Ave, Dalton OH 44618, 330-828-2928, tbex303@netzero.net [OH] IIB2 [AC] Youth Pastor, Pleasant View Menn Ch, North Lawrence OH

Martin, Warren W. (Verna) 416 Memorial Hwy, Fleetwood PA 19522, 610-944-0574 [LAN] [RE]

Martin, William G. (Sharon) 167 S Main St, Dublin PA 18917, 215-249-0259, bmartin@deeprunE.org [FRC] IIA [AC] Associate Pastor, Deep Run Menn Ch E, Perkasie PA

Martinez, Esther, PO Box 227153, Dallas TX 75222, 972-286-1342, emartine@airmail.net [SC, WDC] IIA [AW] Co-Pastor, Ch of Many Peoples, Dallas TX

Martino, David (Susan) 1584 Park Rd, Winfield PA 17889, 717-743-0326, david@cmfmilton.org [LAN] IIB1 [AC] Pastor, Community Menn Fell, Milton PA

Martz, Robert (Sherry) 27847 Crestview Dr, Elkhart IN 46517, 574-361-0975, robert@martz.us [IM] IIB1 [AC] Pastor, Olive Menn Ch, Elkhart IN

Martzall, Dorcas J. (Glenn) 316 S Railroad Ave, New Holland PA 17557, 717-354-8188 [LAN] IIC [AC] Chaplain, Mennonite Home Communities, Lancaster PA

Masih, Jai Prakash (Shireen) Orchard Village Apt 1, 1280 W Indian Trails Dr, Aurora IL 60506, 680-896-9217, jaiis53@hotmail.com [CDC] IIB1 [AC] Pastor, Asian Menn Community Ch, Aurora IL

Mason, Chad, 205 NE Grant St, Ankeny IA 50021 [CP] IIA [AC] Pastor, Christ Community Ch, Des Moines IA

Massanari, Eric (Yolanda Kauffman) 319 S Pine St, Newton KS 67114, 316-283-5281 [SC, WDC] IIB1 [AC] Pastor, Shalom Menn Ch, Newton KS

Mast, Conrad (Donna) 531 Scottdale Ave, Scottdale PA 15683, 724-887-5563 [ALL] IIB1 [AC] Co-Pastor, Scottdale Menn Ch, Scottdale PA

Mast, Dale (Kathy) PO Box 7736, Richmond VA 23231-0236 [VA] IIC [AC]

Mast, Donna (Conrad) 531 Scottdale Ave, Scottdale PA 15683, 724-887-5563 [ALL] IB3, IIB1 [AC] Co-Pastor, Scottdale Menn Ch, Scottdale PA

Mast, Fremon E., 6193 Chestnut Ridge, Wooster OH 44691, 330-264-0945 [OH] [RE]

Mast, LeRoy J. (Sherry Lee) PO Box 91, Hammondsport NY 14840, 607-569-3283, lsmast2@sg23.com [NY] IIB1 [AC] Pastor, Pleasant Valley Menn Ch, Hammondsport NY

Mast, Mattie Marie, 505 Smith Ave, Dalton OH 44618, sonnenbergmc@juno.com [OH] IIA [AC] Associate Pastor, Sonnenberg Menn Ch, Kidron OH

Mast, Michael M. (Mattie Marie) 505 Smith Ave, Dalton OH 44618-9039, 330-828-0491, mmmast@juno.com [OH] IIB1 [AC] Pastor, Sonnenberg Menn Ch, Kidron OH

Mast, Moses (Sadie) 4708 Outpost Dr, Spencer OK 73084, 405-771-4743, mosesmast@aol.com [WDC] IIB1 [AC] Pastor, Joy Menn Ch, Oklahoma City OK

Mast, Robert W. (Esther) 2314 Mount Pleasant Rd, Chesapeake VA 23322, 757-482-3435 [VA] [RE]

Mast, Russell Lowell (Alma Hilty) 2635 Walnut St Box 59, Walnut Creek OH 44687-0059, 330-893-2356 [CDC] [RE]

Mast, Wesley S. (Elsie) 2665 Sutton Pl, Lancaster PA 17601, 717-560-3470, wmast@juno.com [LAN] IIB3a [AC] Chaplain, Hospice of Lancaster Co, Lancaster PA

Matos, Eugenio (Sergia) 762 Centre St, Trenton NJ 08611, 609-396-1901 [LAN] IIA [AC] Pastor, Nueva Vida en Cristo, Trenton NJ

Matteson, F. Matthew (Mary Lou) 2720 Tsawsi Rd,

MINISTERS

6

Knoxville TN 37931, 865-691-5347, matteson@mfire.com [VA] IIB1 [AC] Pastor, Concord Menn Ch, Knoxville TN

Maurer, David Thomas (Beth) 6090 Lugabill Rd, Columbus Grove OH 45830, 419-369-4474, DTMaurer@hotmail.com [CDC] IIA [AC] Minister of Youth and Christian Education, Grace Menn Ch, Pandora OH

Maust, Duane E. (Elaine L.) 135 Fairchild Rd, Meridian MS 39307, 601-485-2248, Duelchna@aol.com [GS] IIB1 [AC] Co-Pastor, Jubilee Menn Ch, Meridian MS

Maust, Elaine (Duane Earl) 135 Fairchild Rd, Meridian MS 39307, 601-485-2248, Duelchna@aol.com [GS] IIB1 [AC] Co-Pastor, Jubilee Menn Ch, Meridian MS

Maust, Norman (Wilmetta) 57365 CR 23, Goshen IN 46528, 574-295-6511 [IM] IIB3c [AC] Ordained Deacon, Pleasant View Menn Ch, Goshen IN

Maven, G. Craig (Wendy Myers) 1326 Yoderstrasse, Berne IN 46711, 260-589-9911, craig@firstmennonite.org [CDC] IIB1 [AC] Pastor, First Menn Ch, Berne IN

McClintic, David (Terry) PO Box 328, Concord MI 49237, 517-524-7489, dtmcclin@frontiernet.net [IM] IIB1 [AC] Pastor, Liberty Menn Ch, Concord MI

McDorman, Lewis E., 326 SW 6th St, PO Box 1278, Premont TX 78375-1278, 361-348-2872 [SC] IIB1 [AC] Pastor, United Menn Ch, Premont TX

McDougal, Kent, 680 56th St, Des Moines IA 50312 [CP] IIA [AC] Pastor, Christ Community Ch, Des Moines IA

McFarland, John (Mabel) D-90 Kalkaji, New Delhi 110019, India [VA] IIB3b [AC]

McFarren, Patrick J. (Janet Elaine) 94 Hickory Tree Rd, Asheville NC 28805, 828-298-3233, avlmenno@juno.com [VA] IIB1 [AC] Pastor, Asheville Menn Ch, Asheville NC

McKinney, Karl (Kellie M.) 4206 LaSalle Ave, Baltimore MD 21206, 410-485-2775, pastarkam@msn.com [ACC] IIB3b [AC] Minister of Church Planting, Mennonite Mission Network, Elkhart IN

McKnight, Hugh (Joyce) 705 Somerset St, Johnstown PA 15901, 814-535-1688 [ALL] [AW]

McPhee, Art (Evelyn L.) AMBS, 3003 Benham Ave, Elkhart IN 46517, 574-296-6210, amcphee@ambs.edu [IM] IIB3c [AC] Professor, Associated Mennonite Biblical Seminary, Elkhart IN

McVay, Darrel, 48655 Center St, St Clairsville OH 43950, 740-695-0303 [OH] IIB1 [AC] Pastor, Fairpoint Menn Ch, Fairpoint OH

Meador, James B. (Judy Poole) 2209 Silver Ln, Willow St PA 17584-9613, 717-464-0475, JJ.Meador@verizon.net [LAN] IIB1 [AC] Pastor, Willow St Menn Ch, Willow Street PA

Mears-Driedger, June (Kevin) 2315 S Washington St, Lansing MI 17584-9613, 517-346-7610, jmdriedger@mindspring.com [CDC, IM] IIB1 [AC] Pastor, MSU Menn Fell, East Lansing MI

Meck, John D. (Jane) 109 Snake Ln, Kinzers PA 17535, 717-768-8334, j6meck@dejazzd.com [LAN] IIB1 [AC] Pastor, Meadville Menn Ch, Kinzers PA

Meck, John Dwight (Deborah) 371 Walnut Run Rd, Willow St PA 17584, 717-687-7120, jd.meck@juno.com [LAN] IIB1 [AC] Pastor, Strasburg Menn Ch, Strasburg PA

Mejia, René, 1129 Ayersville St, Defiance OH 43512, 419-782-6761, reneme@defnet.com [OH] IIB1 [AC]

Melendrez, John (Sissy) 11551 E 169th St, Artesia CA 90701-1706, 310-860-3464 [PSW] IIB1 [AC] Pastor, Bethel Community Ch, Santa Fe Springs CA

Mellinger, James W. (Ruth) 615 W Ames Pl, Williamsport PA 17701, 717-323-9779, jrmel@chilitech.net [LAN] IIB1 [AC] Associate Pastor, Agape Fell, Williamsport PA

Menard, Martin (Rosette) PO Box 381282, Miami FL 33238, 305-891-1651, PastorMenard@yahoo.com [SE] IIC [AC] Pastor, Good Shepherd Evangelical, Miami FL

Mendoza, Irene (Rafael) 328 S Azusa Ave, La Puente CA 91744, 626-912-1983, holfmc1@juno.com [PSW] IIA [AC] Associate Pastor, House of the Lord Fell, La Puente CA

Meneses, Michael A. (Eloise Hiebert) 1109 Allentown Rd, Lansdale PA 19446, 215-393-9836, meneses1@juno.com [FRC] IIB1 [AC] Pastor, Wellspring Ch of Skippack, Skippack PA

Mengistu, Yeshitela (Ebebach) PO Box 16668, St Louis MO 63105, 314-725-63105 [IL] IIC [AC] Teacher/Director, Jesus The Fountain of Life Institute, Addis Ababa, Ethiopia

Mentzer, Mark W. (Cathy) 15 Church Rd, New Providence PA 17560, 717-786-9198, PastorMark1@verizon.net [LAN] IIB2 [AC] Youth Pastor, Willow Street Menn Ch, Willow Street PA

Messenger, David, PO Box 150777, Cape Coral FL 33915-0777, 239-772-5683, Dmessenger@capechristian.com [SE] IIA [AC] Worship Pastor, Cape Christian Fell, Cape Coral FL

Metzler, Duane L. (Kristine) 707 Millwood Rd, Willow Street PA 17584, 717-464-3361 [LAN] IIB1 [AC] Pastor, University Christian Fell, Millersville PA

Metzler, Edgar J. (Ethel Yake) 211 E Douglas St, Goshen IN 46526-4061, 574-534-2245, etheled@juno.com [CDC, IM] [RE]

Metzler, Everett G. (Margaret J.) 1311 Cosmo St, Goshen IN 46528, 574-534-5491, MetzlerUSA@aol.com [IM] [RE]

Metzler, Glenn D. (Betty) 2646 Pinewood Rd, Lancaster PA 17601, 717-581-5399 [LAN] IIC [AC] Chaplain, Landis Homes, Lititz PA

Metzler, John B., 266 Panorama Dr, Denver PA 17517, 717-445-6769 [LAN] [RE]

Meyer, Brenda Hostetler (Rich) 13416 CR 44, Millersburg IN 46543, 574-642-3963, brendam@maplenet.net [IM] IIB1 [AC] Pastor, Benton Menn Ch, Goshen IN

Meyers, Garland L. (Janice Martin) 44 William Penn Dr, Schwenksville PA 19473, 610-948-6130 [FRC] IIB3a [AC] Chaplain, Heartland Hospice

Michaels, Thomas L. (Cheryl D.) 5359 PR 382, Millersburg OH 44654, 330-893-3750 [OH] IIB1 [AC]

Middleton, Glenn (Ardis) 70245 Kime Rd, Sturgis MI 49091, 269-651-6046 [IM] IIB1 [AC] Pastor, Christian Fell Center, Sturgis MI

Mierau, Jake (Lucille Mae) 1478 Willow Ct Lot 45, Goshen IN 46526, 574-534-8102 [CDC] [RE]

Miiller, Walter Jay (Sonia) 2470 520th St SW, Kalona IA 52247, 319-683-3158, jaymiiller@hotmail.com [CP] IIB1 [AC] Pastor, East Union Menn Ch, Kalona IA

Miller, Abner G. (Betty) 1001 E Oregon Rd, Lititz PA

17543, 717-509-5428 [LAN] [RE]

Miller, Alvin R., 28648 CR 38, Wakarusa IN 46573, 574-862-4300 [IM] [RE]

Miller Jr., Andrew G. (Naomi) 631 Fruitville Pk, Manheim PA 17545-9718, 717-664-5023 [LAN] IIB2 [AC] Associate Pastor, Erisman Menn Ch, Manheim PA

Miller, Arthur H. (Ethel) 475 Church St, Landisville PA 17538, 717-898-7896 [LAN] [RE]

Miller, Beth (Marcus) Box 62, 914 5th St, Wellman IA 52356, 319-646-2856 [CP] IIB3a [AC] Chaplain, Parkview Nursing Home, Wellman IA

Miller, Chadwick, 12130 Jerome Ave, Hartville OH 44632, chad@hartvillemennonite.org [OH] IIA [AC] Assoc Pastor of Student Ministries/Worship Arts, Hartville Menn Ch, Hartville OH

Miller, Corey Lee (Nancy Sue) 891 Chisholm Trail, Newton KS 67114, 620-367-4672, cmiller@tabormennonite.org [WDC] IIB1 [AC] Pastor, Tabor Menn Ch, Newton KS

Miller, D. Richard, 1639 Magnolia Ct, Goshen IN 46526-6529 [IM] [RE]

Miller, Daniel G. (Joyce Elaine) 1119 Chestnut St, Lebanon PA 17042, 717-270-1904, millers@paonline.com [LAN] IIB2 [AC] Pastor, Freedom in Christ Fell, Lebanon PA

Miller, Daniel Z. (Nadine) 62436 CR 17, Goshen IN 46526, 574-534-3229, SuspndrDan@aol.com [IM] IIB1 [AC] Interim Pastor, Marion Menn Ch, Shipshewana IN

Miller, David B. (Mary) 884 Bayberry Dr, State College PA 16801, 814-861-5612 [ALL] IB3, IIB1 [AC] Pastor, University Menn Ch, State College PA

Miller, David F. (Martha Pearl) 231 Mockingbird Dr, Souderton PA 18964, 215-723-9345 [VA] [RE] Fund Consultant, Miller Ministries, Souderton PA

Miller, Edgar (Martha) 2351 Breckenridge Ct, Harrisonburg VA 22801, 540-433-6558 [VA] [RE]

Miller, Edmond F. (Wendy) 11054 Phillips Store Rd, Broadway VA 22815, 540-896-5216 [VA] [RE]

Miller, Edward J., 16203 E Princeton Cr, Aurora CO 80013, 303-699-7510 [RM] [RE]

Miller, Eldo J., 315 W 6th, La Junta CO 81050, 719-775-2145 [RM] [RE]

Miller, Eli (Irene) RR 2 Box 2269, Seligman MO 65745, 417-341-1005 [SC] III [AC] Elder, Rogers Menn/Ch of the Brethren, Pea Ridge AR

Miller, Elsie, 179 Norwood Ct, Box 411, Smithville OH 44677, 216-669-2193 [CDC] [RE]

Miller, Eugene N. (Sharon) 3231 Palmer Rd, Wellsville NY 14895, 716-593-3287, Genemile@aol.com [NY] IIB1 [AC] Pastor, Yorks Corners Menn Ch, Wellsville NY; Camp Administrator, Penn-York Camp, Ulysses PA

Miller, Frederic A. (Judy) 13153 Hackett Rd, Orrville OH 44667, 330-857-6521, bethmill@sssnet.com [OH] IIB3c [AC]

Miller, Freeman J. (Naomi) 2027 N Carlisle St, Philadelphia PA 19121, 215-765-3676, fjmiller@erols.com [LAN] IB3 [AC] Bishop/Overseer, Philadelphia District, Philadelphia PA

Miller, Gordon, 109 Mohican Ave, Orrville OH 44667, 330-683-9398, chpastor@neobright.net [OH] IIB1 [AC] Pastor, Crown Hill Menn Ch, Rittman OH

Miller, Harold N. (Karen A.) 280 Park Ave, Corning NY 14830, 607-937-4390, HNMiller@juno.com [NY] IIB1 [AC] Pastor, Community Menn Fell of Corning, Corning NY

Miller, Harold W., 604 Sumneytown Pk, PO Box 1001, North Wales PA 19454, 215-699-4227 [FRC] IIB3a [RE]

Miller, Howard I. (Carolyn) 4368 Zion Church Rd, Broadway VA 22815, 540-896-4614 or 540-421-4944, howard@lindale.com [VA] IIB2 [AC]

Miller, J. Brian (Heather) 200 Nordick Dr, Lancaster PA 17602, 717-464-5287, brianheather4@juno.com [LAN] IIC [AC] Associate Pastor, Sunnyside Menn Ch, Lancaster PA

Miller, J. Daniel, 5022 Avoca Ave, Ellicott City MD 21043, 410-465-1233 [LAN] IIB1 [AC] Pastor, First Menn Ch of Columbia, Ellicott City MD

Miller, J. John J. (Mabel) PO Box 305, Kalona IA 52247, 319-656-5457 [CP] [RE]

Miller, J. Robert (Irene) RR 1 Box 61, Liberty PA 16930-9757, 570-324-5405 [LAN] [RE]

Miller, John H. (Anna) 197 Quarry Hill Ln, Schuyler VA 22969, 804-831-2383 [VA] IIB1 [AC]

Miller, John M. (Mary Christine) 15297 Arnold Rd, Dalton OH 44618, 330-828-8593, johnmiller1950@sbcglobal.net [OH] IIB1 [AC] Pastor, Pleasant View Menn Ch, North Lawrence OH

Miller, Joseph S. (Julie Zimmerman) 1301 Sweet Clover Dr, Goshen IN 46526, 574-534-4448, joe@waterfordchurch.org [IM] IIB1 [AC]

Miller, Keith Allen Graber (Ann Maureen) 208 River Vista Dr, Goshen IN 46526, 574-534-3891 [IM] IIB3d [AC] Professor, Goshen College, Goshen IN

Miller, Kenton Tod (Cynthia June) 10907 Market Ave, Uniontown OH 44685, 330-877-3217, k-cmiller@juno.com [OH] IIB2 [AC] Associate Pastor, Dayspring Christian Fell, North Canton OH

Miller, Lee E. (Vina) 2869 Wood St, Sarasota FL 34232, 941-316-0861 [SE] IIB2 [AC] Minister of Administration, Bay Shore Menn Ch, Sarasota FL

Miller, Leo J., 418 E Sassafras St, Orrville OH 44667, 330-684-1213 [OH] [RE]

Miller, Leon J. (Susan K.) 279 Black Oak Dr, Lancaster PA 17602-3477, 717-299-2709, miller1765@comcast.net [LAN] [AW] Staff, Eastern Mennonite Missions, Salunga PA

Miller, Lester, 6190N 100E, Howe IN 46746, 260-562-2812 [IM] IIC [AC] Prison Ministry, LaGrange IN

Miller, Levi (Gloria) 903 Arthur Ave, Scottdale PA 15683, 724-887-5515 [ALL] IIC [AC]

Miller, Lewis W. (Norma Jean) 719 7th St, Milford NE 68405 [CP] IIB1 [AC] Pastor, Milford Menn Ch, Milford NE

Miller, Lloyd L. (Joan Yoder) 64308 CR 21, Goshen IN 46526, 574-534-4486, cdcllm@hoosierlink.net [CDC] IB2 [AC] Conference Minister, Central District Conference, Goshen IN

Miller, Lloyd R., 1425 Greencroft Apt 278, Goshen IN 46526, 574-537-4680 [IM] [RE]

Miller, Lynn Arthur (Linda J.) 11088 N Phillips Rd, Bluffton OH 45817, 419-358-2296, LynnAMiller@Juno.com [CDC] IIB3c [AC] Stewardship Minister, Mennonite Mutual Aid, Bluffton OH

Miller, Lynn Roger (Janice Fay) 2758 S Shore Dr, Albany OR 97322, 541-926-3493, lynnjanicemiller@aol.com [PNW] IIB3a [AC] Chaplain, Albany Mennonite Home, Albany OR

Miller, Mahlon D. (Dorothy) 57377 CR 29, Goshen IN

MINISTERS

6

46526 [IM] [RE]

Miller, Marilyn Ferne (Maurice Lee) 2000 Dartmouth Ave, Boulder CO 80305, 303-499-5229, marilynfmiller@comcast.net [WDC] [RE]

Miller, Mark A., 629 Crescent Dr, Hesston KS 67062, mark@wmc.kscoxmail.com [OH] IIB2 [AC] Pastor, Whitestone Menn Ch, Hesston KS

Miller, Mark G. (Debbie) 1222 S Owens, Lakewood CO 80226, 303-986-2969 [RM] [AW]

Miller, Mark R. (Joyce Moyer) 2517 Proctor Ln, Baltimore MD 21234, 410-663-4554, mark.miller@mmyfc.org [ACC] IIC [AC] Staff, Metro-Maryland Youth for Christ, Baltimore MD

Miller, Marlin M. (Karen) 180 N Main St, Bolivar NY 14715, 716-928-1452 [LAN] IIB2 [AC] Associate Pastor, Kossuth Community Chapel, Bolivar NY

Miller, Merlin L. (Linda) 953 Bedford St, Chesapeake VA 23322, 757-482-4495 [VA] IIB1 [AC] Pastor, Landstown Community Ch, Virginia Beach VA

Miller, Mervin, 55251 SR 13, Middlebury IN 46540, 574-825-4970 [IM] IIB1 [AC] Intentional Interim Pastor, Forks Menn Ch, Middlebury IN

Miller, Philip (Verna Mae) 728 Bedford St, Chesapeake VA 23322, 757-482-1836 [VA] [RE]

Miller, Raymond (Ruth) 803 Anderson Ferry Rd, Mount Joy PA 17552, 717-653-8762 [LAN] [RE]

Miller, Robert L. (Belinda) PO Box 111, Mt Eaton OH 44659, 330-359-5595, bobbeem@hotmail.com [OH] IIB1 [AC] Pastor, Salem Menn Ch, Wooster OH

Miller, Robin Dean (Cynthia Howell) 3533 Hildana Rd, Shaker Heights OH 44120, 216-561-8142, RobinDeanMiller@hotmail.com [OH] IIB1 [AC] Pastor, Lee Heights Community Ch, Cleveland OH

Miller, Rocky (Diane) 1951 Racimo Dr, Sarasota FL 34240, 941-378-5536, RockyMiller@compuserve.com [SE] IIB2 [AC] Interim Pastor, Bay Shore Menn Ch, Sarasota FL

Miller, Roderick, 185 Noteman Rd, Plain City OH 43064, 614-873-1908 [OH] IIA [AC] Pastor, Cornerstone Menn Fell, Plain City OH

Miller, Ross A., 844 Basel St, Sugarcreek OH 44681, 330-852-2575, ross@wcmenn.org [OH] IIB1 [AC] Pastor, Walnut Creek Menn Ch, Walnut Creek OH

Miller, S. Paul, 1300 Greencroft Apt 78, Goshen IN 46526, 574-537-3581 [IM] [RE]

Miller, Sharon Wyse (Duane) 1226 Cedar Rd, Ambler PA 19002, 215-646-7924, swmiller@verizon.net [FRC] IIB1 [AC] Pastor, Ambler Menn Ch, Ambler PA

Miller, T. Lee (Marty) 3309 N 600 E, Kokomo IN 46901, 765-628-2984, howardmiami@mennonite.net [IM] IIB1 [AC] Co-Pastor, Howard-Miami Menn Ch, Kokomo IN

Miller, Thomas H. (Christine) 7 Greenwood Hills, Mountaintop PA 18707, 717-678-3010 [LAN] IIB1 [AC] Pastor, Cornerstone Christian Fell, Mountain Top PA

Miller, Timothy O. (Kathy) PO Box 127, 6097 Pearl St, Naubinway MI 49762, 906-477-8090, tomiller@portup.com [IM] IIB1 [AC] Pastor, Rexton Menn Ch, Naubinway MI; Pastor, Naubinway Christian Fell, Naubinway MI

Miller, Vern L., 2043 Sycamore Dr, Bedford Heights OH 44146, 440-735-1988, hmiller13@juno.com [OH] [AW]

Miller, Vernon U., 27727 CR 36, Goshen IN 46526, 574-862-2748 [IM] [RE]

Miller, Waldo E. (Neva A.) 211 Lake Vista Cr, Hesston KS

67062, 620-327-2172 [WDC] [RE]

Miller, Wendy, 629 Crescent Dr, Hesston KS 67062, wendy@wmc.kscoxmail.com [OH] IIB2 [AC] Associate Pastor, Whitestone Menn Ch, Hesston KS

Miller, Wendy J., 11054 Phillips Store Rd, Broadway VA 22815, 540-896-5216 [VA] IIB3d [AC]

Miller, Willis A., 357 Main St, Harleysville PA 19438, 215-256-8240 [FRC] [RE]

Miller Jacobs, Rachel (Randall M.) 505 S 5th St, Goshen IN 46526, 574-534-5964, rachelkrmc@juno.com [IM] IIA [AC] Pastor of Faith Formation, Kern Rd Menn Ch, South Bend IN

Miller-Eshelman, Jon Chester (Holly) 12611 Kornett Ln, Bowie MD 20715-0444, 301-809-4246 [LAN] IIB2 [AC]

Mininger, Joseph H. (Eleanor) HC 70 Box 68, Harman WV 26270, 304-227-4370 [VA] [RE]

Mininger, Mary (Phil) 2589 N CR 100 W, Paoli IN 47454, 812-723-2414, mennos@iquest.net [CDC, IM] IIB1 [AC] Co-Pastor, Paoli Menn Fell, Paoli IN

Mininger, Philip A. (Mary Kauffman) 2589 N CR 100 W, Paoli IN 47454, 812-723-2459, mininger@blueriver.net [CDC, IM] IIB1 [AC] Co-Pastor, Paoli Menn Fell, Paoli IN

Mininger, Richard Huber (Linda) 37 Sycamore Ave, Halifax PA 17032-9055, 717-896-2637, rlhm@pa.net [LAN] IIB1 [AC] Pastor, Halifax Community Fell, Halifax PA

Minino, Vincente (Carmen) 10868 Oak Green Ct, Burke VA 22015-2336, vicarm6@juno.com [LAN] IB3, IIB1 [AC] Pastor, Iglesia Menonita Hispana Vida Nueva, Burke VA; Bishop/Overseer/Supervisor, Spanish District, South Supervisor, Burke VA

Minnich, Abram D. (Marolyn J.) 30376 Charles Barnes Rd, Wover MD 21871, 410-957-3755 [ACC] [RE]

Minnich, R. Herbert (Shirley S.) 300 Nebraska Dr, Goshen IN 46526, 574-533-9965 [IM] [RE]

Mishler, David E. (Becky) 999 Blough Rd, Johnstown PA 15905, 814-288-3420 [ALL] IB3 [AC]

Mishler, Donald Paul (Catherine Yoder) 5793 US Hwy 340N, Rileyville VA 22650, 540-743-6972, pmishler@shentel.net [VA] [RE]

Mishler, Dorsa J., 1412-6 Pembroke Cr, Goshen IN 46526, 574-534-4998 [IM] [RE]

Mohler, David W. (Mildred) 220 Akron Rd, Ephrata PA 17522-2604, 717-733-4359, damohler@localnet.com [LAN] III [AC] Ordained Deacon, Gehman Menn Ch, Adamstown PA

Mohr, James R. (Roberta R.) 502 Rosalind Ave, Wadsworth OH 44281, 330-336-2797, mohr@wadsnet.com [CDC] IIB1 [AC] Pastor, First Menn Ch, Wadsworth OH

Molina, Oscar Enrique (Sandra) 420 Green St, Lancaster PA 17602, 717-299-9423 or 717-299-9414 [LAN] IIB1 [AC] Pastor, Iglesia Menonita Roca de Salvación, Lancaster PA

Monroe, Earl B. (Joy Magdalene) 80 Lake Rd, Stuarts Draft VA 24477, 540-337-1062, earlshome@rica.net [VA] IIB1 [AC] Pastor, Mountain View Menn Ch, Lyndhurst VA

Montanez, Emilio (Migdalea) 1116 Kittatiny St, Harrisburg PA 17104, 717-233-8412 [LAN] IIB1 [AC] Pastor, Jesu Cristo es la Respuesta, Harrisburg PA

Montes, Juan V. (Carmen A.) PO Box 111, Reedley CA 93654, 559-638-8493, jmontesimh@juno.com [PSW]

IIB2 [AC] Pastor, Primera Iglesia Menonita, Reedley CA; Associate Pastor, First Menn Ch of Reedley, Reedley CA

Moore, Irene, 5121 Serena Dr E, Rm 142, Tampa FL 33617, 813-985-0727 [SE] IIC [AC] Minister of Visitation, College Hill Menn Ch, Tampa FL

Moore, Jerry A. (Ida Jane) 419 W Fifth St, Box 544, Buhler KS 67522-0544, 620-543-2403 [WDC] [RE]

Moore, Jon E., 1939 W Page St, Philadelphia PA 19121-1513, 215-232-4579, Jonfeliciamoore@aol.com [FRC] IIA [AC] Pastor, New Beginnings Community Ch, Bristol PA

Morales, Eduardo P. (Lourdes) 419 2nd Rd Apt 3, Arlington VA 22203, 703-528-2417, peraza2@juno.com [LAN] IIB1 [AC] Pastor, Buenas Nuevas, Falls Church VA

Moran, Samuel (Orflia R. Lopez) PO Box 68008, Oak Grove OR 97268, 503-653-4164 [PNW] IIB1 [AC] Pastor, Ministerios Restauración, Tualatin OR

Moreno, Justo, 717 Elsberry Ave, Valinda CA 91744, 818-336-7656, holfmc@juno.com [PSW] IIB1 [AC] Senior Pastor, House of the Lord Fell, La Puente CA

Morrow, David Marvin (Irene Schomus) 802 S Pine, PO Box 766, Warden WA 98857, 509-349-0577, dmmorrow@mennonite.net [PNW] IIB1 [AC] Pastor, Warden Menn Ch, Warden WA

Morton, Craig Daniel (Karla Crydermann) 2743 W Wave, Meridian ID 83642, 208-288-2378, ccdmort@velocitus.net [PNW] IIB1 [AC] Co-Pastor, Emmaus Christian Fell, Meridian ID; Interim Pastor, First Menn Ch, Nampa ID

Mosemann, Clyde R. (Anna Burkhart) 324 Spring Rd, Warfordsburg PA 17267, 717-573-2504 [ACC] [RE]

Moser, David Palmer, 15406 Watercress Dr, Cassopolis MI 49031, 616-476-9989, moser@friendswald.org [CDC] IIB1 [AC] Pastor, Lima Menn Ch, Lima OH; Program Director, Camp Friedenswald, Cassopolis MI

Moser, Teresa (Phil Rempel) 4586 Geary St SE, Albany OR 97322, 541-812-1168, teresamoser@spearnet.net [PNW] IIB3a [AC] Chaplain, Mennonite Home of Albany, Albany OR

Motley, Alvin, 809 Glen Ter, Chester PA 19013, 610-872-5539 [LAN] IIB1 [AC] Pastor, Way Thru Christ Ministry, Chester PA

Moua, Shoua (Chou Vang) 9980 W 59th Pl #1, Arvada CO 80004-5015, 303-463-0257 [RM, WDC] IIB1 [AC] Pastor, Hmong Menn Ch, Arvada CO

Moyer, Ann Bender (Bradley Dean) 4361 35th St, San Diego CA 92104-1504, 619-281-3240, ann.moyer@sharp.com [PSW] IIB1 [AC]

Moyer, Bradley Dean (Ann Bender) 4361 35th St, San Diego CA 92104, 619-281-3240 [PSW] [AW]

Moyer, Jay (Cindy) 642 Rittenhouse Pl, Telford PA 18969, 215-723-0780, jmoyer@cc-fellowship.org [FRC] IIB1 [AC] Co-Pastor, Covenant Community Fell, Lansdale PA

Moyer, Larry G. (Loretta) 70 E Ridge Ave, Telford PA 18969, 215-723-5233, larrymoyer@juno.com [FRC] IIB1 [AC] Pastor, Rockhill Menn Ch, Telford PA

Moyer, Norman W., RR 5 Box 78, Middleburg PA 17842-9805, 717-374-4266 [ALL] [RE]

Moyer, Richard A. (Fern Walter) PO Box 504, 116 Green St, Green Lane PA 18054, 215-234-8286, richfern@verizon.net [FRC] IIB1 [AC] Pastor, Shalom Christian Fell, E Greenville PA; Treasurer, Franconia Mennonite Conference, Souderton PA

Moyer, Wellington (Evangeline) 6220 Greedy Hwy,

Hickory NC 28602, 704-324-7652, wemoyer8@twave.net [VA] IIB2 [AC]

Mull, Kenneth A. (Edna) 2345 Little Hill Rd, Narvon PA 17555, 610-286-9096 [LAN] [RE]

Mullett, Isabel Margaret (S. James) 4181 SR 788, Wellston OH 45692, 740-384-3055 [OH] [RE]

Mullett, James, 4181 SR 788, Wellston OH 45692, 740-384-3055, jmullett@etrademail.com [OH] [RE]

Mungai, Simon (Gladys Maina) 2104 W Bryden Dr, Muncie IN 47304, 317-289-5436, smungai@regenstrief.org [CDC, IM] IIB2 [AC] Associate Pastor, Morning Star Ch, Muncie IN

Murr, Robert G. (Lois) 36 Cleversburg Rd, Shippensburg PA 17257-9410, 717-530-9179, bmurr@pa.net [ACC] IIB1 [AC] Pastor, Bethel Menn Ch, Gettysburg PA

Murray, John C. (Krista Anne Miller) 413 Rosewood, Hesston KS 67062, 620-327-0486, jcmurray@dtnspeed.net [SC] IIB1 [AC] Pastor, Hesston Menn Ch, Hesston KS

Murray, John F. (Marilyn) 303 E Indiana, Kouts IN 46347, 219-766-3981 [IM] [RE]

Murray, Mick (Julie) 1136 Ginkgo Ave, Wellman IA 52356-9248, 319-646-6810, kmcmick@kctc.net [CP] IIB1 [AC] Pastor, Kalona Menn Ch, Kalona IA

Murray, Randy B. (Amy Justine) 2522 Tannerville Rd, Orrville OH 44667, 330-683-0158, martinsmennonite@myfishonline.net [OH] IIB1 [AC] Pastor, Martins Menn Ch, Orrville OH

Murti, Samuel, Indonesian Menn Church, 1419 S 3rd St, Alhambra CA 91803, 626-588-1665 [PSW] IIB2 [AC] Associate Pastor, Indonesian Worship Ch, Alhambra CA

Musselman, Betty (Paul) 622 Morwood Rd, Telford PA 18969, 215-723-4922 [EDC] IIC [AC] Chaplain, Lutheran Home of Telford, Telford PA

Musselman, David L. (Brenda) 985 Sunset Ave, New Holland PA 17557, 717-354-2246, dlmusselman@juno.com [LAN] IIB2 [AC] Associate Pastor, Village Chapel Menn Ch, New Holland PA

Musselman, Glenn E., 1352 Greencroft Dr, Goshen IN 46526, 574-534-2275 [IM] IB3 [AC] Overseer for Liberty Mennonite, Somerset Center MI

Musselman, Henry S. (Lois L.) 114-D Menno Home Dr, Souderton PA 18964, 215-723-0145 [FRC] [RE]

Musselman, Steven Alan (April Lynn) 27 Park View Dr, Reinholds PA 17569, 717-336-2206, steve@zionmennonite.com [ACC] IIB1 [AC] Pastor, Zion Menn Ch—Birdsboro, Birdsboro PA

Musser, Aldine, 5542 Valley Pk, Stephens City VA 22655, 540-868-0136, musser@visuallink.com [VA] IIB2 [AC] Co-Pastor, Stephens City Menn Ch, Stephens City VA

Musser, David W. (Ella) 213 W Bahney Ave, Myerstown PA 17067-1202, 717-866-7787 [LAN] [AW]

Musser, Eric (Rebecca Lynn) 490 Godshall Rd, Souderton PA 18964, 215-721-1813, emusser@franconiamennonite.org [FRC] IIB2 [AC] Minister of Evangelism/Young Adults, Franconia Menn Ch, Telford PA

Musser, James W., 5542 Valley Rd, Stephens City VA 22655, 540-868-0136, musser@visuallink.com [VA] IIB1 [AC] Pastor, Stephens City Menn Ch, Stephens City VA

Musser, Roy W. (Joyce) 20 Union St, Pottsville PA 17901, 570-622-5681 [LAN] III [AC] Ordained Deacon, Palo Alto Menn Ch, Pottsville PA

Musser, Wilmer S. (Janelle) 510 S Farmersville Rd, Ephrata PA 17522, 717-354-4347 [LAN] IIB1 [AC] Pastor, Hammer Creek Menn Ch, Lititz PA

Mustangin, Slamet, 826 Woodward Blvd, Pasadena CA 91107, 626-584-3935, mustangin@hotmail.com [PSW] IIA, IIB2 [AC] Associate Pastor, Gereja Kristus Injili, Pasadena CA

Myer, Landis E. (Esther) 2000 Temple Ave, Lancaster PA 17603, 717-299-6968 [LAN] [RE]

Myers, D. Glenn (Emma Bender) 315 Northwood Dr, Philadelphia MS 39350, 601-656-3514, gemyers@bbimail.net [GS] IB3, IIB1 [AC] Pastor, Pearl River Menn Ch, Philadelphia MS

Myers, Herman F., 3363 Friendsville Rd, Wooster OH 44691-1237, 330-264-3404, herman@kidronmennonite.com [OH] IIB2 [AC] Associate Pastor, Kidron Menn Ch, Kidron OH

Myers, J. Vernon (Becky) 145 Bethel Rd, Oxford PA 19363, 610-932-4429, bishopvern@juno.com [LAN] IB3 [AC] Bishop/Overseer, LMC Willow Street-Strasburg, PA

Myers, John M. (Kim) 515 S Market St, Elizabethtown PA 17022, 717-361-2133, pastorjohnm@earthlink.net [LAN] IIA [AC] Associate Pastor, Elizabethtown Menn Ch, Elizabethtown PA

Myers, Ralph, 2415 Long St, Sweet Home OR 97386, 541-367-6617 [PNW] [RE]

N

Nachtigall, Ray (Karen) 716 Tremont St, PO Box 254, Hopedale IL 61747, 309-449-6031, rnach@juno.com [IL] IIB1 [AC] Lead Pastor, Hopedale Menn Ch, Hopedale IL

Nachtigall, Wilbur G. (Grace M.) 1921 S Ridge Dr, Coralville IA 52241-1058, 319-338-3839 [CP] [RE]

Nafziger, Randall K. (Diane F.) 5175 CR 19, Wauseon OH 43567, 419-445-3486, parson@wcnet.org [OH] IIB1 [AC] Pastor, Tedrow Menn Ch, Wauseon OH; Hospice Chaplain, Hospice of Wms and Fulton Co, Archbold OH

Nafziger, Robert D. (Nadine) 6349 Springfield Rd, Delavan IL 61734, 309-244-7153 [IL] IIB1 [AC] Pastor, Menn Ch of Dillon, Delavan IL

Nafziger-Meiser, Linda E. (Gary) 5218 Castle Dr, Boise ID 83703, 208-331-8529, lindanm@mindsprng.com [PNW] IIB1 [AC] Pastor, Hyde Park Menn Fell, Boise ID

Naranjo, Luis E. (Ana) 812 Wedgewood Dr, Lansdale PA 19446, 215-368-5839, messiahisrael@aol.com [EDC] IIB1 [AC] Pastor, Iglesia Menonita Comunidad de Amor, Philadelphia PA

Nauman, Donald O. (Erla) 31 Oakwood Ln, Manheim PA 17545, 717-665-3096 [LAN] IB3 [AC]

Nauman, Kenneth E. (Miriam W.) 922 W Hickory St, Arcadia FL 34266, 941-993-9353, KenMirNa@sunline.net [SE] IB2, IB3 [AC] Conference Minister, SE Mennonite Conference, Sarasota FL; District Minister, SE Mennonite Conference, SW District, FL

Naylor, Ruth Eileen (Stanley Fred) 123 Villanova Dr, Bluffton OH 45817, 419-358-6309, snaylor@wcoil.com [CDC] [RE]

Neff, Clarence R., 249 Esbenshade Rd, Ronks PA 17572, 717-687-6406 [LAN] [RE]

Neff, Daniel W. (Carol) 465 Long Rd, Manheim PA 17545, 717-569-0812 [LAN] III [AC] Ordained Deacon, E Petersburg Menn Ch, East Petersburg PA

Neff, Earl L., 8 Stone Rd, Quarryville PA 17566, 717-786-3487 [LAN] III [AC]

Neff, L. Delmar (Nancy) 569 Georgetown Rd, Ronks PA 17572-9534 [LAN] [RE]

Neil, Marlin A. (Freda) 16062 Mountain Green Rd, Spring Run PA 17262, 717-349-7160, mfneil@innernet.net [FRK] IIB1 [AC] Pastor, Shady Pine Menn Ch, Willow Hill PA

Neis Jr., Thomas A. (Patricia) 94 Fairfax Village N, Harrisburg PA 17112-9555, 717-540-5280 [LAN] III [AC] Elder, Locust Ln Menn Chapel, Harrisburg PA

Nelson, Dawn Ruth (Paul Joseph) 318 W Broad St, Harleysville PA 19438, 215-256-9606 [FRC] IIB3a [AC] Pastor, Methacton Menn Ch, Norristown PA; Chaplain, Indian Creek Foundation, Harleysville PA

Nelson, James H. (Odie) 3405 Corvair Ln, Saginaw MI 48602, 517-249-5894 [IM] IIA [AC] Pastor, Grace Chapel, Saginaw MI

Ness, Charles A. (Janet) PO Box 228, Skippack PA 19474, 610-584-6624, perkmc@juno.com [FRC] IIB1 [AC] Pastor, Perkiomenville Menn Ch, Perkiomenville PA

Neufeld, Bonnie Beth (Chuck) 3316 W 163rd, Markham IL 60426, 708-333-9827, chuckneufeld@mennonite.net [CDC, IL] IIB1 [AC] Co-Pastor, Community Menn Ch, Markham IL

Neufeld, Chuck T. (Bonnie Beth) 3316 W 163rd St, Markham IL 60426, 708-333-9827, chuckneufeld@mennonite.net [CDC, IL] IIB1 [AC] Lead Pastor, Community Menn Ch, Markham IL

Neufeld, Ernest Wiens (Lila) PO Box 53, Mt Lake MN 56159-2828, 507-427-2828 [CP] [RE]

Neufeld, Peter J. (Onalee Diann) 312 Robert, Hutchinson KS 67502-0312, 620-663-2581 [WDC] [RE]

Neufeld, Walter P. (Frieda Braun) 901 E Hoch, Moundridge KS 67107-7138, 620-345-2547 [WDC] [RE]

Newswanger, Carl K. (K. Louise Myers) 1970 Engel Ct NW, Salem OR 97304, 503-391-2772, newswanger2@attbi.com [PNW] IIB1 [AW]

Newswanger, Ricky L. (Wilda) 3155 Rothsville Rd, Ephrata PA 17522, 717-859-1682 [LAN] IIC [AC] Youth Pastor, Hammer Creek Menn Ch, Lititz PA

Newton, Elbert Walker (Gloria Martyn), bnewton@pop.pacificnet.net [PSW] IIB2 [AC] Associate Pastor, Pasadena Menn Ch, Pasadena CA

Nguyen, Peter Simon (Minh Le) 3804 Munson Rd, Falls Church VA 22041 [VA] IIA [AC] Pastor, Vietnamese Christian Fell, Falls Church VA

Nice, Aaron D., 16270 Union St, Morrison IL 61270, 815-722-2541 [IL] [RE]

Nice, Frank E. (Evelyn) 1161 Stuart St, Harrisonburg VA 22802, 540-434-4441 [VA] IB3 [AC]

Nicholson, Ransford, 1806 N Euclid Ave, Sarasota FL 34237, 941-365-6878 [SE] [RE]

Nickels, Christian J. (Beth) 201 Lexington Rd, Schwenksville PA 19473, 610-287-3681, chrisnbeth@nni.com [EDC] IIA [AC] Youth Pastor, Grace Menn Ch, Lansdale PA

Nimon, James R. (Lydia) 273 Mount Airy Rd, New Providence PA 17560, 717-786-4583, Jimmy@ConsumingFireMinistries.org [LAN] IIB2 [AC] Associate Pastor, Living Stones Fell, Peach Bottom PA

Nisly, Paul W. (Laura) PO Box 262, Grantham PA 17027-0262, 717-766-4937 [LAN] IB3 [AC]

Nisly, Weldon D. (Margaret A.) 13773 30th Ave NE,

Seattle WA 98125-3509, 206-368-7529, weldonNisly@mennonite.net [PNW] IIB1 [AC] Pastor, Seattle Menn Ch, Seattle WA

Nissley, Addona H. (Mary Elizabeth) 1554 Park Rd, Harrisonburg VA 22802, 540-434-9427 [VA] [RE]

Nissley, Clair R. (Ruth) 1832 Pecks Rd, Middletown PA 17057-5349, 717-367-2033, crnissley@juno.com [LAN] [RE]

Nissley, Darin, 227 Tyler Ave SE, Canton OH 44707, 330-452-2416, cantonlighthouse@sbcglobal.net [OH] IIB2 [AC] Youth Pastor, First Menn Ch of Canton, Canton OH

Nissley, Elizabeth G. (Kenneth) 127 N Market St, Mount Joy PA 17552-1305, 717-653-2550, enissley@earthlink.net [LAN] IIC [AC] Associate Pastor, James St Menn Ch, Lancaster PA

Nissley, Jay W. (Elta) 1487 Breneman Rd, Manheim PA 17545, 717-665-7367, jayeltaniss@juno.com [LAN] IIB1 [AC] Associate Pastor, Kauffman Menn Ch, Manheim PA

Nissley, M. John (Lois C. Musselman) 430 Bright Rd, Findlay OH 45840-7043, 419-425-6708, jnissley@winebrenner.edu [OH] IIB3d [AC] Program Committee, Yokefellow Spiritual Retreat Center, Defiance OH

Nitzsche, Mary Erb (Wayne Arthur) 917 Patrick Pl, Wooster OH 44691, 330-264-1516, rpmary@juno.com [CDC, OH] IB3 [AC] Regional Pastor, Ohio Conference of the Mennonite Church, Wooster OH

Nitzsche, Wayne A. (Mary Erb) 917 Patrick Pl, Wooster OH 44691, 330-264-1516, waynen@sssnet.com [OH] IB3 [AC] Regional Pastor, Ohio Conference of the Mennonite Church, Kidron OH

Nofziger, Donald D. (Vietta K) 307 S Higbee St, Milford IN 46542, 574-658-3245 [CDC] [RE]

Nofziger, Pauline Ann (Donald Lee) 8038 Witts Mill Ln, Cincinnati OH 45255, 513-474-0637, cmfoffice@juno.com [CDC, OH] IIB1 [AC] Pastor, Cincinnati Menn Fell, Cincinnati OH

Nolt, M. Luke (Dorothy) 160 Forest Hill Rd, Leola PA 17540, 717-656-7817 [LAN] IIB2 [RE]

Nolt, Martin R., 271 Bucknoll Rd, Manheim PA 17545, 717-665-2962 [LAN] [RE]

Nolt, Robert E. (Anna) 1701 W 4th St, Newton KS 67114, 316-284-0218 [SC] IB2 [AC] Conference Minister, South Central Conference, North Newton KS

North, Wayne G. (Doris) 466 Eckert Cr, Harrisonburg VA 22801, 540-433-3538, wayne@lindale.org [VA] IB3 [AC]

Norton, Steve (Sharon) Beyschlag Strasse #17, Halle 06110, Germany, 011-49-345-1200820 [IM] IIB3b [AC] Missionary, Eastern Mennonite Missions, Halle, Germany

Nowlin, Preston (Carolyn) 1915-B Old Tavern Rd, Powhatan VA 23139, 804-598-7289 [VA] [RE]

Nunez, Andrew (Carmen) 1475 Popham Ave #1E, Bronx NY 10453, 718-716-6579, acnunez2001@yahoo.com [LAN] IIA [AC] Pastor, Believers Menn Garifuna Ministries, Brooklyn NY

Nussbaum, Delvin, 13877 Emerson Rd, Dalton OH 44618, 330-857-2463 [OH] [RE]

Nussbaum, Gary, 15511 Hackett Rd, Dalton OH 44618, 330-857-4392 [OH] IIB3a [AC]

Nussbaum, Gerald C. (Virginia Kay) 266 Oak Hill Dr, Westerville OH 43081, 614-523-2515; 614-898-4024 (work), gnussbaum@mchs.com [CDC] IIB3a [AC]

Nussbaum, Harold Walden (Marie W.) 505 W Main St ,

Berne IN 46711, 260-589-2461, harold@firstmennonite.org [CDC] IIB2 [RE]

Nussbaum, Irvin A. (Nelda) 23899 Banyan Cr, Elkhart IN 46516, 574-875-1324 [IM] [RE]

Nussbaum, Larry (Cheryl L.) 547 N Roosevelt, Wichita KS 67208-3723, 316-684-5448, lamcassocpastor@prodigy.net [WDC] IIB3a [AC]

Nwani, Clement (Evelyn) 2926 W Florence Ave, Los Angeles CA 90043, 323-778-4063, clevychic@yahoo.com [PSW] IIB1 [AC] Co-Pastor, Abundant Life Miracle Christian Center, Los Angeles CA

Nwani, Evelyn (Clement) 2926 W Florence Ave, Los Angeles CA 90043, 323-778-4063, clevychic@yahoo.com [PSW] IIB1 [AC] Co-Pastor, Abundant Life Miracle Christian Center, Los Angeles CA

Nyce, R. Keith (Yvonne) 736 Bob Bea Ln, Harleysville PA 19438, 215-256-0522, Knyce@cc-fellowship.org [FRC] IIB1 [AC] Co-Pastor, Covenant Community Fell, Lansdale PA

Nyce, Steven C., 19 S School Ln, Souderton PA 18964, 215-721-0167 [FRC] IIB3a [AC]

O

Oberholtzer, Jay R. (Rhoda) PO Box 318, Lititz PA 17543, 717-626-5658 [LAN] [RE]

Oberholtzer, Leon H. (Leona) 2251 Creek Hill Rd, Lancaster PA 17601, 717-393-7747, mmc@proclaim.net [LAN] IB3, IIB2 [AC] Pastor, Mellinger Menn Ch, Lancaster PA; Bishop/Overseer, LMC Mellinger District, PA

Oberholzer, Richard, 13315 Cearfoss Pk, Hagerstown MD 21740, 301-739-5036 [FRK] [RE]

Obold, Frederick J. (Ruth W.) 716 Lewis Dr, Hesston KS 67062, 620-327-4435 [WDC] IIB3a [AC] Chaplain, Reno Co Hospice, Hutchinson KS

O'Connell, Darwin, 989 W Tremont Ave, Lima OH 45801, 419-223-3266 [OH] [RE]

Oesch, H. Duane, 11161 Moss Ln, Nampa ID 83651, 208-466-1897 [PNW] [AW]

Olesh, Steve (Edna) 522 Beagle Rd, Bethel PA 19507-9518, 717-933-8373 [LAN] [RE]

Onelangsy, Aaron S., 92 Greenwood Dr, New Cumberland PA 17070, 717-938-8552 [LAN] IIA [AC] Pastor, Lao Menn Fell/Slate Hill, Camp Hill PA

Ontjes, Kenneth Loren (Alice Marie) PO Box 19, Bridgewater SD 57319-0019, 605-729-2745 [CP] IIB1 [AC] Pastor, Neu Hutterthal Menn Ch, Bridgewater SD

Opong, Charles, 5125 S Crenshaw Blvd, Los Angeles CA 90043-1853, 323-291-2235 [PSW] IIA [AC] Pastor, All Souls Christian Center, Los Angeles CA

O'Reilly II, George Christopher II (Karen L.) 1217 9th Ave, Mt Lake MN 56159, 507-427-2002 [CP] IIB1 [AC] Pastor, Bethel Menn Ch, Mountain Lake MN

Orr, David E. (Sharon Fay) 809 Wellmon St, Bedford OH 44146, 440-786-2401, dorr614248@aol.com [OH] IIB1 [AC]

Ortiz, Henry, 1750 Skippack Pk, Blue Bell PA 19422-1339, 610-292-8243 [FRC] [RE]

Ortiz, Jose M. (Iraida) 21 Village Ln, New Holland PA 17557, 717-354-2601, [ACC] [RE]

Ortiz, Marquel (Charlotte) 41 James St, Bernville PA 19506-8617, newlifebernville@juno.com [ACC] IIB1 [AC] Pastor, New Life Christian Fell, Bernville PA

Osborne, Millard Edmond (Joyce Nyce) 3430 Dawn Dr,

Harrisonburg VA 22801, 540-438-8390, mosborne001@sprintmail.com [VA] [RE]

Ostlund, James W., PO Box 942, Moundridge KS 67107, edenyouth@hotmail.com [WDC] IIB2 [AC] Associate Pastor, Eden Menn Ch, Moundridge KS

Oswald, Leland (Doretta) 537 W Gay St, Harrisonburg VA 22802, 540-432-0308 [VA] [RE]

Otto, Darrel D. (Ruth Ann) 4422 Zephyr St, Wheat Ridge CO 80033, 303-657-5908 [RM] [RE]

Otto, John D. (Edna) 406 E F Ave, South Hutchinson KS 67505, 620-665-8966 [SC] [RE]

Overholt, Lewis (Mary E. Mast) 329 Wildwood Cr, Americus GA 31709, 912-924-0652, overholt@sowega.net [SE] [RE]

Ozor, Chibuzor Vincent (Chima Edith) 1455 Kelly Green Dr, Ann Arbor MI 48103-2614, 313-996-9198, ozotas@aol.com [CDC, IM] IIB1 [AC] Pastor, Ann Arbor Menn Ch, Ann Arbor MI

P

Pacheco, Reinaldo (Ray) (Ana) Mansiones de Coamo, Calle C, #1, Coamo PR 00769, 718-253-7267 or 347-229-4265 (cell), arpac@aol.com [ACC] [AW]

Paetkau, Brenda Sawatzky (Donald William) 1002 Leroy Ave, Goshen IN 46526, 574-533-9972, dpaetkau@bnin.net [CDC] IIB2 [AC] Pastor, Eighth St Menn Ch, Goshen IN

Pagan, Samuel (Mayra) c/o Ramsey Memorial Methodist Church, 5900 Hull St, Richmond VA 23244 [VA] IIB3b [AC]

Pam, Chuwang Rwang (Grace) 4541 August St , Los Angeles CA 90008, 323-299-1499, chuwang@webtv.net [PSW] IIA [AC] Pastor, Los Angeles Faith Chapel, Inglewood CA; Mission Associate, Center for Anabaptist Leadership

Parks, Burt Preston (Melanie Dawn Miller) 133 Carter Grove Ln, Smithville OH 44677, 330-669-9256, bpparks@smithvillemennonite.org [OH] IIB1 [AC] Pastor, Smithville Menn Ch, Smithville OH

Parks, Lynn S. (Vandy L.) 6269 Walker St, Philadelphia PA 19135, 215-333-5868, lynn_parks@msn.com [LAN] IIC [AC] Associate Pastor, Oxford Cr Menn Ch, Philadelphia PA

Parks, Vandy L. (Lynn) 6269 Walker St, Philadelphia PA 19135, 215-333-5868, lynn_parks@msn.com [LAN] IIB2 [AC]

Pascacio, Egbert, 7860 S Wern Ave, Los Angeles CA 90047, 323-466-4117 [PSW] IIA [AC] Pastor, Miracle of Faith Menn Ch, Los Angeles CA

Patterson, Allan, 36 Morgan St, Oberlin OH 44074, 440-774-4675, pmcpastor@aol.com [OH] IIB1 [AC] Pastor, Peace Menn Ch, Elyria OH

Patterson, Donald A. (Sharlene) 231 F Pl, Kalona IA 52247, 319-656-2600, donpatt@kctc.net [CP] IIB1 [AC] Pastor, Lower Deer Creek Menn Ch, Kalona IA

Pauls, Jeffrey G. (Donna) 12 S Kinzer Rd, Kinzers PA 17535, 717-442-8008, jgpdep@epix.net [LAN] IIB2 [AC] Associate Pastor, Kinzer Menn Ch, Kinzer PA

Payne, Justin Franklin (Ruby Mae) 331 Milton St, Eon PA 18042, 610-252-4109, rogpastor@verizon.net [FRC] IIA [AC] Pastor, River of God Fell, Eon PA

Peachey, B. Frank (Carol) 31 Fairview Dr, Akron PA 17501-1613, peacheys@juno.com [LAN] [AW]

Peachey, C. David (Carol Ann) 420 Turkey Run Rd,

Mifflinburg PA 17844, 717-966-1458, pchykeen1@chilitech.net [LAN] IIB1 [AC] Co-Pastor, Buffalo Menn Ch, Lewisburg PA

Peachey, Gerald, 162 N Kish St, Belleville PA 17004, 717-935-2583 [ALL] IIB1 [AC] Pastor, Barrville Menn Ch, Reedsville PA

Peachey, John Stephen (Suzi Christina) 10 Highfield Oval, Harpenden, Herts AL5 4BX, England, johnpeachey@mail.com [SE] IIC [AC]

Peachey, Laban (Helen) 1251-B Old Windmill Cr, Harrisonburg VA 22802, 540-574-2950, Labanpeach@aol.com [VA] IIB2 [AC] Interim Pastor, Huntington Menn Ch, Newport News VA

Peachey, Mark E., 602 Eleanor, Scottdale PA 15683 [ALL] IB3 [AC]

Peachey, Raymond S., 6671 SR 655, Belleville PA 17004, 717-667-3097 [ALL] [RE]

Peachey, Timothy R., 102 Poe St, Belleville PA 17004, 717-935-2763 [ALL] IB3 [AC]

Peachey, Urbane (Gwendolyn Wenger) 242 Cats Back Rd, Ephrata PA 17522, 717-354-7001, UPeach@aol.com [ACC] [RE] Individual and Family Counselor, Bethany Counseling Ministry, Ephrata PA

Peak, Michael Wayne (Joylyn June) 58073 Diener Dr, Goshen IN 46528, 574-875-4288, mpeak@maplenet.net [IM] IIB1 [AC] Associate Pastor, Pleasant View Menn Ch, Goshen IN

Pegarella, David A. (Tammy) 146 Main St, Mountaintop PA 18707, 717-474-2955, davidp146@verizon.net [LAN] IIB1 [AC] Pastor, Nanticoke Christian Fell, Nanticoke PA

Peifer, Jane Hoober (Daryl Eugene) 125 N Shippen St, Lancaster PA 17602, 717-396-0683, jhp125@juno.com [VA] IIB1 [AW] Pastor, Blossom Hill Menn Ch, Lancaster PA

Pellecer, Byron (Hildalejandra) 135 SW 113 Ct, Miami FL 33174, 305-207-5299, bpellece@bellsouth.net [SE] IIB1 [AC] Pastor, Iglesia Menonita Encuentro de Renovación, Miami FL; Tutor, IBA/USA & Guatemala, Miami FL; District Minister, SE Mennonite Conference, South Florida District, FL

Pellman, Hubert R. (Mildred) 1307 Woodland Dr, Harrisonburg VA 22802, 540-434-5797 [VA] [RE]

Pendleton, Joe (Jean) 9785 S Bagley Rd, Ashley MI 48806, 989-838-2588, joe_pendleton@hotmail.com [IM] IIB1 [AC] Pastor, Bethel Menn Ch, Greenville MI

Penner, Bradley B. (Viola K.) 330 E Washington, Kingman KS 67068, 620-532-5330, darev@kans.com [WDC] IIB1 [AC] Pastor, Kingman Menn Ch, Kingman KS

Penner, Bruno (Julia E.) 1313 2nd Ave, Mt Lake MN 56159, 507-427-2030 [CP] [RE]

Penner, Don (Sandy) 402 Willow, Rocky Ford CO 81067, 719-254-7590, donpen@rural-rural.com [RM] IIA [AC] Pastor, Rocky Ford Menn Ch, Rocky Ford CO

Penner, Galen (Cindy) PO Box 68, Cheraw CO 81030, 719-853-6377 [WDC] IIB1 [AC] Pastor, E Holbrook Menn Ch, Cheraw CO

Penner, Marvin Wesley (Sue) HC 30 Box 2071, Wolf Point MT 59201-9702, 406-392-5215 [CP] IIB1 [AC] Pastor, Bethel Menn Ch, Wolf Point MT

Penner, Ruth (Marvin J.) 1426 Willow Rd, Newton KS 67114, 316-284-2261, mcfc@southwind.net [WDC] IIB1 [AC] Pastor, New Creation Fell, Newton KS

Penner, Stephen J. (Glena Schroeter) 195 Ponderosa,

Reedley CA 93654, 559-638-5565, sngpenner@telis.org [PSW] IIB2 [AC] Pastor, First Menn Ch of Reedley, Reedley CA

Penner, Vicki Lynn (Richard Warren Minder) 1511 Rhode Island St, Lawrence KS 66044-4271, 785-830-9547, vickipenner@sunflower.com [WDC] IIB1 [AW]

Perez, Gilberto (Elizabeth) 1385 S Tuttle Ave, Sarasota FL 34239 [SE] [RE]

Perez, Rafael (Xiomara) 1241 Church St, Reading PA 19601, 610-372-1812 [LAN] IIA [AC] Pastor, New Revival Menn Ch, Reading PA

Perri, Mark D. (Annabelle) 42-45 149th Pl, Flushing NY 11355, 718-539-6702, MPerri2804@aol.com [ACC] IIC [AC] Pastor, Immanuel Community Ch, Flushing NY

Peters, Jay M. (Margie) 1064 Fairview Rd, Manheim PA 17545-8100, 717-664-2814 [LAN] IIB2 [AC] Associate Pastor, Hernley Menn Ch, Manheim PA

Petersheim, Isaac R., 957 Weaverland Rd, East Earl PA 17519, 717-354-7328 [LAN] III [AC] Ordained Deacon, Cambridge Menn Ch, Gordonville PA

Petersheim, John R. (Ruby) 3475 Apple Tree Dr, Harrisonburg VA 22802, 540-867-5568, johnorruby@att.net [VA] [RE]

Petersheim, Robert L. (Cindy A.) 1543 Morgantown Rd, Morgantown PA 19543, 610-913-7413, rlpckp@juno.com [FRC] IIB1 [AC] Interim/Transitional Pastor, Towamencin Menn Ch, Kulpsville PA

Peterson, Kenneth James (Carol Jean) 13101 Warwick Blvd, Newport News VA 23602, 757-249-2702, providence@mennonite.net [VA] IIB1 [AC] Pastor, Providence Menn Ch, Newport News VA

Peterson, Neville John (Joan Ellen) PO Box 190, Glendive MT 59330, 409-377-7574, nevpeter@miDrrs.com [NC] IIB1 [AC] Pastor, White Chapel Menn Ch, Glendive MT

Pham, Thanh Cong, 530 Main St Apt E-507, Harleysville PA 19438-2246, 215-513-4117, tcpham1@netzero.net [FRC] IIB1 [AC] Pastor, Vietnamese Gospel Menn Ch, Allentown PA

Pham, Xuan (Lisa) Huong (Can Le) 3871 Scibilia Rd, Fairfax VA 22033, 703-802-0139, lpham@forministry.com [VA] [AW]

Pitts, Katherine Jameson (Kenneth Duane) 1851 Conestoga Dr, Lancaster PA 17602, 717-672-0645, kjpitts@mennonite.net [ACC] [AW]

Poirot Sr., Clifford S. (Judy) PO Box 307, Lacey Springs VA 22833, 540-433-1367 [VA] IIB3b [AC]

Ponce, Teofilo, 707 N 6th St A, Goshen IN 46526, 574-533-7267 [IM] [RE]

Porter, Ike, 58726 CR 657, Mattawan MI 49071, 269-668-2562 [IM] IIB3a [AC] Chaplain, Mattawan MI

Porzelius, Ernest Eugene (Violet Janet) 173 Albert St, Bluffton OH 45817-1401, 419-358-8481 [CDC] [RE]

Possinger, David (Glenda) 14634 St Paul Rd, Clear Spring MD 21722, 301-842-1279, dgp14634@earthlink.net [FRK] IIB2 [AC] Associate Pastor, Mercersburg Menn Ch, Mercersburg PA

Post, Stephen (Mary Ellen) PO Box 109, Grand Marais MI 49839, 906-494-2724, smpost@jamadots.com [IM] IIA [AC] Pastor, Grand Marais Menn Ch, Grand Marais MI

Powell, John H. (Shirley J.) 50 Allenhurst Rd, Buffalo NY 14214, 716-837-1751, fjPowell@aol.com [NY] IB3, IIB3c [AW]

Preheim, Lois Janzen (Lyle Orie) 44229 281st St, Freeman SD 57029, 605-925-7760 [CP] IIB3b [AC] Director, Victim Offender Reconciliation Program, Sioux Falls SD

Preheim, Patrick (Patty Jo) 2211 28th Ave S, Minneapolis MN 55406, 612-724-0733 [CP] IIB1 [AC] Pastor, Faith Menn Ch, Minneapolis MN

Price, Brian (Becky) PO Box 43, Wolford ND 58353-0043, 701-583-2102 [NC] IIA, IIC [AC]

Prichard, George F. (June L.) 2921 Silk Oak Dr, Sarasota FL 34232-5403, 941-377-8051 [EDC] [RE]

Pride, Ronnie B. (Louvenia) 1001 Tarboro St, Rocky Mount NC 27801, 919-977-1901 [VA] IIB1 [AC] Pastor, Fell of Christ, Rocky Mount NC

Pruitte-Sorrells, Vikki, 4132 Princeton Blvd, South Euclid OH 44121, sorrells64@ameritech.net [OH] IIA [AC] Associate Pastor, Lee Heights Community Ch, Cleveland OH

Q

Quackenbos, Gary (Vickie) PO Box 338, Hancock MD 21750, 301-678-6526 [FRK] IIB1 [AC] Pastor, Bethel Community Ch, Warfordsburg PA

Quackenbos, Robert A. (Phyllis J.) 414 Spring Lakes Blvd, Bradenton FL 34210, 941-756-3245 [SE] [RE]

Quintela, Helen Wells (Alberto Jr.) 622 Bidwell St, St Paul MN 55107, 651-222-4863 [CP] IIB3a [AC] Staff Chaplain, Regions Hospital/Gillette Children's Specialty, St Paul MN

Quintero, Ceferino, Shalom Mennonite (Spanish), (information unknown) Venezuela [LAN] IIA [AC] Associate Pastor, Shalom Mennonite, Venezuela

R

Raab, Myra (Glenn) 1619 Bramoor Dr, Kokomo IN 46902, 317-963-2156 [IM] IIB3a [AC] Chaplain, Kokomo IN

Raber, Chester, 139 S Duke St, Lancaster PA 17603, 717-397-4596 [IM] [RE]

Raber, Daniel A. (Erma June) 4828 NE 12th St, Newton KS 67114, 316-283-4530 [WDC] [RE]

Rada, Cruz (Margarita) 122 Evergreen Ln, Fruitland IA 52749, 319-262-9670 [CP] IIB1 [AC] Pastor, Muscatine Menn Ch, Fruitland IA

Raines, William, PO Box 61, Huntertown IN 46748, 260-637-8807 [IM] [AW]

Ralph, James (Anna) 132 S Main St, Quakertown PA 18951-1120, ballypj@juno.com [FRC] IIB1 [AC] Pastor, Bally Menn Ch, Bally PA

Ramer, Derrick Devon, 1651 E Market St, Nappanee IN 46550, 574-773-3579, dram144@yahoo.com [IM] IIA [AC] Youth Pastor, North Main St Menn Ch, Nappanee IN

Ramer, Milton D., 1053 S Trappe Rd, Collegeville PA 19426, 610-489-2336 [FRC] [RE]

Ramseyer, Alice Ruth (Robert Lewis) 107 Magnolia Ln, Bluffton OH 45817, 419-358-0835, ramseyer@wcoil.com [CDC] [RE]

Ramseyer, Robert Lewis (Alice Ruth) 107 Magnolia Ln, Bluffton OH 45817, 419-358-0835, ramseyer@wcoil.com [CDC] [RE]

Ranchod, Flinn John (Vasanthi Karen) 142 Cherry Ave, Hampton VA 23661, 757-380-6220 [VA] IIB1 [AC] Pastor, Calvary Community Ch Chesapeake, Chesapeake VA

MINISTERS

6

Ranck, Dawn J., 610 Derstine Ave, Lansdale PA 19446, 215-631-1610, dawn.ranck@verizon.net [FRC] IIA [AC] Associate Pastor, Plains Menn Ch, Hatfield PA

Ranck, Edwin H. (Rosanna) 1127 White Oak Rd, Christiana PA 17509-9765, 610-593-6488, reranck2@juno.com [LAN] [RE]

Ranck, J. Elvin (Charlotte) Rte 4 Box 298, Mifflintown PA 17059, 717-438-9142, elvchar@juno.com [LAN] IIC [AC] Evangelist, Orphanage Director, Lauver Menn Ch, Richfield PA

Ranck, Jay L., 1950 Lancaster Pk, Peach Bottom PA 17563, 717-548-3155 [LAN] IIB1 [AC] Pastor, Mechanic Grove Menn Ch, Peach Bottom PA

Ratzlaff, Harold Cecil (Ruth Leona) 1116 E 7th St #6, Newton KS 67114-2818, 316-283-6169 [WDC] [RE]

Ratzlaff, Richard (Velma) 27606 S Halstead St, Pretty Prairie KS 67570, 620-459-6203 [WDC] [RE]

Ratzlaff, Steve C. (Lynette Friesen Ratzlaff) 6039 N Roosevelt, Fresno CA 93704, 559-447-1481, ratzlaffs@sbcglobal.net [PSW] [AC] Pastor, Menn Community Ch, Fresno CA

Rauschenberger, Elizabeth D., 452 Beck Rd, Souderton PA 18964, 215-723-9853, rbcd4@netcarrier.com [EDC] IIC [AC]

Reber, Donald, 1506 Winsted Dr, Goshen IN 46526, 574-534-1783 [IM] [RE]

Rediger, Anita Pauline (Martin) 3077 W 950 S, Geneva IN 46740, 260-368-9143, redigerfarm@adamswells.com [CDC] IIB3a [AC]

Rediger, Terry Ray (Jerilee Anne) 1378 N Damon Rd, Ritzville WA 99169-8717, 509-659-0690, trediger@ritzcom.net [PNW] IIB1 [AC] Pastor, Menno Menn Ch, Ritzville WA

Reed, Harold E. (Barbara K.) 451 Delp Rd, Lancaster PA 17601, 717-560-2252, hereed@characterlink.net [LAN] IIB3a [AC] Chaplain, Garden Spot Village, New Holland PA

Reed, Harold S. (Ethel) 219 Lancaster Ave, PO Box 186, Terre Hill PA 17581, 717-445-6673 [LAN] IIB2 [RE]

Reed, Marvin S., 309 W Maple Grove Rd, Denver PA 17517, 717-445-7276 [LAN] IIB3a [AC]

Reese, Richard, 2017 W 74th St, Los Angeles CA 90047, 213-758-0248 [PSW] IIB2 [AC] Associate Pastor, Calvary Christian Fell, Inglewood CA

Regier, Daniel George (Goldie Jane) 331 W Spruce, Hesston KS 67062 [WDC] [RE]

Regier, Delbert (Eveline Viola) PO Box 247, Protection KS 67127, 620-622-4499, delregier@aol.com [SC] IIA [AC] Pastor, Protection Menn Ch, Protection KS

Regier, Harold Richard (Rosella Ruth) 1404 Axtell Rd, Newton KS 67114-1327, 316-283-7991 [WDC] [RE]

Regier, Richard James, 10518 S Heinz Rd, Canby OR 97013, 503-651-2430 [PNW] IIB1 [AC]

Rehwalt, Daniel William (Charlotte Ann) 76470 High St, Oakridge OR 97463, 541-782-2508 [PNW] [AC]

Reichenbach, Douglas Alan (Paulette Jean) 14275 92nd St SE, Freeport MI 49325, 616-765-3592 [CDC] IIB1 [AC] Pastor, Hope Church of the Brethren, Freeport MI

Reid, Kathryn Goering (Stephen Breck) 1801 South B St, Richmond IN 47374, kathy@thn.org [WDC] IIB1 [AW]

Reimer, Raymond H. (Rosella E. Epp) 3916 E Ronning Dr, Sioux Falls SD 57103-1152, 605-332-8964 [CP] IIB3d [AC]

Reinford, Daniel J., 304 Whitechapel Rd, Lancaster PA 17603, 717-399-8912 [LAN] [RE]

Reinford, Nelson L., 10 School House Rd, Souderton PA 18964, 215-723-4175 [FRC] [RE]

Reinford, Ralph, 1359 Oil City Rd, Wooster OH 44691, 330-264-1660, ralphr@sssnet.com [OH] IIB1 [AC] Pastor, Wooster Menn Ch, Wooster OH

Reitz, Melvin N. (Pauline) 120 E Deer Park Dr, Gaithersburg MD 20877-2013, 301-258-0762, melreitz@juno.com [LAN] III [AC] Deacon, Washington-Baltimore District, MD

Reitz, Raymond E. (Nancy) 67 Charlestown Rd, Washington Boro PA 17582, 717-684-7192, rayreitz@onemain.com [LAN] IIB1 [AC] Pastor, Mountville Menn Ch, Mountville PA

Rempel, Amanda J. (Clarence E.) 1004 W 10th St, Newton KS 67114, 316-284-0470 [WDC] IIB3a [AC] Chaplain, Kidron Bethel, North Newton KS

Rempel, Clarence E. (Amanda J.) 1004 W 10th St, Newton KS 67114, 316-284-0470, arempel@iwichita.com [WDC] IIB1 [AC] Pastor, First Menn Ch, Newton KS

Rempel, Cornel George (Martha Maria) 202A N President Ave, Lancaster PA 17603-3142, 717-209-7380, cgrempel@canada.com [LAN] IIB3a [AC] CPE Supervisor, Philhaven, Mt Gretna PA; Director of Pastoral Services, Philhaven, Mt Gretna PA

Rempel, Edwin F. (Kathrine M.) 2391 W Caley Ave, Littleton CO 80120, 303-347-9266, ekrempel@msn.com [RM] IB2 [AC] Conference Minister, Rocky Mountain Mennonite Conference, Littleton CO

Rempel, Erwin Henry (Angela Marie Albrecht) 342 Victoria Rd, Newton KS 67114, 316-283-6807, earempel@southwind.net [WDC] IIB3c [AC] Senior Executive, Mennonite Mission Network, Newton KS

Rempel, Jeanne (Dennis Lee) 2266 NE 177th St , Shoreline WA 98155, 206-367-5518 [PNW] IIA [AC] Pastor, Evergreen Menn Ch, Bellevue WA

Rempel, John Donald, 109 W Lafayette St, Goshen IN 46526, 574-534-2223, jrempel@ambs.edu [ACC] IIB3d [AC] Professor of Old Testament, AMBS, Elkhart IN

Rempel, Kathrine M. (Edwin F.) 2391 W Caley Ave, Littleton CO 80120, 303-347-9266, ekrempel@msn.com [RM] IB2 [AC] Conference Minister, Rocky Mountain Mennonite Conference, Littleton CO

Rempel, Vernon K. (Marilyn Yvonne) 3319 S Lafayette St, Englewood CO 81110, 303-781-4481, YKWE@aol.com [RM] IIB1 [AC] Pastor, First Menn Ch of Denver, Denver CO

Rempel, Wendell, 1266 N Klein, Reedley CA 93654-2006, 559-637-1195 [PSW] [AW] Administrator, Sierra View Homes, Reedley CA

Rendon, Simon, 115 NW 9th St, McMinnville OR 97128, 503-472-6264 [PNW] IIB1 [AC] Pastor, First Menn Ch, McMinnville OR; Pastor, Centro Cristiano Pentecostes de McMinnville, McMinnville OR

Renno, Tom (Betty J.) 2156 E Leewynn Dr, Sarasota FL 34240, 941-379-0782, TRenno@aol.com [SE] IIC [AC] Interim Pastor, Peace Christian Fell, North Port FL; Secretary of Outreach, SE Mennonite Conference, Sarasota FL

Resch, Miriam, 26067 Walnut Valley, Elkhart IN 46517,

574-294-4781, Miriam1220@juno.com [IM] IIB3a [AC] Dove Counseling, Elkhart IN

Ressler, Elvin J. (Melanie Joyce) 5923 Strasburg Rd, Atglen PA 19310, 610-593-7247, ejressler@copper.net [LAN] IB3, IIB1 [AC] Bishop/Overseer, LMC Millwood District, PA

Ressler, Jeffrey D. (Cynthia A.) 66 Glenbrook, Fisher IL 61843, 217-897-1713, ebassocpastor@earthlink.net [IL] IIB2 [AC] Associate Pastor, East Bend Menn Ch, Fisher IL

Reyes, Carlos (Constance) 15122 Mt Savage Rd NW, Mt Savage MD 21545, 301-264-3039 [ALL] IIA [AC] Pastor, Red Run Menn Ch, Grantsville MD

Rheinheimer, Ben, 1006 Mervin Ave, Goshen IN 46526, 574-534-9984, benjirh@yahoo.com [IM] IIA [AC] Youth Pastor, Yellow Creek Menn Ch, Goshen IN

Rheinheimer, Don (Jan) 3285 Spaatz Rd, Monument CO 80132, 719-488-9051, dondr@juno.com [RM, WDC] IIB1 [AC] Co-Pastor, Mountain Community Menn Ch, Palmer Lake CO

Rheinheimer, Jan Lynette (Donald Dean) 3285 Spaatz Rd, Monument CO 80132, 719-488-9051 [RM, WDC] IIB1 [AC] Co-Pastor, Mountain Community Menn Ch, Palmer Lake CO

Rice, Howard H. (Mei-Lie) 915 Wood St, Bethlehem PA 18018, 610-814-3416, harryri@mail.sy.ln.cn [LAN] IIB3b [AC] Missionary/Church Worker, PA

Rice, Jack, 951 Copella Rd, Bath PA 18014, 610-759-0211, bendersp@epix.net [LAN] IIB1 [AC] Pastor, Great Shepherd Christian Fell, Pen Argyl PA

Richard, Gary (Anne) 1706 Sheridan St, Warsaw IN 46580, 574-269-7745 [IM] [AW]

Richard, Glen (Margaret) 422 Becky Ln, Mount Pleasant IA 52641, 319-385-4962 [CP] [RE]

Richards, E. Joe (Emma E. Sommers) 1502 Brookfield Ct, Goshen IN 46526, 574-534-6357 [IM] [RE]

Richards, Emma Elizabeth (E. Joe) 1502 Brookfield Ct, Goshen IN 46526, 574-534-6357 [IM] [RE]

Richards, George R. (Clemmie) 223 Peabody St NW, Washington DC 20011, 202-829-1940 [LAN] IIB1 [AC] Pastor, Peabody St Menn Ch, Washington DC

Richer, Roger (Florence Arlene) 1364 Orchard Cr, Upland CA 91786, 909-981-4533 [PSW] IIB1 [AC] Pastor, Mountain View Menn Ch, Upland CA

Richert, Irvin E. (Shirley I.) 207 W Summit St, Souderton PA 18964, 215-723-7267 [EDC] [RE]

Richter Sr, Gerald B. (Charlotte A.) 508 E Bacon St, Pottsville PA 17901, 717-622-8382, jerry01@localnet.com [LAN] [AW]

Riegsecker, Marilyn, PO Box 127, Millersburg IN 46543, marilynr@maplenet.net [IM] IIA [AC] Minister of Christian Education, Clinton Frame Menn Ch, Goshen IN

Ring, Paul, 4275 Mount Tabor Rd, Vinton OH 45686, 740-388-9305 [OH] IIB1 [AC] Pastor, Fell Chapel, Vinton OH

Risser, Gerald E. (Joyce E.) 1246 Nissley Rd, Bainbridge PA 17502, grisser@dejazzd.com [LAN] III [AC] Ordained Deacon, Goods Menn Ch, Bainbridge PA

Risser, Harold L. (Dorothy) 1520 Harrisburg Pk MVG41, Lancaster PA 17601-2632 [LAN] [RE]

Risser, Isaac M. (Mildred) 3363 Melody Ave, Roanoke VA 24018, 540-725-1184 [VA] [RE]

Rissler, Jason R., 428 Nectarine St, Harrisburg PA

17104, jasonrissler@paonline.com [LAN] IIA [AC] Pastor, New Hope Community Ch, Harrisburg PA

Ritchie, Amy Suzanne Gall (Kurt) 15143 Featherstone Rd, Constantine MI 49042, 269-435-7732, amy.kurtritchie@juno.com [CDC] [AW]

Ritchie, Kurt (Amy Gall) 15143 Featherstone Rd, Constantine MI 49042, 269-435-7732, amy.kurtritchie@juno.com [CDC] [AW]

Rittenhouse, Mary Yunginger (Dennis) 6 Fairway Dr, Denver PA 17517, 717-445-6241, denmarrit@1usa,com [LAN] IIC [AC] Chaplain, Landis Homes, Lititz PA

Ritz, Lee Roy (Joyce) 1101 Schoffers Rd, Birdsboro PA 19508, 610-582-8915, his.servants7@juno.com [LAN] IIB1 [AC] Pastor, Hampden Menn Ch, Reading PA

Rivera, Juan Jose (Maria Elena) PO Box 50292, Sarasota FL 34278, 941-954-7189 [SE] IIB1 [AC] Pastor, Iglesia Seguidores de Cristo, Sarasota FL

Rivera, Oswaldo, 511 Glenn Ave, New Carlisle OH 45344, 937-846-1356 [OH] IIB2 [AC] Spanish Pastor, Huber Menn Ch, New Carlisle OH

Roberson, Ellis Wayne (Janice) 6005 Adamstown Rd, Adamstown MD 21710, 301-831-8812, pastor@dawsonvillechurch.org [LAN] IIB1 [AC] Pastor, Dawsonville Menn Ch, Poolesville MD

Roberts, Gary L. (Sue) 1 Lighthouse Dr, Kirkwood PA 17536, 717-529-6071, mtvernonmennonite@juno.com [LAN] IIB1 [AC] Pastor, Mt Vernon Menn Ch, Kirkwood PA

Robinson, Lindsey A., 226 Reily St, Harrisburg PA 17102, 717-232-6252, locustLnmenn@paoline.com [LAN] IB2, IIB1 [AC] Pastor, Locust Ln Menn Chapel, Harrisburg PA; Conference Minister, Lancaster Mennonite Conference, Harrisburg PA

Robles, Isaias, 8630 Fawn Creek Dr, Tampa FL 33626 [SE] IIA [AC] Pastor, North Tampa Christian Fell, Tampa FL

Rodman, Jerry (Carolyn) 1850 N SR 827, Angola IN 46703, 260-665-6364 [IM] [RE]

Rodriguez, Damian (Dilcia Matilde) 4308 Frank St, Dallas TX 75210, 214-428-7731, damain_rodriguez@msn.com [WDC] IIB1 [AC] Pastor, Comunidad de Esperanza, Dallas TX

Rodriguez-Lora, Nancy, 65818 Harwood Dr, Goshen IN 46526, 574-533-5619, loramuneca@aol.com [IM] IIA [AC] Pastor, True Vine Tabernacle, Goshen IN

Roeschley, Jane Thorley (Mark Alan) 14524 N 800 E Rd, Graymont IL 61743, 815-743-5978, jroeschley.mcn@verizon.net [CDC, IL] IIA [AC] Associate Pastor, Menn Ch of Normal, Normal IL

Rogers, Terry (Karen S.) 508 N Main St, Morton IL 61550, 309-263-7407, 7rogers@dpc.net [IL] [AW]

Rohrer, Casey Eugene (Rachel Ann) 1669 Creek Rd, New Columbia PA 17856, 570-568-1381, Casey@cmfmilton.org [LAN] IIA [AC] Youth/Assistant Pastor, Community Menn Fell, Milton PA

Rohrer, Larry D. (Sharon Jayne) 66 N Cross St, Columbiana OH 44408, 330-482-3420 [OH] IIB1 [AC] Pastor, Midway Menn Ch, Columbiana OH

Rohrer, Raymond E. (Elizabeth) 105 Ebrook Rd, Ronks PA 17572, 717-397-7044 [LAN] [RE]

Romain Jr., Victor H. (Oneisha) 21 Olde Forge Dr, Elizabethtown PA 17022-9341 [LAN] IIB1 [AC] Pastor, Steelton Menn Ch, Steelton PA

Roman, Carmen, 37 Reliance Rd, Souderton PA 18964,

MINISTERS

6

215-721-7087 [FRC] IIA [AC]

Romero, Carlos (Celina) 61536 CR 35, Goshen IN 46528, 574-825-0808, carlosr@mennoniteeducation.org [IM] IB1 [AC] staff, Mennonite Education Agency, Elkhart IN

Romero, Eugenio (Aurelia) PO Box 7438, Nogales AZ 85628-7438 [LAN] IIB3b [AC] church planter, Spanish, Nogales, AZ

Ropp, Herman E. (Gladys) 1630 Park Rd, Harrisonburg VA 22802, 540-433-1780 [VA] [RE]

Ropp, Janice Kennel (Lonnie D.) 2325 W Weathersfield Way, Schaumburg IL 60193, 847-985-0178, janiceropp@comcast.net [CDC, IL] IIC [AC] Minister of Counseling, Christ Community Menn Ch, Schaumburg IL

Ropp, Ronald David (Martha Jo Emerick) RR 8 Box 73-A, Normal IL 61761-9725, 309-452-8534 [CDC, IL] [RE] Pastoral Counselor, Private Practice, Normal IL

Ropp, Stephen A. (Cindy Renee) 601 E Taylor, Bloomington IL 61701, 309-829-7428, steverym@juno.com [CDC, IL] IIB2 [AC] Youth Pastor, Menn Ch of Normal, Normal IL

Rosa, Jose A. (Magdalena) PO Box 593, Lewisburg PA 17837-0593 [LAN] IIA [AC] Pastor, Shalom Menn Ch, Milton PA

Rose, Carol Ann 1820 W Cullerton, Chicago IL 60608, 312-421-6796, carolarose@juno.com [WDC] IIB3b [AC] Co-Director, Christian Peacemaker Teams, Chicago IL

Rosemberg, Rojas, 1601 W 4th St, Wilmington DE 19805, 302-654-3587 [LAN] IIB1 [AC] Pastor, Centro Evangelistico Cristiano, Wilmington DE

Ross, Richard, 436 E Sassafras, Orrville OH 44667, 330-684-2573 [OH] IIB3a [RE]

Roth, Arnold C. (Lucille) 6402 Cedar Trail, South Bend IN 46614 [IM] [RE]

Roth, Arthur J. (Marjorie) 320 W 7th St, Julesburg CO 80737, 970-474-2580 [CP] IIB1 [AC] Pastor, Julesburg Menn Ch, Julesburg CO

Roth, Charlene, 1515 30th Ave, Greeley CO 80634, 970-304-0417, rcroth@juno.com [RM] IIB1 [AC] Pastor, Greeley Menn Ch, Greeley CO

Roth, Cloy (Ora) 200 Meadowbrook Dr, Hot Springs AR 71913, 501-624-8722, ceoroth@cccusa.net [CP] IIB1 [AC] Interim Pastor, Wood River Menn Ch, Wood River NE

Roth, David Willis (Connie Sue) PO Box 803, Victoria Ln, Des Allemands LA 70030, 985-758-3927 [GS] IIA [AC] Pastor, Des Allemands Menn Ch, Des Allemands LA

Roth, Earl, 114 Hickory Cr, Elkhart IN 46517-9700, 574-294-5729 [CDC] [RE]

Roth, James L. (Ann Marie) 412 7th St NE, Hickory NC 28601, 828-328-4761, jimannroth@yahoo.com [VA] IIB1 [AC] Pastor, Hickory Menn Ch, Hickory NC

Roth, Jerry A. (Anna) PO Box 106, Marion PA 17235, 717-375-2037 [FRK] IIB1 [AC] Pastor, Chambersburg Menn Ch, Chambersburg PA

Roth, Lester, 203 Farmington Rd, Archbold OH 43502, 419-446-9477 [OH] [RE]

Roth, Mark Ray (Carol Lee) 11150 Rd 781, Philadelphia, MS 39350, 601-656-9302, croth@choctaw.org [GS] IIB2 [AC] Senior Pastor, Nanih Waiya Indian Menn Ch, Philadelphia MS

Roth, Melissa S., 3832 Blaine Ave, St Louis MO 63110, 314-772-1880, msroth7@juno.com [CDC, IL] IIA [AC] Pastor, St Louis Menn Fell, St Louis MO

Roth, Nelson M., 15385 Lakeview Ct, Gulfport MS 39503-8305 [GS] IIA [AC] Pastor, Gulfhaven Menn Ch, Gulfport MS

Roth, Oliver (Verda) RR 1, Milford NE 68405, 402-761-2065 [CP] [RE]

Roth, Randall J. (Mary) 3107 Madison Ave, Des Moines IA 50310, 515-255-9127, RRoth13@aol.com [CP] IIB1 [AC] Pastor, Des Moines Menn Ch, Des Moines IA

Roth, Ron, 1515 30th Ave, Greeley CO 80634, 970-304-0417, rcroth@juno.com [RM] IIB1 [AC] Pastor, Greeley Menn Ch, Greeley CO

Roth, Roy D., 2211 Oakway Rd, Eugene OR 97401, 541-344-8547 [PNW] [RE]

Roth, Willard Edward (Alice Metzler) 1077 Greenleaf Blvd #311, Elkhart IN 46514-3565, 574-266-7684, waroth@juno.com [CDC, IM] [RE]

Roth, Willis (Darlene) 7457 W Abbott Rd, Grand Island NE 68803, 308-382-8039 [CP] [RE]

Rowe, Robert C. (Naomi) 8614 Pine Tree Rd, Jessup MD 20794, 301-725-0540 [LAN] IIB1 [AC] Pastor, Guilford Rd Menn Ch, Jessup MD

Roynon, James (Nancy A.) V986 CR 20, Archbold OH 43502, 419-446-2967, njroynon@fulton-net.com [OH] IIB1 [AC] Pastor, W Clinton Menn Ch, Wauseon OH

Royster, D. David (Pamela) 762 Paddock Pl, Northwales PA 19454-2706 [LAN] [AW]

Rozier, Jacqueline, 945 E 239th St, Euclid OH 44123, godaboveal@aol.com [OH] IIA [AC] Associate Pastor, Lee Heights Community Ch, Cleveland OH

Rudy, Carl J. (Ruth) 2021 College Dr, La Junta CO 81050, 719-384-9297, carlrudy@iguana.rural.net [RM] [RE]

Rudy, John H. (Lucy) 89 Linda Ave, Lancaster PA 17602, 717-299-6031 [ACC] [RE]

Ruffin, Jimmie (Kim) 1823 Woodhaven Dr, Fort Wayne IN 46819, 260-447-9566, jimmie.ruffin@verizon.net [IM] IIB1 [AC] Pastor, Fairhaven Menn Ch, Fort Wayne IN

Rupp, Anne Neufeld (Kenneth Edward) 13844 Sycamore, Olathe KS 66062, 913-782-1793 [WDC] [RE]

Rush, John L. (Esther) 638 Mountain View Rd, Reading PA 19607, 610-777-0171, rushjoes@aol.com [ACC] IIB3b [AC] Executive Director, 2 State-Wide Prison Ministries; Executive Director, Justice & Mercy Ministries, Reading PA

Rush, Paul D., 1419 Richland Town Pk, Quakertown PA 18951, 215-536-3103 [FRC] [RE]

Russell, Rick (Marilyn) 210 Clairmont St, Jackson MS 39209, 601-354-9444 [GS] [AW]

Rust, C. Timothy (Janine J.) 55238 CR 31, Bristol IN 46507-9569, 574-825-1111, tim@rusthollar.com [CDC] [AW]

Ruth, John L., 760 Salfordville Rd, Harleysville PA 19438, 610-287-5487 [FRC] [RE]

Ruth, Marvin L. (Lizzie) 595 N Mountain Rd, Newville PA 17241, 717-776-3084 [LAN] [RE]

Rutherford Jr., Richard E. (Dorothy E.) 272 Picture Mountain Dr, Martinsburg WV 25401-0660, 304-263-7850, pastor@blackoakmennonite.net; reugenejr@msn.com [ACC] IIB1 [AC] Pastor, Black Oak Menn Ch, Warfordsburg PA

Ruth-Heffelbower, Clare Ann (Duane) 3198 E Menlo Ave, Fresno CA 93710, 559-297-4578 [PSW] IB2 [AC] Regional Conference Minister, Pacific SW Mennonite Conference, Fresno CA

MINISTERS

6

Ruth-Heffelbower, Duane Fredric (Clare Ann) Fresno Pacific University, Center for Peacemaking and Conflict Studies, 1717 S Chestnut Ave, Fresno CA 93717, 559-455-5840, duanerh@fresno.edu [PSW] IIB3d [AW]

Rutschman, Laverne (Harriet Anne Fischbach) PO Box 103, North Newton KS 67117, 316-283-5749, rutsch@southwind.net [WDC] [RE]

Rutt, Harry W. (Julia) 390 W Newport Rd, Ronks PA 17572-9718, 717-656-6244, harryrutt1@juno.com [LAN] [AW]

Rutter, Allen G., 21-377 CR H-50, Stryker OH 43557, 419-682-5096, alrutter@bright.net [OH] IIB1 [AC] Pastor, Lockport Menn Ch, Stryker OH

S

Sabatine, Leonard J. (Norma) 1740 Howell Rd RD1, Eon PA 18042-9221, 610-253-0086, lensabsr@juno.com [LAN] III [AC] Ordained Deacon, Maranatha Family Christian Fell, Nazareth PA

Sahle, Endalkachew (Bethlehem) 772 Providence Rd Apt B-408, Aldan PA 19018, 610-623-1409, endalks@yahoo.com [LAN] IIB1 [AC] Pastor, Ethiopian Evangelical Ch of Philadelphia, Upper Darby PA

Sanchez, Moises H. (Stor) 800 Macon St Apt 1R, Brooklyn NY 11233, 718-399-1345 [ACC] IIA [AC] Pastor, First Menn Ch, Brooklyn NY

Saner, John R. (Virginia) HCR 67, Box 37, Mifflin PA 17058, 717-436-6621 [LAN] [RE]

Sangree, Paul C. (Martha) 1125 River Rd, Marietta PA 17547, 717-426-4584, mariettachapel@juno.com [LAN] IIB1 [RE]

Sangrey, Landis K. (Martha) 109 Turnbridge Dr, Lancaster PA 17603, 717-397-6053 [LAN] [RE]

Santiago, Jose A. (Agdelia) 511 Oak Grove Dr, Lancaster PA 17601, 717-299-6789, j.santiago511@juno.com [LAN] IIB3, IIB1 [AC] Interim Pastor, Luz Verdadera, Reading PA; Supervisor, Spanish District, Lancaster PA

Santiago, Noel (Juanita) 210 S Main St, Sellersville PA 18960-2529, 215-257-1126, NoelS@FMC-online.org [FRC] IIB3c [AC] Conference Minister, Franconia Mennonite Conference, Souderton PA

Sarmiento, Luis D. (Patricia) A Apartado 43A, Charavalle, Venezula [LAN] IIB1 [AC]

Sauder, Bruce L. (Wanda) 409 Linden Rd, East Earl PA 17519, 717-445-9280, blwjsauder@hydrosoft.net [LAN] IIB2 [AC] Pastor, Goodville Menn Ch, Goodville PA

Sauder, Donald M. (Myrtle) 5530 Levering Ave, Elkridge MD 21075, 410-796-5274 [LAN] III [AC] Ordained Deacon, Guilford Rd Menn Ch, Jessup MD

Sauder, Eugene H. (Grace) 274 W Maple Grove Rd, Denver PA 17517-8929, 717-445-6119 [LAN] [RE]

Sauder, Glenn E. (Brenda) 518 W Broad St, New Holland PA 17557, 717-354-9990, sauderspot@juno.com [LAN] IIA, IIB1 [AC] Pastor, Hinkletown Menn Ch, Ephrata PA

Sauder, James, 1225 Fern Ave, Reading PA 19607, 610-796-1528, jarhosa@juno.com [LAN] IIB1 [AC] Pastor, Shiloh Menn Ch, Reading PA

Sauder, Joseph P. (Geneva) 5670 Waterloo Rd Apt A, Columbia MD 21045-2627, 410-465-1863, joe@sauder.org [LAN] [RE]

Sauder, Marty (Jean) 1050 North Kiowa St, Allentown PA 18103, 610-770-1409, msauder@erols.com [FRC] IIB1 [AC] Pastor, Spruce Lake Fell, Canadensis PA

Sauder, Mona, 16449 SR 2, Wauseon OH 43567 [OH] IIA

[AC] Pastor of Senior Care/Small Groups, Zion Menn Ch, Archbold OH

Sauder, Steve (Anna) 809 Heritage Dr, Oakland MD 21550-1746, 301-334-7969, ssauder@pennswoods.net [ALL] IB3, IIB1 [AC] Pastor, Gortner Union Ch, Oakland MD

Sauder, Steven A. (Becky) 5755 Elkridge Heights Rd, Elkridge MD 21075-5326, 410-579-8714, ssauder@ineva.com [LAN] IIA [AC] Associate Pastor, Guilford Rd Menn Ch, Jessup MD

Savage, Regan (Janice Histand) 35 Millstone Ct, Langhorne PA 19047, 215-757-3209 [FRC] IIB1 [AC] Pastor, MillCreek Community Ch, Langhorne PA

Sawatsky, Margaret (Walter) 2406 Roys Ave, Elkhart IN 46517, 574-522-1806, msawatsky@juno.com [CDC] IIB3a [AC] Chaplain, Greencroft Retirement Center, Goshen IN

Sawatzky, Erick (Beverley Ann) 405 Park W Dr, Goshen IN 46526, 574-533-1830, EBSawatzky@cs.com [CDC] [RE] Prof. of Pastoral Ministry/Dir. of Field Ed., Associated Mennonite Biblical Seminary, Elkhart IN

Sawatzky, Sheldon Victor (Marietta G. Landis) PO Box 12-89, Taoyuan City 330-99, TAIWAN ROC [WDC] IIB3c [AC] Associate Director, Mennonite Mission Network, Newton KS

Sawatzky, Walter (Joy) 222 W Broad St, Souderton PA 18964, 215-721-4776, WalterS@MRN.org [FRC] IC [AC] Conference Minister, Franconia Mennonite Conference, Souderton PA

Scaggs, Sam R. (Beverly) 441 Wenger Rd, Chesapeake VA 23322 [VA] [AW]

Scandrett, Kendrick J. (Catherine) 441 Saint Bernadine St, Reading PA 19602, 610-796-7397, jclea7@juno.com [LAN] IIB1 [AC] Pastor, Ephrata Menn Ch, Ephrata PA

Schaadt, Michael Alan, 819 Muschlitz St, Bethlehem PA 18015, 610-866-8433, pastormikeis@msn.com [EDC] IIB1 [AC] Interim/Transitional Pastor, Alpha Menn Ch, Alpha NJ; Drug and Alcohol Counselor, Allentown Rescue Mission, Allentown PA

Schanz, Philip (Barbara) 1470 Reiff Rd, Lansdale PA 19446, 215-855-4752 [EDC] III [AC]

Schertz, Dale E. (Virginia Florence) 503 W Short St, Remington IN 47977-9801, 219-261-2731 [CDC] [RE]

Schertz, Vernon E. (Betty I.) 2010 Albany Dr SW, Atlanta GA 30311, 404-758-3096, verbetz@juno.com [SE] [RE]

Schildt, Kenneth E. (Charlene) 74 Engle Rd, Marietta PA 17545, 717-426-1579, schildts@paonline.com [LAN] IIC [AC] Licensed Deacon, Bossler Menn Ch, Elizabethtown PA

Schipani, Daniel, 57995 River Lake Ct, Elkhart IN 46516, 574-875-8913 [IM] IIB3d [AC] Staff, Associated Mennonite Biblical Seminary, Elkhart IN

Schlabach, Mark (Starla) 248 Meadow Ln, Conestoga PA 17516, 717-871-3002, mschlabach@life-ministries.com [LAN] IIA [AC] Pastor, Life Menn Fell, Conestoga PA

Schloneger, Craig (Ann) 950 Buckwalter Rd, Lititz PA 17543, 717-627-4166, schloneg@yahoo.com [ACC] IIA [AC] Pastor, Neffsville Menn Ch, Lancaster PA

Schloneger, Enid Elaine, 822 Orchard Rd, Sellersville PA 18960, 215-257-6999, bobenid@comcast.net [FRC] IIB1 [AC] Lead Pastor, Blooming Glen Menn Ch, Blooming Glen PA

Schloneger, Florence Eileen (Weldon Ray) 1501 Bell

MINISTERS

6

St , Beatrice NE 68310, 402-223-2897, floschloneger@hotmail.com [WDC] IIB1 [AC] Co-Pastor, First Menn Ch, Beatrice NE

Schloneger, Robert (Enid Elaine) 822 Orchard Rd, Sellersville PA 18960, 215-257-6999, bobenid@comcast.net [FRC] IIB1 [AC] Lead Pastor, Blooming Glen Menn Ch, Blooming Glen PA

Schloneger, Weldon Ray (Florence Eileen) 1501 Bell St, Beatrice NE 68310, 402-223-2897 [WDC] IIB1 [AC] Co-Pastor, First Menn Ch, Beatrice NE

Schlosser, Lynn, PO Box 236, 501 Houck, Pawnee Rock KS 67567-0236, 620-982-4886, ltschlosser@mpks.net [WDC] IIA [AC] Co-Pastor, Bergthal Menn Ch, Pawnee Rock KS

Schlosser, Todd, PO Box 236, 501 Houck, Pawnee Rock KS 67567-0236, 620-982-4886, ltschlosser@mpks.net [WDC] IIA [AC] Co-Pastor, Bergthal Menn Ch, Pawnee Rock KS

Schmell, Barry Lee (Deborah Lee) 6133 Cordava Ct, Fort Wayne IN 46815, 260-493-7867, bdschmell@aol.com [CDC] IIB1 [AC] Pastor, Maplewood Menn Ch, Fort Wayne IN

Schmell, Rodger K. (Diana) 552 Irish Meetinghouse Rd, Perdasie PA 18944, 215-766-9659, rdschmell@juno.com [EDC] IIB1 [AC] Pastor, Deep Run W Menn Ch, Perkasie PA

Schmidt, Debra Ann (Donald Ray) 901 S Pine, Newton KS 67114, 316-283-8186, hutchfmc@sbcglobal.net [WDC] IIB1 [AC] Pastor, First Menn Ch, Hutchinson KS

Schmidt, Dennis (Dianne Kay) 525 N Jefferson St, Berne IN 46711-1517, 260-589-9877, dennis@firstmennonite.org [CDC] IIB2 [AC] Pastor of Christian Education, First Menn Ch, Berne IN

Schmidt, Melvin D. (Charlotte G.) 4212 Longfellow St , Hyattsville MD 20781, 301-927-0420, pastor@columbusmennonite.org [ALL] IIB1 [AC]

Schmidt, Steven Gary (Wanda Ream) 10 Chaparral Ct, La Junta CO 81050-3803, 719-384-9359, pastor@emclj.org [RM] IIB1 [AC] Pastor, Emmanuel Menn Ch, La Junta CO

Schmidt, Vyron Lloyd (Elvina Ruth) 906 Player Dr, Goshen IN 46526-2726, 574-533-0671 [IM] IIB3c [AC]

Schmitt, Howard S. (D. Jean) 1003 Willow Creek Dr, Plain City OH 43064, 614-873-0670, howjean@prodigy.net [OH] IIB1 [AC] Interim Pastor, Oak Grove Menn Ch, West Liberty OH

Schmucker, Eli S. (Myrtle) PO Box 257, New Paris IN 46553, 574-831-4432 [IM] IIB1 [AC] Pastor, Family Worship Center at the Lighthouse, Goshen IN

Schrag, Charlene, 25411 S Holman, Estacada OR 97023, 503-630-7216, pmcyouth@teleport.com [PNW] IIA [AC] Youth Pastor, Portland Menn Ch, Portland OR

Schrag, James Frederick (Judith A.) 3225 Southwood Ct, Newton KS 67114, 316-283-0608 [WDC] IB1 [AC] Executive Director, Mennonite Church USA, Newton KS

Schrag, Laverle (Ronald D.) 222 W 20, Hutchinson KS 67502, 620-663-4958, verls@midusa.net [WDC] IIB2 [AC] Associate Pastor, First Menn Ch, Hutchinson KS

Schrag, Myron Dave (Ericka Koop) 1201 S 14th St, Goshen IN 46526, 574-533-8366, schrags@npcc.net [CDC] [RE]

Schrag, Rhoda M., 1105 S 8th St, Goshen IN 46526, 574-534-7873, rmschrag@juno.com [CDC, IM] IIA [AC] Pastor, Southside Fell, Elkhart IN

Schrag, Tim E. (Sue Hertzler) 105 Sandra Ln, Normal IL 61761, 309-862-1880, t.schrag@verizon.net [CDC, IL] IIB1 [AC] Pastor, Menn Ch of Normal, Normal IL

Schrag, Willard A. (Ruth R.) 113 W Lincoln, Moundridge KS 67107-9701, 620-345-6433 [WDC] [RE]

Schreiner Youngquist, Sally (Orland) 810 Reba Place, Evanston IL 60202, 847-86-9395, sallylwcc@aol.com [IL] IIB1 [AC] Senior Pastor, Living Water Community Ch, Chicago IL

Schrock, Daniel P. (Jennifer Halteman) 64366 Meadow Ridge Dr, Goshen IN 46526, 574-533-1729, danschrock@juno.com [IM] IIB1 [AC] Pastor, Berkey Ave Menn Fell, Goshen IN

Schrock, Elwood G. (Lorene) 166 N SR 40, Exeland WI 54835-2176, 715-943-2317, eschrock@indianheadtel.net [NC] IIB1 [AC] Pastor, Exeland Menn Ch, Exeland WI

Schrock, Homer E. (Debbie) 10 Schapansky Rd, Cochranville PA 19330, 610-593-6462 [ACC] [RE]

Schrock, James A., PO Box 67, Pettisville OH 43553, 419-445-3311 [OH] IIC [AC]

Schrock, John L. (Melissa Kauffman) 192 Garmatter St, Bluffton OH 45817, 419-358-0958, FMC.john@bluffton.edu [CDC] IIB2 [AC] Associate Pastor, First Menn Ch, Bluffton OH

Schrock, Thomas L. (Jeanette A.) RR 1 Box 23, Putnam IL 61560, 815-646-4678 [IL] IIB1 [AC] Pastor, New Life Community Ch, Henry IL

Schrock-Hurst, Carmen (Luke) MCC Philippines, PO Box 2541, Central Post Office, 1165 Quezon City, PHILIPPINES, carmenschrock@qinet.net [ALL] IIB3b [AC]

Schrock-Hurst, Luke (Carmen) MCC Philippines, PO Box 2541, Central Post Office, 1165 Quezon City, PHILIPPINES, carmenschrock@qinet.net [ALL] IIB3b [AC]

Schroeder, Joel R. (Kay J.) 1019 Country Lane, Newton KS 67114-1492, 316-215-2497, jkjjschroeder@sbcglobal.net, [WDC] [CP] IIB2 [AC] Associate Pastor, First Menn Ch, Newton KS

Schultz, Timothy J., 5625 Kraus Rd, Clarence NY 14031-1342, 716-480-4013, tim@buffalo.com [NY] [AW]

Schulz, Eugene, PO Box 167, Walsenburg CO 81089, 719-738-2037 [RM] [RE]

Schumacher, Kevin John, 12642 S Hiefield Ct, Oregon City OR 97045, 503-722-2304 [PNW] IIA [AC] Pastor, Calvary Menn Ch, Aurora OR

Schumm, Clare (Katie Ann) 24452 Reiner Ct, Elkhart IN 46517-9482, 574-534-2343 [IM] IIB3a [AC] Chaplain, Greencroft Inc, Goshen IN

Schwartz, Jacob B., 23641 Findley Rd, Sturgis MI 49091, 269-467-6253 [IM] IIB3a [AC] Jail Chaplain, St. Joseph Co Jail, IN

Schwartz, Thomas (Leanell) 138 Keathly Dr, Battle Creek MI 49017, 616-964-9214 [IM] IIB1 [AC] Pastor, Pine Grove Menn Ch, Battle Creek MI

Schwartzentruber, Hubert (Mary Rittenhouse) 711 Rising Sun Rd, Telford PA 18969, 215-723-1460 [FRC] IIB3a [AC] Chaplain, Souderton Mennonite Homes, Souderton PA

Schweitzer, James Roland (Carol Ann) 2455 E Mountain View Dr SE, Albany OR 97322, 541-928-4304 [PNW] IIC [AC]

Scott Jr., William L. (Vivian) 2821 Chamber St, Saginaw MI 48601, 989-755-7159, billy.boy@juno.com [IM] IIB1 [AC] Pastor, Ninth St Menn Ch, Saginaw MI

Scoville, Gordon (Marie Gotfredson) RR1 Box 27, Croghan NY 13327, 315-346-6847, gordmar@northnet.org [CP] IIB1 [AC] Interim Pastor, Beemer Menn Ch, Beemer NE

Sears, Earl (Jane) 7273 1575 E St , Tiskilwa IL 61368, 815-646-4497, esears@theramp.net [IL] [RE] Interim Pastor, Menn Congregation of Boston, Cambridge MA

Seitz Jr., Kenneth L. (Kathryn F.) Mennonite Central Committee, PO Box 113-5157, Hamra, Beirut, Lebanon, 961-365-4106, lebanon@mennonitecc.ca [PSW] IIB1 [AC]

Seitz Sr., Kenneth L. (Grace) 1285 Shank Dr #125, Harrisonburg VA 22802, 540-564-6532 [VA] [RE]

Sell, Glen M. (Ethel) 677 Lititz Rd, Manheim PA 17545-9726, 717-626-1566, gmsell@juno.com [LAN] IIB1 [AC] Interim/Transitional Pastor, Manheim Menn Ch, E Petersburg PA

Sell, Menno D., 1001 E Oregon Rd, Lititz PA 17543 [LAN] [RE]

Sensenig, Craig G. (Denise) 122 W Main St, PO Box 644, Terre Hill PA 17581, 717-445-6916, craigs@groffdale.com [LAN] IIB1 [AC] Assistant/Youth Pastor, Groffdale Menn Ch, Leola PA

Sensenig, David E. (Marilyn) 103 Edgewood Dr, New Holland PA 17557, davmarsen5@aol.com [LAN] IIB2 [AC] Associate Pastor, Martindale Menn Ch, Ephrata PA

Sensenig, Donald M. (Doris) 106 S 4th St, Akron PA 17501, 717-859-2940, dondors@juno.com [LAN] [AW]

Sensenig, Earl M. (Dorothy) 391 Akron Rd, Ephrata PA 17522, 717-859-2103 [LAN] [AC]

Sensenig, Gary (Joanne) Mennonite Guesthouse, PO Box 14646, Nairobi, Kenya [LAN] IIC [AC] Missionary/Church Worker, EMM, Nairobi, Kenya, Africa

Sensenig, J. Carl (Julia A.) 173 Wheatland Dr, Denver PA 17517, 717-445-9641, jcsensen@yahoo.com [LAN] IIA [AC] Pastor, Red Run Menn Ch, Denver PA

Sensenig, Jennifer Davis (Kent) 580 N Los Robles Ave #10, Pasadena CA 91101-1062, 319-277-5611, jennifer@pmcweb.org [PSW] IIB2 [AC] Associate Pastor, Pasadena Menn Ch, Pasadena CA

Sensenig, Joanne E. (Gary) Mennonite Guesthouse, PO Box 14646, Nairobi, Kenya, Africa, 717-354-0234 [LAN] IIC [AC] Missionary, Mennonite Guesthouse, Nairobi, Kenya

Sensenig, Luke Nolt (Anna) 5135 Laurel Ln, New Holland PA 17557, 717-355-0391, lukannsen@juno.com [LAN] IIA [AC] Associate Pastor, Millwood Menn Ch, Bird In Hand PA

Seville, D.C., 7108 W Cholla, Peoria AZ 85345, 602-486-9160 [PSW] IIB1 [AC] Pastor, Emmanuel Menn Ch, Surprise AZ

Seymour III, William A., 128 Cherry St, Orrville OH 44667. 330-682-5804 [OH] IIA [AC] Pastor, Orrville Menn Ch, Orrville OH

Shank, David A., 26430 Banker St Rd, Sturgis MI 49091, 269-659-4047 [IM] [RE]

Shank, Dorothy J. (Orval) 2272 Lake Terrace Dr, Harrisonburg VA 22802, 540-438-0866, dorvals@aol.com [VA] [RE]

Shank, Luke J., 1001 E Oregon Rd, Lititz PA 17543, 717-581-0297, lukejs@dejazzd.com [LAN] [RE]

Shank, Orval M. (Dorothy) 2272 Lake Terrace Dr, Harrisonburg VA 22802, 540-438-0866, dorvals@aol.com [VA] [RE]

Shank, Raymond W. (Gladys) 860A Hillside Ave,

Harrisonburg VA 22802, 540-433-5495 [VA] IIB2 [AC]

Shank, Rowland (Thelma) 2967 Westwind Dr, Harrisonburg VA 22801, 540-564-0568 [VA] [RE]

Shantz, Kathy Keener (Stan R.) 4351 W Vista Ave, Glendale AZ 85301, 623-939-7773, KKShantz@aol.com [PSW] IIB2 [AC]

Shantz, Stan, 4351 W Vista Ave, Glendale AZ 85301, 623-939-7773, srshantz@aol.com [PSW] IIB1 [AC]

Sharp, Donald D. (Loretta) 1696 Billview Dr, Lancaster PA 17601, 717-560-6352, dlsharp102@yahoo.com [LAN] IIB1 [AC] Lead Pastor, Stumptown Menn Ch, Bird In Hand PA

Sharp, Galen (Donna) 75 Allison Gap Rd, Belleville PA 17004, 717-483-6063 [ALL] IIB3a [AC]

Sharp, Harold E. (Vonnie) 102 Forest Ln, Belleville PA 17004, 717-483-6929 [ALL] IB3, IIB1 [AC] Pastor, Rockville Menn Ch, Belleville PA

Sharp, Harold R., 1411 N Abbe Rd, Fairview MI 48621, 517-848-5280 [IM] [RE]

Sharp, John E. (Michele Miller) 416 Marilyn Ave, Goshen IN 46526, 574-534-6685, johnes@goshen.edu [IM] IB3, IIB3c [AC] Overseer, Assembly Mennonite, Goshen IN; Overseer, N Main St Mennonite, Nappanee IN

Shaub, Andrew H. (Ruth C.) 529 Saratoga Rd, Lancaster PA 17603, 717-397-0424 [LAN] [RE]

Shearer, Harold F. (Irene) 3901 Bahia Vista St, Lot 441, Sarasota FL 34232, 941-371-7649, hishearer@comcast.net [SE] [RE]

Shearer, John (Vel) 1560 Jody Ave, Lebanon PA 17046, 717-270-5302 [ACC] [RE]

Sheats, Earl (Pansy) 8610 Mennonite Church Rd, Wover MD 21871, 410-957-2097, epsheats@yahoo.com [ACC] [AW]

Sheeler, Timothy J. (Joyce) 4275 Enola Rd, Newville PA 17241, 717-776-6263, tjsheeler@pa.net [LAN] III [AC] Ordained Deacon, Diller Menn Ch, Newville PA

Shellenberger, Shelley R. (Mildred) 1001 E Oregon Rd, Lititz PA 17543, 717-569-0269 [LAN] [RE]

Sheller, Gayle, 952 C St, Springfield OR 97477, 541-726-9382, eugmenno@efn.org [PNW] IIB1 [AC] Pastor, Eugene Menn Ch, Eugene OR

Shelly, Eugene (Martine S.) 3234 Irwin Ave, Bronx NY 10463-3705, 212-549-1569, GShelly@aol.com [LAN] IIB3a [AC]

Shelly, Karl S (Michelle Schirch) 605 N Greene Rd, Goshen IN 46526, 574-534-0185, kmshelly85@juno.com [CDC, IM] IIB2 [AC] Co-Pastor, Assembly Menn Ch, Goshen IN

Shelly, Maynard (Griselda Gehman) 3017 Ivy Ct, North Newton KS 67117-8072, 316-283-0518 [WDC] [RE]

Shelly, Patricia Joyce, 533 W Broadway, Newton KS 67114 [WDC] IIB3d [AC] Professor of Bible, Bethel College, North Newton KS

Shenk, Calvin E. (Marie) 1055 Blue Ridge Dr, Harrisonburg VA 22802, 540-433-8125 [LAN] [RE]

Shenk, Charles B. (Ruth) 3505 Lindstrom Dr, Columbus OH 43228, 614-274-5552, CBShenk@aol.com [CDC, OH] [RE]

Shenk, Charles E. (Marian) 206 Newcomer Dr, Scottdale PA 15683, 724-887-7641, shenk@Wol.com [ALL] IB3 [AC]

Shenk, Clayton O. (Dorothy) 3346 Redbud Ln, Harrisonburg VA 22801-5313, 540-433-3296 [VA] [RE]

Shenk, Dale (Trish) 1505 S 8th St, Goshen IN 46526-4701, 574-534-3537, deshenk@bethanycs.net [IM] IB3,

MINISTERS

6

IIB3d [AC] Bible Teacher, Bethany Christian Schools, Goshen IN; Overseer, First Mennonite Ch, Middlebury IN

Shenk, David W. (K. Grace) Lithuania Christian College, Malunininku 4, 5813 Klaipeda, Lithuania [LAN] IIB1 [AC]

Shenk, Donna Lois (James W.) 37 Third St, Akron PA 17501, 717-859-3512, jimshenk@juno.com [ACC] IIB3a [AC] Chaplain, Ephrata Community Hospital, Ephrata PA

Shenk, Edith N. (Joseph C.) PO Box 1040, Musoma, Tanzania, jesh@worldnet.att.com [VA] IIB3b [AC]

Shenk, Evelyn Landis (John) 1560 College Ave, Harrisonburg VA 22802, 540-434-8220 [VA] IIB3a [AC]

Shenk, Ezra W. (Sara) 300 13th St, Wellman IA 52356, 319-648-4434 [CP] IIB1 [AC] Pastor, Daytonville Community Ch, Wellman IA

Shenk, Glenn H. (Helen) 186 Buck Heights Rd, Quarryville PA 17566, 717-284-4744 [LAN] [RE]

Shenk II, H. Michael (Peggy Brackbill) 1345 Hillcrest Dr, Harrisonburg VA 22802, 540-434-0578 [VA] IB3, IIB1 [AC] Pastor, Valley View Menn Ch, Harrisonburg VA

Shenk III, H. Michael (Ramona) 5532 Greenhill Rd, Linville VA 22834, 540-833-4727 [VA] IIB1 [AC] Pastor, Valley View Menn Ch, Harrisonburg VA

Shenk, Harold A. (Mary Grace) 13233 Glendale Dr, Hagerstown MD 21742, 301-797-5062, h-mgshenk@juno.com [ACC] IIB1 [AC] Co-Pastor, Hebron Menn Ch, Hagerstown MD

Shenk, Henry G. (Irene) 742 Bruce Ave, Mount Joy PA 17552, 717-653-5819 [LAN] [RE]

Shenk, J. B. (Betty) 1607 Kentfield Way, Goshen IN 46526, 574-534-8432 [IM] [RE]

Shenk, Jean Kraybill (Norman G.) 4050 Old Harrisburg Pk, Mount Joy PA 17552, 717-653-5256, normans@supernet.com [LAN] IIC [AC]

Shenk, John B. (Myrtle) 6138 Sundra Cr, East Petersburg PA 17520, 717-569-1589 [LAN] [RE]

Shenk, Joseph C. (Edith N.) PO Box 1040, Musoma, Tanzania, jeshenk@africaonline.co.tz [VA] IIB3b [AC]

Shenk, Mary Grace (Harold) 13233 Glendale Dr, Hagerstown MD 21742, 301-797-5062, h-mgshenk@juno.com [ACC] IIB1 [AC] Co-Pastor, Hebron Menn Ch, Hagerstown MD

Shenk, Nelson J. (June Yoder) 145 S 5th St, Bally PA 19503, 610-845-3240, ballyshenk@comcast.net [FRC] IIB1 [AC] Pastor, Boyertown Menn Ch, Boyertown PA

Shenk, Norman G. (Jean Kraybill) 4050 Old Harrisburg Pk, Mount Joy PA 17552, 717-653-5256, normans@supernet.com [LAN] [RE]

Shenk, Philip L., 4650 Ridgewood Rd E, Springfield OH 45503, 937-399-9941 [IM] IIB3b [AC]

Shenk, Ruth F. (Charles B.) 3505 Lindstrom Dr, Columbus OH 43228, 614-274-5552, CBShenk@aol.com [CDC, OH] [RE]

Shenk, Stanley C. (Doris) 1801 Greencroft Blvd Apt 434, Goshen IN 46526, 574-533-3511 [IM] [RE]

Shenk, Wilbert, 570 N Madison #6, Pasadena CA 91101, 626-683-3494 [IM] IIB3d [AC] Professor, Fuller Theological Seminary, Pasadena CA

Sherer, Joseph N. (Mary Lou) 26 Donegal Springs Rd, Mount Joy PA 17552, 717-653-1578, joesherer@mjmc.org [LAN] IIB1 [AC] Pastor, Mount Joy Menn Ch, Mount Joy PA

Sherrill, Mike (Teresa Thompson) Higashi Moto Machi 2-2-10, Kokubunji, Tokyo 185-0022, Japan, 011-81-042-301-2911, journey@sherrill.com [PSW] IIB3b [AC]

Sherrill, Teresa Thompson (Mike) Higashi Moto Machi 2-2-10, Kokubunji, Tokyo 185-0022, Japan, 011-81-042-301-2911, journey@sherrill.com [PSW] IIB3b [AC]

Shertzer, Norman C. (Verna) 530 Habecker Ch Rd, Lancaster PA 17603, 717-285-5307 [LAN] [RE]

Shertzer, Philip L. (Joyce) 91 Mill St, Washington Boro PA 17582-9705, 717-684-8820, joyphil@localnet.com [LAN] IIA [AC] Associate Pastor, Mountville Menn Ch, Mountville PA

Shertzer, W. Lynn (Dawn) 832 Fisher Rd, Mechanicsburg PA 17055-9601, 717-766-4142, shertzer@paonline.com [LAN] IIA [AC] Pastor, Slate Hill Menn Ch, Camp Hill PA

Shirk, Frank E. (Erica) 177-A E Main St, Leola PA 17540-1945, 717-656-6658, frankeshirk@comcast.net [LAN] IB3 [AC] Interim Bishop/Overseer, Lancaster District, Lancaster PA

Shirk, Hazel (Mervin) 1019 Ponder Ave, Sarasota FL 34232, 941-371-2005 [SE] IIB2 [AC] Minister of Special Care, Bay Shore Menn Ch, Sarasota FL

Shirk, S. Allen (Elsie Kreider) 1001 E Oregon Rd #J117, Lititz PA 17543, 717-560-9384 [LAN] [RE]

Shisler, Barbara, 93 Klingerman Rd, Telford PA 18969, 215-723-9326 [FRC] [RE]

Shonk, Roy Lee Kenneth (Pam) 290 Newberry Rd, Middletown PA 17057-3515, 717-944-1520 [LAN] IIA [AC] Associate Pastor, Fountain of Life Ch, Middletown PA

Short, Joel A. (Karen Joy) 8201 Smucker Rd, Smithville OH 44677, 330-669-2302, joelandkarenshort@juno.com [CDC, OH] IIA [AC] Associate Pastor, Oak Grove Menn Ch, Smithville OH

Short, Reid, 408 High St, Archbold OH 43502, 419-445-5094, reidshort@earthlink.net [OH] IIB1 [AC] Pastor, Emmanuel Menn Ch, Monclova OH

Short, Tim A., 130 E Good Ave, Wadsworth OH 44281-1916, 330-336-8467, tim19nov@hotmail.com [OH] IIB1 [AC] Pastor, Bethel Menn Ch, Rittman OH

Showalter, Ann, 321 E 12th St #105, Newton KS 67114-1972, asho@ourtownusa.net [WDC] [RE]

Showalter, Gerald W. (Evonne Shank) 552 Harpersville Rd, Newport News VA 23601, 757-595-9221, gshowaltr@aol.com [VA] IIB2 [AC]

Showalter, Glenn D. (Elinor) 44 Social Island Rd, Chambersburg PA 17201, 717-375-2180 [FRK] III [AC] Ordained Deacon, Rock Hill Mennonite Church, McConnellsburg PA

Showalter, Nathan D. (Christina Lee) 25 Red Leaf Ln, Lancaster PA 17602, 717-390-1034, nate@showalter.cc [LAN] IIB3b [AC] Country Strategists for China, Eastern Mennonite Missions, Jinqiao, Pudong Shanghai, China

Showalter, Omar V., 1631 Park Rd, Harrisonburg VA 22802-2465, 540-434-5181 [VA] [RE]

Showalter, Richard A. (Jewel Wenger) 150 James St, Landisville PA 17538, 717-898-5886 [LAN] IIB3c [AC] President, Eastern Mennonite Missions, Salunga PA

Showalter, Richard H. (Bertha) 3912 Stuarts Draft Hwy, Waynesboro VA 22980, 540-943-5827 [VA] [RE]

Shrock Jr., Henry, 13820 Market Ave N, Hartville OH 44632, 330-877-6384, henrich98@aol.com [OH] IIB2 [AC] Associate Pastor, Hartville Menn Ch, Hartville OH

Shue, Jeremy, 2118 W High St, Orrville OH 44667, jeremy@kidronmennonite.com [OH] IIA [AC] Youth Pastor, Kidron Menn Ch, Kidron OH

Shue, Laura, 2118 W High St, Orrville OH 44667,

MINISTERS

6

laura@kidronmennonite.com [OH] IIA [AC] Youth Pastor, Kidron Menn Ch, Kidron OH

Shue, Terry W. (Kay Y.) 4000 Steinwood Dr, Dalton OH 44618, 330-857-8866, tkshue@bright.net [OH] IIB1 [AC] Pastor, Kidron Menn Ch, Kidron OH

Shuford, Robert Weir (Lois Farley) 943 Wesley Ave, Evanston IL 60202, 847-328-6312, blshuford@attbi.com [IL] IIB3a [AC] Chaplain, Our Lady of the Resurrection Medical Center, 5645 W. Addison, Chicago IL

Shull, Jeff (Melodi) 540 New St, Roaring Spring PA 16673, 814-224-9955, JMMSHULL@msn.com [ALL] IIB1 [AC] Pastor, Martinsburg Menn Ch, Martinsburg PA

Shull, Randall (Kristina) 4117 Green Park Dr, Mount Joy PA 17552, 717-653-9340, randallshull@mjmc.org [LAN] IIB2 [AC] Associate Pastor, Mount Joy Menn Ch, Mount Joy PA

Shultz, Alma M. (Harold B.) 1967 Millport Rd, Lancaster PA 17602, 717-393-2376, hashultz@juno.com [LAN] IIC [AC] Licensed Deaconess, Sunnyside Menn Ch, Lancaster PA

Shultz, Harold B. (Alma) 1967 Millport Rd, Lancaster PA 17602, 717-393-2376, hashultz@juno.com [LAN] [RE]

Shutt, Joyce Musselman (Earl E.) 878 Mt Carmel Rd, Orrtanna PA 17353-9703, 717-642-5219, jms555@blazenet.net [EDC] [RE]

Sider, Ronald J. (Arbutus) 312 W Logan St, Philadelphia PA 19144-4120, 215-844-1031, ronsider@esa-online.org [LAN] IIB2 [AC]

Sieber, Paul C. (Martha) 1642A CR 500 E, Champaign IL 61821, 217-863-2514 [CDC, IL] [RE]

Siebert, Audrun, 303 S C, Milford NE 68405, 402-761-4674 [CP] IIA [AC] Pastor, Beth-El Menn Ch, Milford NE

Siegrist, E. Donald (Anne) 3465 SR 417, Jasper NY 14855, 607-792-3710, asiegrist@yahoo.com [NY] IB3 [AC]

Siegrist, Wesley D. (Teresa) 885 Newport Rd, Manheim PA 17545, 717-665-7516 [LAN] IIB1 [AC] Pastor, Erb Menn Ch, Lititz PA

Simmons, Mary Lou E., 517 N Lafayette St, Allentown PA 18104, (h) 610-782-0523 (c) 610-349-7279, Loubeellens@enter.net [EDC] IIB3a [AC] Chaplain, Country Meadows Retirement Communities, Allentown PA

Simonsick, Robert (Patti) 204 S Main St, Davidsville PA 15928 [ALL] IIB1 [AC] Pastor, Blough Menn Ch, Hollsopple PA

Sitther, Thinager Paulraj (Perpetua) 3487 Beechwood Blvd, Pittsburgh PA 15217-2964, thinagars@yahoo.com [ALL] IIB1 [AC]

Slabach, Albert C., 1729 SR 643, Baltic OH 43804, 330-852-2216 [OH] [RE]

Slabach, Monroe C. (Bea) 2044 Paradise Rd, Orrville OH 44667, 330-682-0838 [OH] [RE]

Slabaugh, Daniel (Ethel Lehman) 25039 W US12 #181, Sturgis MI 49091, 269-651-4996, danslabaugh@hotmail.com [IM] [RE]

Slabaugh, Phil L. (Brenda) 207 W Front St, Wayland IA 52654, 319-256-6073, pslabaugh@farmtel.net [CP] IIB1 [AC] Pastor, Bethel Menn Ch, Wayland IA

Slagel, Dean, 605 Maple Crest Dr, Goshen IN 46526, 574-533-9915 [IM] [RE]

Slagel, Steve E. (Barbara Jean) 12924 CR 44, Millersburg IN 46543, 574-642-4554,

steves@Egoshenmc.org [IM] IIB1 [AC] Pastor, East Goshen Menn Ch, Goshen IN

Slaubaugh, Tobias, 4738 Banks Ln, Sarasota FL 34232, 941-377-9841 [IM] [RE]

Slough, Rebecca Jo (Joseph M. S. Miller) 7634 Morning Mist Cr, Trotwood OH 45426, 513-854-9222, rslough@ambs.edu [CDC] IIB3d [AC]

Smeltzer, Carl L., 103 Hillcrest Ave, Souderton PA 18964-1150 [FRC] IIB3a [AC] Chaplain

Smeltzer, Walter (Doris) 2026 W Kellogg St, Peoria IL 61604, 309-674-1777, wdsmeltzer@webtv.net [IL] IIB2 [AC] Associate Pastor, Living Love Ministries, Peoria IL

Smith, Cynthia Neufeld (Roger) 1331 SW Jewell, Topeka KS 66604, 785-232-5781, neufeldsmith@att.net [WDC] IIB1 [AC] Associate Pastor, Southern Hills Menn Ch, Topeka KS

Smith, Dale Wendell (Justina Peters) 400 W 24th Apt 7, North Newton KS 67117, 316-282-0041 [WDC] [RE]

Smith, Duncan James (Charlene K. Epp) 1292 NW Fall Ave, Beaverton OR 97006-4031, 971-570-4216, dsmith@pnmc.org [PNW] IB2 [AC] Conference Minister, Pacific NW Mennonite Conference, Portland OR

Smith, Gordon Louis (Mindy) 202 Windward Ct, Newton KS 67114, gosmith@sbcglobal.net [WDC] IIB1 [AC] Pastor, Faith Menn Ch, Newton KS

Smith, H. James (Phyllis) 19975 Peach Ridge Rd, Goshen IN 46526-9104 [IM] IIB3c [AC] Church Relations, Mennonite Mutual Aid, Goshen IN

Smith, James (Karla) c/o Roy Williams, 22642 Newfield Court, Land O' Lakes FL 34639, Jim_Smith@sil.org [SE] IIC [AC]

Smith, Jeffrey Wayne (Kathy Lynn) 205 Christine Dr, Archbold OH 43502, 419-445-0287 [OH] IIB1 [AC] Pastor, Central Menn Ch, Archbold OH

Smith, Jonathan A. (Cindi) 315 Curtis St, Hutchinson KS 67502, 620-669-1455, jasmith@ourtownusa.net [SC] [AW]

Smith, Karla (James) c/o Roy Williams, 22642 Newfield Ct, Land O' Lakes FL 34639, Jim_Smith@sil.org [SE] IIC [AC]

Smith, Margaret Richer (Robert) 21 Wolf Brook Cr, Iowa City IA 52240, 319-338-7642 [CP] IIB1 [AC] Pastor, First Menn Ch of Iowa City, Iowa City IA

Smith, Michael G. (Missy) 96 Fawn Ridge Ct, White Haven PA 18661, 570-443-8631, mandmsmith3@juno.com [LAN] IIB2 [AC] Associate Pastor, Cornerstone Christian Fell, Mountain Top PA

Smith, Randy W. (Ann Yoder) 1106 Mordecai Dr, Raleigh NC 27604, 919-835-1474, rws.ays@juno.com [WDC] IIB3a [AC] Interim Pastor, Greensboro Menn Fell, Greensboro NC

Smith, Robert (Margaret) 21 Wolf Brook Cr, Iowa City IA 52240, 319-338-7642 [CP] IIB1 [AC] Pastor, First Menn Ch of Iowa City, Iowa City IA

Smith, Roger Neufeld (Cynthia) 1331 SW Jewell, Topeka KS 66604, 785-232-5781, neufeldsmith@att.net [WDC] IIB1 [AC] Pastor, Southern Hills Menn Ch, Topeka KS

Smoker Jr., Arthur E. (Nova Jean) 1304 S 15th St, Goshen IN 46526, 574-533-0968, ansmoker@maplenet.net [IM] IB3, IIB1 [AC] Pastor, North Goshen Menn Ch, Goshen IN; Overseer, North Leo Mennonite Ch, Fort Wayne IN; Overseer, Walnut Hill Mennonite, Goshen IN

Smoker, Kevin S. (Carol) 55 Whitehall Rd, Reinholds PA 17569, 717-336-8407 [LAN] [AW]

Smoker, Vernon D. (Ada Nancy) 425 S Belmont Rd, Ronks PA 17572, 717-687-8536 [LAN] [RE]

Smucker, Daniel M. 3515 Willow Run Rd, Harrisonburg VA 22802, 540-434-7944 [VA] [RE]

Smucker, Donovan Ebersole (Barbara Claassen) 410 W Elm St, Bluffton OH 45817 [CDC] [RE]

Smucker, John I. (Irene) 149-03 Sanford Ave 1A, Flushing NY 11355, 718-961-1463 [ACC] [RE]

Smucker, John R. (Donna Louise Gerber) 2513 College Ave, Goshen IN 46526, 574-534-0841 [IM] [RE]

Smucker, Klaudia (Robert Craig) 2510 S Main St, Goshen IN 46526, 574-534-8710, klaudia@collegemennonite.org [IM] IIB2 [AC] Pastor, College Menn Ch, Goshen IN

Smucker, Marcus G., 2747 Old Philadelphia Pk, Bird In Hand PA 17505-9707, 717-768-3064 [IM] [RE]

Smucker, Merle E. (Tonya) 131 Hill Rd, New Holland PA 17557, 717-354-3306, MTJ34@juno.com [LAN] III [AC] Licensed Deacon, Shiloh Menn Ch, Reading PA

Smucker, Stan J. (Marlene Rufenacht) PO Box 93, North Newton KS 67117, 316-283-3750, smuckersm@juno.com [WDC] [RE]

Snader, Paul E. (Carolyn) 200 Weidmansville Rd, Ephrata PA 17522, 717-733-6718, psnader@juno.com [LAN] III [AC] Ordained Deacon, Indiantown Menn Ch, Ephrata PA

Snavely, Carl H. (Alma) 4295 Colebrook Rd, Hershey PA 17033, 717-367-3634 [LAN] III [AC] Ordained Deacon, Stauffer Menn Ch, Hershey PA

Snider, Howard Mervin (Marie) Box 332, North Newton KS 67117-0332, 316-283-2309 [WDC] [RE]

Snyder, James R. (Brenda) 487 Sportsman Club Rd, Nazareth PA 18064, 610-614-0371, jimbrensny@juno.com [LAN] IIB1 [AC] Pastor, Maranatha Family Christian Fell, Nazareth PA

So, Lemuel (Leona) 169 W Chew Ave, Philadelphia PA 19120, 215-224-7622, lemuelso@netscape.net [LAN] IIB1 [AC] Pastor, Love Truth Chinese Menn Ch, Philadelphia PA

So, Sing Kin (Louisa) Box 25305, Tempe AZ 85285-5305, kinso@hotmail.com [LAN] [AW]

Sollenberger, Menno B. (Joyce) 4169 New Franklin Rd, Chambersburg PA 17201, 717-263-8336 [FRK] [RE]

Sollenberger, Samuel (Patricia) 1255 Candice Ln, Chambersburg PA 17201, 717-264-1125, tssol@pa.net [FRK] IIB1 [AC] Pastor, Rock Hill Menn Ch, Chambersburg PA

Sommers, Clayton, 904 N Korby St, Kokomo IN 46901, 317-452-7109 [IM] [RE]

Sommers, Elvin J., 14242 SR 61, Plain City OH 43064, 614-873-8910 [OH] [RE]

Sommers, Michael Kent (Julia Gay) 23589 Allen Dr, Elkhart IN 46516, 574-875-5916, mjsommers@msn.com [CDC] IIB1 [AC] Pastor, Hively Ave Menn Ch, Elkhart IN

Sosa, Rolando, 708 College Ave, Goshen IN 46526, rolandoas@goshen.edu [IM] IIB1 [AC] Pastor, Iglesia Menonita del Buen Pastor, Goshen IN

Souder, Eugene K. (Alice) 13241 Port Republic Rd, Grottoes VA 24441, 540-249-4368, eksouder@aol.com [VA] [RE]

Souders, Aaron H. (Mary) 3095 Miller Rd Apt A, Washington Boro PA 17582-9717, 717-872-8201 [LAN] [RE]

Spaulding, Randall L. (Laura) 3342 Glouster St, Sarasota FL 34235, 941-951-0743, randy118@comcast.net [SE] IIA [AC] Pastor, Covenant Menn Fell, Sarasota FL

Spayde, Robert J. (Karen) 2327 Andrew Ave, Mount Joy PA 17552, 717-653-0327, rspayde@comcast.net [LAN] IIB1 [AC] Pastor, Stauffer Menn Ch, Hershey PA

Speigle, Donald E. (Grace) 5689 Somerset Pk, Boswell PA 15531, 814-629-5947 [ALL] IIB3b [AC]

Speigle, Wayne (Joanne Brenneman) 862 Hunsicker Rd, Telford PA 18969, 215-256-1995, wjspeigle@aol.com [EDC] IIB1 [AC] Pastor, West Swamp Menn Ch, Quakertown PA

Spory, Ron (Denise) 125 Noble Rd, Johnstown PA 15905, 814-288-5617, rls173@aol.com [ALL] IIB1 [AC] Pastor, New Life Menn Ch, Listie PA

Sprague, Jerry, PO Box 150777, Cape Coral FL 33915-0777, 239-772-5683, Jsprague@capechristian.com [SE] IIC [AC] Associate Pastor, Cape Christian Fell, Cape Coral FL

Springer, Ed M. (Esther) 1113 Sunset Dr, Newberg OR 97132, 503-538-2659 [PNW] [RE]

Sprunger, Charles E. (Geraldine K.) 46 Marian Rd, Trappe PA 19426, 610-489-4688, chsprunger@yahoo.com [EDC] [RE]

Sprunger, John Walter (Deborah Lynn) 401 S Grant St, Scottdale PA 15683, 724-887-5337 [ALL] IIB3d [AC]

Sprunger, Lyman W. (Adeline E.) RR 1 Box 66, Canton OK 73724-9801, 405-886-3398 [WDC] [RE]

Sprunger, Robert John, 3834 Cobblestone CV, New Haven IN 46774-2074, 260-493-0244, bobgldc@myvine.com [CDC] IIB3b [AC]

Stackley, Muriel T., 2303 S Early, Kansas City KS 66103-1808, 913-677-7036, murielts@earthlink.net [WDC] [RE]

Stafford, Rod (Molly Susan Day) 2524 NE 42nd Ave, Portland OR 97213, 503-331-6993, pmcpastr@teleport.com [PNW] IIB1 [AC] Pastor, Portland Menn Ch, Portland OR

Stahl, Mark William (Karen Kay) 1434 Golfview Dr, Nappanee IN 46550, 574-773-3306, mwstahl@hoosierlink.net [CDC] IIB1 [AC] Pastor, First Menn Ch, Nappanee IN

Stahl-Wert, John (Milonica) 7215 Thomas Blvd, Pittsburgh PA 15208, 412-731-8014, stahlwert@plf.org [ALL] IIB3b [AC] President, Pittsburgh Leadership Foundation, Pittsburgh PA

Stair, Tim, 1900 S Main St, Goshen IN 46526, 574-535-7262, cmc@collegemennonite.org [IM] IIB1 [AC] Pastor, College Menn Ch, Goshen IN

Stalter, Edwin J. (Marcella R.) PO Box 576, Flanagan IL 61740, 815-796-2918, Staltere@frontiernet.net [IL] [RE]

Stambaugh, Carlton D. (Arlene) 1115 Moulstown Rd North, Hanover PA 17331-9424, 717-632-8641, card@superpa.net [LAN] IB3, IIB1 [AC] Bishop, Christian Community Fell, Manchester PA; Bishop/Overseer, LAN York-Adams District, PA

Stauffer, Carl S. (Carolyn) 52 Maud St, 1709, Florida, South Africa, c.stauffer@global.co.za [VA] IIB3b [AC]

Stauffer, Clarence S. (Grace) 6480 Main St, East Petersburg PA 17520, 717-569-1586 [LAN] [RE]

Stauffer, Faye L. (Steven) 730 W Newport Rd, Lititz PA 17543-9444, 717-665-3570, sfstauffer@dejazzd.com [LAN] IIC [AC] Chaplain, Lancaster Co Prison, Lancaster PA

Stauffer, James K. (Ruth) 1250 Parkway Dr, Harrisonburg VA 22802, 540-574-6141 [VA] [RE]

Stauffer, Leon L. (Dolores) 60 Hospital RD, Wernersville PA 19565-9406, 610-927-4668, pastorleon@pro-usa.net [LAN] IIB1 [AC] Pastor, Green Terrace Menn Ch, Wernersville PA

Stauffer, P. Eugene (Mabel E.) 545 Indiantown Rd, Ephrata PA 17522, 717-733-7152 [LAN] III [AC] Ordained Deacon, Green Terrace Menn Ch, Wernersville PA

Stauffer, Steven B. (Faye L.) 730 W Newport Rd, Lititz PA 17543, 717-665-3570, sfstauffer@dejazzd.com [LAN] IIB1 [AC] Pastor, Kauffman Menn Ch, Manheim PA

Stauffer, William Henry (Esther Baldwin) 5157 Troendly Rd SW, Stonecreek OH 43840, 216-897-7932 [CDC] [RE]

Steckly, Kenneth (Darlene) 91 Walnut St, Garden City MO 64747, 816-862-6477 [SC] IIB1 [AC] Co-Pastor, Sycamore Grove Menn Ch, Garden City MO

Steelberg, Donald R. (Elsie Steelberg) 201 N Broadview, Wichita KS 67208, 316-681-3538 [WDC] [RE]

Steffen, Harlan (Evelyn) RR 3 Box 46, Syracuse IN 46567, 574-457-4594 [IM] IIB1 [AC] Pastor, Wawasee Lakeside Chapel, Syracuse IN

Steffy, Jason J. (Maribelle) 299 E Main St, Leola PA 17540, 717-656-7506 [LAN] [RE]

Steffy, Karl E. (Ellen) 467 Fruitville Pk, Manheim PA 17545, 717-665-2611, kesteffy@dejazzd.com [LAN] IIB1 [AC] Pastor, East Petersburg Menn Ch, East Petersburg PA

Steffy, Roger L. (Carol A.) 205 E Keller St, Mechanicsburg PA 17055, 717-795-9106, randc.steffy@verizon.net [LAN] [AW]

Steiner, Elno, 1509 Dogwood Ct, Goshen IN 46526, 574-537-4955 [OH] [RE]

Steiner, Glenn M. (Arneda) 2256 Cork Oak St W, Sarasota FL 34232-6810, glennbvmenno@comcast.net [SE] IIB1 [AC] Pastor, Bahia Vista Menn Ch, Sarasota FL

Stevens, David A. (Carole Diane) 174 Green St, Sellersville PA 18960, 215-257-5835 [FRC] IIB2 [AC] Pastor, Blooming Glen Menn Ch, Blooming Glen PA

Stevenson, Robert L., Cd Lopez Mateos, Edo de, CP 52901, Mexico, 525-686-5421 [FRC] IIB3b [AC] Missionary, Franconia Mennonite Conference, Mexico

Stillman, Roger (Karen) 1322 Susquehannock Dr, Drumore PA 17518, 717-284-4797, bettergetready2000@yahoo.com [LAN] IIB2 [AC] Associate Pastor, Living Stones Fell, Peach Bottom PA

Stobaugh, James Parris (Karen) 510 Swank Rd, Hollsopple PA 15935, 814-479-7710, JPStobaugh@aol.com [ALL] IIB3c [AC]

Stobaugh, Karen, 510 Swank Rd, Hollsopple PA 15935 [ALL] IIC [AC]

Stoll, Alvin E. (Rita Marie) N3455 Hwy 73, Glen Flora WI 54526, 715-668-5583, alvines@centurytel.net [NC] IIB1 [AC] Pastor, South Lawrence Menn Ch, Glen Flora WI

Stoll, Don (Mary) 618 SW 15th Ave, Perryton TX 79070, 806-434-1790, stdon@juno.com [RM] IIB1 [AC] Pastor, Perryton Menn Ch, Perryton TX

Stoll, Owen, 2265 Hazel St, Hartville OH 44632, 330-877-9217 [OH] [RE]

Stoltzfus Jr., Amos K. (Rowena M.) 333 S 13th St, Harrisburg PA 17104, 717-232-4224, alive05@juno.com [LAN] IIB3b [AC] Staff, Discipleship

Center, Harrisburg PA

Stoltzfus, Dale W. (Doris) 270 Ivy Terrace, Lancaster PA 17601, 717-560-5696, dordalew@aol.com [LAN] IB1, IB3 [AC] Denominational Minister, Congregational & Ministerial Leadership Team, Mennonite Church USA, Lancaster PA; Bishop/Overseer, LMC Landisville District, PA

Stoltzfus, Daniel H., 409 E Broadway, South Bend IN 46618, 574-288-8192 [IM] [RE]

Stoltzfus, Ed (Mildred) 255 Hartman Dr, Harrisonburg VA 22802, 540-434-9849 [VA] [RE]

Stoltzfus, Eldon (Rachel Lehman) 18399 Northrop Dr, Goshen IN 46526, 574-831-5946 [IM] IIA [AC] Interim Pastor, Bonneyville Menn Ch, Bristol IN

Stoltzfus, George B. (Mae Mast) 1737 Crabtree Ln, Elkhart IN 46514, 574-266-4407, geobs@juno.com [IM] [AW]

Stoltzfus, Harvey Z. (Lillian) 158 Swamp Rd, Morgantown PA 19543-9476, 610-286-5974, beewatcher@juno.com [ACC] IIB1 [AC] Interim Pastor, Oley Valley Menn Ch, Oley PA

Stoltzfus, John M. (Paula) 593 S Fairfield Ave, Lombard IL 60148, 630-678-0480, jmstoltzfus@mennonite.net [IL] IIA [AC] Associate Pastor, Lombard Menn Ch, Lombard IL

Stoltzfus, Mervin R. (Janet E.) 23 Carriage Dr, Gordonville PA 17529, 717-768-3116, woodray@aol.com [ACC] IB2 [AC] Youth Minister/Associate Conference Minister, Atlantic Coast Conference, Morgantown PA

Stoltzfus, Milton L. (Lois) 282 Baumgardner Rd, Willow St PA 17584, 717-464-9072 [LAN] IIB3a [AC] Director of Development, Friendship Community, Lititz PA; Chaplain, Friendship Community, Lititz PA

Stoltzfus, Nathan G. (Marian) PO Box 19, Morgantown PA 19543, 610-286-5080 [ACC] [RE]

Stoltzfus, Noah S., 36 Fredericksville Rd, Mertztown PA 19539, 610-641-0543, noah.edie@juno.com [ACC] [RE]

Stoltzfus, Regina Shands (Art) 808 Strong Ave, Elkhart IN 46517 [IM] IIB3c [AC] Assistant Campus Pastor, Goshen College, Goshen IN; Minister of Urban Ministries, Mennonite Mission Network, Elkhart IN

Stoltzfus, Ruth Brunk, 1111 Mount Clinton Pk, Harrisonburg VA 22802, 540-434-7705 [VA] [RE]

Stoltzfus, Sherman M. (Heather) 1013 Fern Ave, Reading PA 19607-1626, 610-775-9970, smandhm@aol.com [LAN] IIA [AC] Pastor, Alsace Christian Fell, Temple PA

Stoltzfus, Victor, 607 College Ave, Goshen IN 46526, 574-533-4550 [IM] [RE]

Stoltzfus Schlabach, Kristina Marie, 2705 S Main St, Goshen IN 46526, 574-533-7651 [IM] IIA [AC] Pastor, Waterford Menn Ch, Goshen IN

Stoner, Andre Gingerich (Cathy) 628 Cushing, South Bend IN 46616, 574-289-4623, andrekrmc@juno.com [IM] IIB1 [AC] Pastor, Kern Rd Menn Ch, South Bend IN

Stoner, Barry Lee (Brenda) 1455 Hollywood Dr, Lancaster PA 17601, 717-291-1127, barry@proclaim.net [LAN] IIA [AC] Associate Pastor, Mellinger Menn Ch, Lancaster PA

Stoner, John Andrew (Anita L.) 11026 Old Oak Trail, Ft Wayne IN 46845, 877-321-3289 pin 7093, rpandy@juno.com [CDC] IIB3a [AC]

Stoner, John David (Martha L.) 29 Mayfield Dr, Leola

MINISTERS

6

PA 17540, 717-656-7744 [LAN] [RE]

Stopher, Wanda, 205 E Holland St, Archbold OH 43502, 419-445-1568, wstopher@centralmennonite.org [OH] IIA [AC] Associate Pastor, Central Menn Ch, Archbold OH

Stoudt, Curtis, 763 Ruth Rd, Telford PA 18969, 215-723-4637 [FRC] [RE]

Strayer, Sally C. (Charles) 1010 Lakewood Dr, Harrisburg PA 17109, 717-540-1228, sallystrayer@aol.com [LAN] IIC [AC] Chaplain, Harrisburg State Hospital, Harrisburg PA

Strite, Clarence B. (Mary Grace) 1561 Pin Oak Dr, Chambersburg PA 17201, 717-264-5798, cnmstrite@pa.net [ACC] [RE]

Strite, James L. (Norma) 5975 Reeves Rd, East Petersburg PA 17520-1530, 717-569-1720, jlstrite@yahoo.com [LAN] III [AC] Ordained Deacon, Manheim Menn Ch, East Petersburg PA

Strunk, Stephen Carl (Naomi K.) 1460 Doerr Rd, Quakertown PA 18951, snstrunk@enter.net [EDC] [AW]

Stuckey, Anne, 14277 Killybegs Ln, Somerset MI 49281, annestuckey@bnnorth.net [OH] IIB2 [AC] Associate Pastor, Zion Menn Ch, Archbold OH

Stuckey, Earl, 18526 CR K, West Unity OH 43570, 419-924-2535 [OH] [RE]

Stuckey, Robert, 18540 CR O, Alvordton OH 43501, 419-924-2130, bobnem@williams-net.com [OH] IIB1 [AC] Preaching Minister, Salem Menn Ch, Waldron MI

Stuckey, Walter, 10334 CR 21N, West Unity OH 43570, 419-445-6225 [OH] [RE]

Stucky, Edwin R. (Doris G.) 514 Spruce Ave, Moundridge KS 67107-9501, 620-345-2589 [WDC] [RE]

Stucky, Gary L., PO Box 188, North Newton KS 67117 [WDC] IIC [AC]

Stucky, Harley J. (Ruby L.) 2117 N Main, Box 394, North Newton KS 67117, 316-283-3029 [WDC] [RE]

Stucky, Nathan T. (Janel Denise) 7271 Boggs School House Rd, Wover MD 21871, 410-957-6857, natestucky@hotmail.com [ACC] IIA [AC] Youth Pastor, Holly Grove Menn Ch, Wover MD

Stucky, Willard L. (Marjorie A.) 600 Bluestem, PO Box 55, North Newton KS 67117, 316-283-0648 [WDC] [RE]

Studer, Gerald C. (Marilyn) 1260 Orchard Ln, Lansdale PA 19446, 215-368-8455 [FRC] [RE]

Stutzman, Benjamin S. (Katrina Derstine) 402 W Callowhill St, Perkasie PA 18944, 215-258-0338 [FRC] IIB2 [AC] Pastor, Blooming Glen Menn Ch, Blooming Glen PA

Stutzman, Bonita (Ervin) 1315 Harmony Dr, Harrisonburg VA 22802-5545, 540-442-8331, stutzerv@emu.edu [VA] IIB3a [AC]

Stutzman, David J. (Donna P.) 1966 Wimbledon Ct NW, Salem OR 97304, 503-581-3236, ddstutz@hotmail.com [PNW] IIB1 [AC] Pastor, Wern Menn Ch, Salem OR

Stutzman, Dennis (Ronda Jean) 3610 E Longview Rd, Haven KS 67543, 620-665-0207, ddstutz@yahoo.com [SC] IIB1 [AC] Pastor, Yoder Menn Ch, Haven KS

Stutzman, Ervin R. (Bonita) 1315 Harmony Dr, Harrisonburg VA 22802-5545, 540-442-8331, stutzerv@emu.edu [VA] IIB3d [AC] Associate Professor of Church Ministries, Eastern Mennonite Seminary, Harrisonburg VA; Dean, Eastern Mennonite Seminary, Harrisonburg VA

Stutzman, Linford (Janet) 1083 Smith St, Harrisonburg VA 22802, 540-432-1714, stutzmal@emu.edu [VA]

IIB3d [AC]

Stutzman, Marvin (Yvonne) 1285 Shank Dr #116, Harrisonburg VA 22802, 757-482-7023 [VA] [RE]

Styer, Jack (Sandra K.) 2728 Younts Rd, Bedford PA 15522-7547, 814-623-2119, jstyer@bedford.net [ALL] IIA [AC] Assistant Pastor, Canan Station Menn Ch, Altoona PA

Suter, Daniel B. (Grace) 102 Old Rte 33, Harrisonburg VA 22801, 540-434-6168 [VA] [RE]

Sutter, David L. (Janice Yordy) 233 E Irvington Ave, South Bend IN 46614, 574-288-5520, davekrmc@juno.com [IM] IB3, IIB1 [AC] Pastor, Kern Rd Menn Ch, South Bend IN; Overseer, Hudson Lake Mennonite, New Carlisle IN

Sutter, Janice Yordy (David) 233 E Irvington Ave, South Bend IN 46614, 574-288-5520, janickrmc@juno.com [IM] IIB1 [AC] Pastor, Kern Rd Menn Ch, South Bend IN

Sutter, Lester L. (Marietta) 6042 Westview Dr, Ferndale WA 98248-9214 [LAN] [RE]

Sutter, Stanley Ray (Catherine) 529 Greeley Ave, Staten Island NY 10306, 718-351-8163, Est1man@aol.com [LAN] IIA [AC] Pastor, Redeeming Grace Fell, Staten Island NY

Sutton, James, 62 Harmon Ave, Painesville OH 44077, 440-357-6040, jdsutt@ncweb.com [OH] IIB1 [AC] Pastor, New Mercies Community Ch, Burton OH

Sutton, Norma S., 5218 N Sawyer, Chicago IL 60625, 312-463-3044 [CDC, IL] IIB3d [AC] Librarian, Mellander Seminary, Chicago IL

Swarr, Paul L. (Bertha) 1311 Carlisle Ave, Richmond VA 23231, 804-222-4345 [VA] [RE]

Swartley, Willard M. (Mary) 57697 7th St, Elkhart IN 46517, 574-522-0314, wswartley@ambus.edu [IM] IIB3c [AC] Staff, Associated Mennonite Biblical Seminary, Elkhart IN

Swartz, Delores, 58204 CR 23, Goshen IN 46528, 574-875-0098 [IM] IIB3a [AC] Chaplain, Greencroft Retirement Center, Goshen IN

Swartz, Joseph J., 4750 E CR 300 N, North Vernon IN 47265, 812-458-6323 [IM] [RE]

Swartz, Ronald Duane (Lucretia Ann) 66 W 6 Mile Rd, Sault Ste Marie MI 49783, 906-635-0459, rswartz@northernway.net [IM] [AW]

Swartz, Sam, PO Box 327, West Liberty OH 43357, 937-465-7867 [OH] [RE]

Swartzendruber, Dean (Lois) 831 3rd Pl, Kalona IA 52247, 319-656-2999 [CP] [RE]

Swartzendruber, Loren, PO Box 3000, Hesston KS 67062 [VA] IIB3c [AC] President, EMU, Harrisonburg VA

Swartzendruber, Scott (Jan) 918 10th St, Kalona IA 52247, 319-656-3945, kmcscott@kctc.net [CP] IIB1 [AC] Pastor, Kalona Menn Ch, Kalona IA

Swartzendruber, Steve, 1200 Park Rd, Harrisonburg VA 22802, 540-432-4260, info@emu.edu [VA] IIB2 [AC] Youth Pastor, Grace Menn Fell, Linville VA

Swartzentruber, Clayton L., 209 Dock Dr, Lansdale PA 19446, 215-393-0955 [FRC] [RE]

Swihart, James, PO Box 579, Kalida OH 45853, 419-532-3598, kfoc@bright.net [OH] IIB1 [AC] Pastor, Kalida Family Outreach Center, Kalida OH

Swora, Mathew (Rebecca J.) 4715 Laura Ln, Shoreview MN 55126, 651-482-9620, emmanuel@visi.com [CP] IIB1 [AC] Pastor, Emmanuel Menn Ch, Shoreview MN

Tadeo, Raul (Vanita M.) 405 W Schultz Ave, Dalton OH 44618, 330-828-0040, rvtadeo1934@valkyrie.net [OH] IIB3b [AC] Open Arms Hispanic Ministry Coordinator, Wayne/Holmes Mennonite Churches, Wayne/ Holmes counties, OH

Tannelus, Jean, 7103 Mauna Loa Blvd, Sarasota FL 34241-5840, jtannelus@comcast.net [SE] IIA [AC] Pastor, New Jerusalem Menn Ch, Sarasota FL

Taylor, Owen (Rosetta) 2201 Rebourde Dr, South Bend IN 46628, 574-273-0059 [CP] IIB1 [AC] Pastor, Northside Christian Family Center, Omaha NE

Teague, Norman (Fannie) 5191 Kratzer Rd, Linville VA 22834, 540-833-2402 [VA] [RE]

Telgren, Joe, 701 Los Arboles, Carlsbad NM 88220, 505-628-8679, cmchurch@cavemen.net [RM] IIA [AC] Pastor, Carlsbad Menn Ch, Carlsbad NM

Thacker, John David, 3903 Arkansas Dr, Anchorage AK 99517, 907-677-9394, johndavidthacker@hotmail.com [PNW] IIB1 [AC] Pastor, Prince of Peace Menn Ch, Anchorage AK

Thieszen, Eugene Roy, PO Box 20513, Maun, Botswana, 267-686-3248, genet@mainstaycomm.net [CP] IIB3b [AC]

Thieszen, Harold Daniel (Esther M.) 606 Bluestem St, North Newton KS 67117-8020, 316-283-8623, harolddt@southwind.net [WDC] [RE]

Thomas, Aldine (Esther) 59456 CR 35, Middlebury IN 46540, 574-825-2506, altom2@juno.com [IM] IIC [AC] Minister of Visitation, Clinton Frame Menn Ch, Goshen IN

Thomas, Everett J. (Barbara Gunden) 1817 Woodgate Dr, Goshen IN 46526-6456, 574-533-6143, editor@themennonite.org [IM] IIB3c [AC] Editor, The Mennonite, Goshen IN

Thomas, J. Samuel (Marian J.) 1361 Nissley Rd, Landisville PA 17538, 717-898-8662, samthomas.lmc@verizon.net [LAN] IIB1 [AC] Pastor, Landisville Menn Ch, Landisville PA

Thomas, James (Sherry) 425 Moonshine Hollow Rd, Johnstown PA 15905, 814-288-5763, jetsetjj@juno.com [ALL] IIB1 [AC] Pastor, Living Way Fell, Tire Hill PA

Thomas, Marlin E. (Janice) 104 Urban Dr, Lancaster PA 17603, 717-393-9964, mthomas@mennonitechurch.org [LAN] IIB1 [AC] Pastor, Bethel Menn Ch of Lancaster, Lancaster PA

Thomas, Melvin (Marie) 670 Royal View Dr, Lancaster PA 17601, 717-581-1491, m520j717@aol.com [LAN] IIB3a [AC] Chaplain; Director of Pastoral Care, Mennonite Home Communities, Lancaster PA

Thomas, Stephen B. (Linda) 1011 S 7th St, Goshen IN 46526, 574-534-7118, s-lthomas@juno.com [IM] IIB1 [AC] Pastor, Walnut Hill Menn Ch, Goshen IN

Thomas, Vincent J. (Martha) 4125 Board Rd, Manchester PA 17345, 717-266-4108 [LAN] [AW]

Thomassen, Donald L. (Barbara Norma) 659 Glen Eyrie Cr, Colorado Spring CO 80904, 719-471-4753, thethomassens@aol.com [RM] IIB1 [AC] Pastor, First Menn Ch of Colorado Springs, Colorado Springs CO

Thompson, Kenneth Lee (Victoria) 2089 Ryer Ave, Bronx NY 10460, 718-733-6975, FCC2283@juno.com [ACC] IIB1 [AC] Pastor, Friendship Community Ch, Bronx NY

Thomsen, June E. (Ib) 4824 S Knox Ave, Chicago IL 60632, 773-767-1977, thomsen@avenew.com [CDC] [AW]

Thornton, Jim (Kathy) 305 Moss Ave, Seaford VA 23696, 757-898-3970, kktjwt@aol.com [VA] IIC [AC] Minister of Preaching/Teaching, Huntington Menn Ch, Newport News VA

Tice, Ezra M. (Joan Van Antwerp) 25 Vicki Cr, Gettysburg PA 17325, 717-334-5068, ezratice@supernet.com [ACC] [AW]

Tijerina, David G. (Corina) 109 Pleasant St, Archbold OH 43502, 419-445-0016, goodshepherdmc@earthlink.net [OH] IIB1 [AC] Pastor, Iglesia Menonita del Buen Pastor, Archbold OH

Tijerina, Guillermo G., 613 N Defiance, Archbold OH 43502, 419-445-6502 [OH] [RE]

Tippett, Thomas Arthur (Teresa Ann) 4505 S State Rd, Harbor Springs MI 49740, 231-526-6034 [IM] IIC [AC] Chaplain/Pastoral Counselor, Stutsmanville Chapel, Harbor Springs MI

Tobin, George E. (Carol) 4 Prince Edward Ln, Media PA 19063, 610-566-1611 [LAN] IIC [AC] Missionary/Church Worker, Ubon Ratchathani, Thailand

Todd, Jay (Ruth) 866 Quarry Rd, Manheim PA 17545, 717-569-1345 [LAN] III [AC] Ordained Deacon, East Petersburg Menn Ch, East Petersburg PA

Toews, Russell G. (Cynthia Ann) PO Box 711, Hotevilla AZ 86030, 520-734-6630 [PSW] IIA [AC] Pastor, Bacavi Menn Ch, Hotevilla AZ

Torres, Neftali, c/o Shirley Powell, Elder, 184 Barton, Buffalo NY 14213, 716-837-1751, SJHP@aol.com [NY] IIB1 [AW]

Townsend, James D. (Debra) 834 High St, Alpha NJ 08865, 908-454-1314, alphamenno@juno.com [FRC] [AW]

Townsend, Raleigh, 253 McClellandtown Lambert Rd, McClellandtown PA 15458 [ALL] IIA [AC]

Tran, Quang Xuan, 101 Powell Ln, Upper Darby PA 19082, 610-352-8689, msquang@go.com [LAN] IIB1 [AC] Pastor, Vietnamese Menn Ch, Philadelphia PA

Tribby, Phyllis, 6047 Flower St, Arvada CO 80004, kptribby@juno.com [WDC] IIB1 [AC] Pastor, Arvada Menn Ch, Arvada CO

Trobaugh, Peter, Maranatha School for the Deaf, Top Hill PO, St Elizabeth, Jamaica [VA] IIC [AW]

Trobaugh, Shirley, Maranatha School for the Deaf, Top Hill PO, St Elizabeth, Jamaica [VA] IIC [AW]

Troyer, James L. (Anna) 1671 River Rd, Manistique MI 49854, 906-341-5007, jtroyer@up.net [IM] IB3, IIB1 [AC] Pastor, Cedar Grove Menn Ch, Manistique MI; Overseer, Menominee River Fell, Menominee MI; Overseer, Grand Marais Mennonite, Grand Marais MI

Troyer, John L. (Maxine) W15537 Sandtown Rd, Engadine MI 49827, 906-586-6421, maxinetroyer@webtv.net [IM] IIB1 [AC] Pastor, Wildwood Menn Ch, Engadine MI

Troyer, John M. (Sheila W.) 27077 Baker Dr, Sturgis MI 49091, john.troyer@lgrove.org [IM] IIB1 [AC] Pastor, Locust Grove Menn Ch, Burr Oak MI

Troyer, John V. (Ina May) 7321 Springfield Rd, Delavan IL 61734, 309-244-8674 [IL] [RE]

Troyer, Lowell Ovid (Mary Wineland) 2301 Morton Ave, Elkhart IN 46517, 574-294-6272 [CDC] [RE]

Troyer, Martin Bradley, 209 S Roupp, Hesston KS 67062 [SC] IIA [AC] Associate Pastor for Youth, Hesston Menn Ch, Hesston KS

MINISTERS

6

Troyer, Rick (Joanie) 705 S Forest Park Dr, Eureka IL 61530, 309-467-3787, rickrmc@mtco.com [IL] IIB1 [AC] Pastor, Roanoke Menn Ch, Eureka IL

Troyer, Robert L. (Marcia) PO Box 583, Milford NE 68405, 402-761-3500 [CP] IIB3a [AC]

Troyer, Samuel J. (Betsy) 2440 Mc Cleary Dr, Chambersburg PA 17201, 717-264-1366 [IM] [RE]

Troyer, Stanley J. (Marilyn Ann) 7291 N Maple, Mancelona MI 49659, 616-587-0715, stroyer@freeway.net [IM] IIB3b [AC] Missionary, Church Resource Ministries, Mancelona MI

Trupe, Robert L. (Sylvia) 958 Rettew Mill Rd, Ephrata PA 17522, 717-733-0291 [LAN] IIB1 [AC] Pastor, Martindale Menn Ch, Ephrata PA

Tsai, Caleb Tsan (Esther Kuei Mei Tsai) 258 Chaumont Cr, Foothill Ranch CA 92610-2344 [PSW] [RE]

Tschetter, Peter William (Beulah Margene) PO Box 538, Mountain Lake MN 56159-0536 [CP] [RE]

Tschetter, Randall LaMont (Wanette Jane) 2300 Carter Place, Sioux Falls SD 57105, 605-331-5034 [CP] IIB1 [AC] Pastor, Bethany Menn Ch, Freeman SD

Tschetter, Richard Daniel (Ruth Eileen) 3386 Rd R, Pandora OH 45877-9779, 419-358-4593 [CDC] [RE]

Tu, Truong (Dorcas Hua) 738 Moore St, Philadelphia PA 19148-1718, 215-271-5018, alcmc@juno.com [LAN] IIA [AC] Pastor, Abundant Life Chinese Menn Ch, Philadelphia PA

Tyson, Warren L. (Linda A.) 66 Millstone Dr, PO Box 785, Brownstown PA 17508-0785, 717-661-7266, warrent@frontiernet.net [ACC] IB2 [AC] Conference Minister, Eastern District Conference, Souderton PA; Conference Minister, Atlantic Coast Conference, Morgantown PA

U

Ulloa, Marco Antonia (Patricia) 111 School Ln, Landisville PA 17538-1247, 717-898-9815 [LAN] IIB3c [AC] Staff, Eastern Mennonite Missions, Salunga, PA

Ulrich, Wilfred D. (Betty Stutzman) 504 Crestwood Dr, Eureka IL 61530, 309-467-2194 [CDC, IL] [RE]

Umble, Jeni Hiett (Arthur K.) 60251 Surrey Ln, Elkhart IN 46517, 574-875-5904, ajumble@juno.com [CDC] IIB3b [AC] Church Community Service, Elkhart IN

Umble, Leroy D. (Fern) 5661 Strasburg Rd, Atglen PA 19310, 215-593-2943 [ACC] [RE]

Umble, R. Clair (Miriam) 46 Newlin Rd, Parkesburg PA 19365, 717-442-8667 [ACC] [RE]

Umble, Richard (Ruth) c/o Spruce Lake, RR 1, Box 605, Canadensis PA 18325-9749, 570-595-7505, rrrumble@juno.com [ACC] IIB3b [AW]

Unruh, Ervey A. (Norma J.) 831 S New York Ave, Liberal KS 67901, 620-624-6818, eunruh@swdtimes.com [WDC] IIB1 [AC] Pastor, Calvary Menn Ch, Liberal KS

Unruh, James Michael, 1710 E 2nd Ave, Hutchinson KS 67501 [SC] IIA [AC] Pastor, Faith Menn Ch, South Hutchinson KS

Unruh, Raymond (DeMaris) RR 3 Box 84, Hydro OK 73048-9124 [WDC] IIB1 [AC] Pastor, Bethel Menn Ch, Hydro OK

Unruh, Verney (Belva) 3012 Ivy Dr, North Newton KS 67117-8002, 316-283-2298 [WDC] [RE]

V

Vallejos, Jorge (Ruth) PO Box 1245, Elkhart IN 46515-1245, JorgeV@MennoniteUSA.org [IM] IIB3c [AC] Director of Convention Planning

Van Etten, Percy N., 2 Ivey Ln Apt 19, PO Box 3221, Harrisburg PA 17105-3221, 717-234-2548 [LAN] [RE]

Van Voorhis, Laura, 6130 Carvel Ave, Apt 17, Indianapolis IN 46220, 317-722-0715, vanvols@msn.com [IM] [AW]

VanderPlate, Joshua R., 1298 Breneman Rd, Conestoga PA 17516, 717-872-0772, pastorjvp@hotmail.com [LAN] IIC [AC] Youth Pastor, Habecker Menn Ch, Lancaster PA

Vang, Neng Chue, 706 Clearbooks Ln, Vadnais Heights MN 55127 [CP] IIB1 [AC] Pastor, Hmong Menn Ch of St Paul, Vadnais Heights MN

Vanpelt, Steven C. (Joy) 234 Brenneman Rd, Lancaster PA 17603, 717-464-4283, svanpelt1@juno.com [LAN] IIB1 [AC] Pastor, Lyndon Menn Ch, Lancaster PA

Vargas, Blanca (Victor) 211 E Edgewood Pl, San Antonio TX 78209, 210-533-2727, blancavargas@earthlink.net [SC, WDC] IIA [AC] Pastor, Iglesia Menonita Comunidad de Vida, San Antonio TX

Vargas, Victor M. (Virginia) 1225 Bair Rd NE, Keizer OR 97303, 503-390-1944, vvargas@pnmc.org [PNW] IIB1 [AC] Pastor, Iglesia Menonita Pentecostes, Woodburn OR; Hispanic Conference Minister, Pacific NW Mennonite Conference, Keizer OR

Vargas, Victor Serafin (Blanca) 1710 Lynette #606, San Antonio TX 78209, victorvargast@earthlink.net [SC, WDC] IIA [AC] Pastor, Iglesia Menonita Comunidad de Vida, San Antonio TX

Vaughn, Jr., William (Irene) 6501 Pierce St, Norfolk VA 23513, 757-855-8822 [VA] IIB1 [AC] Pastor, Word of Life Menn Ch, Norfolk VA

Vellaramala, Baby John (Ponomma) 105-B St No 12, Prathap Nagar, Phase 1, Myur Vihar, New Delhi 110091, INDIA, bvellaramal@yahoo.com [LAN] IIB3b [AC] Missionary/Church Worker, Eastern Mennonite Missions, Myur Vihar, New Delhi, INDIA

Ventura, John (Hope) 94 S Xavier St, Denver CO 80219, 303-935-0722 [RM] [RE]

Versluis, Paul (Joi) 1346 Ravenwood St, Ann Arbor MI 48103, 734-827-0741, pversluis@comcast.net [CDC] IIB1 [AC] Pastor, Shalom Community Ch, Ann Arbor MI

Vielman, Jorge, 1703 Lawndale Pl, Goshen IN 46526, jorgeev@juno.com [IM] IIB1 [AC] Pastor, Iglesia Menonita del Buen Pastor, Goshen IN

Villalobos, Carlos Caleb (Cynthia) 214 1st St, Broadway NC 27505, 919-776-1487 [LAN] IIA [AC] Associate Pastor, Iglesia Menonita Bethel Ch, Sanford NC

Villalobos Mora, Carlos L. (Nubia) 301 Carbonton Rd, Sanford NC 27330-4012, 919-776-1487 [LAN] IIB1 [AC] Pastor, Iglesia Menonita Bethel, Sanford NC

Vincent, Lorie L. (Mark LaVon) W325 S7418 Squire Ln, Mukwonago WI 53149, DesignForMinistry@prodigy.net [CDC, IL] [AC] Design for Ministry, Mukwonago WI

Vincent, Mark (Lorie) W325 S7418 Squire Ln, Mukwonago WI 53149, 262-392-9771, marklv@designforministry.com [CDC, IL] IIB3c [AC] Interim Pastor, Freeport Menn Ch, Freeport IL; Lead Partner, Design for Ministry, Mukwonago WI

Vogt, Royce W. (Marla) 910 E 14th, Harper KS 67058,

620-896-2093 [SC] IIB1 [AC] Pastor, Pleasant Valley Menn Ch, Harper KS

Vogt, Virgil (Joan) 726 Monroe, Evanston IL 60202, 846-869-4599, vvvogt@ameritech.net [IL] [RE]

Voran, Peter Willard (Lois June) 3057 Ivy Ct, North Newton KS 67117, 316-284-2343 [WDC] [RE]

Voth, James Joel (Barbara Ruth) 1400 Westborough Dr, Newton KS 67114-1476, 316-283-2644, jvoth@cox.net [WDC] IIB1 [AC] Pastor, Grace Hill Menn Ch, Whitewater KS

Voth, John Wesley (Carolyn Ruth) 105 N Vann, PO Box 845, Chouteau OK 74337, 918-476-5166 [WDC] [RE]

W

Wade, Andrew Frost (Susan) c/o Hong Kong Menn Centre, 76 Waterloo Rd, 1/F, Kowloon, Hong Kong, 011-852-2714-2852 [PNW] IIB3b [AC]

Wadel, Mark N. (Betty Anne) PO Box 3, Westminster MD 21158, 410-876-2808 or 410-848-1500 [FRK] [AW]

Wagler, Howard L. (Cathy) 317 E Trails W Rd, South Hutchinson KS 67505, 620-663-5803, pastorhoward@shmc-online.net [SC] IIB1 [AC] Lead Pastor, South Hutchinson Menn Ch, South Hutchinson KS

Wagner, Dennis William Kinde (Marsha Lynn) 1238 Chaucer Pl, Maineville OH 45039-9750, 513-677-2349, DWKWagner@aol.com [CDC] IIB3a [AC]

Waite, Donald N. (Anna) 622 Watterson Rd, Cochranville PA 19330, 610-593-6601 [LAN] [RE]

Waite, Phil (Elizabeth Bontrager) 1620 Wisconsin, Berwyn IL 60402, 708-484-6756, pewaite@mennonite.net [CDC, IL] IIB1 [AC] Pastor, Chicago Community Menn Ch, Chicago IL

Walcott, Carl A. (Annette) 4913 Headland Hills, Tampa FL 33624, 813-961-1114 [SE] IIC [AC] Associate Pastor, College Hill Menn Ch, Tampa FL

Walker, Kurt (Marla) 1343 US Hwy 136, Armington IL 61721, 309-392-2460, kmkmjd@juno.com [IL] IIB2 [AC] Associate Pastor, Hopedale Menn Ch, Hopedale IL

Walks Along Sr, Joe (Victoria) PO Box 232, Lame Deer MT 59043, 406-477-8388 [CP] IIB1 [AC] Pastor, Lame Deer Menn Ch, Lame Deer MT

Wall, Elmer A. (Winifred E.) 415 Fairview Dr, Goshen IN 46528, 574-534-1995, elwinwall@juno.com [CDC] [RE]

Walters, Robert G., 2187 Skyline Dr, Bethlehem PA 18105, 610-865-3316 [FRC] [RE]

Waltner, Erland (Winifred Schlosser) 2806 Benham Ave, Elkhart IN 46517-1950, 574-522-6042 [CDC] [RE]

Waltner, Harris H. (Christine M.) 3053 Ivy Ct, North Newton KS 67117 [WDC] [RE]

Waltner, James H., 1717 Mayflower Pl, Goshen IN 46526, 574-534-5474, jwaltner@tln.net [IM] IB3 [AC] Overseer, Belmont Mennonite Ch, Elkhart IN; Overseer, Kern Rd Mennonite, South Bend IN; Overseer, North Goshen Mennonite, Goshen IN; Overseer, East Goshen Mennonite, Goshen IN

Waltner, Stacey (Jeremy) PO Box 777, Freeman SD 57029, estaceyk@hotmail.com [CP] IIA [AC] Associate Pastor, Salem Menn Ch, Freeman SD

Walton, Robin W. (Gregory F.) 5233 Hitesman Way, Columbus OH 43214, 614-431-5233 [CDC] IIB3a [AC]

Ward, Frank Gene (Margaret Makino) 95223 Ainakuai Place, Miliana HI 96789, 808-626-0350 [WDC] [RE]

Warfel, Amos H. (Joanne) 2100 Millstream Rd, Lancaster PA 17602-1428, 717-393-1643 [LAN] [RE]

Warner, Edward (Mary) RR 2 Lightfoot Rd, Harbor Springs MI 49740, 616-526-6971 [IM] IIB1 [AC] Pastor, Stutsmanville Chapel, Harbor Springs MI

Watkins, Larry G., RR 4, Box 20900, Inola OK 74036 [WDC] IIC [AC]

Weaver, A. Richard (Ruth) 230 Penn Ave, Ephrata PA 17522, 717-733-1891, arweaver@ptd.net [ACC] [RE]

Weaver, Christopher Z. (Sheri Lynn) 6918 Rock Lodge Rd, Accident MD 21520, gladechurch@iceweb.net [ALL] IIB2 [AC] Pastor, Glade Menn Ch, Accident MD

Weaver, Clair H. (Betsy J.) 538 Waterside Cr, Lebanon PA 17042-9487, 717-273-9710, cweaver705@aol.com [LAN] IIB3c [AC] Director, Jubilee Ministries, Lebanon PA

Weaver, Dale L. (Ida M.) 18 Oak Hill Dr, Paradise PA 17562, 717-687-9583 [ACC] IIA [AC] Senior Pastor, Sandy Hill Menn Ch, Coatesville PA

Weaver, Daryl L., 25 Hahnstown Rd, Ephrata PA 17522, 717-733-2895 [LAN] IIC [AC] Missionary/Church Worker, Lancaster Mennonite Conference, Grenada

Weaver, David L. (Dawn) 1944 Hemlock Rd, Lancaster PA 17603, 717-399-7354, davidweaver@juno.com [LAN] IIB1 [AC] Pastor, Rohrerstown Menn Ch, Lancaster PA

Weaver, David M. (Martha) 925 Fallowfield Rd, Atglen PA 19310, 610-593-5064 [LAN] [RE]

Weaver, David M. (Esther) RR 1 Box 113, Roaring Branch PA 17765, 717-673-5083 [LAN] [RE] Interim Pastor, Menn Bible Fell, Morris PA

Weaver, David W. (Pauline) RD 1 Box 600, McAlisterville PA 17049-9606, 717-463-2672 [LAN] [RE]

Weaver Jr., David W. (Sue) 21170 D'Herde Rd, Gulfport MS 39503, 228-832-0661, dweaver@starvisionsat.com [GS] IIB2 [AC] Assistant Pastor, Gulfhaven Menn Ch, Gulfport MS; Conference Minister, Gulf States Mennonite Conference, Gulfport MS

Weaver, Don R. (Linda) 607 Gault Rd, New Holland PA 17557-9007, 717-354-5001, DLHGRDW@aol.com [LAN] IIB1 [AC] Pastor, Weaverland Menn Ch, East Earl PA

Weaver, Dorothy Jean, 1514 College Ave, Harrisonburg VA 22802-5509, 540-433-3336 [VA] IIB3d [AC]

Weaver, Earl S. (Marilyn) 224 White Oak Rd, New Holland PA 17557, 717-354-7510, esweaver@juno.com [LAN] IIC [AC] Associate Pastor, Weaverland Menn Ch, East Earl PA

Weaver, Eugene Z. (Elaine) Olive Branch Mennonite Mission, PO Box 156 Tikini Rd, Cherry Creek SD 57622 [LAN] IIB3b [AC] Missionary/Church Worker, Olive Branch Mennonite Mission, Cherry Creek SD

Weaver, Harold K., 527 Dock Dr, Lansdale PA 19446, 215-368-5783 [FRC] [RE]

Weaver, Irvin D., 6322 Acker Ln, Linville VA 22834, 540-833-4232 [VA] [RE]

Weaver, Jay S. (Shirley A.) 195 Speedwell Forge Rd, Lititz PA 17543, 717-626-4314, jsw195@dejazzd.com [LAN] IIB2 [AC] Associate Pastor, Indiantown Menn Ch, Ephrata PA

Weaver, Jerry, 8157 Kline St, Arvada CO 80005, 303-420-4417 [RM] [AW]

Weaver, Kenneth, PO Box 15402, Fort Wayne IN 46885 [IM] IIB3a [AC]

Weaver, L. Keith (JoAnne) 115 Swamp Church Rd, Reinholds PA 17569-0091, 717-336-5253, keith@lanmenconf.org [LAN] IB1, IB3 [AC]

MINISTERS

6

Bishop/Overseer, LMC Ephrata District, PA; Conference Moderator, Lancaster Mennonite Conference, Lancaster PA

Weaver, Luke W. (Joanne) 25 Hahnstown Rd, Ephrata PA 17522, 717-733-2895, lweaver8@juno.com [LAN] III [AC] Ordained Deacon, Martindale Menn Ch, Ephrata PA

Weaver Jr., M. Lloyd (Sarah Marie Yoder) 198 Colony Rd, Newport News VA 23602, 757-877-1925, LWeaver10@AOL.com [VA] [RE]

Weaver, Marion C. (Jean) 539 Augusta Farms Rd, Waynesboro VA 22980, 540-337-2639 [VA] [RE]

Weaver, Marvin L. (Lois H.) 145 Rose Dr, Lancaster PA 17602, 717-397-7279 [LAN] IIB3a [AC] Chaplain, Auntie Anne's Pretzels, Inc, Lancaster PA

Weaver, Paul G. (Shirley A.) 9 Shupp Ln, Denver PA 17517, 717-484-4899 [LAN] [RE]

Weaver, Paul H., 1001 E Oregon Rd G 13, Lititz PA 17543, 717-560-7809 [LAN] [RE]

Weaver, Richard S. (Virginia) 3842 Rawley Pk, Harrisonburg VA 22801, 540-867-5600 [VA] [RE]

Weaver, Samuel O. (Sarah) 1550 N College Ave, Harrisonburg VA 22802, 540-434-2985, weaverso@emu.edu [VA] IB3 [AC]

Weaver, Stanley (Arlie Virginia) 10607 N 9th Dr, Phoenix AZ 85029, 602-906-0512 [PSW] IIB2 [AC]

Weaver, Stephen Souder (Ann) 1069 Rawlinsville Rd, Willow Street PA 17584-9736, 717-284-2508, ssweaver@paonline.com [LAN] IIB1 [AC] Pastor, Strasburg Menn Ch, Strasburg PA

Weaver, Timothy D. (Juanita) 421 Campus Dr, Perkasie PA 18944, 215-453-0554 [FRC] [AW]

Weaver, Victor R., 681 Meadow Dr, Honey Brook PA 19344, 610-273-3010, vweaver@ptdprolog.net [LAN] IIB1 [AC] Associate Pastor, Cambridge Menn Ch, Gordonville PA

Weaver, Wayne S. (Edna G.) 155 Weidmansville Rd, Ephrata PA 17522, 717-733-3323 [LAN] [RE]

Weaver, William M. (Viola) 1501 Virginia Ave Apt 148, Harrisonburg VA 22802-2497 [LAN] [RE]

Weber, Floyd S. (Salinda) 287 Panorama Dr, Denver PA 17517, 717-445-5805 [LAN] [RE]

Weber, George G. (Gladys) 123 Farm Crest Dr, Ephrata PA 17522, 717-351-0834 [LAN] [RE]

Weber, Larry H. (Sandra) 368 Boulder Hill Rd, Mohnton PA 19540-9425, 717-445-5229, laweb@juno.com [LAN] IIC [AC] Associate Pastor, Bowmansville Menn Ch, East Earl PA

Weidner, Mark L. (Susan Ann) 1119 Old Post Rd, Perkasie PA 18944, mweidner@ambs.edu [FRC] IIB1, IIB3c [AC] Pastor, Perkasie Menn Ch, Perkasie PA

Welty, Lavon Jerry (Carol Ann) 211 Devonshire Ave, Lima OH 45804-3319, 419-222-6102, lavonw@wcoil.com [CDC] IB2 [AC] Conference Minister, Central District Conference, Ohio and Michigan, Lima OH

Welty, Merritt (Linda) 12048 W Arkansas Pl, Lakewood CO 80228, 303-985-2287, mlwelty@i70W.com [RM] IIB3a [AC]

Welty, Russell Ralph (Ellen Louise) 264 Acacia Dr, Stockbridge GA 30281, 770-389-4316 [CDC] [RE]

Wendland, Wolfgang (Sarah Rebecca) 1124 Arcadia St, Bethlehem PA 18018-3002, 610-861-4409, wkwendland@netcarrier.com [LAN] IIB1 [AC] Pastor,

Bethlehem Community Fell, Bethlehem PA

Wenger, Alma E. (Nelson H.) 690 Earhart Rd, Manheim PA 17545, 717-665-7233, wenger690@desupernet.net [LAN] IIC [AC] Licensed Deaconess, Erisman Menn Ch, Manheim PA

Wenger, Chester L. (Sara Jane) 2186 Old Philadelphia Pk, Lancaster PA 17602, 717-397-3065, clwsjw@juno.com [LAN] [RE]

Wenger, Esther Elizabeth (Malcolm) 3049 Ivy Court, North Newton KS 67117-8072, 316-283-2903, emwenger@southwind.net [WDC] [RE]

Wenger, Harold Paul, 4670 Elk Creek Rd, Middletown OH 45042-9659, 513-988-9080, halois@siscom.net [CDC] [RE]

Wenger, Harold Robert (Christine Headings) 1042 N Main St Apt C, Mount Joy PA 17552, 549-574-0617 [VA] IIB1 [AC] Pastor, Stuarts Draft Menn Ch, Stuarts Draft VA

Wenger Jr., James L. (Melani) 63 Poplar St, Penns Grove NJ 08069, 856-299-4385, jamesnmel@aol.com [LAN] IIB1 [AC] Pastor, Friendship Menn Ch, Carney's Point NJ

Wenger, James Rodney (Faith Ann) 5805 Berkeley Ave, Baltimore MD 21215, jaswenger@aol.com [ACC] IIB1 [AC] Pastor, North Baltimore Menn Ch, Baltimore MD

Wenger, Kathryn W. (Mark) 177 Nottingham Ln, Waynesboro VA 22980, 540-943-5970, sprngdle@ntelos.net [VA] IIB1 [AC] Co-Pastor, Springdale Menn Ch, Waynesboro VA

Wenger, L. Larry (RaeDella A.) 1036 Edgemoor Ct, Lancaster PA 17601, 717-392-3589, larry.wenger@juno.com [LAN] III [AC] Ordained Deacon, James St Menn Ch, Lancaster PA

Wenger, Linden M. (Esther) 1285 Shank Dr Apt 319, Harrisonburg VA 22802, 540-564-3745 [VA] [RE]

Wenger, Lloyd (Pauline) 816 Tuska Ave, Millville NJ 08332, 856-451-0508 [LAN] III [AC] Deacon, Norma Menn Ch, Norma NJ

Wenger, Mark R. (Kathy Weaver) 177 Nottingham Ln, Waynesboro VA 22980, 540-943-5970, sprngdle@ntelos.net [VA] IIB1 [AC] Co-Pastor, Springdale Menn Ch, Waynesboro VA

Wenger, Michael W. (Donna) 126 Bomberger Rd, Akron PA 17501, 717-859-1671, mwenger@ptd.net [LAN] IIC [AC]

Wenger, Nelson H. (Alma E.) 690 Earhart Rd, Manheim PA 17545, 717-665-7233, wenger690@desupernet.net [LAN] IIC [AC] Licensed Deacon, Erisman Menn Ch, Manheim PA

Wenger, O. Martin, PO Box 45, International Falls MN 56649, 218-286-3316, mart-diane@juno.com [NC] IIB1 [AC] Pastor, Point O' Pines Menn Ch, International Falls MN

Wenger, Robert G. (Lois) HC 70 Box 67A, Harman WV 26270, 304-227-3647, rolowenger@juno.com [VA] IIB1 [AC] Pastor, Riverside Menn Ch, Harman WV

Wenger, Ruth Yoder (David A.) 3304 Steuben Ave, Bronx NY 10467-3006, 718-882-8924, wengermail@aol.com [LAN] IIC [AC] Pastor, North Bronx Menn Ch, Bronx NY

Wenger, Tonya Ramer (Jonathan) 1805 Frisch Rd, Madison WI 53711-3248, 608-276-9311, tramer@prairienet.org [CDC, IL] IIB1 [AC] Pastor, Madison Menn Ch, Madison WI

Wenger, Warren M., 52C Fairview Ave, Perkasie PA 18944, 215-453-9286 [FRC] [RE]

Wengerd, Robert D., 7852 Glenwood Ave, Boardman OH 44512, 330-758-2597, bobwengerd@aol.com [OH] IIB1 [AC] Pastor, North Lima Menn Ch, North Lima OH

Wentland, Theodore (Frieda Marie Herbstreit) 411 N 3rd, Fisher IL 61843, 217-897-1577, tedwent@juno.com [IL] [RE] Pastor, Fullerton Presbyterian, Farmer City IL

Wero, George, 1111 James Cr, Bloomfield NM 87413, 505-632-1380 [RM] IIB1 [AC] Pastor, Light of Life Menn Ch, Farmington NM

Wert, Boyd M. (Martha R.) 1001 E Oregon Rd, Lititz PA 17543, 717-591-2605 [LAN] [RE]

Wert, Charles W. (Mildred) 84 Quarry Rd, Leola PA 17540, 717-656-8546 [LAN] [RE]

Westmoreland Jr., James M., 991 Olive St, Coatesville PA 19320, 610-383-6695 [LAN] IIB2 [AC] Associate Pastor, Newlinville Menn Ch, Coatesville PA

Whaley, Alan H. (Carol Ann) 3502 W Lamar Rd, Phoenix AZ 85019, 602-841-8044, menn1ofphx@aol.com [PSW] IB2, IIB1 [AC] Pastor, First Menn Ch of Phoenix, Phoenix AZ; Area Minister, Pacific SW Mennonite Conference, AZ

Wheeler, Susan, 101 Willow, Hesston KS 67062 [SC] IIA [AC]

Whigham Jr., Ertell M., 977 Trinity Ln, Gulph Mills PA 19406, 610-834-1024, NNLErtell1@juno.com [FRC] IIB1, IIB3c [AC] Associate Pastor, Norristown New Life Menn Ch, Norristown PA; Conference Minister, Franconia Mennonite Conference, Souderton PA

White, Richard (Betty) HC 68 Box 209, Bowden WV 26254, 304-636-8667 [VA] IIB2 [AC] Associate Pastor, Lambert Menn Ch, Belington WV

Whitehead, Grace E., 1515 W Havens, Kokomo IN 46901, 317-452-1130, rewgew@aol.com [IM] IIB3b [AC] Restoration Ministries, Kokomo IN

Whitermore, David Malcolm, 2951 N Governeour Unit 206, Wichita KS 67226, 316-683-2963 [WDC] [RE]

Whitman, Alice W. (Vincent) 1417 Brunnerville Rd, Lititz PA 17543, 717-626-9130, vawhitman@yahoo.com [LAN] IIC [AC] Licensed Deaconess, Crossroads Menn, Lancaster PA

Whitman, Vincent (Alice W.) 1417 Brunnerville Rd, Lititz PA 17543, 717-626-9130, vawhitman@yahoo.com [LAN] IIB1 [AC] Pastor, CrossRds Menn, Lancaster PA

Wickey, William (Florence Edna) 28314 Findley Rd, Burr Oak MI 49030, 574-646-2545 [IM] [RE]

Wideman, Louise Renee, 131 N Spring St, Bluffton OH 45817, 419-369-4573, lrwideman@wcoil.com [CDC] IIB1 [AC] Associate Pastor, First Menn Ch, Bluffton OH

Widmer, Rosemary (David) 23238 CR 32, Goshen IN 46526, 574-875-1009, rose@collegemennonite.org [IM] IIB2 [AC] Pastor, College Menn Ch, Goshen IN

Wiebe, Carl, 6009 CR 203, Millersburg OH 44654, 330-674-0189, carl@mcmc.org [OH] IIB1 [AC] Pastor, Martins Creek Menn Ch, Millersburg OH

Wiebe, Edward J. (Velma L) 2328 23rd St, Rockford IL 61108, 815-397-7946 [CDC] [RE]

Wiebe, Gordon Wayne (Delphia Mae) RR 1 Box 59, Doland SD 57436, 605-266-2588, gwiebe@willinet.net [CP] IIB1 [AC] Pastor, Emmanuel Menn Ch, Doland SD

Wiebe, Leonard C. (Joan E.) 2701 Goldenrod Rd, North Newton KS 67117, 316-283-4711, ljwiebe@southwind.net [WDC] [RE]

Wiebe, Peter B. (Rheta Mae) 4436 W Vista Ave, Glendale AZ 85301, 623-842-1145, PWiebe@meda.org [PSW] IIB3c [AW]

Wiebe-Johnson, Stephen Michael (Dorothy Lucille) 919 E Hively Ave, Elkhart IN 46517, 574-522-1172, wiebejohn@hotmail.com [IM] IIB3b [AC] Missionary, Mennonite Mission Agency, Benin, West Africa

Wiens, Mark Allen (Gayle Ann) PO Box 256, Goessel KS 67053-0256, 620-367-2528, wiensmg@mtelco.net [WDC] IIB2 [AC] Associate Pastor, Alexanderwohl Menn Ch, Goessel KS

Wightman, Margaret, 110 E Weaver Ave, Harrisonburg VA 22801, 540-434-0097, cmc_meg@ntelos.net [VA] IIB1 [AC] Co-Pastor, Community Menn Ch, Harrisonburg VA

Wikerd, Paul H. (Loretta M.) 253 State St, Hamburg PA 19526, 610-562-3936, pwikerd@enter.net [EDC] [RE]

Wilder, Kevin, 316 S Main, Hesston KS 67062, 620-327-3185, kevinw@hesston.edu [SC] IIA [AC]

Willems, Frank J. (Velma Elsie) 303 S Birch, Hillsboro KS 67063, 620-947-2543 [SC] [RE]

Willems, John (Dora E.) 2796 Goldfinch Loop SE, Albany OR 97322, 541-926-2006, jwillems@pacifier.com [PNW] [RE]

Williams, Dean E. (Cindy) 20721 Lower Highland, Bergton VA 22811, 540-852-3241 [VA] IIB1 [AC] Pastor, Mathias Menn Ch, Bergton VA

Williams, Nan (Robert) 5 Wentworth Pl, Hampton VA 23666, 757-826-4224 [VA] IIB2 [AC] Associate Pastor, Calvary Community Ch, Hampton VA

Williams, Robert (Nan) 5 Wentworth Pl, Hampton VA 23666, 757-826-4224 [VA] IIB2 [AC] Associate Pastor, Calvary Community Ch, Hampton VA

Williams, Roy W. (Ruth) 22642 Newfield Ct, Land O' Lakes FL 34639, 813-247-2798, RRRSJW@aol.com [SE] IB3, IIB1 [AC] Pastor, College Hill Menn Ch, Tampa FL; Urban Ministry Director of Tampa Bay, SE Mennonite Conference, Tampa FL; District Minister, SE Mennonite Conference, Tampa FL

Williams, Sharon K. (James P.) 1625 New Hope St, Norristown PA 19401, 610-277-1729, SharonW@MRN.org [FRC] IIB3c [AC] Congregational Resources/Anti-racism Consultant

Wilson, Larry J. (Lydia Jane) 1398 E CR 2250 N, White Heath IL 61884, 217-687-4132, ljwilson@net66.com [CDC, IL] IIB1 [AC] Pastor, First Menn Ch of Champaign-Urbana, Urbana IL

Wilson, Mike, 318½ Petoskey St Apt 5, Petoskey MI 49770, 231-487-1658, michael_ray_wilson@yahoo.com [IM] IIC [AC] Chaplain, Petoskey MI

Wilson, Nita, 1304 K-15 Hwy, PO Box 8, Goessel KS 67053-0008, 620-367-8192, alexyouth@mtelco.net [WDC] IIC [AC] Youth Pastor, Alexanderwohl Menn Ch, Goessel KS

Wilson, Samuel A. (Jackie) 5285 Balfour, Detroit MI 48224, 313-885-1485 [IM] IIB1 [AC] Pastor, Community Christian Fell Ch, Detroit MI

Wilson, Scot (Sharon) 7023 Clabeusch St, Pigeon MI 48755, 517-453-3632, mamc@avci.net [IM] IIB1 [AC] Pastor, Michigan Ave Menn Ch, Pigeon MI

Winey, Dawn R. (Rich) 577 E High St, Elizabethtown PA 17022, 717-367-9150, dawnwiney@mjmc.org [LAN] IIC [AC] Minister of Worship, Mount Joy Menn Ch, Mount Joy PA

MINISTERS

6

Winey, Richard L. (Dawn) 577 E High St, Elizabethtown PA 17022, 717-367-9150, richwiney@mjmc.org [LAN] IIC [AC] Minister of Worship, Mount Joy Menn Ch, Mount Joy PA

Wingard, Aldus, 4480 Egypt Rd, Smithville OH 44677, 330-669-2110 [ALL] [RE]

Winslow, Mark Howard (Judith Ann) 9025 E Rainsage St, Tucson AZ 85747, 520-574-7755 [PSW] IIB3a [AC]

Wintermote, Jeffrey Dale (Tamara Jean) RR 2 Box 21, Turpin OK 73950, 580-259-6439, jeffmote@yahoo.com [WDC] IIB2 [AC] Pastor, Turpin Menn Ch, Turpin OK

Winters, John W. (Ida E.) 1001 E Oregon Rd, Lititz PA 17543, 717-569-7790 [LAN] [RE]

Wise, Arthur C. (Betty J.) 5520 Antoinette St, Sarasota FL 34232, 941-377-3104 [SE] [RE] Executive Director/Chaplain, Sunnyside Retirement Village, Sarasota FL

Wise, Glenn D. (Dorothy) 12864 Path Valley Rd, Willow Hill PA 17271, 717-349-7061 [FRK] III [AC] Ordained Deacon, Shady Pine Menn Ch, Willow Hill PA

Witmer, Amos (Julia Ann) 4732 Witmer Ln, Dayton VA 22821, 540-879-9376 [VA] III [AC]

Witmer, Dale E. (Jeanne M.) 6109 Geneva Dr, East Petersburg PA 17520-1240, 717-569-5247, dewy@voicenet.com [LAN] IIC [AC] Licensed Deacon, Erisman Menn Ch, Manheim PA

Witmer, Dennis Lamar (Lori) 717 Shed Rd, Newville PA 17241, 717-776-4488, witmer4@pa.net [LAN] IIA [AC] Pastor, Diller Menn Ch, Newville PA

Witmer, E. Ray (Meredyth) 1729 Lincoln Hwy E, Lancaster PA 17602, 717-393-9800, rmwitmer@juno.com [LAN] III [AC] Ordained Deacon, CrossRds Menn, Lancaster PA

Witmer, H. Howard (Miriam) Dogwood Dr, Cottage 46, 1001 E Oregon Rd, Lititz PA 17543, 717-581-3970, hhwitmer@juno.com [LAN] [RE]

Witmer, Irwin L. (Mary) 1318 Mount Gretna Rd, Elizabethtown PA 17022, 717-367-3037 [LAN] [RE]

Witmer, Jeanne M. (Dale E.) 6109 Geneva Dr, East Petersburg PA 17520-1240, 717-569-5247, dewy@voicenet.com [LAN] IIC [AC] Licensed Deaconess, Erisman Menn Ch, Manheim PA

Witmer, John E. (Evelyn) 1067 Hearthstone Rd, Lancaster PA 17603-9452, 717-871-0686 [LAN] [RE]

Witmer, Kenneth R. (Lorraine) PO Box 363, Bowmansville PA 17507-0363, 717-445-7458, krwitmer@hydrosoft.net [LAN] IIB1 [AC] Co-Pastor, Bowmansville Menn Ch, East Earl PA

Witmer, Meredyth Ann (E. Ray) 1729 Lincoln Hwy E, Lancaster PA 17602, 717-393-9800, rmwitmer@juno.com [LAN] IIC [AC] Licensed Deaconess, Crossroads Menn, Lancaster PA

Witmer, Paul M. (Mary K.) 5033 Martin Dr, East Petersburg PA 17520, 717-581-7805 [LAN] [RE]

Witmer, Randall L. (Lorretta) 235 Hershey Ave, Lancaster PA 17603, 717-393-5840, rlwitmer@dejazzd.com [LAN] IIB1 [AC]

Wittrig, Jerry (Ruth Ann) 1008 N Indiana Ave, Goshen IN 46526, 574-533-2408, jwtrg@aol.com [IM] IIB2 [AC] Co-Pastor, North Goshen Menn Ch, Goshen IN

Woelk, Frank, 241 Bergen Rd, Newport WA 99156, 509-447-2224, fwoelk@juno,com [PNW] IIB1 [AC] Pastor, Spring Valley Menn Ch, Newport WA

Woldeabe, Mulugeta Abate (Tihute Yohannes) 1687 Castle Hill Ave Apt 3, Bronx NY 10462-4249, 718-246-7263, abatem@worldnet.att.net [LAN] IIB1 [AC] Pastor, Emmanuel Worship Center, Bronx NY

Wolgemuth, Herbert R. (Kathleen M.) RR 1 Box 202-A, Covington PA 16917, 570-659-5479, herbw@ticopa.quik.com [LAN] [AW]

Wright, Jeff (Debra Yvonne Thesman Wright) Box CAL, 1539 E Howard St, Pasadena CA 91104, 626-720-8100, wrightstuff@pacificsouthW.org [PSW] IB2, IIB1, IIB3b [AC] Lead Pastor, First Menn Ch of Upland, Upland CA; Director of Strategic Projects, Center for Anabaptist Leadership, Pasadena CA; Area Minister for Southern California, Pacific SW Mennonite Conference, Pasadena CA

Wright, Timothy Lee (Linda Lou) 1704 Empire Blvd, Apt 10, Rochester NY 14580, 716-670-9987, channels@frontiernet.net [NY] IIB1 [AC] Pastor, Jesus Ch, Webster NY

Wyatt Jr., Boyd (Shirley) RR 3 Box 70, Belington WV 26250, 304-823-1466 [VA] IIB1 [AC] Pastor, Lambert Menn Ch, Belington WV

Wyse, Dale, 30 Willow Way, Archbold OH 43502, 419-445-2765 [OH] IIB2 [AC] Minister of Visitation, Central Menn Ch, Archbold OH

Wyse, Don (Joyce) 5384 Olentangy River Rd, Columbus OH 43235-3442, 614-451-9169 [CDC] [RE]

Wyse, Elmer J. (Deloris J.) 524 Alana Dr, Goshen IN 46526, 574-533-2358, edwyse@maplenet.net [IL] [RE]

Wyse, Joyce M. (Don Gene) 5384 Olentangy River Rd, Columbus OH 43235-3442, 614-451-9169, wyse.5@osu.edu [CDC] [RE]

Wyse, Ned, 11080 Frontier Rd, Camden MI 49232, 517-254-4552, nlwyse@dmci.net [OH] IIB2 [AC] Preaching Minister, Salem Menn Ch, Waldron MI

Y

Yao, Ted Tchen (Mary) 4800 N 11th St, Philadelphia PA 19141, 215-455-6099 [LAN] [RE]

Yates, Bob, 1023 Madison, Harper KS 67058, 620-896-7398 [SC] IIB1 [AC] Associate Pastor, Pleasant Valley Menn Ch, Harper KS

Yeakey II, Michael Aaron (Kathleen Faye Nofziger) 6085S 1000W, Topeka IN 46571, 260-593-2594 [CDC] IIB3a [AC]

Yigzaw, Guenetu, 450 W Forest Ave, West Chicago IL 60185, 630-293-7331, bwec@msn.com [IL] IIB1 [AC] Pastor, Berhane Wongel Ethiopian Ch, West Chicago IL

Yoder, Aden J., 1006 Mervin Ave, Goshen IN 46526, 574-534-5573 [IM] [RE]

Yoder, Alvin, 321 Linden St, West Liberty OH 43357, 937-465-2263, ayoder@logan.net [OH] IIB1 [AC] Pastor, Bethel Menn Ch, West Liberty OH

Yoder, Amanda A. (Jonathan D. Schrock) 5857 Noble Dr, Indianapolis IN 46234, 317-858-9054, yorocks@juno.com [IM] IIA [AC] Associate Pastor, First Menn Ch, Indianapolis IN

Yoder, Amos W. (Gertrude) 1055 Simmontown Rd, Gap PA 17527, 717-442-4265 [LAN] [RE]

Yoder, Amzie (Elena) 1605 Wridge, Carlsbad NM 88220, 505-887-7658, amziey@cavemen.net [RM] [AW]

Yoder, Anita, 60575 CR 27, Goshen IN 46528, 574-534-7374, anitay@maplenet.net [IM] IIA [AC] Minister of Worship/Music, Clinton Frame Menn Ch, Goshen IN

Yoder, Arlin David (Mary Lou) 1704 6th Ave N, Wellman IA 52356 [CP] [RE]

Yoder, Beth Ranck (Jerold) 1209 Telegraph Rd, Perkasie PA 18944, 215-257-1850, jyoder@enter.net [FRC] IIB1 [AC] Pastor, Perkasie Menn Ch, Perkasie PA

Yoder, Brenda J., 706 C St, Springfield OR 97477, 541-726-4478 [PNW] IIB3a [AC]

Yoder, Bruce, BP 2624, Cotonou 01, Benin [ALL] IIC [AC]

Yoder, Calvin L. (Lorie B.) 24 Diane Ave, Lititz PA 17543, 717-626-9364, calyoder@foresthillschurch.org [ACC] IIB1 [AC] Pastor, Forest Hills Menn Ch, Leola PA

Yoder, Carl V., 402 Walnut St, Archbold OH 43502, 419-445-4676 [OH] [RE]

Yoder, Chester (Patricia Jane) 1202 Harman Rd, Accident MD 21520 [ALL] IIC [AC]

Yoder, Chester E. (Sandra) 214 Spruce St, Denver PA 17517, 717-445-4782, yoders@hydrosoft.net [LAN] IIB1 [AC] Co-Pastor, Bowmansville Menn Ch, East Earl PA

Yoder, Daniel J. (Lois Beachy) 8301 Nathanael Greene, Charlotte NC 28227, 704-531-6010 [VA] [AW]

Yoder, David D. (Shirley) 1539 Hillcrest Dr, Harrisonburg VA 22802, 540-434-4776 [VA] [RE]

Yoder, Delmar (Tammy) 33068 Cty Hwy 34, Ogema MN 56569, 218-983-3490 [NC] IIB1 [AC] Pastor, Strawberry Lake Menn Ch, Ogema MN

Yoder, Derek, 108 Willow Ln, Hesston KS 67062, derek@wmc.kscoxmail.com [SC] IIA [AC] Youth Pastor, Whitestone Menn Ch, Hesston KS

Yoder, Duane Allen (Barbara Jill) 2290 Lake Terrace Rd, Harrisonburg VA 22802, 540-434-5813, duane@lindale.org [VA] IIB1 [AC] Pastor, Lindale Menn Ch, Harrisonburg VA

Yoder, Earl A., PO Box 275, Springs PA 15562, 814-662-2210 [ALL] [RE]

Yoder, Earl D., 20 Osage Dr, Belleville PA 17004, 717-667-9710 [ALL] [RE]

Yoder, Edwin M., RR 4 Box 10, Harrisonburg VA 22801 [OH] [RE]

Yoder, Elena, 1605 Wridge, Carlsbad NM 88220, 505-887-7658 [RM] IIB3a [AC] Hospice Counselor, Carlsbad Hospital, Carlsbad, NM

Yoder, Glen, 336 Robin, Waverly OH 45690 [OH] [RE]

Yoder, Glen J. (Ellen) 321 Primrose Ln, Mountville PA 17554, 717-285-3906 [LAN] [AW]

Yoder, Harold, 1310 S 14th St, Goshen IN 46526, 574-825-2701 [IM] [RE]

Yoder, Harold J. (Ruth Anne) 26175 Woodridge Dr, Elkhart IN 46517, 574-293-5080 [IM] IIB2 [AC] Pastor, Yellow Creek Menn Ch, Goshen IN

Yoder, Harvey (Alma Jean) 1135 Hamlet Dr, Harrisonburg VA 22802, 540-432-0531, harvyoder@aol.com [VA] IIB1 [AC] Pastor, Family of Hope, Harrisonburg VA

Yoder, Helen, 5465 Black Hawk Ave SW, Wellman IA 52356, 319-646-6835, HLHYoder@yahoo.com [CP] IIA [AC] Staff Deacon, W Union Menn Ch, Parnell IA

Yoder, Herbert L. (Dorothy Beason) 415 7th Ave, PO Box 169, Wellman IA 52356, 319-646-2622, hdyoder@hotmail.com [CP] [RE]

Yoder, Irvin C., 1312 Copley Ct, Goshen IN 46526, 574-533-9084 [IM] [RE]

Yoder, J. David (Nancy) 2280 Lake Terrace Dr, Harrisonburg VA 22802-6193, 540-434-4769 [VA] IIB3c [AC]

Yoder, John O. (Arlene H.) PO Box 362, Maytown PA 17550, 717-426-1560, joytwo@paonline.com [LAN]

IIB1 [AC] Pastor, Erisman Menn Ch, Manheim PA

Yoder, Jon, 5902 S Whiskey Hill Rd, Hubbard OR 97032, 503-651-2743, jzyoder@web-ster.com [PNW] IIA [AC] Pastor, Pacific Covenant Menn Ch, Canby OR

Yoder, Joshua (Rebecca Kirkpatrick) 418 W Hubbard Ave, Elkhart IN 46516, 574-389-9624, joshuapyoder@juno.com [IM] IIA [AC] Pastor, Fell of Hope Menn Ch, Elkhart IN

Yoder, June Alliman, 200 Westwood Rd, Goshen IN 46526, 574-533-4943 [IM] IIB3d [AC] Professor, Associated Mennonite Biblical Seminary, Elkhart IN

Yoder, Kevin (Sharon) 60790 CR 101, Elkhart IN 46517 [IM] IIA [AC] Missionary, Eastern Mennonite Missions, Kenya, Africa

Yoder, Lawrence M. (Shirlee K.) 1301 Mount Clinton Pk, Harrisonburg VA 22802, 540-434-1058, yoderlm@emu.edu [VA] IIB3d [AC]

Yoder, Lawrence Richard (Bonnie L.) 3246 Hemlock St, Harrisonburg VA 22801, 540-574-4659 [VA] IIC [AC]

Yoder, Leanne, 4950 E Second St, Tucson AZ 85711, 520-323-8611, eyoder@gci-net.com [PSW] IIC [AC]

Yoder, Lonnie D. (Teresa Boshart) 1066 Smith Ave, Harrisonburg VA 22802, 540-432-6467 [VA] IIB3d [AC]

Yoder, Mark (Alice) 2726 Conestoga Creek Rd, Morgantown PA 19543, 610-286-9445 [LAN] [RE]

Yoder, Marvin D. (Rachel) 61205 CR 17, Goshen IN 46526, 574-875-7850 [IM] [RE]

Yoder, Marvin K. (Neta Faye) 104 Fairview Dr PO Box 166, Wellman IA 52356, 319-646-2451 [CP] [RE]

Yoder, Mary Lehman (Michael) 216 Gorham Rd, Goshen IN 46526, 574-534-3741, mmyoder1@cs.com [CDC, IM] IIB1 [AC] Co-Pastor, Assembly Menn Ch, Goshen IN

Yoder, Monroe J. (Rachel) 268 Van Cortlandt Ave E Apt 2, Bronx NY 10467-3008, 718-652-2307, myrybronx@earthlink.net [LAN] IB3 [AC] Pastor, Seventh Ave Menn Ch, New York NY; Bishop/Overseer, LAN New York City District, New York NY

Yoder, Nathan E. (Miriam Grace) 1545 Shank Dr, Harrisonburg VA 22802, 540-432-9326, yoderne@emu.edu [VA] IIB3d [AC]

Yoder, Nelson S. (Pat) 5948 Michele Dr, Narvon PA 17555, 717-355-9130, npyoder1@juno.com [ACC] IB2, IIB2 [AC] Conference Minister, Atlantic Coast Conference, Morgantown PA; Associate Pastor, Ridgeview Menn Ch, Gordonville PA; Mental Health Therapist, Philhaven, Mt Gretna PA

Yoder, Ottis (Violet) 32553 County Hwy 34, Ogema MN 56569-9605, 218-983-3477 [NC] IB3 [AC] Bishop, Strawberry Lake Menn Ch, Ogema MN

Yoder, Pamela (Robert) 19321 Yoder Dr, Goshen IN 46528, 574-875-1862, pamela@firstmennonite.net [IM] IIA [AC] Associate Pastor, Pastoral Care, First Menn Ch, Middlebury IN

Yoder, Paul E. M. (Helen) 1009 9th Ave, Wellman IA 52356, 319-646-2316 [CP] [RE]

Yoder Sr., Paul R. (Grace W.) 1591 Pine Ct, Harrisonburg VA 22802, 540-438-4260, yowing819@cs.com [VA] [RE]

Yoder, Paul T. (Daisy) 1588 Pine Ct, Harrisonburg VA 22802-2484, 540-432-7200, twopilgrims@ttmol.com [VA] IIB1 [RE]

Yoder, Ray K. (Edna) 794 Moccasin Dr, Harleysville PA 19438, 215-256-6356, rayyoder@excelonline.com [FRC] IIB1 [AC] Intentional Interim Pastor, Rocky Ridge,

Quakertown PA

Yoder, Richard W. (Barbara A.) 1410 Pembroke Cr #3, Goshen IN 46526, 574-534-0287, barw@bnin.net [IM] [RE]

Yoder, Robert D. (Vickie Dee) 14201 Germantown Rd, Columbiana OH 44408, 330-482-2123, bc958@wmconnect.com [OH] IIB1 [AC] Pastor, Sharon Menn Ch, Plain City OH

Yoder, Robert E. (Pamela Sue) 19321 Yoder Dr, Goshen IN 46528, 574-875-1862, bob@im.mennonite.net [IM] IB2 [AC] Conference Minister of Youth/Young Adults, Indiana-Michigan & Central District Conferences, Goshen IN

Yoder, Robert K. (Elvira) 903 K Ave, Kalona IA 52247, 319-656-3910 [CP [RE]

Yoder, Roy K. (Sandra Fay) PO Box 33 560 Kulps Rd, Bally PA 19503, 610-845-3650, rsyoder@excelonline.com [FRC] IIB3b [AW]

Yoder, Ruth Anne, 59193 Green Valley Parkway, Elkhart IN 46517-3427, 574-875-4512 [IM] IIB1 [AC] Pastor, Union Center Church of the Brethren, Nappanee IN

Yoder, Samuel J. (Mary Ann) RR 1 Box 73, Mifflinburg PA 17844, 717-966-2392 [ALL] IIB1 [AC]

Yoder, Sharon (Kevin) 60790 CR 101, Elkhart IN 46517 [IM] IIA [AC] Missionary, Eastern Mennonite Missions, Kenya Africa

Yoder, Shirlee K. (Lawrence M.) 1301 Mount Clinton Pk, Harrisonburg VA 22802, 54-434-1058 [VA] IIB3a [AC]

Yoder, Steven J. (Janet J.), Bluffton OH, sjyoder@southwind.net [CDC] IIB2 [AC] Pastor, First Menn Ch, Bluffton OH

Yoder, Vickie (Robert D.) 14201 Germantown Rd, Columbiana OH 44408, 330-482-2123, bc958@cboss.com [OH] IIB3a [AC]

Yoder, W. Harvey (Karen S.) 311 Jensen St, Macon MS 39341, 662-726-2542, whyksy@crawdat.com [GS] IIA [AC] Assistant Pastor, Nanih Waiya Indian Menn Ch, Philadelphia MS

Yoder-Schrock, John Lamar (Marcia Ann) PO Box 722, Moundridge KS 67107, 620-345-8500, Wzionmc@netks.net [WDC] IIB1 [AC] Co-Pastor, West Zion Menn Ch, Moundridge KS

Yoder-Schrock, Marcia Ann (John L.) 1281 16th St, PO Box 69, Henderson NE 68371, 402-723-5300 [WDC] IIB1 [AC] Co-Pastor, West Zion Menn Ch, Moundridge KS

Yordy, Maurice J. (Pat) 1397 CR 700 N, Eureka IL 61530, 309-467-3109, mpyord@mtco.com [IL] IIB1 [AC] Pastor, E Peoria Menn Ch, Eureka IL

Yost, Burton George (Elnore Ruth) 184 Garmatter St, Bluffton OH 45817-1165, 419-358-9495 [CDC] [RE]

Yovanovich, William Z. (Ruth B. Brubaker) 405 College Ave, Elizabethtown PA 17022-2222, 717-367-3713 or 367-4992, billyo@lancnews.infi.net [LAN] [RE]

Yutzy, Homer E. (Elizabeth G.) 13169 CR 16, Wauseon OH 43567, 419-452-6756 [OH] [RE]

Yutzy, Melvin E., 8740 PC Georgesville Rd, Plain City OH 43064, 614-873-4144 [OH] [RE]

Yutzy, Oliver (Miriam) 2220 N 675 W, Shipshewana IN 46565, 260-768-4238 [IM] IIB3c [AC] Manager, Menno-Hof, Shipshewana IN

Z

Zabriskie, Kristin Klompeen (W. Tyler) World Vision, Central Post Office, PO Box 479, Phnomh Penh, Cambodia, kristi@onlin [PSW] IIB2 [AC]

Zacheus, Stephen, 1499 Ridgecrest #22, Montery Park CA 91754, 323-526-4585 [PSW] IIA [AC] Assistant/Associate Pastor, Jemaat Kristen Indonesia Anugrah, Pasadena CA

Zeager, J. Frank (Rhoda) 2405 Colebrook Rd, Middletown PA 17057, 717-944-5008 [LAN] IIB2 [AC] Associate Pastor, Stauffer Menn Ch, Hershey PA

Zehr, Calvin Dean (Carol Ann) 130 N Galena St, Tiskilwa IL 61368, 815-646-4819 [IL] IIB1 [AC] Pastor, Willow Springs Menn Ch, Tiskilwa IL

Zehr, Douglas J. (Miriam R.) PO Box 281, Leo IN 46765, 260-627-5867 [IM] IB3, IIB1 [AC] Pastor, North Leo Menn Ch, Leo IN; Overseer, First Mennonite, Fort Wayne IN

Zehr, Evan (Amy Lynn) 5574 Highland Ave, Lowville NY 13367, 315-376-3082, eazehr@northnet.org [NY] IIB1 [AC] Pastor, Lowville Menn Ch, Lowville NY

Zehr, Keith (Connie) 111 Main St, Akron NY 14001, 716-542-9848, daisymae2000@hotmail.com [NY] IIB1 [AC] Pastor, Clarence Center-Akron Menn Ch, Akron NY

Zehr, Lidia, 1024 E 12th St, Harper KS 67058, 620-896-7895 [SC] IIA [AC] Pastor, Crystal Springs Menn Ch, Harper KS

Zehr, Loren (Ethel M.) 1918 SE 40th Terrace, Cape Coral FL 33904, 239-772-5683 and 239-945-4421, elzehr@juno.com; LZehr@capechristian.com [SE] IIC [AC] Pastor of Nurture, Cape Christian Fell, Cape Coral FL

Zehr, Marvin Jay (Jeannie K.) 824 Trinity Dr, Newton KS 67114, 316-283-8308 [WDC] IIA [RE]

Zehr, Michael M. (Lois Shenk) 19839 Peach Ridge Rd, Goshen IN 46526, 574-534-2453 [IM] IB3 [AC] Overseer, Holdeman Mennonite, Wakarusa IN

Zehr, Michael R. (Rebecca A.) 699 Parkside Dr, Wauseon OH 43567, 419-337-6797, michael.zehr@northclinton.org [OH] IIB2 [AC] Associate Pastor, North Clinton Menn Ch, Wauseon OH

Zehr, Milton J. (Dorothy Leora) 5549 Alger Rd, Martinsburg NY 13404, 315-376-3734, dotconf@northnet.org [NY] IB2, IB3 [AC] Conference Minister, NY Mennonite Conference, Martinsburg NY

Zehr, Nathan (Ruth) 8343 VanAmber Rd, Castorland NY 13620, 315-376-2593, nrzehr@hotmail.com [NY] IIB1 [AC] Pastor, Pine Grove Menn Ch, Castorland NY

Zehr, Paul M. (Mary Martin) 209 Henrietta Ave, Lancaster PA 17602-3911, 717-299-6104, zehrpm@emu.edu [LAN] IB3 [AC] Bishop/Overseer, LMC Mellinger District, PA

Zehr, Robert O. (Vivian Margaret Guengerich) 134 Maloney Rd, Des Allemands LA 70030, 985-785-2974, bobzehr@cox.net [GS] IB3, IIB1 [AC] Interim Pastor, Open Door Menn Ch, Jackson MS

Zehr, Terry (Cheryl June) 3017 Pleasant Plain, Elkhart IN 46517, 574-522-6972, sunnysidemc@juno.com [IM] IIB1 [AC] Pastor, Sunnyside Menn Ch, Elkhart IN

Zehr, Terry J. (Lisa R.) 7630 Park Ave, Lowville NY 13367, 315-376-5514, tzehr1@twcny.rr.com [NY] IIB1 [AC] Pastor, Watertown Menn Ch, Watertown NY

Zehr Jr., Vernon, 2721 Skylark Rd, Wilmington DE 19808, 302-994-8698 [LAN] IIB2 [AC] Associate Pastor,

Frazer Menn Ch, Frazer PA

Zeiset, Nelson B. (Esther) 111 Hopeland Rd, Newmanstown PA 17073, 717-949-2478 [LAN] IIB2, IIB3a [AC] Associate Pastor, Green Terrace Menn Ch, Wernersville PA; Chaplain, Prison Ministry, PA

Zeiset, Samuel W., 420 Radcliff Rd, Willow St PA 17584-9752, 717-464-3340 [LAN] IIB3a [AC] Pastor, Mennonite & Brethren Marriage Encounter, PA

Zewdie, Kinfe (Adanech) 7432 Maury Rd, Baltimore MD 21244, 410-298-6053 [LAN] [AW]

Ziemer, Richard Carl (Adella W.) 325 Cedar Crest Dr, Quakertown PA 18951, 215-536-8895 [EDC] [RE] Chaplain, Delaware Valley College, Quakertown PA

Zimmerman, Earl S. (Ruth Hoover) 1181 Lincolnshire Dr, Harrisonburg VA 22802, 540-433-5227, zim1181@intergate.com [VA] IIB1 [AC] Pastor, Shalom Menn Congregation, Harrisonburg VA

Zimmerman, George L. (Lois) 20 Evergreen St, Thompsontown PA 17094-9733, 717-535-9941, georgelois@nmax.net [LAN] IIB1 [AC] Interim Pastor, Krall Menn Ch, Lebanon PA

Zimmerman, Ivan R. (Vera Mae) 85 Millstone Dr, Denver PA 17517, 717-445-8297 [LAN] [RE]

Zimmerman, James Seibel (Lillian) 3110 Mount Joy Rd, Mount Joy PA 17552, 717-653-7366, jimandlilz@yahoo.com [LAN] IIC [AC] Associate Pastor, Risser Menn Ch, Elizabethtown PA

Zimmerman II, John Charles, 56 Market St, Myerstown PA 17067, 717-933-5235, zimmermanii@hotmail.com [LAN] IIC [AC] Associate Pastor, Schubert Menn Ch, Bethel PA

Zimmerman, Lester L. (Thelma) 1407 Brunnerville Rd, Lititz PA 17543, 717-626-2641 [LAN] [RE]

Zimmerman, M. Craig (Grace) 966 Lower Bodines Rd, Trout Run PA 17771, 570-995-9171 [LAN] IIA [AC] Pastor, Mountain View Fell, Trout Run PA

Zimmerman, Marlin M. (Bonnie) 708 E Linden St, Richland PA 17087, 717-866-5323, zimmb@ptd.net [LAN] III [AC] Ordained Deacon, Schubert Menn Ch, Bethel PA

Zimmerman, Michael S. (Marlene Faye) 528 E 28th Division Hwy, Lititz PA 17543, 717-627-2461, mandmzimm@paonline.com [LAN] IIB2 [AC] Associate Pastor, Erb Menn Ch, Lititz PA

Zimmerman, Norman L. (Betty) 524 Appalachian Ave, Mechanicsburg PA 17055, 717-766-0536 [LAN] [RE]

Zimmerman, R. Eugene (Edith) 315 E Wesner Rd, Blandon PA 19510, 610-926-4074 [LAN] [AW]

Zimmerman, Titus N. (Ursula) 345 Stevens Rd, Stevens PA 17578, 717-336-7154 [LAN] [RE]

Zoll, David Eugene (Florence) 1715 Swamp Bridge Rd, Stevens PA 17578, 717-336-3369, zoll@ptdprolog.net [LAN] IIB2 [AC] Associate Pastor, Metzler Menn Ch, Akron PA

Zook, Darrell E. (Patricia Ann) PO Box 100, Pulaski IA 52584 [SC] [AC] Pastor, Pulaski Menn Ch, Bloomfield IA

Zook, Edward L. (Martha E.) 1626 Green St, Harrisburg PA 17102, 717-232-1480, ezook@statepa.us [LAN] IIA [AC] Associate Pastor, Herr St Menn Ch, Harrisburg PA

Zook, Gary L. (Teresa) 11842 Williamsport Pk, Greencastle PA 17225, 717-597-3294, zookie17225@peoplepc.com [FRK] IIB1 [AC] Pastor, North Side Menn Ch, Hagerstown MD

Zook, Gordon D. (Bonnie) 156 Robinhood Ln, Newport News VA 23602, 757-877-4247 [VA] IIB3d [AC]

Zook, Herbert, Wild Cherry Rd, New Castle PA 16101, 724-652-5436 [OH] [RE]

Zook, Judith E. (Ronald) 35 N Whisper Ln, New Holland PA 17557, 717-354-5387, jzook@frontiernet.net [LAN] IIC [AC] Associate Pastor, New Holland Menn Ch, New Holland PA

Zook, Lester L. (Grace E.) PO Box 302, 315 S Ash St, Pretty Prairie KS 67570-0302, 620-459-7389, lzook@southwind.net [WDC] IIB1 [AC] Pastor, First Menn Ch, Pretty Praook, Robert G. (Ethel) 223 Howard Ave, Lancaster PA 17602, 717-393-2867, BobZook@lgms.pvt.k12.pa.us [LAN] [AW]

Zook, Ronald E. (Judith) 35 N Whisper Ln, New Holland PA 17557, 717-354-5387, rzook@frontiernet.net [LAN] IIB1 [AC] Pastor, New Holland Menn Ch, New Holland PA

Zuercher, Marvin (Glenda) 330-682-8418 [VA] IIA [AC] Pastor, Chestnut Ridge Menn Ch, Orrville OH

MINISTERS

6

Congregations by location

7

This section lists congregations according to their location. It includes all congregations that are affiliated with member and provisional member area conferences of Mennonite Church USA (all congregations in section 2). In addition to congregations in the United States, congregations relating to Mennonite Church USA in Canada and Mexico also are included.

Congregations are listed in order by state and city. Congregations are included under the city of their mailing address. Included with the name of the congregation are the congregational ID number, the area conference affiliation and the page number where more details can be found.

For a listing of congregations in alphabetical order, check the online directory on the Mennonite Church USA website (www.MennoniteUSA.org).

United States

ALABAMA
Atmore
Native Christian Fell (11140) (GS) 57
Poarch Community Ch (16535) (GS) 57

ALASKA
Anchorage
Prince of Peace Menn Ch (10051) (PNW) 94

ARIZONA
Chandler
Koinonia Menn Ch (23044) (PSW) 97
Glendale
Trinity Menn Ch (18333) (PSW) 98

Phoenix
First Menn Ch of Phoenix (5312) (PSW) 96
Sunnyslope Menn Ch (18317) (PSW) 98
Surprise
Emmanuel Menn Ch (18325) (PSW) 96
Tucson
Shalom Menn Fell (22418) (PSW) 98

ARKANSAS
Calico Rock
Calico Rock Menn Fell (17855) (SC) 102
El Dorado
First Menn Ch (10777) (GS) 57
Pea Ridge
Rogers Menn/Ch of the Brethren (29745) (SC) 103

CALIFORNIA
Alhambra
Indonesian Worship Ch (11078) (PSW) 97
Chino
Jemaat Kristen Indonesia Hosana (10282) (PSW) . . .97
Claremont
Peace House Fell (10027) (PSW) 97
Cupertino
Cupertino Menn Ch (5697) (PSW) 96
Downey
Faith Menn Ch (18259) (PSW) 96
Jemaat Kristen Indonesia Imanuel (10309) (PSW) . . .97
Fresno
Hmong Community Ch (10247) (PSW) 96
Menn Community Ch (28373) (PSW) 97
Inglewood
Calvary Christian Fell (18242) (PSW) 96
Los Angeles Faith Chapel (11088) (PSW) 97
Irvine
Trinity Chinese Menn Ch (5183) (PSW) 98
La Mirada
Gereja Kristen Injili Indonesia Zion (10311) (PSW) . .96
La Puente
House of the Lord Fell (24885) (PSW) 97
Los Angeles
Abundant Life Miracle Christian Center (11318) (PSW) .96
All Souls Christian Center (11583) (PSW) 96
Faith and Love Christian Center (11584) (PSW) 96
Family Menn Ch (11109) (PSW) 96

Great Commission Deliverance Ch (11172) (PSW) . . .96
Hollywood Christian Center (11586) (PSW) 96
Labor for Christ Ministry (11269) (PSW) 97
Miracle of Faith Menn Ch (24612) (PSW) 97
Prince of Peace Anabaptist Fell (18267) (PSW) 97
Riches of Christ Fell (11080) (PSW) 97
Royal Dominion Family Chapel (11319) (PSW) 97
Pasadena
Gereja Kristus Injili (11079) (PSW) 96
Jemaat Kristen Indonesia Anugrah (10289) (PSW) . . .97
Pasadena Menn Ch (28142) (PSW) 97
Paso Robles
First Menn Ch of Paso Robles (5409) (PSW) 96
Reedley
First Menn Ch of Reedley (5321) (PSW) 96
Reseda
Jemaat Kristen Indonesia Maranatha (10259) (PSW) . .97
San Diego
San Diego Menn Ch (10001) (PSW) 98
San Francisco
First Menn Ch of San Francisco (23226) (PSW) 96
San Francisco Chinese Menn Ch (5692) (PSW) 98
Santa Fe Springs
Bethel Community Ch (5075) (PSW) 96
South Gate
Iglesia Monte Sinai (24232) (PSW) 97
Sun Valley
Iglesia Evangelica Bethel (25429) (PSW) 97
Upland
First Menn Ch of Upland (5330) (PSW) 96
Mountain View Menn Ch (18309) (PSW) 97

COLORADO
Arvada
Arvada Menn Ch (6020) (WDC) 115
Hmong Menn Ch (11119) (RM, WDC) 117
Aurora
Peace Menn Community Ch (28605) (RM, WDC) .90, 118
Boulder
Boulder Menn Ch (6153) (WDC) 115
Cheraw
East Holbrook Menn Ch (20834) (RM) 99
Colorado Springs
Beth-El Menn Ch (20792) (RM) 99
First Menn Ch of Colorado Springs (20867) (RM) . .99
Denver
First Menn Ch of Denver (20859) (RM) 100
Fort Collins
Fort Collins Menn Fell (24687) (RM, WDC) 42, 116
Glenwood Springs
Glenwood Menn Ch (20891) (RM) 100
Greeley
Greeley Menn Ch (20917) (RM) 100
Julesburg
Julesburg Menn Ch (13300) (CP) 65
La Jara
Menn Ch of La Jara (20925) (RM) 100
La Junta
Emmanuel Menn Ch (20842) (RM) 99
Lakewood
Glennon Heights Menn Ch (20883) (RM) 100
Palmer Lake
Mountain Community Menn Ch (25247) (RM,
WDC) 97, 118

Pueblo
Pueblo Menn Ch (21774) (RM) 100
Rocky Ford
Rocky Ford Menn Ch (20966) (RM) 100
Walsenburg
Walsenburg Menn Ch (20982) (RM) 100

DELAWARE
Claymont
Jesus Power and Love Ministries (10070) (LAN) 74
Greenwood
Tressler Menn Ch (10462) (ALL) 36
Wilmington
Centro Evangelistico Cristiano (26724) (LAN) 71

DISTRICT OF COLUMBIA
Germantown
Iglesia del Evangelio Completo Alpha y O (23465)
(VA) 111
Washington
Christian Conquest Fell (10010) (VA) 110
Peabody Street Menn Ch (14993) (LAN) 78
Washington Community Fell (24778) (VA) 112

FLORIDA
Apopka
Ebenezer Christian Ch (25049) (SE) 107
Arcadia
Pine Creek Chapel (22376) (SE) 107
Blountstown
Oak Terrace Menn Ch (12823) (SE) 107
Cape Coral
Cape Christian Fell (28175) (SE) 106
Fort Myers
Iglesia Menonita Arca de Salvación (27904) (SE) . .107
Gainesville
Emmanuel Menn Ch (25080) (SE) 107
Homestead
Homestead Menn Ch (14332) (SE) 107
Immokalee
Assemblee de la Grace (11299) (SE) 106
Tabernacle of Bethlehem (12502) (SE) 107
Lakeland
Luz y Verdad (10212) (SE) 107
Lauderdale Lakes
Evangelical Garifuna Ch (12051) (SE) 107
Miami
Ch of God Prince of Peace (11169) (SE) 106
Eglise du Nouveau Testament (28449) (SE) 107
Good Shepherd Evangelical (10972) (SE) 107
Iglesia Menonita Encuentro de Renovación (10284)
(SE) 107
Unity Pentecostal Ch of God (11153) (SE) 107
Miami-Dade
Tabernacle of Bethlehem (10253) (SE) 107
North Port
Peace Christian Fell (10241) (SE) 107
Sarasota
Ashton Menn Ch (13524) (SE) 106
Bahia Vista Menn Ch (18903) (SE) 106
Bay Shore Menn Ch (15693) (SE) 106
Covenant Menn Fell (12196) (SE) 106
Iglesia Evangelica Nueva Vida (11622) (SE) 107
Iglesia Seguidores de Cristo (25072) (SE) 107

New Jerusalem Menn Ch (12501) (SE) 107
Newtown Gospel Chapel (18762) (SE) 107
St Petersburg
New Beginning Community Ch (19531) (SE) 107
Tampa
College Hill Menn Ch (13797) (SE) 106
North Tampa Christian Fell (14886) (SE) 107

GEORGIA
Americus
Americus Menn Fell (10067) (SE) 106
Atlanta
Atlanta Menn Fell (10291) (CDC) 41
Berea Menn Ch (13565) (SE) 106

HAWAII
Honolulu
New Life Christian Fell (29157) (LAN) 77
Vietnamese Christian Fell (29215) (LAN) 79

IDAHO
Aberdeen
First Menn Ch (5335) (PNW) 93
Boise
Hyde Park Menn Fell (23663) (PNW) 93
Caldwell
Evergreen Heights Menn Ch (10050) (PNW) 93
Filer
Filer Menn Ch (17525) (PNW) 93
Meridian
Emmaus Christian Fell (11305) (PNW) 93
Nampa
First Menn Ch (17533) (PNW) 93

ILLINOIS
Arthur
Arthur Menn Ch (11817) (IL) 59
Aurora
Asian Menn Community Ch (16719) (CDC) 41
Centro Cristiano Vida Abundante Aurora (20606) (IL) .59
Carlock
Carlock Menn Ch (2195) (CDC) 41
Chenoa
Meadows Menn Ch (2540) (CDC) 42
Chicago
Bethel Menn Community Ch (11825) (IL) 59
Chicago Community Menn Ch (24653) (CDC, IL) . .41, 59
Englewood Menn Ch (11882) (IL) 60
First Menn Ch (2359) (CDC) 42
Grace Community Ch (2400) (CDC) 42
Iglesia Cristiana Peniel (11097) (IL) 60
Lawndale Menn Ch (11973) (IL) 60
Living Water Community Ch (11151) (IL) 60
Cicero
Centro Cristiano Vida Abundante (28928) (IL) 59
Sonido de Alabanza (23432) (IL) 61
Danvers
North Danvers Menn Ch (2620) (CDC) 43
Delavan
Menn Ch of Dillon (11866) (IL) 61
East Chicago
Iglesia Menonita Getsemani (10638) (IL) 60
Eureka
East Peoria Menn Ch (11940) (IL) 60

Maple Lawn Fell (10049) (IL) 61
Roanoke Menn Ch (12070) (IL) 61
Evanston
Evanston Menn Ch (11890) (CDC, IL) 41, 60
Reba Place Ch (22343) (IL) 61
Fisher
East Bend Menn Ch (11874) (IL) 60
Flanagan
Prairieview Menn Ch (12138) (CDC, IL) 43, 61
Freeport
Freeport Menn Ch (11932) (IL) 60
Henry
New Life Community Ch (26732) (IL) 61
Hopedale
Boynton Menn Ch (2160) (CDC) 41
Hopedale Menn Ch (11957) (IL) 60
Lombard
Lombard Menn Ch (11981) (IL) 60
Markham
Community Menn Ch (28332) (CDC, IL) 41, 60
Metamora
Metamora Menn Ch (12013) (IL) 61
Moline
Templo Alabanza Menonita (13284) (CP) 47
Morton
First Menn Ch of Morton (11908) (IL) 60
Trinity Menn Ch (23549) (IL) 61
Mundelein
North Suburban Menn Ch (27557) (CDC, IL) . . .43, 61
Normal
Menn Ch of Normal (11833) (CDC, IL) 42, 61
Pekin
Bethel Menn Ch (2125) (CDC) 41
Peoria
First Norwood Menn Ch (11916) (IL) 60
Joy Fell Ch (27391) (CDC, IL) 42, 60
Living Love Ministries (11096) (CDC, IL) 42, 60
Roanoke
Cazenovia Menn Ch (11841) (IL) 59
Schaumburg
Christ Community Menn Ch (29397) (CDC, IL) . .41, 60
Comunidad de Fe (2207) (CDC) 41
St Anne
Rehoboth Menn Ch (12062) (IL) 61
Sterling
Science Ridge Menn Ch (12104) (IL) 61
Tiskilwa
Plow Creek Menn Ch (22335) (CDC, IL) 43, 61
Willow Springs Menn Ch (12146) (IL) 61
Urbana
First Menn Ch of Champaign-Urbana (11924)
(CDC, IL) 42, 60
W Chicago
Berhane Wongel Ethiopian Ch (11025) (IL) 59
Washington
Calvary Menn Ch (2190) (CDC) 41

INDIANA
Berne
First Menn Ch (2344) (CDC) 41
Bloomington
Menn Fell of Bloomington (11426) (IM) 65
Bristol
Bonneyville Menn Ch (12245) (IM) 63

CONGREGATIONS BY LOCATION

7

Elkhart
Belmont Menn Ch (12187) (IM) 63
Ch Without Walls (10244) (IM) 63
Fell of Hope Menn Ch (22210) (IM) 64
Hively Avenue Menn Ch (2455) (CDC) 42
Hively Jesus Village Ch (10005) (CDC) 42
House of Power (10961) (IM) 65
Olive Menn Ch (21758) (IM) 66
Prairie Street Menn Ch (12880) (IM) 66
Southside Fell (12930) (CDC, IM) 43, 66
Sunnyside Menn Ch (12997) (IM) 66
True Vine Tabernacle (12914) (IM) 67

Fort Wayne
Carroll Community Worship Center (12153) (IM) . . .63
Fairhaven Menn Ch (12435) (IM) 64
First Menn Ch (12476) (IM) 64
Maplewood Menn Ch (2530) (CDC) 42

Goshen
Assembly Menn Ch (22582) (CDC, IM) 41, 63
Benton Menn Ch (12195) (IM) 63
Berkey Avenue Menn Fell (24323) (IM) 63
Clinton Brick Menn Ch (12336) (IM) 63
Clinton Frame Menn Ch (12328) (IM) 63
College Menn Ch (12518) (IM) 63
East Goshen Menn Ch (12393) (IM) 64
Eighth Street Menn Ch (2270) (CDC) 41
Faith Menn Ch (10127) (CDC, IM) 41, 64
Family Worship Center at the Lighthouse (12526)
    (IM) 64
Iglesia Menonita del Buen Pastor (12377) (IM) 65
North Goshen Menn Ch (21998) (IM) 66
Pleasant View Menn Ch (12872) (IM) 66
Praise Chapel Christian Fell (10079) (IM) 66
Silverwood Menn Ch (2715) (CDC) 43
Walnut Hill Menn Ch (13045) (IM) 67
Waterford Menn Ch (13060) (IM) 67
Yellow Creek Menn Ch (13128) (IM) 67

Indianapolis
First Menn Ch (12450) (IM) 64
Shalom Menn Ch (10196) (IM) 66

Kokomo
Howard-Miami Menn Ch (12583) (IM) 65
Parkview Menn Ch (12849) (IM) 66

Kouts
Hopewell Menn Ch (12575) (IM) 64

Lafayette
Lafayette Menn Fell (26021) (CDC, IM) 42, 65

Leo
North Leo Menn Ch (12773) (IM) 66

Middlebury
First Menn Ch (12468) (IM) 64
Forks Menn Ch (12492) (IM) 64
Pleasant Oaks Menn Ch (2645) (CDC) 43

Montgomery
Providence Menn Ch (12898) (IM) 66

Muncie
Morning Star Ch (29652) (CDC, IM) 43, 65

Nappanee
First Menn Ch (2401) (CDC) 42
North Main Street Menn Ch (12781) (IM) 66

New Carlisle
Hudson Lake Menn Ch (12591) (IM) 65

Paoli
Paoli Menn Fell (22624) (CDC, IM) 43, 66

Rensselaer
Burr Oak Menn Ch (12278) (IM) 63

Shipshewana
Marion Menn Ch (12708) (IM) 65
Shore Menn Ch (12963) (IM) 66

South Bend
Kern Road Menn Ch (12617) (IM) 65

Syracuse
Wawasee Lakeside Chapel (13078) (IM) 67

Topeka
Emma Menn Ch (12419) (IM) 64
Topeka Menn Ch (2775) (CDC) 43

Valparaiso
Valparaiso Menn Ch (13037) (IM) 67

Wakarusa
Holdeman Menn Ch (12567) (IM) 64

Warsaw
Menn Ch of Warsaw (10007) (IM) 65

Wolcottville
Lake Bethel Menn Ch (12625) (IM) 65

IOWA

Ames
Ames Menn Ch (23424) (CDC) 40

Burlington
Peace Menn Ch (28787) (CP) 46

Cedar Falls
Cedar Falls Menn Ch (24935) (CP) 45

Davenport
Casa de Oración Emanuel (11629) (CP) 45

Des Moines
Christ Community Ch (11628) (CP) 45
Des Moines Menn Ch (13219) (CP) 45

Donnellson
Zion Menn Ch (2860) (CP) 47

Fort Dodge
Evangelical Menn Ch (13250) (CP) 45

Fruitland
Muscatine Menn Ch (13375) (CP) 46

Iowa City
First Menn Ch of Iowa City (13276) (CP) 46

Kalona
East Union Menn Ch (13243) (CP) 45
Kalona Menn Ch (13318) (CP) 46
Lower Deer Creek Menn Ch (13334) (CP) 46

Manson
Manson Menn Ch (13342) (CP) 46

Mount Pleasant
Pleasant View Menn Ch (13425) (CP) 46

Parnell
West Union Menn Ch (13474) (CP) 47

Pulaski
Pulaski Menn Ch (2650) (CP) 46

Washington
Iglesia Roca de Salvación (10126) (CP) 46
Washington Menn Ch (13458) (CP) 47

Wayland
Bethel Menn Ch (13177) (CP) 45
Eicher Emmanuel Menn Ch (2265) (CP) 45
Sugar Creek Menn Ch (13441) (CP) 47
Wayland Menn Ch (2815) (CP) 47

Wellman
Daytonville Community Ch (13201) (CP) 45
Wellman Menn Ch (13466) (CP) 47

KANSAS

Buhler
Buhler Menn Ch (6165) (WDC) 115

Burrton
Burrton Menn Ch (6170) (WDC) 115

Canton
Spring Valley Menn Ch (18127) (SC) 104

Elbing
Zion Menn Ch (6865) (WDC) 118

Goessel
Alexanderwohl Menn Ch (6005) (WDC) 115
Goessel Menn Ch (6370) (WDC) 116

Greensburg
Greensburg Menn Ch (17939) (SC) 102

Halstead
First Menn Ch (6374) (WDC) 116

Hanston
Hanston Menn Ch (6430) (WDC) 116

Harper
Crystal Springs Menn Ch (17889) (SC) 102
Pleasant Valley Menn Ch (18051) (SC) 103

Haven
Yoder Menn Ch (18192) (SC) 104

Hesston
Hesston Menn Ch (17962) (SC) 102
Whitestone Menn Ch (18184) (SC) 104

Hillsboro
First Menn Ch (6376) (WDC) 116
Trinity Menn Ch (6780) (WDC) 118

Hutchinson
First Menn Ch (6382) (WDC) 117

Inman
Bethel Menn Ch (6095) (WDC) 115
Hoffnungsau Menn Ch (6460) (WDC) 117
Inman Menn Ch (6505) (WDC) 117

Kansas City
Argentine Menn Ch (17798) (SC) 102
Rainbow Menn Ch (18093) (WDC) 118

Kingman
Kingman Menn Ch (6511) (WDC) 117

Lawrence
Peace Menn Ch (23853) (SC, WDC) 103, 118

Liberal
Calvary Menn Ch (6185) (WDC) 115

Manhattan
Manhattan Menn Ch (24174) (SC, WDC) 103, 117

McPherson
First Menn Ch (6391) (WDC) 116

Montezuma
Gospel Fell Ch (27425) (SC, WDC) 102, 116

Moundridge
Eden Menn Ch (6255) (WDC) 116
First Menn Ch of Christian (6330) (WDC) 116
West Zion Menn Ch (6830) (WDC) 118

Newton
Faith Menn Ch (6325) (WDC) 116
First Menn Ch (6403) (WDC) 116
New Creation Fell (6596) (WDC) 118
Shalom Menn Ch (10130) (SC, WDC) 118
Tabor Menn Ch (6765) (WDC) 118

North Newton
Bethel College Menn Ch (6070) (WDC) 115

Pawnee Rock
Bergthal Menn Ch (6045) (WDC) 115

Pretty Prairie
First Menn Ch (6315) (WDC) 116

Protection
Protection Menn Ch (18085) (SC) 103

Ransom
First Menn Ch (6318) (WDC) 116

Salina
Salina Menn Ch (6691) (WDC) 118

South Hutchinson
Faith Menn Ch (24356) (SC) 102
South Hutchinson Menn Ch (18101) (SC) 104

Topeka
Southern Hills Menn Ch (6740) (WDC) 118

Whitewater
Grace Hill Menn Ch (6390) (WDC) 116

Wichita
Hope Menn Ch (6468) (WDC) 117
Lorraine Avenue Menn Ch (6525) (WDC) 117
Menn Ch of the Servant (23317) (SC, WDC) . .103, 117

KENTUCKY

Ages-Brookside
Harlan Menn Fell (23333) (IM) 64

Morgantown
Ridgeview Menn Ch (12740) (IM) 66

Talcum
Talcum Menn Ch (13003) (IM) 66

West Liberty
West Liberty Menn Ch (18457) (VA) 112

LOUISIANA

Buras
Lighthouse Fell Ch (25403) (GS) 57

Des Allemands
Des Allemands Menn Ch (17897) (GS) 57

Metairie
Iglesia Amor Viviente (28258) (GS) 57

MARYLAND

Accident
Glade Menn Ch (10231) (ALL) 35

Baltimore
Ethiopian Evangelical Ch of Baltimore (11108) (LAN) .72
North Baltimore Menn Ch (27920) (ACC) 39
Wilkens Avenue Menn Ch (15081) (LAN) 80

Boonsboro
Mount Zion Menn Ch (14746) (FRK) 55

Ellicott City
First Menn Ch of Columbia (14027) (LAN) 72

Grantsville
Oak Grove Menn Ch (10348) (ALL) 35
Red Run Menn Ch (10397) (ALL) 36

Hagerstown
Hebron Menn Ch (23572) (ACC) 38
North Side Menn Ch (16345) (FRK) 55

Hyattsville
Hyattsville Menn Ch (10223) (ALL) 35

Jessup
Guilford Road Menn Ch (14209) (LAN) 73

Laurel
Capital Christian Fell (13805) (LAN) 70

Marion
Community Menn Ch (14738) (FRK) 54

CONGREGATIONS BY LOCATION

7

Oakland
Gortner Union Ch (22632) (ALL) 35
Ocean City
Ocean City Menn Christian Fell (26476) (ACC) 39
Pinto
Pinto Menn Ch (10363) (ALL) 36
Poolesville
Dawsonville Menn Ch (13847) (LAN) 71
Swanton
Meadow Mountain Menn Ch (10322) (ALL) 35
Walkersville
Faith Community Menn Ch (11309) (FRK) 54
Westover
Holly Grove Menn Ch (16089) (ACC) 38

MASSACHUSETTS
Cambridge
Menn Congregation of Boston (16246) (ACC,
    EDC) 39, 49
Dorchester
Boston Bethel Missionary Ch (11433) (LAN) 70
Malden
Chinese Christian Ch of Malden (10743) (LAN) 71

MICHIGAN
Ann Arbor
Ann Arbor Menn Ch (13508) (CDC, IM) 40, 63
Shalom Community Ch (23242) (CDC) 43
Battle Creek
Pine Grove Menn Ch (12559) (IM) 66
Brutus
Maple River Menn Ch (12682) (IM) 49
Burr Oak
Locust Grove Menn Ch (12666) (IM) 65
Centreville
Wasepi Menn Chapel (13052) (IM) 67
Comins
Comins Menn Ch (2205) (CDC) 41
Concord
Liberty Menn Ch (12641) (IM) 65
Constantine
Florence Ch of the Brethren-Menn (11315) (CDC) . .42
Detroit
Community Christian Fell Ch (10243) (IM) 64
Peace Community Menn Ch (12385) (IM) 66
East Lansing
MSU Menn Fell (12757) (CDC, IM) 65
Engadine
Wildwood Menn Ch (13110) (IM) 67
Escanaba
Soo Hill Community Ch (12971) (IM) 66
Germfask
Germfask Menn Ch (12500) (IM) 64
Grand Marais
Grand Marais Menn Ch (12542) (IM) 64
Greenville
Bethel Menn Ch (12237) (IM) 63
Harbor Springs
Stutsmanville Chapel (12989) (IM) 66
Holland
Centro Cristiano Vida Abundante Holland (20605)
    (IL) 59
Kalkaska
Coldsprings Christian Fell (12344) (IM) 63

Manistique
Cedar Grove Menn Ch (12302) (IM) 63
Menominee
Menominee River Fell (10135) (IM) 65
Midland
Midland Menn Ch (12724) (IM) 65
Naubinway
Naubinway Christian Fell (12807) (IM) 65
Rexton Menn Ch (12906) (IM) 66
Petoskey
Hilltop Menn Fell (12856) (IM) 64
Pigeon
Michigan Avenue Menn Ch (12716) (IM) 65
Pinckney
Good News Community Chapel (12286) (IM) 64
Saginaw
Grace Chapel (12534) (IM) 64
Ninth Street Menn Ch (12815) (IM) 65
Sturgis
Christian Fell Center (28951) (IM) 63
Waldron
Salem Menn Ch (16618) (OH) 90

MINNESOTA
Frazee
Lake Region Menn Ch (15578) (NC) 85
International Falls
Point O' Pines Menn Ch (15610) (NC) 85
Minneapolis
Faith Menn Ch (23127) (CP) 45
Mountain Lake
Bethel Menn Ch (4120) (CP) 45
First Menn Ch (4397) (CP) 46
Ogema
Strawberry Lake Menn Ch (15644) (NC) 85
Rochester
Rochester Menn Ch (4667) (CP) 46
Shoreview
Emmanuel Menn Ch (11125) (CP) 45
St Paul
St Paul Menn Fell (28555) (CP) 47
Vadnais Heights
Hmong Menn Ch of St Paul (10128) (CP) 46

MISSISSIPPI
Gulfport
Gulfhaven Menn Ch (17947) (GS) 57
Jackson
Open Door Menn Ch (22046) (GS) 57
Macon
Choctaw Christian Ch (15891) (GS) 57
Cornerstone Community Ch (16212) (GS) 57
Meridian
Jubilee Menn Ch (24547) (GS) 57
Philadelphia
Nanih Waiya Indian Menn Ch (16352) (GS) 57
Pearl River Menn Ch (21790) (GS) 57
Quitman
Grace Menn Christian Fell (11144) (GS) 57

MISSOURI
Birch Tree
Berea Menn Community Ch (17806) (SC) 102

Garden City
Sycamore Grove Menn Ch (18135) (SC) 104
Leonard
Mount Pisgah Menn Ch (18002) (SC) 103
Palmyra
Pea Ridge Menn Ch (18044) (SC) 103
St Louis
Bethesda Menn Ch (17814) (IL) 59
St Louis Menn Fell (24182) (CDC, IL) 43, 61

MONTANA
Bloomfield
Bethlehem Menn Ch (4145) (NC) 84
Red Top Menn Ch (15628) (NC) 85
Busby
White River Cheyenne Menn Ch (4171) (CP) 47
Colstrip
Ashland Christian Fell (4025) (CP) 45
Dagmar
Coalridge Menn Ch (15529) (NC) 84
Glendive
White Chapel Menn Ch (15594) (CP, NC) 47, 85
Kalispell
Mountain View Menn Ch (10082) (PNW) 94
Lame Deer
Lame Deer Menn Ch (4635) (CP) 46
Wolf Point
Bethel Menn Ch (4130) (CP) 45

NEBRASKA
Beatrice
Beatrice Menn Ch (6030) (WDC) 115
First Menn Ch (6341) (WDC) 116
Beemer
Beemer Menn Ch (13144) (CP) 45
Henderson
Bethesda Menn Ch (4135) (CP) 45
Lincoln
First Menn Ch (13268) (CP) 45
Milford
Bellwood Menn Ch (13151) (CP) 45
Beth-El Menn Ch (13169) (CP) 45
Milford Menn Ch (13367) (CP) 46
Omaha
Northside Christian Family Center (24166) (CP) 46
Shickley
Salem Menn Ch (13433) (CP) 46
Wood River
Wood River Menn Ch (13482) (CP) 47

NEVADA
North Las Vegas
Emmanuel Faith Chapel (10123) (PSW) 96

NEW JERSEY
Alpha
Alpha Menn Ch (23051) (FRC) 51
Camden
Iglesia Evangelical Menonita Manantial de Vida
(29116) (LAN) 74
Carney's Point
Friendship Menn Ch (15008) (LAN) 35
New Song Congregation (11581) (LAN) 77

Dover
Garden Chapel (11544) (FRC) 51
Marlton
Crossroads Christian Community (10631) (LAN) . . .71
Norma
Norma Menn Ch (14860) (LAN) 78
Trenton
Iglesia Menonita Puerta de Sion (22897) (LAN) 74
Nueva Vida en Cristo (11436) (LAN) 78
Vineland
Faro Ardiente (22111) (LAN) 72

NEW MEXICO
Albuquerque
Albuquerque Menn Ch (11311) (RM) 99
Carlsbad
Carlsbad Menn Ch (20818) (RM) 99
Farmington
Light of Life Menn Ch (10656) (RM) 100

NEW YORK
Akron
Clarence Center-Akron Menn Ch (16980) (NY) 82
Alden
Alden Menn Ch (10496) (NY) 82
Bolivar
Kossuth Community Chapel (25395) (LAN) 75
Bronx
Emmanuel Worship Center (10016) (LAN) 72
Evangelical Garifuna (29660) (LAN) 72
Friendship Community Ch (16253) (ACC) 38
Iglesia Evangelica Menonita Eben-Ezer (28589)
(ACC) 38
King of Glory Tabernacle (14043) (LAN) 74
North Bronx Menn Ch (29561) (LAN) 78
Brooklyn
Believers Menn Garifuna Ministries (27599) (LAN) . .70
First Menn Ch (15958) (ACC) 38
Iglesia Christiana Valle de Jesus (25338) (LAN) 74
Iglesia Unida de Avivamiento (22350) (LAN) 74
International Christian Community Ch (11123) (LAN) .74
Menn Evangelical Tabernacle (26849) (LAN) 76
Buffalo
Westside Menn Ch (10068) (NY) 83
Castorland
Pine Grove Menn Ch (11072) (NY) 83
Corning
Community Menn Fell of Corning (23614) (NY) 82
Flushing
Immanuel Community Ch (26468) (ACC) 38
Hammondsport
Pleasant Valley Menn Ch (15057) (NY) 83
Lowville
First Menn Ch of New Bremen (21964) (NY) 82
Lowville Menn Ch (10892) (NY) 83
New York
Manhattan Menn Fell (3602) (ACC) 39
Seventh Avenue Menn Ch (15198) (LAN) 79
Penfield
Rochester Area Menn Fell (21956) (NY) 83
Queens
Ephesians Menn Ch (23762) (ACC) 38
Rochester
Bethsaida Evangelical Ch (11118) (NY) 82

Schoharie
Grace Fell (11170) (NY) 82
Staten Island
Redeeming Grace Fell (24588) (LAN) 78
Watertown
Watertown Menn Ch (21980) (NY) 83
Webster
Jesus Ch (10138) (NY) 82
Wellsville
Independence Gospel Fell Menn (14357) (NY) 82
Yorks Corners Menn Ch (15487) (NY) 83
Williamson
Community of Faith (11479) (NY) 82
Williamsville
Harris Hill Menn Ch (10504) (NY) 82

NORTH CAROLINA
Asheville
Asheville Menn Ch (24281) (VA) 109
Chapel Hill
Chapel Hill Menn Fell (11621) (VA) 109
Durham
Durham Menn Ch (18481) (VA) 110
Greensboro
Greensboro Menn Fell (29744) (VA) 110
Hickory
Hickory Menn Ch (18580) (VA) 110
Mountain View Menn Ch (18713) (VA) 111
Raleigh
Raleigh Menn Ch (28266) (VA) 112
Robbins
Iglesia el Verbo (11571) (LAN) 74
Rocky Mount
Fell of Christ (23473) (VA) 110
Sanford
Iglesia Menonita Bethel Ch (11435) (LAN) 74

NORTH DAKOTA
Alsen
Swiss Menn Ch (4755) (CP) 47
Surrey
Prairie Peace Fell (15545) (NC) 85
Wolford
Lakeview Menn Ch (15586) (NC) 85

OHIO
Archbold
Central Menn Ch (15842) (OH) 88
Iglesia Menonita del Buen Pastor (16022) (OH) 89
Zion Menn Ch (16873) (OH) 91
Aurora
Aurora Menn Ch (15677) (OH) 88
Barberton
Summit Menn Ch (16741) (OH) 91
Bedford Heights
Friendship Menn Ch (16006) (OH) 89
University Euclid Christ New Testament (16774)
(OH) 91
Bellefontaine
Jubilee Menn Ch (11111) (OH) 89
Berlin
Berlin Menn Ch (15727) (OH) 88
Bluffton
First Menn Ch (2347) (CDC) 42

Burton
New Mercies Community Ch (10899) (OH) 90
Canton
First Menn Ch of Canton (15982) (OH) 89
Chesterville
Gilead Menn Ch (16014) (OH) 89
Cincinnati
Cincinnati Menn Fell (23325) (CDC, OH) 88
Springdale Chapel (16717) (OH) 91
Cleveland
Lee Heights Community Ch (16139) (OH) 89
Columbiana
Midway Menn Ch (16261) (OH) 90
Columbus
Agora Christian Fell (11103) (CDC, OH) 40, 88
Columbus Menn Ch (16378) (CDC, OH) 41, 88
Defiance
Primera Iglesia Menonita (15974) (OH) 90
Dover
Dover Christian Fell (10709) (CDC, OH) 41, 89
Elida
Pike Menn Ch (16469) (OH) 90
Salem Menn Ch (16634) (OH) 90
Elyria
Peace Menn Ch (25825) (OH) 90
Fairpoint
Fairpoint Menn Ch (15925) (OH) 89
Hartville
Hartville Menn Ch (16048) (OH) 89
Helena
Primera Iglesia Menonita (24695) (OH) 90
Jackson
Hillside Chapel (16071) (OH) 89
Kalida
Kalida Family Outreach Center (16311) (OH) 89
Kidron
Kidron Menn Ch (16113) (OH) 89
Salem Menn Ch (2680) (CDC) 43
Sonnenberg Menn Ch (18846) (OH) 91
Leetonia
Leetonia Menn Ch (16147) (OH) 89
Lima
Lima Menn Ch (16402) (CDC, OH) 89
Logan
St Johns Menn Chapel (16725) (OH) 91
Louisville
Beech Menn Ch (15701) (OH) 88
Stoner Heights Menn Ch (16733) (OH) 91
Lucasville
Owl Creek Menn Ch (16451) (OH) 90
Millersburg
Martins Creek Menn Ch (16196) (OH) 90
Millersburg Menn Ch (16279) (OH) 90
Moorhead Menn Ch (16295) (OH) 90
Monclova
Emmanuel Menn Ch (10037) (OH) 89
New Carlisle
Huber Menn Ch (16097) (OH) 89
North Canton
Dayspring Christian Fell (27334) (OH) 88
North Lawrence
Pleasant View Menn Ch (16527) (OH) 90
North Lima
North Lima Menn Ch (16337) (OH) 90

Orrville
Chestnut Ridge Menn Ch (18416) (VA) 110
Martins Menn Ch (16204) (OH) 90
Orrville Menn Ch (16444) (OH) 90
Pandora
Grace Menn Ch (2420) (CDC) 42
St John Menn Ch (2670) (CDC) 43
Pedro
Wayside Chapel (16816) (OH) 91
Plain City
Cornerstone Menn Fell (28225) (OH) 88
Sharon Menn Ch (16659) (OH) 91
Rio Grande
Community Christian Fell (16485) (OH) 88
Rittman
Bethel Menn Ch (15768) (OH) 88
Crown Hill Menn Ch (15883) (OH) 88
Smithville
Oak Grove Menn Ch (16428) (CDC, OH) 43, 90
Smithville Menn Ch (16667) (OH) 91
Springfield
Southside Menn Ch (24034) (OH) 91
Stryker
Lockport Menn Ch (16154) (OH) 89
Pine Grove Menn Ch (16477) (OH) 90
Sugarcreek
First Menn Ch (2324) (CDC) 42
Toledo
Toledo Menn Ch (15685) (OH) 91
Trenton
Trenton Menn Ch (2779) (CDC) 43
Wadsworth
First Menn Ch (2333) (CDC) 42
Walnut Creek
Walnut Creek Menn Ch (16808) (OH) 91
Wauseon
Inlet Menn Ch (16105) (OH) 89
North Clinton Menn Ch (16329) (OH) 90
Tedrow Menn Ch (16766) (OH) 91
West Clinton Menn Ch (16824) (OH) 91
West Lafayette
Lafayette Christian Fell (28191) (OH) 89
West Liberty
Bethel Menn Ch (15750) (OH) 88
Oak Grove Menn Ch (16410) (OH) 90
South Union Menn Ch (16683) (OH) 91
Winesburg
Longenecker Menn Ch (16162) (OH) 89
Wooster
Salem Menn Ch (16626) (OH) 91
Wooster Menn Ch (16840) (OH) 91
Youngstown
Berean Fell Ch (15719) (OH) 88

OKLAHOMA
Clinton
First Menn Ch (6362) (WDC) 116
Koinonia Menn Ch (6575) (WDC) 117
Cordell
Herold Menn Ch (6445) (WDC) 117
Deer Creek
Deer Creek Menn Ch (6230) (WDC) 115
Enid
Grace Menn Ch (6410) (WDC) 116

Foss
Bethel Menn Ch (6085) (WDC) 115
Ft Cobb
Greenfield Menn Ch (6425) (WDC) 116
Hydro
Bethel Menn Ch (6090) (WDC) 115
Pleasant View Menn Ch (18069) (SC) 103
Inola
Eden Menn Ch (6250) (WDC) 116
Oklahoma City
Joy Menn Ch (6642) (WDC) 117
Seiling
Menn Indian Ch (6558) (WDC) 117
Turpin
Turpin Menn Ch (6785) (WDC) 118

OREGON
Adair Village
Prince of Peace Community Ch (17509) (PNW) 94
Albany
Albany Menn Ch (17434) (PNW) 93
Plainview Menn Ch (17590) (PNW) 94
Aurora
Calvary Menn Ch (5180) (PNW) 93
Iglesia Cristiana Roca de Salvación (17493) (PNW) .93
Canby
Pacific Covenant Menn Ch (10142) (PNW) 94
Corvallis
Corvallis Menn Fell (10141) (PNW) 93
Eugene
Eugene Menn Ch (17517) (PNW) 93
Hubbard
Zion Menn Ch (17640) (PNW) 94
Lebanon
Lebanon Menn Ch (17574) (PNW) 93
Logsden
Logsden Neighborhood Ch (17582) (PNW) 93
McMinnville
Centro Cristiano Pentecostes de McMinnville (11620)
(PNW) 93
First Menn Ch (10278) (PNW) 93
Portland
Anawim Christian Community (11602) (PNW) 93
Peace Menn Ch (24380) (PNW) 94
Portland Menn Ch (17608) (PNW) 94
Salem
Jerusalem Iglesia (28315) (PNW) 93
Salem Menn Ch (17616) (PNW) 94
Western Menn Ch (17632) (PNW) 94
Sweet Home
River of Life Fell (10270) (PNW) 94
Tualatin
Ministerios Restauración (11073) (PNW) 94
Woodburn
Comunidad Cristiana de Vida Nueva (11533) (PNW) . .93
Iglesia Menonita Pentecostes (23556) (PNW) 93

PENNSYLVANIA
Adamstown
Gehman Menn Ch (14100) (LAN) 73
Akron
Akron Menn Ch (15651) (ACC) 38
Metzler Menn Ch (14613) (LAN) 76
Pilgrims Menn Ch (24513) (LAN) 78

**CONGREGATIONS
BY LOCATION**

7

Allentown
First Menn Ch (3338) (EDC) 49
Vietnamese Gospel Menn Ch (11128) (FRC) 53
Altoona
Canan Station Menn Ch (10173) (ALL) 35
Cornerstone Fell of Mill Run (10330) (ALL) 35
Ambler
Ambler Menn Ch (11353) (FRC) 51
Atglen
Maple Grove Menn Ch of Atglen (16188) (ACC) . . .39
Athens
New Life Menn Ch (10013) (FRC) 52
Bainbridge
Goods Menn Ch (14142) (LAN) 73
Bally
Bally Menn Ch (11361) (FRC) 51
Belleville
Maple Grove Menn Ch (21931) (ALL) 35
Rockville Menn Ch (10405) (ALL) 36
Bernville
New Life Christian Fell (29249) (ACC) 39
Bethel
Meckville Menn Ch (14597) (LAN) 76
Schubert Menn Ch (15180) (LAN) 79
Bethlehem
Bethlehem Community Fell (29124) (LAN) 70
Steel City Menn Ch (11759) (FRC) 53
Bird In Hand
Millwood Menn Ch (14654) (LAN) 77
Stumptown Menn Ch (15297) (LAN) 79
Birdsboro
Zion Menn Ch—Birdsboro (16865) (ACC) 39
Blooming Glen
Blooming Glen Menn Ch (11403) (FRC) 51
Boyertown
Ark Bible Chapel (15669) (ACC) 38
Boyertown Menn Ch (11411) (FRC) 51
Bristol
New Beginnings Community Ch (11429) (FRC) 52
Camp Hill
Lao Menn Fell/Slate Hill (11560) (LAN) 75
Slate Hill Menn Ch (15206) (LAN) 79
Canadensis
Spruce Lake Fell (26203) (FRC) 53
Canton
Canton Menn Ch (25098) (LAN) 70
Chambersburg
Cedar Street Menn Ch (19000) (FRK) 54
Chambersburg Menn Ch (19018) (FRK) 54
Marion Menn Ch (19034) (FRK) 54
Pleasant View Menn Ch (19042) (FRK) 55
Pond Bank Menn Ch (19059) (FRK) 55
Rock Hill Menn Ch (19067) (FRK) 55
Chester
Way Thru Christ Ministry (10073) (LAN) 80
Claysburg
Roaring Spring Menn Ch (3665) (EDC) 49
Coatesville
Coatesville Menn Ch (13755) (LAN) 71
Newlinville Menn Ch (14845) (LAN) 77
Sandy Hill Menn Ch (16642) (ACC) 39
Collegeville
Providence Menn Ch (11668) (FRC) 52

Columbia
Chestnut Hill Menn Ch (13714) (LAN) 71
Columbia Menn Ch (13771) (LAN) 71
Conestoga
Life Menn Fell (11294) (LAN) 75
River Corner Menn Ch (15131) (LAN) 78
Conneaut Lake
Sunnyside Menn Ch (16758) (OH) 91
Corry
Beaverdam Menn Ch (22004) (OH) 88
Davidsville
Carpenter Park Menn Ch (10181) (ALL) 35
Kaufman Menn Ch (10256) (ALL) 35
Denver
Red Run Menn Ch (15115) (LAN) 78
Downingtown
Downing Hills Christian Fell (13896) (LAN) 72
Doylestown
Doylestown Menn Ch (11445) (FRC) 51
East Earl
Bowmansville Menn Ch (13623) (LAN) 70
Churchtown Menn Ch (13748) (LAN) 71
Weaverland Menn Ch (15420) (LAN) 80
East Greenville
Shalom Christian Fell (10018) (FRC) 52
East Petersburg
East Petersburg Menn Ch (13946) (LAN) 72
Manheim Menn Ch (14530) (LAN) 76
Easton
River of God Fell (11452) (FRC) 52
Elizabethtown
Bossler Menn Ch (13615) (LAN) 70
Cedar Hill Community Ch (13706) (LAN) 70
Elizabethtown Menn Ch (13953) (LAN) 72
Risser Menn Ch (15123) (LAN) 78
Ephrata
Ephrata Menn Ch (13961) (LAN) 72
Hinkletown Menn Ch (14316) (LAN) 74
Indiantown Menn Ch (14365) (LAN) 74
Martindale Menn Ch (14548) (LAN) 76
New Life Fell (27052) (LAN) 77
Fairfield
Fairfield Menn Ch (3300) (EDC) 49
Fleetwood
Hope Community Ch (10039) (ACC) 38
Folcraft
Delaware County Fell (11562) (LAN) 71
Frazer
Frazer Menn Ch (14050) (LAN) 72
Frederick
Frederick Menn Ch (11528) (FRC) 51
Gap
Old Road Menn Ch (14928) (LAN) 78
Gettysburg
Bethel Menn Ch (15743) (ACC) 38
Goodville
Goodville Menn Ch (14159) (LAN) 73
Gordonville
Cambridge Menn Ch (13680) (LAN) 70
Ridgeview Menn Ch (16576) (ACC) 39
Greencastle
Cedar Grove Menn Ch (15834) (ACC) 38
Salem Ridge Menn Ch (19075) (FRK) 55

Halifax
Halifax Community Fell (27060) (LAN) 73
Harleysville
Salford Menn Ch (11718) (FRC) 52
Harrisburg
Herr Street Menn Ch (14266) (LAN) 73
Jesu Cristo Es la Respuesta (10342) (LAN) 74
Locust Lane Menn Chapel (14498) (LAN) 75
New Hope Community Ch (11561) (LAN) 77
Peace Chapel (25353) (LAN) 78
Hatfield
Plains Menn Ch (11643) (FRC) 52
Havertown
Kapatiran Christian Ch (11102) (LAN) 74
Hershey
Stauffer Menn Ch (15230) (LAN) 79
Holland
Ch of the Good Samaritans (3200) (EDC) 49
Hollsopple
Blough Menn Ch (10157) (ALL) 35
Thomas Menn Ch (10454) (ALL) 36
Jersey Shore
Emmanuel Community Ch (24844) (LAN) 72
Johnstown
Crossroads Community Ch (10488) (ALL) 35
First Menn Ch (10215) (ALL) 35
Stahl Menn Ch (10447) (ALL) 36
Kennett Square
Kennett Square Menn Ch (14381) (LAN) 74
Kinzers
Hershey Menn Ch (14282) (LAN) 73
Kinzer Menn Ch (14399) (LAN) 75
Meadville Menn Ch (14571) (LAN) 76
Kirkwood
Mt Vernon Menn Ch (14720) (LAN) 77
Kulpsville
Towamencin Menn Ch (11783) (FRC) 53
Lancaster
Bethel Menn Ch of Lancaster (3100) (EDC) 49
Blossom Hill Menn Ch (14795) (LAN) 70
Community Menn Ch of Lancaster (27441) (ACC) . .38
Crossroads Menn (15172) (LAN) 71
East Chestnut Street Menn Ch (13912) (LAN) 72
El Buen Pastor (14167) (LAN) 72
First Deaf Menn Ch (14019) (LAN) 72
Habecker Menn Ch (14217) (LAN) 73
Iglesia Menonita Roca de Salvación (11301) (LAN) . .74
James Street Menn Ch (15396) (LAN) 74
Landis Valley Menn Ch (14431) (LAN) 75
Laurel Street Menn Ch (14449) (LAN) 75
Lyndon Menn Ch (14514) (LAN) 76
Mellinger Menn Ch (14605) (LAN) 76
Neffsville Menn Ch (16360) (ACC) 39
New Danville Menn Ch (14837) (LAN) 77
Rohrerstown Menn Ch (15156) (LAN) 78
Rossmere Menn Ch (15164) (LAN) 78
Sunnyside Menn Ch (15305) (LAN) 79
Tinsae Kristos Evangelical Ch (11566) (LAN) 79
West End Menn Fell (11174) (LAN) 80
Witmer Heights Menn Ch (11120) (LAN) 80
Landisville
Landisville Menn Ch (14423) (LAN) 75
Langhorne
MillCreek Community Ch (29348) (FRC) 52

Lansdale
Covenant Community Fell (29306) (FRC) 51
Grace Menn Ch (3415) (EDC) 49
Lebanon
Freedom in Christ Fell (11563) (LAN) 73
Gingrichs Menn Ch (14118) (LAN) 73
Krall Menn Ch (14407) (LAN) 75
Lebanon Christian Fell (24562) (LAN) 75
Luz de Salvación (26716) (LAN) 75
Leola
Forest Hills Menn Ch (16287) (ACC) 38
Groffdale Menn Ch (14191) (LAN) 73
Millport Menn Ch (14621) (LAN) 76
Lewisburg
Buffalo Menn Ch (13631) (LAN) 70
Line Lexington
Line Lexington Menn Ch (11593) (FRC) 51
Listie
New Life Menn Ch (10740) (ALL) 35
Lititz
Crossroads Community Fell (14308) (LAN) 71
Erb Menn Ch (13979) (LAN) 72
Hammer Creek Menn Ch (14233) (LAN) 73
Lititz Menn Ch (14480) (LAN) 75
Manheim
Derry Menn Ch (13862) (LAN) 71
Erisman Menn Ch (13987) (LAN) 72
Grace Community Fell (14084) (LAN) 73
Hernley Menn Ch (14290) (LAN) 73
Kauffman Menn Ch (14373) (LAN) 74
Meserete Wongel Ethiopian Evangelical Ch (11565)
(LAN) 76
Marietta
Marietta Community Chapel (24224) (LAN) 76
Martinsburg
Martinsburg Menn Ch (10298) (ALL) 35
Masontown
Masontown Menn Ch (10306) (ALL) 35
Mercersburg
Mercersburg Menn Ch (19109) (FRK) 55
Middleburg
Boyer Menn Ch (10165) (ALL) 35
Middletown
Fountain of Life Ch (25320) (LAN) 72
Mifflintown
Cornerstone Community Ch (3543) (EDC) 49
Lost Creek Menn Ch (14506) (LAN) 75
Millersville
Millersville Menn Ch (14639) (LAN) 77
University Christian Fell (10188) (LAN) 79
Milton
Community Menn Fell (13540) (LAN) 71
Shalom Menn Ch (10076) (LAN) 79
Monroeton
West Franklin Menn Ch (15404) (LAN) 80
Morgantown
Conestoga Menn Ch (15875) (ACC) 38
Morris
Menn Bible Fell (11619) (FRC) 51
Morris Run
Calvary Menn Fell (14670) (LAN) 70
Mount Joy
Mount Joy Menn Ch (14688) (LAN) 77

CONGREGATIONS BY LOCATION

7

Mount Union
Otelia Menn Ch (10355) (ALL) 36
Mountain Top
Cornerstone Christian Fell (27193) (LAN) 71
Mountville
Mountville Menn Ch (14696) (LAN) 77
Mt Pleasant Mills
Susquehanna Menn Ch (15313) (LAN) 79
Nanticoke
Nanticoke Christian Fell (25809) (LAN) 77
Nazareth
Maranatha Family Christian Fell (10119) (LAN) 76
New Castle
Maple Grove Menn Ch (16170) (OH) 90
New Holland
Lichty Menn Ch (14464) (LAN) 75
New Holland Menn Ch (14811) (LAN) 77
New Holland Spanish Menn (14704) (LAN) 77
Village Chapel Menn Ch (22491) (LAN) 79
Welsh Mountain Menn Ch (22061) (LAN) 80
New Providence
New Providence Menn Ch (14829) (LAN) 77
Newville
Diller Menn Ch (13888) (LAN) 71
Norristown
Methacton Menn Ch (11601) (FRC) 52
Norristown New Life Menn Ch (10125) (FRC) 52
Oley
Oley Valley Menn Ch (16436) (ACC) 39
Parkesburg
Parkesburg Menn Ch (14985) (LAN) 78
Peach Bottom
Living Stones Fell (10155) (LAN) 75
Mechanic Grove Menn Ch (14589) (LAN) 76
Pen Argyl
Great Shepherd Christian Fell (13557) (LAN) 73
Pennsburg
Finland Menn Ch (11486) (FRC) 51
Perkasie
Deep Run Menn Ch East (11437) (FRC) 51
Deep Run West Menn Ch (3225) (EDC) 49
Perkasie Menn Ch (11627) (FRC) 52
Perkiomenville
Perkiomenville Menn Ch (11635) (FRC) 52
Philadelphia
Abundant Life Chinese Menn Ch (10102) (LAN) . . .69
Arca de Salvación (22459) (LAN) 70
Christian Life Menn Fell (10122) (LAN) 71
Diamond Street Menn Ch (13870) (LAN) 71
Iglesia Menonita Comunidad de Amor (3212) (EDC) . .49
Indonesian Fell (11568) (LAN) 74
Love Truth Chinese Menn Ch (27995) (LAN) 75
New Mercies Menn Ch (10293) (LAN) 77
Oxford Circle Menn Ch (14951) (LAN) 78
Philadelphia Cambodian Menn Ch (10075) (LAN) . .78
Vietnamese Menn Ch (27045) (LAN) 79
West Philadelphia Menn Fell (27276) (FRC) 53
Phoenixville
Hope Community Fell of Phoenixville (11579)
(ACC) 38
Pine Grove
Roedersville Menn Ch (15149) (LAN) 78
Pittsburgh
Pittsburgh Menn Ch (10371) (ALL) 36

Port Allegany
Birch Grove Menn Ch (15792) (ACC) 38
Pottsville
Palo Alto Menn Ch (14969) (LAN) 78
Quakertown
Rocky Ridge Menn Ch (11684) (FRC) 52
Salem Menn Ch (11700) (FRC) 52
Swamp Menn Ch (11767) (FRC) 53
West Swamp Menn Ch (3825) (EDC) 49
Reading
Hampden Menn Ch (15354) (LAN) 73
Hopewell Menn—Reading (25999) (ACC) 38
La Luz del Mundo (10071) (LAN) 75
Luz Verdadera (15107) (LAN) 75
New Revival Menn Ch (11570) (LAN) 77
Shiloh Menn Ch (10765) (LAN) 79
South 7th Street Menn Ch (15222) (LAN) 79
Reedsville
Barrville Menn Ch (10140) (ALL) 35
Reinholds
Emmanuel Menn Ch (3285) (EDC) 49
Richfield
Lauver Menn Ch (14456) (LAN) 75
Ridley Park
Ch of the Overcomer (11590) (LAN) 71
Schwenksville
Hersteins Menn Ch (11569) (FRC) 51
New Eden Fell (3260) (EDC) 49
Spring Mount Menn Ch (11742) (FRC) 52
Scottdale
Scottdale Menn Ch (10413) (ALL) 36
Skippack
Wellspring Ch of Skippack (11726) (FRC) 53
Souderton
Iglesia Menonita Ebenezer (10093) (EDC) 49
Souderton Menn Ch (11734) (FRC) 52
Zion Menn Ch (3880) (EDC) 49
Spartansburg
Valley View Menn Ch (16782) (OH) 91
Spring City
Vincent Menn Ch (11809) (FRC) 53
Springs
Springs Menn Ch (10439) (ALL) 36
State College
University Menn Ch (10470) (ALL) 36
Steelton
Steelton Menn Ch (15248) (LAN) 79
Stevens
Blainsport Menn Ch (13607) (LAN) 70
Strasburg
Strasburg Menn Ch (15271) (LAN) 79
Susquehanna
Lakeview Menn Ch (11577) (FRC) 51
Talmage
Carpenter Community Ch (13698) (LAN) 70
Telford
Franconia Menn Ch (11502) (FRC) 51
Rockhill Menn Ch (11692) (FRC) 52
Temple
Alsace Christian Fell (13490) (LAN) 69
Terre Hill
Cedar Lane Chapel (11580) (LAN) 70
Thompsontown
Delaware Menn Ch (13854) (LAN) 71

Tire Hill
Living Way Fell (11434) (ALL) 35
Trout Run
Mountain View Fell (29975) (LAN) 77
Upper Darby
Ethiopian Evangelical Ch of Philadelphia (10194)
(LAN) 72
Warfordsburg
Bethel Community Ch (18994) (FRK) 54
Black Oak Menn Ch (15800) (ACC) 38
Washington Boro
Masonville Menn Ch (14562) (LAN) 76
Wernersville
Green Terrace Menn Ch (14183) (LAN) 73
Whitehall
Whitehall Menn Ch (10114) (FRC) 53
Williamsport
Agape Fell (15016) (LAN) 69
Willow Hill
Shady Pine Menn Ch (19083) (FRK) 55
Willow Street
Byerland Menn Ch (13656) (LAN) 70
Willow Street Menn Ch (15461) (LAN) 80
Wyncote
Salam Menn Fell (11099) (LAN) 78
York
Stony Brook Menn Ch (15255) (LAN) 79
Zionsville
Upper Milford Menn Ch (3800) (EDC) 49

SOUTH DAKOTA
Avon
Friedensberg Bible Ch (4350) (CP) 46
Bridgewater
Neu Hutterthal Menn Ch (4610) (CP) 46
Doland
Emmanuel Menn Ch (4275) (CP) 45
Freeman
Bethany Menn Ch (4055) (CP) 45
Hutterthal Menn Ch (4490) (CP) 46
Salem Menn Ch (4675) (CP) 46
Salem-Zion Menn Ch (4690) (CP) 47
Sioux Falls
Good Shepherd Community Ch (4375) (CP) 46
Sermon on the Mount Menn Ch (24018) (CP) 47

TENNESSEE
Goodletsville
Harmony Christian Fell (28035) (IM) 64
Knoxville
Concord Menn Ch (18424) (VA) 110
Knoxville Menn Ch (18622) (VA) 111

TEXAS
Alamo
Casa de Oración (26971) (SC) 102
Austin
Austin Menn Ch (28761) (SC, WDC) 102, 115
Brownsville
Iglesia Menonita del Cordero (17830) (SC) 103
Iglesia Menonita Rey de Gloria (27111) (SC) 103
Corpus Christi
Prince of Peace Menn Ch (18077) (SC) 103

Dallas
Comunidad de Esperanza (6240) (SC, WDC) . .102, 115
Iglesia Menonita Luz del Evangelio (6512)
(SC, WDC) 103, 117
Iglesia Menonita Monte Horeb (11273) (SC, WDC) . .103
Peace Menn Ch (17921) (SC, WDC) 103, 118
Ferris
Iglesia Menonita Sembradores de Buenas Nuevas
(15304) (SC, WDC) 103, 117
Garland
Iglesia Menonita Casa de Dios (15303) (SC,
WDC) 102, 117
Houston
Houston Menn Ch (23184) (SC, WDC) 102, 117
Mathis
Calvary Menn Ch (17863) (SC) 102
Tabernaculo de Fe (28316) (SC) 104
Pasadena
Iglesia Menonita Casa del Alfarero (15302) (SC,
WDC) 102, 117
Perryton
Perryton Menn Ch (20958) (RM) 100
Premont
United Menn Ch (18168) (SC) 104
San Antonio
Iglesia Menonita Comunidad de Vida (27410)
(SC, WDC) 103, 117
San Antonio Menn Ch (25239) (SC, WDC) . . .103, 118
San Benito
New Life Christian Center (29546) (SC) 103
San Juan
Iglesia Menonita Buenas Nuevas (28001) (SC) . . .102
Waco
Hope Fell (10012) (SC, WDC) 102, 117

VERMONT
Bridgewater Corners
Bethany Menn Ch (11387) (FRC) 51
Taftsville
Taftsville Chapel Menn Fell (11775) (FRC) 53

VIRGINIA
Bergton
Mathias Menn Ch (18689) (VA) 111
Bridgewater
New Beginnings Ch (27517) (VA) 111
Broadway
Crossroads Menn Ch (18465) (VA) 110
Trissels Menn Ch (18895) (VA) 112
Zion Menn Ch (18978) (VA) 113
Burke
Iglesia Menonita Hispana Vida Nueva (11572) (LAN) .74
Charlottesville
Charlottesville Menn Ch (18408) (VA) 110
Chesapeake
Calvary Community Ch Chesapeake (27411) (VA) .109
Mount Pleasant Menn Ch (18747) (VA) 111
Christiansburg
Christiansburg Menn Fell (25296) (VA) 110
Fairfax
Northern Virginia Menn Ch (23457) (VA) 111
Falls Church
Buenas Nuevas (10732) (LAN) 70
Vietnamese Christian Fell (10104) (VA) 112

Fulks Run
Hebron Menn Ch (18572) (VA) 110
Grottoes
Mount Vernon Menn Ch (18754) (VA) 111
Hampton
Calvary Community Ch (27409) (VA) 109
Harrisonburg
Community Menn Ch (22178) (VA) 110
Family of Hope (29900) (VA) 110
Gospel Hill Menn Ch (18549) (VA) 110
Harrisonburg Menn Ch (18564) (VA) 110
Immanuel Menn Ch (10144) (VA) 111
Lindale Menn Ch (18655) (VA) 111
Mount Clinton Menn Ch (18721) (VA) 111
Park View Menn Ch (18788) (VA) 111
Ridgeway Menn Ch (18812) (VA) 112
Shalom Menn Congregation (29009) (VA) 112
Valley View Menn Ch (18911) (VA) 112
Weavers Menn Ch (18937) (VA) 112
Linville
Beldor Menn Ch (18341) (VA) 109
Grace Menn Fell (11158) (VA) 110
Woodland Menn Ch (18960) (VA) 113
Luray
Big Spring Menn Ch (18374) (VA) 109
Lyndhurst
Lynside Menn Ch (18671) (VA) 111
Mountain View Menn Ch (18705) (VA) 111
Newport News
Huntington Menn Ch (18614) (VA) 111
Providence Menn Ch (16550) (VA) 112
Warwick River Menn Ch (18929) (VA) 112
Norfolk
Word of Life Menn Ch (18770) (VA) 113
Powhatan
Powhatan Menn Ch (18804) (VA) 111
Richmond
First Menn Ch of Richmond (18523) (VA) 110
Schuyler
Rehoboth Menn Ch (11163) (VA) 112
Singers Glen
Zion Hill Menn Ch (18986) (VA) 113
Staunton
Staunton Menn Ch (18861) (VA) 112
Stephens City
Stephens City Menn Ch (18879) (VA) 112
Stuarts Draft
Greenmonte Menn Ch (18556) (VA) 110
Stuarts Draft Menn Ch (18887) (VA) 112
Virginia Beach
Landstown Community Ch (24349) (VA) 111
Waynesboro
Springdale Menn Ch (18853) (VA) 112
Waynesboro Menn Ch (24760) (VA) 112
Williamsburg
Williamsburg Menn Ch (23135) (VA) 112

WASHINGTON
Bellevue
Evergreen Menn Ch (10145) (PNW) 93
Moses Lake
Iglesia Pentecostes Maranatha (17520) (PNW) 93
Newport
Spring Valley Menn Ch (5730) (PNW) 94

Ritzville
Menno Menn Ch (5550) (PNW) 93
Seattle
Seattle Menn Ch (28381) (PNW) 94
Spokane
Shalom Ch (5723) (PNW) 94
Warden
Cristo Tu Unica Esperanza (17521) (PNW) 93
Warden Menn Ch (5810) (PNW) 94

WEST VIRGINIA
Belington
Lambert Menn Ch (18630) (VA) 111
Fort Seybert
Pleasant Grove Menn Ch (18796) (VA) 111
Harman
Riverside Menn Ch (18820) (VA) 112
Morgantown
Morgantown Ch of the Brethren (27300) (ALL) 35
Philippi
Philippi Menn Ch (26500) (ALL) 36
Wardensville
Crest Hill Community Ch (18432) (VA) 110

WISCONSIN
Exeland
Exeland Menn Ch (15537) (NC) 84
Glen Flora
South Lawrence Menn Ch (15636) (NC) 85
Madison
Madison Menn Ch (10078) (CDC, IL) 42, 61
Stone Lake
Sand Lake Menn Chapel (24620) (NC) 85
Waukesha
Maple Avenue Menn Ch (23697) (CDC, IL) 42, 61

Canada

ONTARIO
Sleeman
Morson Community Bible Fell (15495) (NC) 85

Mexico

TAMAULIPAS
Cd Reynosa
Iglesia Ebenezer (27600) (SC) 102
Cd Valle Hermoso
Primera Iglesia Anabautista de Valle Hermoso
(27603) (SC) 103
H Matamoros
Iglesia Evangelica Menonita Gethsemani (27602)
(SC) 102
Iglesia Menonita Rios de Agua Viva (10681) (SC) . .103
Matamoros
Nueva Jerusalem (27605) (SC) 103
Reynosa
Iglesia Evangelica Galilea (27604) (SC) 102

VERACRUZ
Cd Boca del Rio
Centro Cristiano Menonita Jerusalem (27601) (SC) . .102

Index

INDEX

INDEX

INDEX

Believers Church
Bible Commentary

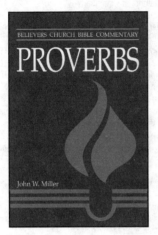

Available November 2004

Proverbs
John W. Miller

The uniqueness of this commentary is its detailed, first-time uncovering of evidence that there were two editions of Proverbs, the first in the time of Solomon and the second created by "the men of Hezekiah" in support of King Hezekiah's historic religious reforms. Up to this time the puzzling features of the book's design, purpose, and message are clarified in this light and the book's relevance for its time and ours greatly enhanced.

"Here is solid scholarship with certain unpopular twists and interpretations. In place of a pedantic verse by verse approach, this thematic treatment of Proverbs provides a surprisingly contemporary manual on some critical issues of Christian discipleship. Miller offers very helpful pastoral insights for the 21st-century preacher."—*James M. Lapp, Franconia Mennonite Conference*

Paper. 400 pages. 0-8361-9292-3: $24.99; in Canada $34.99

These commentaries, informed by recent scholarship, are written for lay leaders, teachers, pastors, college and seminary students, and all those searching the Bible for truth and life.

Available now: Genesis; Exodus; Judges; Ruth, Jonah, Esther; Jeremiah; Ezekiel; Daniel; Hosea, Amos; Matthew; Mark; Acts; Romans; 2 Corinthians; Ephesians; Colossians, Philemon; 1-2 Thessalonians; 1-2 Peter, Jude; and Revelation.

1 800 245-7894
www.heraldpress.com

Herald Press

Mennonite Directory Advertisers

Quickfind

PAGE	NAME AND ADDRESS	TELEPHONE	FAX	E-MAIL AND WEBSITE
120	African-American Mennonite Association (AAMA) 2311 Tower Place, Hampton VA 23666	757-262-0128	757-825-8771	aama_org@yahoo.com www.ammaorg.org
34	Allegheny Mennonite Conference 111 E Main St, PO Box 12, Somerset PA 15501-0012	814-443-2007	814-445-3418	officeamc@cs.com
16	Archives of Mennonite Church USA —see Historical Committee			
122	Associated Mennonite Biblical Seminary 3003 Benham Ave, Elkhart IN 46517-1999	574-295-3726	574-295-0092	rreschly@ambs.edu www.ambs.edu
37	Atlantic Coast Mennonite Conference 115 E Main, New Holland PA 17557	800-238-0126 717-355-0550		atlanticcoast@frontiernet.net www.atlanticcoastconference.org
126	Bethel College 300 East 27th St, North Newton KS 67117	316-283-2500	316-284-5286	webmaster@bethelks.edu www.bethelks.edu
126	Bluffton University 1 University Dr, Bluffton OH 45817-1196	800-488-3257 419-358-3000	419-358-3323	webmaster@bluffton.edu www.bluffton.edu
206	Brethren in Christ General Conference (North America) 431 Grantham Rd, PO Box A, Grantham PA 17027	717-697-2634	717-691-7714	bic@messiah.edu www.bic-church.org
205	*Canadian Mennonite* 490 Dutton Dr, Unit C5, Waterloo ON N2L 6H7	519-884-3810	519-884-3331	editor@canadianmennonite.org www.canadianmennonite.org
40	Central District Conference 1015 Division St, Goshen IN 46528-2000	800-662-2664 574-534-1485	574-534-8654	cdcoffice@hoosierlink.net www.centraldistrict.mennonite.net
44	Central Plains Mennonite Conference 121 E. Third St, PO Box 101, Freeman SD 57029	605-925-4463	605-925-7293	cpmcsd@gwtc.net
206	Church of the Brethren 1451 Dundee Ave, Elgin IL 60120	800-323-8039 847-742-5100	847-742-6103	generalboard@brethren.org www.brethren.org/genbd
131	Christian Peacemaker Teams PO Box 6508, Chicago IL 60680-6508	773-277-0253	773-277-0291	peacemakers@cpt.org www.cpt.org
207	Conservative Mennonite Conference 9910 Rosedale Milford Center Rd, Irwin OH 43029	740-857-1234	740-857-1605	office@cmcrosedale.org www.cmcrosedale.org

PAGE	NAME AND ADDRESS	TELEPHONE	FAX	E-MAIL AND WEBSITE
48	Eastern District Conference 711 Route 113, Souderton PA 18964	215-723-5513	215-723-1211	info@easterndistrict.org www.easterndistrict.org
136	Eastern Mennonite Missions 53 West Brandt Blvd, PO Box 458, Salunga PA 17538-0458	717-898-2251	717-898-8092	info@emm.org www.emm.org
136	Eastern Mennonite Seminary 1200 Park Rd, Harrisonburg VA 22802	540-432-4260	540-432-4444	info@emu.edu www.emu.edu
137	Eastern Mennonite University 1200 Park Rd, Harrisonburg VA 22802	540-432-4000	540-432-4444	info@emu.edu www.emu.edu
50	Franconia Conference of the Mennonite Church 771 Route 113, Souderton PA 18964	215-723-5513	215-723-1211	info@fmc-online.org www.fmc-online.org
54	Franklin Mennonite Conference 4856 Molly Pitcher Hwy S, Chambersburg PA 17201	717-375-4544	717-375-2136	frmc@earthlink.net
141	Goshen College 1700 S Main St, Goshen IN 46526	800-348-7422 574-535-7000	574-535-7660	info@goshen.edu www.goshen.edu
56	Gulf States Mennonite Conference PO Box 526, Des Allemands LA 70030	985-758-7075		secretarygsmc@aol.com
142	Hesston College 325 S College, PO Box 3000, Hesston KS 67062-2093	866-437-7866 620-327-4221	620-327-8300	admissions@hesston.edu www.hesston.edu
16	Historical Committee and Archives Goshen: 1700 S Main St, Goshen IN 46526-4794 North Newton: 300 East 27th St, North Newton KS 67117-0531	574-535-7477 316-284-5360	574-535-7756	archives@goshen.edu www.goshen.edu/mcarchives mla@bethelks.edu www.bethelks.edu/services/mla
147	Iglesia Hispana Menonita 1208 "L" St, Box 111, Reedley CA 93654	(iglesia) 559-638-7723 (casa) 559-637-9787	559-637-0588	jmontesimh@juno.com
58	Illinois Mennonite Conference 214 S Simpson St, PO Box 3, Tremont IL 61568	309-925-2111 309-925-2111	309-925-5612	info@illinois.mennonite.net www.illinois.mennonite.net
62	Indiana-Michigan Mennonite Conference 212 S Main St, Goshen IN 46526	800-288-8486 574-534-4006	574-533-5676	imoffice@im.mennonite.net www.im.mennonite.net
68	Lancaster Mennonite Conference 2160 Lincoln Hwy E #5, Lancaster PA 17602	800-216-7249 717-293-5246	717-431-1987	lmccenter@lanmenconf.org www.lanmenconf.org
148	Lao Mennonite Ministries 71 Lakeshore Dr, St Catharines ON L2N 2T3 Canada	905-646-3651	905-646-3651	kuayingt@mennomission.net
208	Mennonite Brethren Churches, U.S. Conference 315 S Lincoln St, PO Box 220, Hillsboro KS 67063-0220	620-947-3151	620-947-3266 www.usmb.org	offices@usmb.org
158	Mennonite Central Committee 21 S 12th St, PO Box 500, Akron PA 17501-0500 U.S.—21 S 12th St, PO Box 500, Akron PA 17501-0500	888-563-4676 717-859-1151 717-859-3889	 717-859-2171 717-859-3875	 mailbox@mcc.org, www.mcc.org mailbox@mcc.org, www.mcc.org
205	Mennonite Church Canada 600 Shaftesbury Blvd, Winnipeg MB R3P 0M4, Canada	866-888-6785 204-888-6781	204-831-5675	office@mennonitechurch.ca www.mennonitechurch.ca

PAGE	NAME AND ADDRESS	TELEPHONE	FAX	E-MAIL AND WEBSITE
15	Mennonite Church USA Executive Leadership	866-866-2872		www.mennoniteusa.org
	Great Lakes: 500 S Main St, PO Box 1245, Elkhart IN 46515-1245	574-294-7523	574-293-1892	elkhart@mennoniteusa.org
	Great Plains: 722 Main St, PO Box 347, Newton KS 67114-0347	316-283-5100	316-283-0454	newton@mennoniteusa.org
161	Mennonite Disaster Service	717-859-2210	717-859-4910	binational@mds.mennonite.net
	1018 Main St, Akron PA 17501			www.mds.mennonite.net
161	Mennonite Economic Development Associates (MEDA)	800-665-7026	204-942-4001	meda@meda.org
	302-280 Smith St, Winnipeg MB R3C 1K2, Canada			www.meda.org
19	Mennonite Education Agency	866-866-2872	574-642-4863	info@mennoniteeducation.org
	63846 CR 35, Suite 1, Goshen IN 46528-9621	574-642-3164		www.mennoniteeducation.org
165	Mennonite Health Services Alliance	800-611-4007	574-534-3254	info@mhsonline.org
	234 S Main St, Suite 1, Goshen IN 46526	574-534-9689		www.mhsonline.org
186	Mennonite Indian Leaders Council (MILC) —see Native Mennonite Ministries			
174	Mennonite Media	800-999-3534	540-434-5556	info@mennomedia.org
	1251 Virginia Ave, Harrisonburg VA 22802	540-434-6701		www.mennomedia.org
175	Mennonite Men	316-283-5100	316-283-0454	jimg@mennoniteusa.org
	722 Main St, PO Box 347, Newton KS 67114-0347			www.mennonitemen.org
22	Mennonite Mission Network	866-866-2872		www.mennonitemission.net
	Great Lakes: 500 S Main St, PO Box 370, Elkhart IN 46515-0370	574-294-7523	574-294-8669	info@mennonitemission.net
	Great Plains: 722 Main St, PO Box 347, Newton KS 67114-0347	316-283-5100	316-283-0454	info@mennonitemission.net
28	Mennonite Mutual Aid	800-348-7468	574-533-5264	mma@mma-online.org
	1110 N Main St, PO Box 483, Goshen IN 46527-0483	574-533-9511		www.mma-online.org
30	Mennonite Publishing Network	866-866-2872		www.mph.org
	616 Walnut Ave, Scottdale PA 15683-1999	724-887-8500	724-887-3111	info@mph.org
	718 Main St, PO Box 347, Newton KS 67114-0347	316-283-5100	316-283-0454	flp@mph.org
	490 Dutton Dr, Suite C8, Waterloo ON N2L 6H7, Canada	519-747-5722	519-747-5721	hpcan@mph.org
179	Mennonite Women USA	316-283-5100	316-283-0454	
	722 Main St, PO Box 347, Newton KS 67114-0347			office@mennonitewomenusa.org
197	Mennonite World Conference			www.mwc-cmm.org
	8 rue du Fosse des Treize, 67000 Strasbourg, France	(33) 388-15-27-50	(33) 388-15-27-51	strasbourgh@mwc-cmm.org
	50 Kent Ave, Kitchener ON N2G 3R1, Canada	519-571-0060	519-571-1980	kitchener@mwc-cmm.org
	2529 Willow Ave, Clovis CA 93612, USA	559-291-2125	559-291-2065	fresno@mwc-cmm.org
186	Native Mennonite Ministries			
	MILC: 722 Main St, PO Box 347, Newton KS 67114-0347	316-283-5100	316-283-0454	milc@mennonitemission.net
	MILC: 500 S Main St, PO Box 370, Elkhart IN 46515-0370	574-523-3077	574-294-8669	
	UNM: 2121 Hawthorne Dr, Elkhart IN 46517	574-295-8530	574-293-1892	rrhorst@verizon.net
81	New York Mennonite Conference	315-376-3734	315-376-3071	dotconf@northnet.org
	PO Box 99, 5546 Alger Road, Martinsburg NY 13404			www.bfn.org/~nymennon

PAGE	NAME AND ADDRESS	TELEPHONE	FAX	E-MAIL AND WEBSITE
187	North American Vietnamese Mennonite Fel. 7155 Sherbrook St, Vancouver BC V5X 4E3, Canada	604-324-1200		nhienp@hotmail.com
84	North Central Conference of the Mennonite Church 166 N State Rd 40, Exeland WI 54835-2176	715-943-2317		egschrock@indianheadtel.net
86	Ohio Conference of the Mennonite Church 13363 Jericho Rd, PO Box 210, Kidron OH 44636	330-857-5421	330-857-5485	ohmc@zoominternet.net www.ohio.mennonite.net
92	Pacific Northwest Mennonite Conference 19532 NE Gilsan St, Portland OR 97230	503-492-4216	503-492-8965	office@pnmc.org www.pnmc.org
95	Pacific Southwest Mennonite Conference Box CAL, 1539 E Howard St, Pasadena CA 91104	626-720-8100	626-720-8101	admin@pacificsouthwest.org www.pacificsouthwest.org
188	Peace and Justice Support Network 202 S Ann St, Lancaster PA 17602	717-399-8353	717-391-6512	leoh@mennonitemission.net peace@mennoniteusa.org www.mennoniteusa.org
31	Provident Bookstores 616 Walnut Ave, Scottdale PA 15683	800-759-4447 724-887-8500	724-887-3111	pbs@mph.org www.providentbookstores.com
99	Rocky Mountain Mennonite Conference 2391 W Caley Ave, Littleton CO 80120	303-347-9266	303-795-0090	rmmc@rmmc.org www.rmmc.org
101	South Central Mennonite Conference 2517 N Main, PO Box 448, North Newton KS 67117	316-283-7080	316-283-0620	scc@mennoscc.org
105	Southeast Mennonite Conference 35 S Beneva Rd, Suite A, Sarasota FL 34232-1452	941-342-9959	941-342-0318	seconference@verizon.net
158	Ten Thousand Villages 704 Main St, PO Box 500, Akron PA 17501-0500	717-859-8100	717-859-2622	www.tenthousandvillages.org inquiry.us@tenthousandvillages.org
193	The Mennonite Editor: 1700 S Main St, Goshen IN 46526 Newton: 722 Main St, Newton KS 67114	800-790-2498 574-535-6051 316-283-5155	 574-535-6050 316-283-0454	www.themennonite.org editor@themennonite.org editor@themennonite.org
186	United Native Ministries (UNM) —see Native Mennonite Ministries			
195	Virginia Mennonite Board of Missions 901 Parkwood Dr, Harrisonburg VA 22802	800-707-5535 540-434-9727	540-434-7627	info@wmbm.org www.vmbm.org
108	Virginia Mennonite Conference 901 Parkwood Dr, Harrisonburg VA 22802	800-707-5535 540-434-9727	540-434-7627	info@vmconf.org www.vmconf.org
114	Western District Conference 2517 N Main, PO Box 306, North Newton KS 67117	316-283-6300	316-283-0620	wdc@mennowdc.org www.mennowdc.org